GEOGRAPHIES FOR ADVANCED STUDY
EDITED BY PROFESSOR S. H. BEAVER, M.A.

MALAYA, INDONESIA, BORNEO
AND THE PHILIPPINES

GEOGRAPHIES FOR ADVANCED STUDY

EDITED BY S. H. BEAVER, M.A.

The Tropical World: Its Social and Economic Conditions and its future status.   P. GOUROU

West Africa: A Study of the Environment and of Man's use of it.
R. J. HARRISON CHURCH, B.SC.(ECON.), PH.D.

The Soviet Union: The Land and its People.   G. JORRÉ

Malaya, Indonesia, Borneo, and the Philippines.
CHARLES ROBEQUAIN

The Scandinavian World   A. C. O'DELL, M.SC., F.R.S.E.

IN PREPARATION

Geography of Western Europe   F. J. MONKHOUSE, M.A.

Central Europe: A Regional and Human Geography
ALICE F. A. MUTTON, M.A., PH.D.

Introduction to Geomorphology   B. W. SPARKS, M.A.

MALAYA, INDONESIA, BORNEO, AND THE PHILIPPINES

A Geographical, Economic, and Political description of Malaya, the East Indies, and the Philippines

BY

CHARLES ROBEQUAIN

Professor of Tropical Geography in the University of Paris

Translated by

E. D. LABORDE

Sometime Assistant Master in Harrow School

Issued in co-operation with the International Secretariat, Institute of Pacific Relations

1724

LONGMANS

LONGMANS, GREEN AND CO LTD
6 & 7 CLIFFORD STREET, LONDON W1

THIBAULT HOUSE, THIBAULT SQUARE, CAPE TOWN
605–611 LONSDALE STREET, MELBOURNE C1
443 LOCKHART ROAD, HONG KONG
ACCRA, AUCKLAND, IBADAN
KINGSTON (JAMAICA), KUALA LUMPUR
LAHORE, NAIROBI, SALISBURY (RHODESIA)

LONGMANS, GREEN AND CO INC
119 WEST 40TH STREET, NEW YORK 18

LONGMANS, GREEN AND CO
20 CRANFIELD ROAD, TORONTO 16

ORIENT LONGMANS PRIVATE LTD
CALCUTTA, BOMBAY, MADRAS
DELHI, HYDERABAD, DACCA

FIRST PUBLISHED	. . . .	1954
SECOND EDITION	. . . .	1958
NEW IMPRESSION	. . . .	1959

Original edition published in French
by Editions Payot under the title
Le Monde Malais

Made and printed by offset in Great Britain by
William Clowes and Sons, Limited, London and Beccles

TRANSLATOR'S FOREWORD

Monsieur Robequain's book fills a gap in the previously existing descriptions of important regions of the world. No excuse is needed for producing an English edition. For centuries the East Indies have attracted interest in Europe as a source of economic products, as a kind of fairyland to the romantic, and as a field of investigation for the naturalist. The last seventy years have seen the islands become the most important part of the tropical and equatorial world and assume a leading rôle in the production of rubber, tin, sugar, tobacco, vegetable oil, fibres, and other valuable commodities. The rising tide of Japanese ambition brought the region into the political arena, and the war of 1941–5 together with the subsequent Communist activities has made it one of the danger spots to world peace. The volume contains a comprehensive description of the natural layout of the region, its economic and cultural development, and the political setting and trends. The author, who has read widely in his subject and has a first-hand knowledge of parts of the region, is well qualified for the great task he has undertaken in compiling the book. He shows himself particularly interested in the results of the impact of various civilisations on the inhabitants of the region and in comparing the effects of the British, Dutch, and American colonial systems. The rapid course of recent events has made a great deal of revision necessary.

I have to thank Monsieur Robequain for the detailed care he has taken in reading my translation.

CHOLSEY, BERKSHIRE. E. D. L.

AUTHOR'S FOREWORD TO THE SECOND EDITION

The text has been revised mainly with the help of Dr. C. D. Cowan of the School of Oriental and African Studies in the University of London. This help has been especially valuable in Chapters I and V. For this I owe him grateful thanks. I am deeply grateful to Dr. E. D. Laborde for the elegance and closeness to the original of his translation and for the judicious corrections suggested by him. My thanks also go to Messrs. Longmans, Green and Co. for the care they have devoted to the English editions of my work.

C.R.

THE INSTITUTE OF PACIFIC RELATIONS

The Institute of Pacific Relations is an unofficial and nonpartisan organisation founded in 1925 to facilitate the scientific study of the peoples of the Pacific area. It is composed of autonomous National Councils in the principal countries having important interests in the Pacific area, together with an International Secretariat. It is privately financed by contributions from National Councils, corporations, and foundations. It is governed by a Pacific Council composed of members appointed by each of the National Councils.

The Institute as such and the National Councils of which it is composed do not advocate policies or express opinions on national or international affairs. Responsibility for statements of fact or opinion in Institute publications rests solely with the authors.

CONTENTS

PART I

GENERAL FEATURES

PART IV

COLONIAL ACHIEVEMENT

PHOTOGRAPHS

ix

MAPS AND DIAGRAMS

PART I

GENERAL FEATURES

CHAPTER 1

DISCOVERY AND PARTITION

It was only at the beginning of the 16th century that the Western peoples set foot in the Malay world.[1] Of course, in 1292 on his way home from China Marco Polo the Venetian had stayed for a short time in Sumatra and in his account of his travels had recorded something of what he had seen in the island. Possibly in the next two hundred years merchants or travellers, of whom there were many in India, whether Italians, Catalans, Jews, or Levantines, had visited certain ports on the Malay Peninsula or even in the East Indies. Of this there is no safe evidence. All that is certain is that several Western cities—Venice and Bruges among them—had agencies and correspondents on the coast of India (at Calicut, for example) before the arrival of Vasco da Gama. At Goa the explorer met one of them. This was Gaspar the Jew, who was very useful to Vasco da Gama and was two years later to negotiate Cabral's reception at Calicut (1500).

Until the coming of the Europeans the principal traders in the Indian Ocean were Indians and Chinese, whose ships were still frequenting the Persian Gulf in the first half of the 15th century; and from the 11th century onwards, there were the Arabs, who, together with Gujerati Muslims, were gradually edging their way eastwards. These two peoples engaged in very active trade in the ports on the Malabar and Coromandel Coasts and acted as middlemen between Europe and the Far East, bringing spices to Arabia and Egypt, to the warehouses at Aden, Jedda, and Alexandria. These famous commodities, whose place of origin long remained uncertain, were distributed in the West by the Venetians and there

[1] Heyd (6), II, p. 150 and *passim*. 'The Malay world' is here meant to include Malaya with Singapore and the adjacent islands, the East Indies, and the Philippines, but excludes New Guinea and other Melanesian islands. The East Indies comprise Indonesia (i.e. the islands formerly known as the Dutch East Indies), the British Colonies of North Borneo and Sarawak with the State of Brunei, and the whole of Timor.

1

held an important place in the pharmacopœia and the kitchen, being used for seasoning dishes and flavouring drinks. In 1487 Pedro de Covilham observed large plantations of pepper and ginger on the Malabar Coast. These were merely the 'heavy spices' of which Sumatra was the other leading producer. Nutmeg with its delicate arillus, or mace, which 'fortifies and warms the stomach', came with cloves and cinnamon from a more distant and mysterious country, the Moluccas. Here an Italian named Varthema was probably the first European to land (1504). Be it so or not, he was the first to describe the way in which clove buds were picked.

The lure of the spices, the desire to avoid the expense of Venetian, Arab, and Indian middlemen, the effort to ensure control of production itself, and crusading fervour to strike at the economic roots of Muslim strength were the main factors in the rapidity of Portuguese expansion.

European Settlement and Rivalry. The storming of Malacca by Albuquerque in 1511 marks a definite stage. It confirmed the possession of Muscat and Socotra and made the Indian Ocean into a Portuguese lake for nearly a hundred years. Malacca was then a leading market on the long strait which forms a passageway to the Far East. The Muslims had taken it in 1450. The Portuguese found in it several colonies—Chinese, Javanese, and others—each with its autonomous administration. As early as 1512 the Portuguese had established a royal agent in Sumatra, and a Portuguese squadron under the command of Abreu had reached the Moluccas, though all but one ship were lost on the voyage.

For about a hundred years the Moluccas were the centre of European activity in the East Indies. The Portuguese did not long remain the only ones there, for rivals came from the east. After other navigators had in vain sought a passage along the coasts of South America, Magellan, who was in the service of Spain, succeeded during his epic voyage in passing round the continent and crossing the vast expanses of the Pacific. In a fight with natives in 1521 he met his death on one of the St. Lazarus Islands, afterwards called the Philippines. But the Spanish expedition continued on its way and without difficulty reached the Moluccas, which legend—carefully maintained by the Portuguese—claimed to be inacessible in the midst of a sea studded with reefs and darkened by dense fogs. The Spaniards were received at Tidore by King Almanzor,[1] whilst the Portuguese had established themselves on the neighbouring island of Ternate. Then began that undeclared, picturesque, and cruel spice war in which both sides took advantage of the rivalries of native chiefs and also of the ambiguous character of the Treaty of Tordesillas by which the Pope had tried in 1494 to delimit the Portuguese and Spanish

---

[1] Olearius (9) II, p. 422.

hemispheres.[1] It ended in the expulsion of the Portuguese, who were driven back to Amboina from Ternate in 1575. Meanwhile, under a Basque named López de Legaspi, who had arrived from Mexico in 1564, the Spaniards began the conquest of the Philippines.

By this time other competitors for the profitable trade were coming on to the scene. The Dutch, who had hitherto been the distributors in Europe of the spices brought to Lisbon by the Portuguese, became progressively dissatisfied with their position as middlemen as their own economy expanded and were eager to make the voyage to the East on their own account. When in 1594 Philip II gained control of Portugal, they sought the commodities in the country of origin. Dutch seamen tried to reach the Far East through the frozen seas off the north coast of Eurasia; others succeeded in embarking in Portuguese ships sailing round Africa; and in this way Linschoten brought back valuable information from Goa. After very careful preparation a squadron of four ships despatched by the Distant Lands Company under the command of Cornelius Houtman left the Texel and sailed to Bantam on the north coast of Java in 1596. It came home with decimated crews, but certain that the spice trade would yield enormous profits. Between 1598 and 1602 thirteen Dutch expeditions went one after the other to the East Indies. In 1605 the Dutch established themselves at Amboina, the main settlement still retained by the Portuguese in the Spice Islands. In 1610 they became masters of Ternate.

But from then on their interest was not restricted to the Moluccas. The United East India Company had been formed at Amsterdam in 1602. Armed officially with very extensive powers and a monopoly, it skilfully intervened in quarrels between native princes and thus secured commercial privileges in Sumatra and Java. In 1619 Jan Pieterszoon Coen seized Jakarta, a place to the east of Bantam and the residence of one of these princes, where a Portuguese colony had been established. At the mouth of the Chiliwung near by he built a fort, under the protection of which an agency soon sprang up. Thus was founded Batavia, which was destined to become what its founder intended it to be, the focus of Dutch power in the East Indies. It was from here that the Company succeeded partly by the use of force, but even more by its persistent and astute policy, if not in occupying and governing the archipelago, at any rate in

---

[1] Kammerer (7), pp. 58, 439, and *passim.* The Pope's Line was the meridian situated 370 leagues west of the Cape Verde Islands. But of which island in that group? And there was no mention of the antimeridian which passed through the Pacific. Taking advantage of the then existing difficulties of finding the longitude, the Spaniards unfairly pushed the Line westwards. A Portolan chart dated 1522 shows it passing through Sumatra; and at Badajoz in 1524 Spain claimed that it crossed the mouths of the Ganges. In fact, the Moluccas fell just within the Portuguese hemisphere.

controlling most of its trade—to the great profit of its own agents and stockholders.

Thus, its rivals were gradually ousted. After the expedition of merchants from St. Malo, Vitré, and Laval, who reached Sumatra and Java in 1616 and returned with a cargo of spices, scarcely any French ships visited the East Indies until the end of the 18th century.[1] The Spaniards advanced no farther than the Philippines; and as the Portuguese were in a period of decadence, they kept no more than the eastern half of Timor. The English were more persistent and, though they were unsuccessful in their attempts to make settlements in the Moluccas at the beginning of the 17th century, their factory at Bantam lasted until 1682. After that date their holdings were restricted to a few points on the west coast of Sumatra, especially Benkulen.[2] English freebooters, the best known of whom was William Dampier (1652–1715), quite often succeeded in cheating the Dutch attempt to monopolise the trade of the Archipelago and the no less jealous control of the Spaniards in the Pacific. Great Britain took advantage of the Napoleonic Wars to seize the Dutch territories and to hold them till 1816. About 1811 Raffles, the Governor of Java under British occupation and afterwards Governor of Benkulen, dreamt of forming a kind of federation of Malay States under his country's protection. But in 1824 the two nations agreed to an exchange of the settlements and rights which Great Britain held in Sumatra for those the Dutch had on the Malay Peninsula.

This partition became more clearly defined during the 19th century. In 1819 Raffles selected Singapore as the centre of British power in the Far East, and from that point as well as from Madras and Calcutta Great Britain extended her influence over the Malay States in the south of the Peninsula. She also succeeded by means of skilful moves in securing a footing in North Borneo.

Imperial sway was certainly not the aim of the famous Dutch East India Company, whose strength lay wholly in its fleet and its 'factories' and which at first merely wished to reap the harvest of the seas. It had been driven regretfully to political action, and not until after the Company's fall, and especially from 1870 onwards, did the Dutch Government in the East Indies, like the British Government on the Peninsula, gradually achieve the effective occupation of the territories recognised as theirs. The Dutch did not check their eastward advance until they reached the middle of New Guinea, the eastern part of which was shared between Germany and Australia until 1918, when it passed wholly under the administration of the Dominion.

[1] For the voyage of Jean Parmentier to Sumatra in 1529, see Guibon: (5).
[2] See W. Dampier (3) III, p. 196.

The end of the 19th century also saw a most important event, the downfall of Spanish rule in the Philippines after a duration of more than three hundred years. Though Germany had had her eyes on the islands, the advantage accruing from the defeat of Spain fell to the lot of the United States, whose spread across the American continent had now reached the shores of the Pacific.

Exploration of the Malay Lands. Four hundred years of European and American activity have enabled our knowledge of the region to make considerable progress. The singular complexity of its outlines is now accurately shown on our maps. But on the Portolan charts of the 14th century, and frequently in the 15th too, the Golden Chersonese (as the Malay Peninsula was called) was continued by a large island, the Taprobane of the ancients, in which Ceylon and Sumatra seem to have been confused. In the 15th century, however, a distinction was usually made between the islands. For instance, on the *mappemonde* of Fra Mauro (1459) there appear beyond Taprobane–Sumatra a Java Minor and a Java Major on the way to Cipango (Japan). Sumatra is shown for the first time under its real name in the Egerton MS. (1508?) in the British Museum. A little later the Munich Portolan (1516), attributed to the Reinels and now in the Bibliothèque Nationale in Paris, sprinkled the blue water with the bellying sails of caravels and countless islands freakishly shaped like dentate leaves. The Moluccas became better known after the return of del Cano. Sebastian Münster's 'Table of the Oriental Region' (1562) showed a swarm of islands round Java, among which were named Timor, Gilolo (Halmahera), Borne (Borneo), and Puloan (Palawan). The South Sea—Magellan's 'Pacific'—was still for long to separate Asia, then thought to be joined to America, from an enormous Southern Continent. At the end of the 16th century maps by Mercator and Hondius reproduced fairly accurately the general arrangement of the islands, *in quibus Moluccæ celeberrimæ sunt*, and made the Sunda arc curve round from Sumatra to New Guinea. But it was not yet known whether the latter was an island or part of the Southern Continent. The strait now called after Torres was shown on maps of 1771, whilst New Holland (Australia) was given a shape not far removed from reality. Cook's voyages in the last quarter of the 18th century finally killed the legend of the great Southern Continent. The East Indies then appeared like a bridge connecting Asia and Australia and lying between the expanses of the Pacific and Indian Oceans, whose waters extend to the Antarctic Circle.

It must be repeated, however, that the Dutch East India Company took no pride in the advance of geographical knowledge and still less in its publication. Its support was given mistrustfully to voyages into unknown regions and in every case it insisted upon discoveries being kept secret. Unauthorised exploration of the interior of an island by its officers was regarded as absence without leave or desertion, and the offenders were put in chains. The making of a map was classed with theft. Detailed surveys of the coasts and later of the inland areas were the work of the 19th and 20th centuries, and especially of the latter, when the surveys were assisted by official cartographical services. Since Junghuhn's description of Java in about 1850, a large number of documents, mainly in Dutch, but also in English, German, and French, have been published concerning the geology, ethnology, history, and physical, plant, and human geography of Malaya, the East Indies, and the Philippines. To master them wholly is becoming impossible, but an attempt will be made to set out here for the general reader the essential points in the data and conclusions.

Unity of the Malay World. The comprehensive treatment in this book of the region stretching from Malaya to the Philippines inclusive is by no means arbitrary. What strikes one on first glancing at a simple atlas map is the discontinuous and insular character of the region. Even Malaya looks just like an island to the south of the isthmus of Kra, in spite of the railway from Singapore to Bangkok and the road along which the Japanese troops and tanks advanced in 1941. A brisk sea-borne trade soon developed in the relatively sheltered little Mediterraneans which trench deeply between the island groups. Strong cultural influences from the neighbouring continent spread from island to island, those from China and India beginning with the Christian era and the more distant ones from Islam and Western Europe coming later. The history of the Malay thalassocracies is imperfectly known. The relations between them and the Polynesian world and the part they played in those daring migrations which reached as far as Madagascar easily appeal to one's curiosity. It will be seen that the distinguishing features of the Malay (using this word in its widest sense) were mainly those imposed on him by external civilisations.[1] He is a person who, after being refined by age-long contact with India and China, has finally become a Muslim; and he is also a sailor or at any rate a member of a community to whom the sea is familiar. But most of all, Malay unity is expressed by the spread of the Malay tongue over the greater part of Indonesia and by its development into the language of trade even in places far from the Peninsula.

But the Malay world, as thus defined, does not seem ever to have formed a really independent whole. Foreign domination may have relaxed at certain times and principalities may have been established, in which native traditions fused harmoniously with customs and

---

[1] This statement is perhaps exaggerated and is disputed by several writers with special knowledge, most of whom are Dutch.

ideas imported from abroad, especially in Java in the heyday of the Majapahit kingdom. History records neither a Malay empire nor a Malay federation capable of long resistance to a powerful invader. This is in striking contrast with the Japanese Islands, which continue the same system of island festoons off the continent of Asia. A fairly general feature which persists to this day has been the difference between the coastal and inland peoples, the latter of whom, for example, the Bataks of Sumatra, the Dyaks of Borneo, and the Alfurus of Celebes and the Moluccas, though they cannot without exaggeration be termed primitive, have yet had only indirect influence from without by slow infiltration and after a series of delays.

The region consists not only of islands, but of volcanic tropical islands at that. The discontinuity of the dry land favours foreign domination, and the climate and fertility of the soil ensure its persistence. Owing to the qualities of the soil and water, the countries of the north—particularly China and Western Europe—found in the region areas suitable for supplying certain commodities which would season their rather insipid food and give rise to a particularly profitable trade. Later, when European nations became industrial, the same physical advantages together with the abundance and relative docility of the people allowed the cultivation of other crops, some of which, though exotic, have done remarkably well. Recently, mineral resources have come to swell the exports, and Malaya, the East Indies, and the Philippines have become one of the world's chief producers of tropical commodities. In fact, the region may be regarded as among the finest successes achieved by Western colonisation in the tropics, at least so far as economic development is concerned.

CHAPTER 2

LAND AND SEA

The first men from the West to visit the Spice Islands did not find them the earthly paradise that some had hoped to see. But few regions are as attractive as the East Indies to the man of the West who dreams of voyages to far-off lands, and none has a keener interest for the scholar. Situated between Monsoon Asia and three-parts desert Australia, these island groups afford a variety of scene and a wealth of life which raise highly interesting problems for the student. The distribution of plants and animals and of man himself has given rise to a rich crop of published works, but is far from being wholly explained. The swarm of islands, however, is certainly related to the geological evolution.

The Formation of the Archipelago. A glance at even a small-scale map such as is found in every good atlas shows that the distribution of the islands is not chaotic, but on the contrary is subject to definite order. This is especially evident in the huge Sunda arc which forms a convex line of great regularity on the whole from Sumatra to Timor. North of this arc things are less clear and simple; and yet the rows of islands and the grain of the relief, especially in Borneo and the Philippines, evince those curved lines and that festoon-like appearance that characterise the Pacific coastline.

The idea that these lines of islands are all due to a range of fold mountains at once jumps to the mind; and it is to verify this probability, sort out the lines followed by the ranges, discover the dates of their origins, and recognise the vicissitudes through which they have passed, that a large number of scientists—mainly Dutch—have striven. Their work has corrected and completed the masterly synthesis set out by Suess in *The Face of the Earth.* The great Austrian geologist saw in the structure of Indo-China and Indonesia the prolongation of the Himalayan ranges. The curve of the island chain revealed the existence of ancient masses against which had been moulded the sediments accumulated in the marine trenches formed by the geosynclines of Tethys. These masses were not only large blocks of Gondwanaland, like Peninsular India and Australia, but also, lying between these, some less extensive pieces, like Assam, southern China, and, lastly, Cambodia and southern Annam, which form the Indosinia of geologists in French Indo-China.

From Indo-China to New Guinea and Australia the components of Indonesia become smaller and smaller. The massive areas of

8

Sumatra, Malaya, and Borneo are followed by the narrower and far more indented islands of Java, Celebes, Mindanao, and Luzón; and in the end comes a real swarm of small islands round the Banda Sea.

Are the islands a mountain range in process of formation and rising from the sea? Or the ruins of a range that is gradually disintegrating? No proof exists that there was at any time a continuous connexion between Asia and Australia or that Indonesia represents the wreckage of such a bridge and consists of the piers of a broad continental isthmus now submerged.

One of the most interesting and reliable results of geological researches, which have greatly increased in number since the beginning of the century in Indonesia as well as in Indo-China, is that the progress of the orogenic forces has been accurately traced together with the spread of the folds from north to south at the expense of a shrinking Tethys. The complexity of detail is certainly very great. The emersion of the sediments accumulated in the geosynclinal seas was effected by fits and starts with intervals of rest during which the mountains so elevated were eroded and the sediment transported to form the mountains of the succeeding phase. But generally speaking, the farther the folds are from Asia and the nearer to Australia, the more recent they are. As early as the Carboniferous there were well-marked ridges in north-eastern Indo-China. After the Triassic the peninsula stretched westwards as far as the Burmese trenches, where Tethys suddenly turned southwards. It included Banka and Belitong and probably parts of Sumatra, Borneo, and Java. In the whole extent of Indo-China the Tertiary appears only in small patches on geological maps. On the other hand, Indonesia is essentially a Tertiary and Quaternary formation, and rocks of those eras comprise more than 70 per cent. of the surface of the former Dutch East Indies.

Geological research[1] has gathered few safe notions about the history of the archipelago during the Primary and Secondary. The thickness of the pre-Tertiary strata is on the whole imperfectly known. From the fact that the Cambrian, Silurian, and Devonian have not been found, it has sometimes been concluded prematurely that a continent—the 'Æquinoctia' of Abendanon the geologist—covered the site of Indonesia at the beginning of the Primary. The recent discovery of Glossopteris flora in New Guinea seems to indicate a connexion, which was still easy during the Carboniferous, between India and Australia. And it must be remembered that Wegener regarded the festoons of Indonesia as remnants left behind as Asia drifted westwards after the breaking up of Gondwanaland

[1] Good summaries of the results obtained may be found in Rutten (32, 33), Brouwer (24), and Blondel (23). See also Umbergrove's strikingly illustrated work (36a).

had separated Australia from the Deccan. However, it seems likely that since the upper Primary and the Secondary eras an archipelago has always existed here, but that its outline has greatly changed. The region was affected by the vast marine transgressions known to have occurred all over the globe in the Permo-Carboniferous, Upper Triassic, Upper Jurassic, and Middle Cretaceous. The facies resulting from these are all different, but many bear evidence that the seas were shallow. Changes in fauna show that relations with the other end of Tethys—the Mediterranean of Europe—were more or less easy. Already local endemic features appear; for instance, in the Middle and Upper Cretaceous in Sumatra, where a first phase of emersion and folding are clearly indicated.

Movements in various directions took place one after the other during the Tertiary. Numerous unconformities in the strata give proof of the change from continental erosion to marine transgression at periods which vary greatly from place to place; and the distribution of land and sea still underwent many vicissitudes. The progressive deepening of the geosynclines is proved by the great depth of sediments which appear to belong to shallow seas. In western Indonesia as in the Philippines and New Guinea the total depth of Tertiary beds often reaches 15,000 or 30,000 feet. These vast quantities of sediment cannot be explained by erosion from the surfaces now above water. Other land must have existed to the west of Borneo on the site of the South China Sea and also to the south of Java.[1] This land was perhaps wholly submerged during a great part of the Tertiary. The differences between the Indonesian and Western European faunas became more and more striking as the Tertiary period went on, for it seems that the great trenches in the east and west tended to be isolated from each other. The Quaternary was also an era of great changes, but in it destruction was greater than construction.

In Indonesia as a whole two main phases of folding are recognised. An intensive one occurred towards the end of the Secondary and beginning of the Tertiary and was accompanied by the intrusion into the sedimentaries of deep-seated igneous rocks, granites and peridotites. The other phase took place at the end of the Tertiary and was also rather violent, but less so than the first. These movements ended in the formation of those arcs or festoons which are very noticeable on maps, but whose continuity is sometimes more apparent than real (see Fig. 1).

The most clearly marked is that of Sunda. It continues the Arakan Yoma of Burma, the gap being marked by the Andaman and

[1] Rutten (32), p. 229.

Nicobar Islands. It can be traced through Sumatra, Java, and the Lesser Sunda Islands till it bends like a fishhook round the Banda Sea. Dutch geologists distinguish at least two secondary lines in the Sunda arc. From the centre outwards (see Fig. 1) these are:

(*a*) A continuation of the principal arc from Sumatra to Flores and Wetar by a crescent of volcanic islets as far as Banda to the south of Serang and even to Api to the north of Wetar, where the crescent almost curves back on itself. The anticlinal structure is

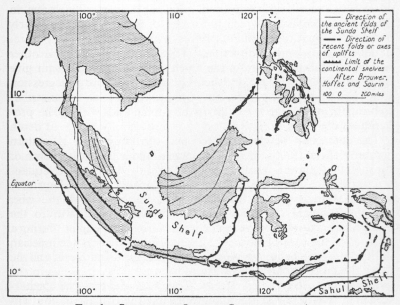

FIG. 1.—STRUCTURAL LINES OF SOUTHEASTERN ASIA

very evident in western Sumatra and in southern Java, in the mountains which dominate the hills and plains of the oil-bearing geosyncline.

(*b*) The arc which appears in the Nias and Mentawai Islands to the west of Sumatra. After a gap of about 1200 miles it rises again in Sumba and Timor, whence it continues through Tenimbar, Kei, Serang, Amboina, and Buru.

A third arc which passes through the Aru Islands and the south-western point of New Guinea probably continues through Misul, Obi, Sula (between Serang and the Moluccas) to Celebes. This arc is mainly Melanesian and interests Indonesia in part only.

Suess himself saw in Celebes and the Moluccas the remains of some peculiar little ranges with an east-to-west direction, continuing the alignment of the mountains in New Guinea. But the curious shape of Celebes seems due rather to very recent fracturing. The structure of Borneo has not yet been satisfactorily analysed. It is like a fan, with a number of ribs converging north-eastwards towards the highest point in the island and opening out towards the south-west. But the relation of these ranges to those of Indo-China has not been explained. The concave arcs formed by the Malay Peninsula and British Borneo suggest the theory of tectonic continuity and of another festoon. But the suggestion is deceptive. The Malay Peninsula, which is formed of ancient rocks, does not consist of a single range, but of a series of about fifteen ridges running obliquely to its general direction. This is the same structure as is seen in the hills of Annam to the north of Hué. In fact, the formations are different in age and belong to different orogenic systems which are not contemporary, but successive. It is as useless to try to bring them into line as to link up the Alpine folds with those of the Pennines or North Wales.[1]

The connexion between Borneo and the Philippines is less uncertain. The northern range in the large island is probably continued through the Palawan Islands towards Luzón. Another arc, marked out farther east by the Sulu group, probably appears again in western Mindanao. On the other hand, the links joining Celebes and the Moluccas to Mindanao remain very hypothetical. The Philippines present a convergence northwards of the main structural lines, as in the case of Borneo, although the two areas seem utterly unlike now, one being the most compact mass in Indonesia and the other the most astonishing swarm of islands.

Continental Shelves and Marine Trenches. Several writers have seen in the East Indies a mountain range like the Himalayas or at any rate the Alps in process of formation. The resemblance has been particularly stressed by Argand and Brouwer.[2] Folding appears most complex in eastern Indonesia, where, moreover, rock waste from Triassic limestones has been transported and laid down on more recent sedimentary beds, to form the 'fatus' which gives a strange appearance to the scenery. Brouwer compares this with the formation of beds of transported matter in eastern Switzerland and likens the position of the Sunda arc in its relation to Australia to that of the Himalayas in relation to the Deccan. He even supposes that this arc will continue to move towards Australia, so that a junction may be expected between the Sunda–Timor bulge and the main Sunda line. After the oceanographic cruise of the

[1] Blondel (23), p. 332.   [2] Brouwer (24), p. 46 ff.

Snellius, however, Kuenen[1] reported that the enormous accumulations of sediment which accompanied the uplift of the Alps and Himalayas are not found in front of the arcs. Yet recent movements have been most widespread in south-eastern Indonesia and orogenic activity continues to be greatest there. The many oceanographic expeditions that have worked in the archipelago have revealed in a progressively more accurate manner great differences in the form of the sea-bottom, differences which correspond to those observed in the configuration of the areas above the sea (see Fig. 2).

To the south of the Sunda arc Indonesia is bounded by a deep trench parallel with the arc and marking the region as belonging wholly to the Pacific. It is like the one which runs along beside the Aleutian Islands, Japan, and the Philippines and plunges down to a depth of more than 5900 fathoms to the east of Mindanao; and only on the far side of the Sunda trench does the Indian Ocean begin. This is a wholly different ocean bounded by the unbroken land masses of western Australia, East Africa, Arabia, and the Deccan, whose smooth coastlines are fringed with no curving island festoons. But on the near side of the long trench, more than 3800 fathoms deep to the south of Java and ending in a point off the south of Timor, the relief of eastern Indonesia, both emerged and submarine, is extraordinarily complex, whilst the big islands farther west lie on the world's largest continental shelf.

On this, the Sunda shelf, the mean depth of the sea is only 30 fathoms, the maximum being nowhere more than 45 fathoms. If the sea level were lowered by that much, Borneo, Sumatra, and Java would be joined to Indo-China, as they have very probably been at various times and even at a relatively recent period. Molengraaff[2] devoted himself to the study of the shelf and thought he found in it confirmation of the geological theories of Daly and Penck. According to these the surface has been carved by normal subaerial agents of erosion, especially running water, has remained stable since the Miocene, and at last emerged about the time of the great Quaternary ice ages. The sea covered it again at the end of the ice ages, but underwater maps still show traces of the former land relief (see Fig. 2). Molengraaff and Umbgrove[3] recognised drowned river valleys belonging to two river systems separated by a ridge now represented between Sumatra and Borneo by the islands of Banka, Belitong, and Karimata. The drainage of the southern basin flowed eastwards along the axis of the existing Java Sea. In the

[1] Kuenen (25), pp. 113–18.
[2] Molengraaff (30) regards the greatest period of continental erosion as having occurred in the Plio-Pleistocene.
[3] Umbgrove (25).

northern basin the rivers flowing down from Sumatra and Borneo discharged north-eastwards across the floor of the modern South China Sea. The streams in north-western Borneo and the whole of eastern Sumatra represent merely the remains of the latter extensive drainage system, and their former connexion is attested by the existence of many species common to the fresh-water fauna of the two islands. Other evidence of positive movement is furnished by the presence of alluvial deposits of tin like those around the island of Singkep to the south of Singapore, which were originally above water, but are now submerged. The movement is recent enough for the rivers, sediment-loaded though they are, not to have had time to build large deltas, but to end as a rule in wide, deep estuaries.

At the eastern end of Indonesia between Australia and New Guinea the Arafura Sea masks a shelf similar to that of Sunda and, like it, covered to the very shallow depth of less than 55 fathoms. This is the Sahul shelf, so called after an enormous sandbank stretching from Timor to New Guinea. It has been far less explored than the Sunda shelf, but the narrow channels which separate the Aru Islands seem, as indeed Wallace thought,[1] very like portions of river valleys which have been scoured by ocean currents. Tertiary rocks have remained horizontal in the Arus.[2] The Sahul shelf seems to extend to the south-west of New Guinea. The centre and north of the island, on the other hand, form an unstable area in which violent earthquakes are frequent and young fold ranges—the highest in the Netherlands Indies (*Snuuwgebergte*)—are cut by deep depressions.

Between the Sunda and Sahul shelves the sea covers one of the most extraordinary surface reliefs in the world. Its main features were known by 1903, and the first bathymetrical map of the archipelago was published by Tydeman in that year; but the last oceanographic expedition, that of the *Snellius*, brought back many new details of knowledge. The systematic use of echo-sounding, by which some 35,000 soundings were taken during the 1929–30 cruise, has permitted the compilation under the editorship of van Riel of bathymetrical maps of the old Dutch East Indies, one on a scale of 1 in 5M, another in twelve colours of the eastern portion of the archipelago on a scale of 1 in 2·5M, and special maps of the straits on a larger scale. To the east of Macassar and Lombok Straits— the famous Wallace Line—the Sunda shelf gives way to a series of deep basins. Submarine relief here is so uneven over relatively small areas that, in spite of the great number of soundings taken, interpolation and even interpretation have often been necessary. It has been possible to deduce from the temperature of the water at

[1] Wallace (63), p. 371.   [2] Rutten (33), p. 149.

different levels the approximate minimum depths of many of the sills separating the basins. These basins—about twenty in number, counting the southern Philippines—form in fact a series of very peculiar seas whose mutual hydrographic relations are often very complicated.

The most fully enclosed of the basins is the Sulu Sea, which goes down to a depth of 3000 fathoms, whilst the sills separating it from the neighbouring seas are nowhere deeper than 250 fathoms. In the Celebes Sea between Celebes and Mindanao one sounding gave

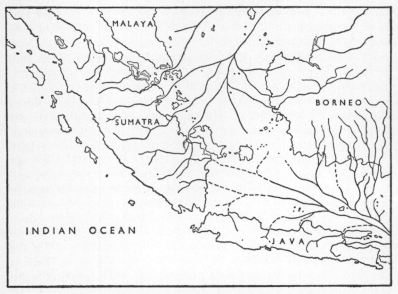

FIG. 2.—SUBMERGED RIVERS ON THE SUNDA SHELF
(From Umbgrove's Structural History of the East Indies, by permission of Cambridge University Press)

a depth of 3000 fathoms. But the greatest depth in the archipelago, apart from the marginal trenches near the Sunda Islands and the Philippines, has been found in the eastern part of the Banda Sea and is 4082 fathoms. The sea is itself subdivided into several secondary basins and offers a good instance of the astonishing complexity of the ocean currents in eastern Indonesia. Water from the Pacific does not reach the northern basin of the Banda Sea from due east, but from the north by a very narrow trough which skirts the west coast of Halmahera and swings round Buru. Except in the Timor and Aru basins to the south of the Sunda arc, the influence of the Pacific prevails throughout these deep-sea basins; and even in the

Savu Sea between Flores and Timor the waters mingle at most levels with the Pacific and not with the Indian Ocean.

The outline of the deep-sea basins is not uniform. Two main types are recognised: one long and narrow is generally considered to be a syncline separating anticlines marked by the island arcs; the other, which is more irregular in shape, drops suddenly down by steep gradients which seem to be fault scarps, has a broad and relatively smooth bottom with a depth of more than 2000 fathoms, and appears to be a rift, or *graben*. Wegener likened them to *crevasses* perpendicular or oblique to the direction of the continental drift. The depressions cut across the Miocene folds and are therefore subsequent to them. Pliocene beds in Serang are uplifted to a height of nearly 10,000 feet.

These facts all clearly reveal the strength of orogenic movements in recent epochs. Further proof of their persistence is furnished by the frequent occurrence of earthquakes which at times cause serious damage to the frail native dwellings, especially around the Banda Sea and in the Philippines. The most serious on record destroyed the town of Amboina on February 17, 1764. In western Indonesia the coasts of Sumatra and Java are the most exposed to this danger, and in particular the district of Benkulen. Fortunately, the epicentres are nearly all under the sea. Disastrous shocks seldom extend as far as Jakarta, where, however, a tremor destroyed a few dozen houses in 1699 and sent into the upper course of the Chiliwung quantities of mud which laid waste several parts of the town.[1]

Coral Structures and the Formation of the Islands. The mature relief of the Sunda shelf is prolonged without a break under the alluvium on the lowlands of Borneo, Sumatra, and Java, under all the Java Sea and the southern part of the South China Sea. In eastern Indonesia, on the other hand, the greatly varying depth of the deep-sea basins is accompanied by a very uneven uplift of the folds along the island arcs. Hence, the islands are smaller and the coasts generally steeper and more broken. Coral formation often affords data for calculating the extent of the recent tectonic movements that have given the archipelago its present shape.

Coral reefs of the most varied forms abound at greatly differing depths. Many corals live in the astonishingly clear water and shelter among their branches a very plentiful and often brightly coloured fauna including bright-blue star-fish, sea-slugs with black and yellow stripes, and queerly shaped fish. In many other cases the reefs are mere ruins and look like polyp graveyards. Off the south-east coast of Borneo a sea reef is forming about 300 miles

---

[1] The danger from earthquakes is far less than in Japan and less too than in Sicily and on the west coast of South America.

long at a maximum distance of 140 miles from the coast. No doubt it marks the position of the former coastline of the Sunda shelf before the sea level rose by about 50 fathoms at the end of the ice ages. The positive movement here must have been uniform and of a eustatic character, for no reefs have been reported as raised above the present sea level in the islands of western Indonesia.

In eastern Indonesia, on the other hand, vertical movements with a great range have affected the islands themselves and have everywhere confused their effects with those of eustatic movements and variations in sea level. Coral formation does not appear here only under the living forms of fringing and barrier reefs resting on a shallow base. Atolls, which have been built up at a rate equal to that of subsidence of the sea bottom, crown foundations of dead coral, whose steep slopes sometimes reach down to 500 or even 1000 fathoms. Of this the atolls of Teger and Tukang Besi to the south of the two southern peninsulas of Celebes are examples.[1] On the other hand, dead coral covers raised beaches now at various heights above sea level. Belts of coral are found as high as 2300 or 2600 feet, as, for instance, on Sumbawa in the main Sunda arc, where they form a series of terraces like those characteristic of some of the small islands.

In one island arc, and on an anticlinal axis at that, recent uplift has perhaps been very unequal. The central parts of Timor show Quaternary coral reefs at a height of 4200 feet above the sea; on the east and west ends these marks are no higher than 950 feet; whilst farther off there are only corals living at sea level. In this same Timor arc dead coral has been brought up from a depth of nearly 170 fathoms. The island may have been affected by a rocking movement, one side sinking, whilst the other rises slowly. Similar phenomena are reported from the Philippines, where coral has been carried up in places to a height of more than 4900 feet above the sea. On the other hand, in this group there are no barrier reefs and atolls are rare. This Davis attributed to a too rapid or too extensive subsidence and, in short, to a far greater instability than existed in the central Pacific.

The straits separating the islands in one and the same arc seem due sometimes not to mere lower height in the anticlinal axis, but to faulting or to a dislocation on the horizontal plane. The hypothesis of river valleys drowned by the sea and widened by currents is not always to be disregarded, particularly in Sunda Strait between Java and Sumatra.[2]

[1] See P. H. Kuenen (25), p. 98. There are many atolls off the eastern end of Serang, among them Pulo Geser, which is perfectly circular in shape.
[2] Umbgrove (25), p. 72.

As may be imagined, zoology can contribute to the solution of the problem of the formation of the islands.[1] Profiting by ever more intensive research from Wallace's time onwards, this science has not ceased to probe the chronology of the events by which Indonesia has moved to its present form. Not surprisingly, scholars are not all agreed. The distribution of the fauna took place in very different and uncertain conditions according as the genera and species were of Asiatic or Australian origin. The abundance of endemic forms may have been due to the occurrence of fairly long periods of complete isolation. Being in the centre of Indonesia, Celebes owes to the peculiarity of its fauna the fact that it is often pointed out as one of the oldest and longest isolated of the islands. In the Miocene it must have received a first wave of Asiatic species and then been connected at intervals with Java, Flores, the Moluccas, and Philippines, whilst it was already separated from Borneo. In fact, it has no species in common with the last named that is not also found in the others previously mentioned; and, inversely, numerous species found in Sumatra, Java, and Celebes do not occur in Borneo. Isolation became final perhaps before the end of the Pliocene, though Abendanon prefers to prolong connexion at least with Mindanao right up to the Pleistocene.

Whilst it is difficult to tabulate the absolute chronology and to fix the dates at which continuity was established or destroyed, the relative succession of events seems less doubtful. After the isolation of Celebes, zoologists often place the separation of a Philippine land—later broken up—among the oldest episodes. The Philippine mammals must have come from Borneo by the bridges of Sulu and Palawan, but many Sunda families are absent.

The faunistic affinities of eastern Indonesia reveal a very complex history. The often very highly developed endemic evolution of types of Australian origin seems to bear witness to an isolation old relatively to that continent. Wallace called attention to the fact that, though species with western affinities are less numerous in the Timor group than those with Australian affinities, they are also far less peculiar and differentiated, as if communication with western Indonesia was relatively easy. The cutting of the Strait of Lombok, however, seems to have occurred before the formation of the Lesser Sunda Islands. Among these Flores was joined to Celebes by the Salayan Islands; and continuity was probable between Timor and Alor, Timor and Wetar, and Timor and the Tenimbar Islands, whilst Alor and Wetar do not seem ever to have been connected.

At the end of the Quaternary Java appears to have been the first island on the Sunda shelf to be cut off from Asia. Borneo, Sumatra,

[1] See below, p. 56.

Belitong, and Banka followed in that order. The fauna of the islands lying off the west coast of Sumatra bears evidence that in time past the islands were joined to each other and to their big neighbour as well.

Volcanoes. Whilst coral formations often give a clue to the age of Indonesian structure, volcanoes afford the strongest and most picturesque manifestation of instability in the region, and those in Indonesia are among the most carefully studied in the world. About three hundred have been counted, fifty of which still show some, though usually very weak, activity. Most of them were formed during the Lower Quaternary. Phases of intense vulcanism occurred in the Secondary and Tertiary, but they can now be recognised only by the nature of the sediments contained in strata of those eras. The Tertiary beds are sometimes almost wholly formed of tuff and lava and nearly everywhere show traces of eruptive rocks emitted under the sea or on land. An increase in vulcanism in south-eastern Asia accompanied the spread of folding towards the south. In Indo-China the Secondary and Tertiary beds contain many eruptive rocks, but volcanic activity is almost wholly extinct today. In Borneo and Celebes its principal manifestations date from the Tertiary and beginning of the Quaternary. In recent times and at the present day volcanic activity is found in the Sunda arc and the Philippines on the margins of Indonesia. Yet the most recent volcanoes do not stand on the very edge of the submarine trenches. Those in Sumatra are separated from the Java deep by the fold on which stand the Nias and Mentawai Islands, and they continue not southwards, but through central Java. Eastwards beyond this the series on the Sunda arc does not pass through Sumba and Timor, but through Sumbawa, Flores, and other islands on the main arc. The islets which form the eastern fringe of the Banda Sea beyond Wetar are just volcanic hills. According to Brouwer this inner arc represents the youngest of all the anticlines which have been folded up against the core of Australia. The outer arcs seem indeed to be older and more developed, for a more complicated deep-seated structure would impede the emission of eruptive magma.

In the Philippines two lines of volcanoes are distinguished, reaching respectively Halmahera and the north-east of Celebes. Here again it is the inner line, the one farther from the Pacific, that usually has the greater number of volcanoes.

Indonesia is an admirable region for studying volcanic relief. The mountains are of many different types which depend on the nature and date of the eruptions (see Fig. 3). Classic volcanoes have scarcely been changed by erosion, their eruptions having hitherto been able to make up for any disintegration, and they present fine, regular cones truncated at the very top, with concave gradients which become gentler towards the bottom and fuse with the plains in long, ample slopes. The summits often wear plumes of smoke and seem to be floating on a sea of cloud. Examples of this are to be found in Salak and Lawu in Java, Sinabung and Sibayak to the south-west of Medan in Sumatra, and Mayon in south-eastern Luzón. The last-named is the most regular of all and is even more majestic than Fuji Yama. Some of them still erupt, others give off fumaroles only or are extinct.

To the south-east of Bandung in Java rises the famous and definitely less simple Papandayan with its asymmetrical silhouette. Its last great eruption, which took place in 1772, destroyed forty villages and caused more than 3000 casualties. It opened on the north-east flank of the mountain an enormous crater into which torrents now drain from its slopes. The chaotic surface of the bottom has been carved in whitish tuff and more or less consolidated mud with lava flows running across it. Solfataras are intensely active, and jets of smoke spurt up from circular or irregularly shaped holes, gush out from tiny orifices as steam does from the boiler of a locomotive, or rise like a screen from narrow fissures. The walls of the fissures are coated with a hard layer of beautiful yellow sulphur crystals which are sometimes built up like a chimney 10 or 20 feet high. Here and there wells up muddy boiling water which spouts up in many jets, and there is an incessant roar deep underground. Papandayan means 'forge' in the Sundanese language.

Other volcanoes have double craters; for instance, Tangkuban Prahu, whose whale-back profile runs along to the north of Bandung. Sometimes mountains, like Tambora in Sumbawa or Bonthain, whose great mass of dilapidated cones forms a celebrated landmark near Macassar in Celebes, have a number of adventitious cones set in more or less regular rows on their sides. Lamongan in eastern Java is attended by a whole set of subordinate cones and crater lakes.

But these relatively simple volcanoes often form part of a far vaster and more complex whole and represent only the final episodes in a long series of eruptions. Thus, huge hill-masses may consist of a collection of volcanoes, imbricated and piled one on the other. Calderas play a leading part in very recent geological history as well as in the scenery. The term is applied not only to the deep, narrow craters which occur at the summits of cones, but also to cavities which may be more than 6 miles in diameter and enclosed by walls of lava rising to a height of 1500 or 3000 feet. In general their formation is not satisfactorily explained as due to eruptions, but rather to a gradual or catastrophic subsidence caused by the removal of the lava below and the fusion of the enclosing rocks all round the crater pipes by the heat of the magma or even merely by hot gases. After this the pipes have been enlarged by rockfalls. This was how Tangkuban Prahu was formed into a huge caldera which today is three-quarters broken down. The Tengger caldera in eastern Java is better preserved. After climbing the chemara-clad slopes above Tosari, the traveller sees opening at his feet the Sand Sea, an elliptical hole about 5½ miles by 4½ miles, surrounded by a precipitous rim between 1000 and 1500 feet high. Sand derived from the decomposition of volcanic matter is piled up in little dunes on its flat bottom, from which rise the recent volcanoes of Widodaren, Batok (an almost perfect cone remarkable for its radial gullies), and Bromo. The last-named ceaselessly belches out clouds of vapour-smoke, and every year the natives throw votive offerings into its crater. These are only some of the features in a volcanic mass about 30 miles in diameter, which is comparable in a way with Cantal (in central France) and includes the still active Semeru, the highest peak in Java (12,000 feet). Dutch geologists recognised successive phases of construction and destruction together with the displacement of the eruptive centres along a line running from NNE. to SSW. Lake Toba in northern Sumatra is the result of still far more impressive phenomena. With Samosir Island this sheet of water has four times the area of Lake Geneva. It occupies a hollow scooped out in an enormous heap of lava and tuff which covers nearly the whole 90 miles of the island's breadth.

Such complex structures suggest that volcanic activity was formerly much more intense, and this is confirmed in many ways. Not a few of the still active volcanoes have left in popular tradition no evidence of violent eruption and are now reduced to the state of fumaroles. Lava flows do not often occur today. Being too viscous, the magma generally fails to flow out of the crater or else it flows out only at intervals. It forms domes inside the craters, like those of Galungung and Merapi in Java, Ruang in the Sangi Isles between Celebes and Mindanao, and Lobelobi Perampuan in Flores. The phenomenon has been well described by Kemmerling.[1] Under pressure from within, the shell of the dome bursts from time to time, emitting a wave of lava which flows on to the external slopes of the mountain and solidifies more or less quickly in the gullies and valleys. The fossil domes which occur here and there prove that the magma has lost its explosive force.

Today nearly all the eruptions are of an explosive type. The most famous was that of Krakatoa, which in 1883 gutted and smashed an island in Sunda Strait. The explosions were heard

[1] Kemmerling, in Rutten (19), p. 92.

(a)

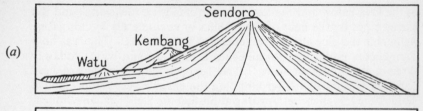

(b)

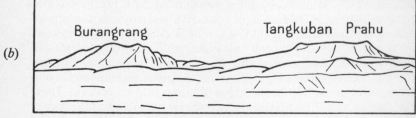

(c)

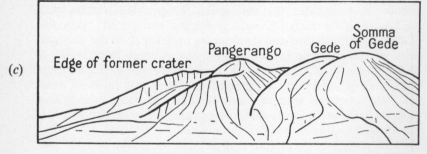

(d)

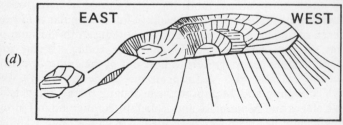

FIG. 3

(a) Simple Volcano: Sendoro in Mid-Java (after Taverne)
(b) Burangrang and Tangkuban Prahu in West Java, from the South (after Taverne)
(c) Volcano System of Gede and Pangerango in West Java, from the South (after Taverne)
(d) The Two Craters of Tangkuban Prahu (after Stehn)
(e) Alignment of Active Craters between Lamongan and Tarub in East Java (after Taverne)
(f) Areas covered by ashes of Kelud in East Java in 1901 and 1919 (after Kemmerling and Rutten)
(g) Extent of *lahars* of Kelud at the time of the Eruption of 1919 (after Kemmerling and Rutten)

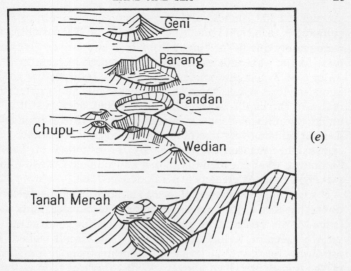

Geni
Parang
Pandan
Chupu-
Wedian
Tanah Merah

(e)

1901 —·—·—
1919 — — —

(f)

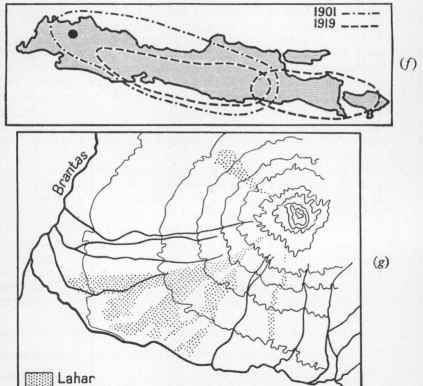

Brantas

Lahar

(g)

throughout the islands, and the upper layers of atmosphere were coloured by ash right round the world; the 36,000 casualties counted were mainly due to the tidal wave which swept over the coasts near by. As the wave entered the deeply indented bays in the Strait, the water rose 75 feet above its normal level at Teluk Betung in southern Sumatra, tore vessels from their anchorages, and carried them far up on to the land. A layer of ash 4 inches thick is still to be seen under the alluvial deposits on the slopes, and the memory of the disaster remains very distinct in the minds of the people. Another catastrophe was caused in 1815 by the eruption of Tambora in Sumbawa, when the quantity of ash and pumice thrown into the air was eight times as great as at Krakatoa in 1883.[1]

It sometimes happens that gases and dust from the volcanoes run down the sides of the cones in incandescent clouds, rather like those from Morne Pelée. The phenomenon has been observed in Java on Mts. Merapi, Kelud, and Semeru. The clouds (called 'ladoes') are always related to the lava flows resulting from the bursting of one of the domes described above. Whilst the lava follows the gullies, the cloud is here not affected by surface relief, but moves straight down asphyxiating every living creature in its way.[2]

A very frequent phenomenon in Indonesia is the *lahar*, a flow of mud, a landslide of volcanic material impregnated with water and moving down gentle slopes carrying blocks of stone at times larger than a native dwelling. The water may come from the heavy falls of rain which occur during eruptions, as on Mt. Semeru in August 1909; and this makes a cold *lahar*. Or else it may come from the sudden emptying of a crater-lake, giving rise to a hot *lahar*, which has been better illustrated by Mt. Kelud in eastern Java than by any other volcano. The water of the lake was thrown out by the swelling up of the lava dome at the bottom of the crater and mingled with the material ejected by earlier eruptions. Such a case occurred in May 1919, when the rush of 52,000,000 cubic yards of water charged with solid matter caused 5500 casualties. Since then a tunnel has been bored to allow the lake to drain regularly.

Today disasters are restricted by organised watching and warnings. Posts are maintained on the more dangerous mountains. Some are permanently occupied by watchers; elsewhere instruments are sufficient to announce the premonitory symptoms of an eruption; and the population can be evacuated in time from the threatened area.

But the benefits of volcanoes greatly exceed the harm they entail.

[1] According to information gathered by Junghuhn about the middle of the 19th century.
[2] Kemmerling in Rutten (19), p. 96.

First, they bring fertility not only to the neighbourhood, but also through the dispersion of the ash to places at great distances away. Their high relief causes condensation and so increases the rainfall. Thanks to the high degree of permeability in the materials of which they are built, they are also reservoirs of water. They assist agriculture by their very forms, for the irrigation of the fertile soil is facilitated by the wide surfaces formed chiefly by the spread of *lahars* at the foot of the cones, but also caused where valleys with interlocking terraces become gradually enclosed downstream by increasingly steep banks. The cultivation of a *sawah*, or irrigated ricefield, may be carried on as high as 5000 feet above sea level. The effect on European colonisation is no less, for the yield from plantations depends partly on the fertility of the land. The association of the traditional food crops with those grown for export has been far easier to bring about here than elsewhere, because export crops are often got from shrubs cultivated on the sides of volcanic hillmasses.

The Variety of the Relief. In spite of the leading part played by volcanoes in the economy of the Malay world, it must not be thought that they always appear in the landscape. The monotonous plains on which they stand sometimes extend so far from the cones that the mountains are lost to sight. The plains themselves vary in origin and altitude. Often they are erosional platforms of Primary or Secondary rocks and are levelled fold ranges dominated by residual buttes, many of which are formed of granite, like the *bukit* of Malaya. Or they may be tables cutting through folds dating from the second half of the Tertiary or even the Lower Quaternary. Some of them rise to more than 3000 feet and are gashed with deeply incised valleys; for example, the high plains in the central mountain range around Mt. Data in northern Luzón; and in central Celebes, where almost horizontal summits rise above 6000 feet. The plains are nearly always much dissected by the later cycles of erosion reinforced by an abundant rainfall as well as by the degree of recent uplifting. Besides, erosion is weakly resisted by deposits which are often soft, like Tertiary marls and shales. The ledges frequently seen on the sides of the valleys do not always mark stages in the deepening of the valleys by the streams, but are usually due to landslides or rockfalls. Such raised surfaces gashed by innumerable gullies are also found in central Java and in Madura, in the Malay Peninsula, south-eastern Sumatra, and eastern Borneo.

The most peculiar relief in sedimentary rocks which have been folded and then worn level is due to limestones that are at times of Primary, but more often of Tertiary, origin. Tropical *karst* forming cliffs of extraordinarily jagged appearance rises above soft material.

In other places there are plateaus with underground drainage, but with dry valleys tracing veritable mazes between swarms of hills with more or less convex profiles; as, for example, in Mt. Sewu to the south of Surakarta in central Java, in the Visayas, and the little island of Nusa Penida to the south of Bali.

Another type of relief which covers large areas in eastern Sumatra and Borneo at any rate, consists of plains built up by mud from the streams at the expense of the sea and often mantled with swamp forest separated from the open sea by a fringe of *Nipa* palms and mangrove. Other plains have been formed inland by the action of rivers in silting up lakes. These lakes are almost all of volcanic origin, as for example those in the highlands of Sumatra or Java.

The rapid rate of erosion combines with tectonic instability and the effects of vulcanism to add variety and change to the scenery.[1] Much heavy rain falling on strata which are often of weak resistance causes the quantity of rockwaste washed away to reach a greater volume than is the case in Europe outside the basins of Mediterranean rivers. Calculations made by the irrigation department in Java show that the mean annual quantity washed away may exceed 1 millimetre over the whole basin and even amounts to 4 millimetres in one district. The average weight of mud carried by the Solo in Java is 4·64 lb. per cubic yard of water. This is fifty times more than is carried by the Rhine above the delta and 1·65 lb. more than the Ganges carries before its junction with the Gangra. From sections drawn across certain islands made of fold mountains it seems that since the Quaternary era rockwaste to a depth of many thousands of feet has been washed away by erosion due to the very rainy climate.

[1] Rutten (33), pp. 154 ff.

CHAPTER 3

CLIMATE

Malaya, the East Indies, and the Philippines lie between 20° N. lat. and 10° S. lat. and are thus situated wholly within the tropics. More than four-fifths of the area of the region lie within 10° of the Equator. The vastness of the space occupied by salt water and the fact that, except in Borneo, no .part of the land is farther than 125 miles from the sea strengthen the characteristics of the climate due to the general geographical position.[1]

General Features. The climate is marked as equatorial by its calm atmosphere and equable temperature. Differences of pressure are very slight, between Asia and Australia the isobars are widely spaced, and barometric readings gradually decrease northwards in July and southwards in January (see Fig. 4). Variations in pressure are regular, gradual, small, and, in fact, identical for more than 1000 miles. They are generally the after-effects of atmospheric disturbances which begin and develop in higher latitudes.

As always, the winds are strongest and least variable over the sea. Three lighthouses situated to the north of the Sunda arc between Java and Timor record more than 88 per cent. of the winds as blowing from the west and north-west in January and February, and more than 90 per cent. from the east and south-east in July and August. From the very numerous observations taken by the *Snellius* in her cruises in 1929–30 it has been found that in 50 per cent. of the cases the wind-velocity was between only 4 and 12 m.p.h. The sea is almost always calm, and navigation far less dangerous than in the temperate belt. Currents are more to be feared by sailors than are storms, for they often rush violently through the straits, those at Flores and Lantar in eastern Indonesia sometimes reaching a speed of 19 m.p.h.[2] For trade between the islands the Dutch East India Company used ships that were not sound enough to make their way back to Europe. On land the winds are more variable, for the regular currents of air that flow across the open sea are often replaced here by land and sea breezes. These are most noticeable on the coasts of the large islands and are sometimes observed in the Celebes Sea nearly 200 miles from Borneo, bringing

[1] The most recent description is by C. Braak: *Klimakunde von Hinterindien und Insulinde*, (38).
[2] Cp. Wallace's observations during his voyage from Waigeu to Ternate, (63), pp. 410–19.

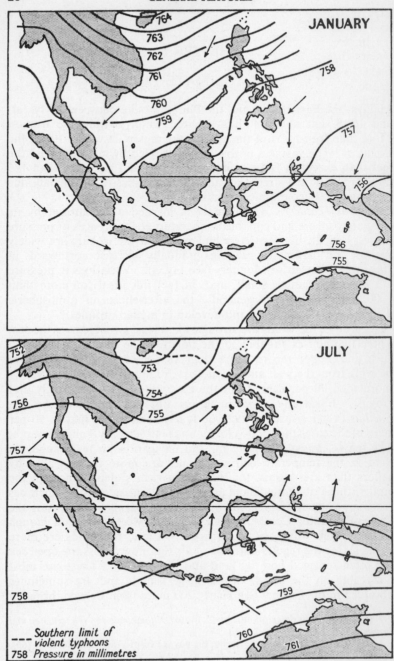

FIG. 4.—PRESSURE AND WINDS IN SOUTHEASTERN ASIA IN
JANUARY AND JULY

with them at a certain time of the year the delicate scent of wild vanilla. The mean velocity of the wind decreases towards the interior of the islands. In Java it is 6 m.p.h. at Semarang, but it scarcely exceeds 2 m.p.h. at Jakarta, a few miles from the coast.

The distribution of temperature clearly illustrates the effects of nearness to the Equator and the sea. There is remarkable uniformity in an area measuring some 2500 miles from north to south and from east to west, and the annual means differ but slightly. At Basco, a little island to the north of Luzón,[1] the mean annual temperature is 78° F.; at Pontianak on the Equator in Borneo 79° F.[2]; at Penang 79° F.; and at Kupang in Timor 79° F. The variations from one month to another are slight and scarcely distinguish the seasons. At Jakarta, where the Royal Observatory has been functioning since 1866, the mean temperature rises to 79° F. in May, but is as high as 78° F. in January, the coolest month. The annual range here is only 1·8° F. and nowhere exceeds 9° F. Life is spent in a continuous sweltering heat like the atmosphere of a hot-house. But whilst great cold is unknown, suffocating heat is rare. All through the year the thermometer generally oscillates between 68° F. and 86° F. in the lowlands. Between 1866 and 1930 the absolute extremes of temperature in Jakarta—65° F. and 96° F. —were recorded in 1877. The shade temperature apparently never reaches 100° F. in any part of Malaya or the East Indies, though the north of the Philippines is an exception. Only in the sheltered plains of Luzón does the mean maximum exceed that figure, whilst the mean minimum falls to 60° F. As is the rule in the tropics, the diurnal range is greater than the mean annual range and is greatest during the dry season. In the Philippines it varies from 10° F. to 25° F.; whilst at Pontianak it averages 13° F.[3]

The days are all much alike not only in length, but also in the sequence of weather, the sequence of climatic phenomena, and the effect of these on the feelings and outlook. Fogs sometimes cover the ground at night, but are quickly dispersed, and the sun rises in a clear sky. By nine o'clock light cumulus clouds begin to form and at the same time a breeze begins to blow. The clouds thicken, become lower in the sky, and in the afternoon merely disperse or else drop heavy showers. In the evening the sky becomes clear

[1] Aparri on the north coast of Luzón has a mean January temperature 9° F. higher than the coast of Annam in the same latitude.

[2] Numerous data of the climate of Pontianak are given in *Die Insel Borneo*, by Fehn (145), p. 44.

[3] The mean annual minima and maxima are: Manila 62° F. and 98° F.; Singapore 70 and 93° F.; and Jakarta 68 and 93° F.

once again and after a short twilight the night is usually superbly calm.

Rain is the most variable element in this climate. Malaya and the East Indies are certainly to be reckoned among the regions with the highest and most regular rainfall in the world. Yet the diversity of the archipelago and the variety of its scenery and modes of life are closely related to the amount of rain and to the rainfall system. Great contrasts occur, and shades of difference are infinite, even if only averages are taken into account. As might be expected, the 21 inches a year that fall at Palu Bay in north-western Celebes and the 166 inches at Buitenzorg Bogor in north-western Java—to mention only lowland districts—make a great difference in the scenery at the two places. And the distribution of this rainfall between the months offers every degree of difference between montonous plenty and a system of well-marked wet and dry seasons.

Differences in Climate, great and small. The rainfall system is affected by nearness not only to the Equator, but also to the two continents between which the East Indies lie. On the whole, the monsoon climate which characterises Southeast Asia extends over the whole archipelago, with local shades of difference due to latitude and to the continuation of the island chain to near the coast of Australia.

The two land masses of Asia and Australia, situated on either side of an equatorial belt occupied mainly by the sea, are always under opposing pressure systems which move alternately from one hemisphere to the other. Relatively very hot in summer, they are centres of low pressure systems which suck in air currents. On the other hand, they are cold and under high pressure in winter; hence, they send out winds. Thus, the trade wind system is greatly modified. In the winter hemisphere the trades are reinforced by winds from the cold continent; whilst in the opposite hemisphere, where it is summer, the direction of the trade wind is reversed. Instead of winds blowing towards the equatorial belt of calms, the East Indies as a whole have winds that blow from one continent to the other alternately (see Fig. 4). When it is summer in the northern hemisphere, winds from Australia blow at first from the south-east, but are more and more deflected by the rotation of the Earth, until they become south-west winds which are felt as far as the north of Luzón and the southern Mariannes and, when at their fullest extent, even in Shanghai and the Bonin Islands. During the winter in the same hemisphere (summer in the southern hemisphere) the north-east winds extend south of the Equator as north-west or even west winds. Though often disguised, the trade wind is not suppressed. It often blows as a gentle breeze over the Philippines during the change of the monsoon and especially in March and April, and it resumes when the south-west monsoon advances too far north and finds itself cut off from its source.

The influence of these alternating winds, or monsoons, combines with, but often exceeds, that of latitude. The rainfall is distributed most evenly near the Equator. The graphs in Fig. 6 show two well-

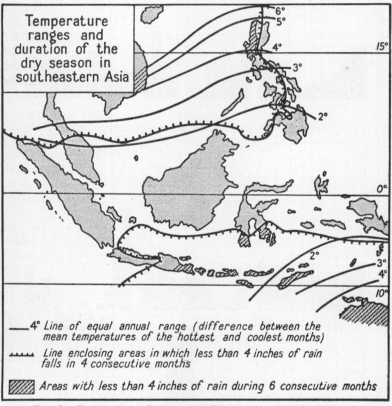

Temperature ranges and duration of the dry season in southeastern Asia

_____4° *Line of equal annual range (difference between the mean temperatures of the hottest and coolest months)*

...... *Line enclosing areas in which less than 4 inches of rain falls in 4 consecutive months*

▨ *Areas with less than 4 inches of rain during 6 consecutive months*

FIG. 5.—TEMPERATURE RANGES AND DURATION OF THE DRY SEASON

marked maxima following the passage of the sun at its zenith; e.g. at Cameron's Highlands. Yet the driest months at Padang get 10 or 12 inches of rain out of a total of 174 inches falling on 190 days.

The farther one goes from the Equator, the greater the influence of the monsoons. But their effect varies according to the distance travelled by the winds across the sea and according to the relief and aspect of the lands they reach. The monsoon from over the sea may blow for several days without disturbing the fine weather, if

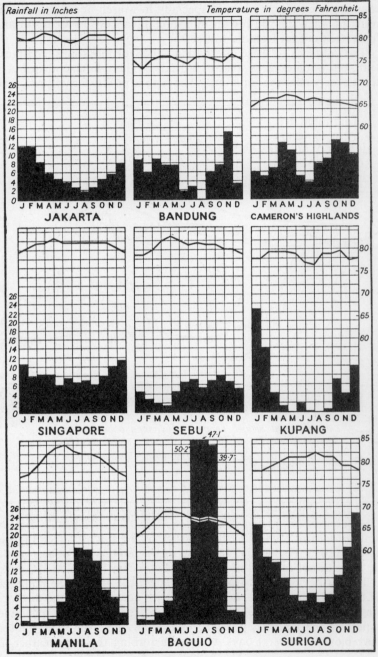

FIG. 6.—TYPES OF TEMPERATURE AND RAINFALL

the wind follows a level path and meets no obstacle. Heavy rain falls only when masses of saturated air are affected by wandering depressions which cause areas of turbulence in the path of the monsoon. In well-sheltered basins the two annual rainfall maxima may be almost equal, as they are at Bandung in western Java. But in other places they often fuse to form a single maximum, which occurs at the height of the summer monsoon. In the southern hemisphere mountain slopes fully exposed to the wind at that juncture get a high rainfall from the north and north-west winds. For instance, in February more than 40 inches fall at Yasareja (5000 feet) on the southern slopes of the central range in Java; and as much as 30 inches at sea level at the foot of the mountains near Macassar in south-western Celebes. In the northern hemisphere, on the other hand, the south-west monsoon causes enormous precipitation in August on the western slopes of Luzón, where about 23 inches fall on the coast and about 50 inches at the hill station of Baguio (5000 feet). The latter place had 133 inches in July 1911.

Though usually dry, the winter monsoon may, however, after a long sea crossing give heavy rain on contact with steep hills. Thus the January mean exceeds 23 inches at certain points on the east coast of Luzón, where the wind is from the north-east. At the same time the west coast is extremely dry, getting 0·5 inch in January at Laoag in north-western Luzón. In August when the south-east wind is blowing, an even sharper contrast is seen between the north and south sides of Ijen in eastern Java. Whilst in the south Pakudo streams with 15·5 inches, Asembagus, which is under the shadow of the volcanic hill-mass, has the extremely low mean of 0·2 inch.

It is impossible to touch on all the particular cases. Combinations of different factors give rise to a very large number of variations in the rainfall system, whose complexity is well illustrated by the fact that every month sees a rainfall maximum and a minimum in some part of Malaya or Indonesia. The dry season may continue normally for several months. It does so in some districts in the Philippines, especially in the west; for instance, on the west coast of Luzón, the station at Vigan records 105 inches of rain a year, but only 0·7 inch in the three driest and 3·1 in the six driest months.

The drought is far more striking in the southern hemisphere and is marked by low annual rainfall totals as well as a brief rainy season. The extraordinarily low precipitation in Palu Bay quite near the Equator in northern Celebes has already been mentioned. The difference between wet and dry seasons gradually increases from south-eastern Celebes and the middle of Java along the eastern section of the Sunda arc. The total annual rainfall at Asembagus in north-eastern Java (32 inches) and on the south coast of Sumba is less than 40 inches. Kupang, near the southern end of Timor, gets 57 inches a year, but only 0·3 inch in the months of July, August, and September, and only 2·7 inches in the six months from May to October. Within 10° of the Equator this is a strong indication of the influence of the Australian desert (see Fig. 5).

The variation in rainfall from year to year is greatest in regions with a well-marked dry season and there entails the most serious consequences for human life. Since the cultivation of food crops is usually restricted to the wet season, a delay in the arrival of the monsoon may have a ruinous effect on a vital harvest. The same result occurs if the rains are interrupted by several weeks of drought caused by the failure of local depressions to give heavy rain in the path of the monsoon. These irregularities upset the tenor of native life, especially in eastern Indonesia and still more in the northern Philippines.

Now that these special cases have been mentioned, it must be emphasised that over the greater part of their area Malaya and the East Indies do not belie their geographical position and are indeed equatorial in the steady, high rainfall as well as their even temperature. According to a table drawn up for the year 1936 only three out of 3354 pluviometrical stations scattered throughout Indonesia had a rainfall of less than 20 inches, thirty-nine less than 40 inches, whilst 2420 had more than 80 inches. No station in the Philippines records a total of less than 40 inches, not one in Malaya less than 60 inches, and the great majority of stations in these two countries record more than 80 inches. Certainly no other region in the world gets such a high rainfall over so large an area. The mean annual totals of the wettest stations exceed 240 inches, among them Bandarbaru between Medan and Lake Toba in northern Sumatra (2820 feet), and Yasareja in central Java, which has already been mentioned. They are both mountain stations; but even places at low altitudes have plenty of rain, provided that mountain ridges behind them force the saturated winds to rise. Thus, Buitenzorg (790 feet) in north-western Java gets 166·5 inches, Padang on the west coast of Sumatra 180, Amboina in south Serang 134, and Surigao in north-eastern Mindanao 136. The mean precipitation in Malaya and the archipelago can scarcely be less than 100 inches.

Rain falls as a rule in very heavy downpours. The greatest intensity over a short time is not much more than occurs in the temperate belt; but heavy showers are far more frequent, and the mean intensity is consequently greater. Braak says that in Indonesia 20 per cent. of the rain falls in showers giving at least 0·003 inch per minute and of at least 5 minutes' duration, whilst the percentage is ten times less in Bavaria. Hence, in the East Indies the showers last a relatively short time.   In Jakarta 72 inches of rain fall in 357 hours as against 23 inches in 657 hours at Potsdam.   A typical equatorial system like that at Pontianak is said to have constant rains; but even there droughts not seldom last a fortnight or even a month.   The hours of sunshine are far more numerous than would be supposed from the continual talk of dismal gloom.   The daily mean is 6 hours 4 minutes at Jakarta and 7 hours 1 minute at Padang, which is, however, one of the wettest parts of Indonesia. Eastern Indonesia has the greatest amount of sunshine during the year.   Kupang has 3072 hours as against 2103 at Manila, 2229 at Pontianak, 2326 at Jakarta, and 2849 at Macassar.   Jakarta has only 103 days in the year which are really overcast, that is when cloud cover is greater than $\frac{8}{10}$; but only 12 days of clear sky— when cloud cover is less than $\frac{2}{10}$.   The play of sunlight on the different shades of green in forest and cultivated field is one of the great charms of Indonesia.   Yet travellers like Conrad have spoken of the oppressive character of the tropical sun, whose light is diffused by the damp atmosphere both at sea and over tin-yielding estuaries with their white beaches and fringes of dark mangrove.

Like rain, thunderstorms are not more violent than in western Europe; but they are more frequent and usually occur in the afternoon at the change of the monsoon and especially in the weeks of at least relative drought preceding the rainy season.   They seldom accompany heavy rains.

Storms and hurricanes do not often occur in the East Indies, and their violence and the damage they do are often exaggerated.   Exceptions must, however, be made of the north and south margins of the archipelago, for there typhoons are rife.   These storms begin in the belt of air forming the equatorial warm front which is displaced by the action of high-pressure belts, and they travel from east to west as a rule.[1]   Those which pass to the south of the Sunda arc are sometimes felt in Java and may cause heavy damage in Timor and nearby islands in April.   Far more frequent and dangerous are the typhoons in the Philippines.   Every year several of them cross the northern part of those islands, nearly always between July and November.   They then make for southern Japan or the coasts of China or Indo-China, causing considerable havoc at times.   House-roofs are torn off, telegraph poles knocked down, and trees uprooted by the violence of the wind.   Floods that are sometimes fatal to man and beast are caused by the heavy rain and even more by the accompanying inrush of the tide reinforced by storm waves.

Differences in climate are further increased by the effects of altitude.   In Indonesia the temperature decreases on an average by

[1] Depperman (40).

1° F. for every 375 feet of ascent. But the thermometer varies no more from one month to the next in the mountains than in the plains. Monthly means do not differ by much more than 4° F. at Baguio or at the summit of Pangerango in western Java (9900 feet) and only by 2° F. at Fort de Kock in Sumatra (3000 feet). Between 1912 and 1918 the absolute minimum recorded on Pangerango was 33° F., and night frost has never been observed in the mountains in Malaya, Sumatra, or the north and centre of Celebes, but hoar-frost has occurred at Kinabalu in northern Borneo. The lowest temperatures have been recorded in the south-east of the archipelago, where frost often occurs above 5000 feet during calm nights at the height of the dry season; for example, at a height of about 6000 feet on the plateau of Dieng in central Java and even no higher than 3000 feet in the crater of Ijen in the eastern part of the same island.

The sky above the mountains is more often overcast, and clouds collect more regularly, in the afternoon and night. At first rainfall increases with height, precipitation consisting more often than in the lowlands of persistent showers of fine rain. On Mt. Singgalang near the Equator in Sumatra observations taken at a height of 9500 feet show that there were 320 days of rain in the year and a mean relative humidity of 93 per cent., the driest month not falling below 89 per cent. But then the rainfall diminishes above a certain altitude, though no general rule can be formulated. On isolated volcanoes the decrease begins about half-way up. On compact hill-masses the belt of greatest rainfall seems to rise higher as the altitude of the hill-mass increases. The air changes more often owing to the existence of vertical ascending or descending currents; so on the heights the relative humidity may pass in a few minutes from a very low figure almost to saturation point.

Acclimatisation. In spite of the equability of the temperature, which is a permanent equatorial feature, hill stations are beneficial to the health of Europeans and enable them to stay in the tropics for a long time with less frequent visits to Europe. The progress in housing and the adoption of a diet and dress suitable to the climate are not enough to prevent anæmia and the nervous diseases which threaten Europeans dwelling in the lowlands. In the loneliness of the bush and the atmosphere of native surroundings these ill-defined maladies, called the 'Philippinite' in Manila, have led to mental depression and an obsession of fear of mysterious and baleful influences.[1] The air in the hills at least delays and weakens the attacks of such diseases. The journey to Buitenzorg has an immediately salutary effect on a resident of Jakarta, though the drop

[1] Cp. the stories of Somerset Maugham, who has travelled in Malaya: *The Trembling of a Leaf, The Casuarina Tree.*

in temperature averages only 2·5° F. The number of holiday
stations above 3000 feet has increased, among the most frequented
being Cameron's Highlands in Pahang on the Perak-Pahang border,
Fraser's Hill (4200 feet) also in Pahang to the north of Kuala
Lumpur in Malaya, Berastagi (5250 feet) to the north of Lake Toba
in Sumatra, Baguio (5000 feet) in the mountains of Luzón, and
Tosari (5700 feet) on the slopes of the Tengger hill-mass in eastern
Java. In the last mentioned the mean temperature is 18·5° F.
lower than in Jakarta. It is a delight to sleep under blankets, yet to
shiver slightly in the morning, and then to set off early under a clear
sky for the casuarina forests and the bare summits of the volcanoes.

CHAPTER 4

VEGETATION AND FAUNA

Malaya and Indonesia have a wealth of living species unique in tropical lands. This is certainly due in part to the heavy rainfall and variety of relief, but it is also the outcome of a position between two very ancient major continental realms. The flora and fauna which evolved in south-eastern Asia and in Australia in very different conditions would naturally spread over Indonesia, where they would meet and mingle. The existing vegetable and animal life there is the outcome of a very complex evolution influenced by geological developments. The formation of the islands was certainly not a regular process. As was said above, its history remains very obscure, and our glimpse of the series of conditions through which the archipelago has passed and of the very numerous changes in its outline during the Tertiary and Quaternary periods is due to botanical and zoological research. As a result of variations in the sea level, in orogenic forces, vulcanism, the activity of coral formation, and the deposition of alluvium, groups of islands have been alternately joined together and separated. The connexion between Asia and Australia has been broken, re-established, and broken again; and animals and plants from the continents have developed local characteristics during the more or less lengthy periods of isolation. Hence, the interest aroused by the exuberance and diversity of life in the region is easily understood.

The problems have in fact caused great enthusiasm in many naturalists, and the theory of natural selection was formulated very largely from observations made in this region. The most striking, of course, were those of A. R. Wallace, who stayed in these parts from 1854 to 1862 and brought back more than 125,000 specimens of the fauna. He confirmed the theory worked out by Darwin as early as 1835, and the years 1858 when Wallace and Darwin read a joint paper before the Linnean Society, and 1859 when *The Origin of Species* was published, are outstanding dates in the history of natural science.

Wallace saw in the Straits of Macassar and Lombok a clear line of separation between species of Asiatic affinity and those of Australian origin. Later researches have proved that the Wallace Line did not have the clearness of definition attributed to it by its author.[1] It is strange, of course, that it should correspond more or

[1] According to Van Steenis (56a) the most significant break in the Sunda arc,

38

less exactly with the transition from the Sunda shelf to the deep seas and small islands of eastern Indonesia. But whilst this structural difference is certainly fairly ancient,[1] the straits separating the islands were, however, not insuperable obstacles to the migration of animal and vegetable species. This was especially true of the latter, which can be more easily carried by winds and currents. The Wallace Line keeps its validity for many zoologists, but, on the other hand, most botanists regard the East Indies as a floral domain in which Asiatic influence prevails. In any case, the relative number of Australian forms increases only gradually, and predominance is reached only in Australia itself.[2]

Distribution of Forest. There is no doubt that the climate of the region is generally favourable to the existence of dense forest. The forest vegetation-type is indeed very extensive, but is far from being everywhere present. No absolute value can be given to the figures quoted for its area, because it has not yet been sufficiently investigated for exact description to be possible, and the statistics very often include under the head of forest associations what should more properly be termed savana or bush (see Fig. 7).[3]

The proportion of woodland to the total area of the region seems to be far below one-half and is probably nearer one-third. But forest is very unevenly spread over the islands and even over parts of the same island. In the Philippines its area is reckoned at 55 per cent. of the whole group; but Mindanao is far more wooded than Luzón, Mindoro than Panay, and Negros than Sebu. The most reliable figures for Indonesia come mainly from Endert's researches and were given recently by van Steenis and illustrated by a very fine map in the *Atlas van Tropisch Nederland.* According to it, forest covers 70 per cent. of the surface in northern and north-eastern Sumatra, the south-eastern half of Borneo, the Moluccas, and New Guinea; but less than 30 per cent. in the Sunda arc from Java to Timor inclusive. Elsewhere the proportion varies between 30 and 70 per cent.

In seeking to discover the causes of these great differences it is

so far as plant geography is concerned, is Sunda Strait between Sumatra and Java, and not Lombok Strait.

[1] According to Rutten there was deep water between Borneo and Celebes right at the beginning of the Miocene.

[2] Cheesman considers the fauna as well as the flora of New Guinea as being on the whole of a mainly Asiatic character. See *Geogr. J.,* vol. xcv, 1940, pp. 208–17.

[3] The chief work on the vegetation of the Dutch East Indies is *Maleische Vegetatieschetsen,* by G. G. J. van Steenis (56). It is accompanied by a map on a scale of 1/75M. The map is reproduced in the *Atlas van Tropisch Nederland,* sheet 7 (33).

CHIEF
FOOD CROPS
Rice
Rice and Maize
Rice and Cassava
Sago ......Coconuts   After Lekkerkerker

VEGETATION
Forest
Savana, Scrub, Moor, and
degenerate Forest
Permanent cultivation
---Western limit of the eucalyptus family
After Van Steenis, Kolb, etc.
100 0 100   400 Miles

FIG. 7.—VEGETATION AND CROPS (after Van Steenis, Kolb, etc.)

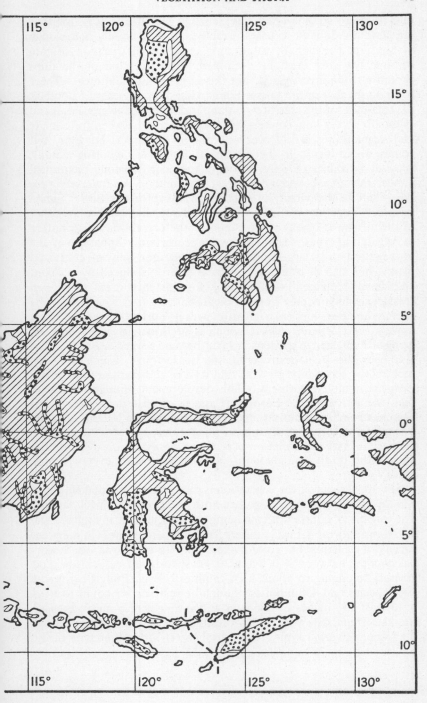

impossible to confine one's researches to climatic factors, for they are certainly difficult to assess exactly. It is definitely not enough to consider the rainfall totals only, and the distribution of rain through the year must be examined. The duration of the rains should also be investigated, but this is generally unknown. There is no doubt that in the Lesser Sunda Islands to the east of Lombok the smallness of the area of woodland is due to the lower rainfall and especially to the long dry season. The relation between the climate and vegetation scarcely ever appears to be direct, however, but comes about through the action of man. If, ignoring details, account be taken of only the main regional divisions mentioned above, the area covered by forest is found to be inversely proportionate to the density of population, except in the Lesser Sunda Islands. Together with the climate and soil, but more than either of them, man is chiefly responsible for the present-day distribution of vegetation-types. His handiwork is certainly apparent in the propagation of a large number of species not only of cultivated plants, but also of others which have been introduced by accident and have remained wild. Such, for instance, are *Eichhornia crassipes*, which comes from tropical America and which clogs the streams and even hinders navigation with its upright leaves and violet flowers; and *Mimosa pudica*, which is of Brazilian origin and, on being acclimatised in gardens in Java, became a weed. But man has also been the great destroyer of the dense forest, which has been replaced by secondary growths that lead to the grass savana, where trees are completely absent. This development, though far earlier than the arrival of the Europeans and in a sense immemorial, has been hastened by colonisation. The forest has diminished not only owing to the spread of European plantations, but also because the increase in native population occasioned an extension of collecting and of the traditional methods of cultivation over ever widening areas.

The appearance of the vegetation is due to the combined action of climate, soil, and man, together with palæogeographical factors. The forest is of course far from being always the same in appearance, for tropical forest naturally differs from temperate forest in the great variety of elements that go to make it up. In Indonesia van Steenis has counted between 20,000 and 30,000 species of trees, shrubs, and grasses, belonging to about 2500 families. Even Endert arrives at 3000 species and 450 families, though he restricts his count to trees of at least $15\frac{1}{2}$ inches in diameter at the height of a man's breast.[1] But the irregularity with which the trees are mingled is not always the same. Even in typical equatorial forest little differences in the

[1] Van Steenis (56), p. 40.

nature of the soil, relief, or climate are reflected in the appearance of the stands. The slight anticlinal ridges of tuff on the lowlands of Sumatra carry fine stands of dipterocarps which show up against the rest of the forest. The Tertiary hills in eastern Java are the favourite home of teak. In places where the layman at first sees only inextricable confusion the botanist recognises an arrangement something like a mosaic, and in the most luxuriant forests he distinguishes stands each of which is characterised by the fairly small number of species they contain. Surveys of this kind have certainly been carried out more carefully in Indonesia than in any other region in the hot belt. Here, however, only the main features of distribution can be touched upon.

Coastal Forests. The mangrove[1] is a well-known form of coastal vegetation in the hot belt. The term includes a group of species belonging to families differing somewhat from each other, but all remarkably well adapted to their environment, that is, to soil periodically covered by the tide. Mangroves are found on limestone shores—for instance, on coral islands—but are of poor growth there. Their favourite home is the half-consolidated mud along the shores of relatively calm bays and lagoons, where they are sheltered from strong currents. They are found to some extent everywhere in the East Indies, but they form an almost continuous fringe on the west coast of the Malay Peninsula, eastern Sumatra, and southern and eastern Borneo. The traveller who goes up deeply indented estuaries like that of the Musi at Palembang tends to exaggerate the width of the mangrove belt, which may be as little as 30 yards and seldom exceeds a mile or two. However, in the district of Port Weld in the North of Perak in Malaya it measures nearly 12 miles. The various species are not scattered about at random, but run in successive belts parallel with the shore. The outer belt generally belongs to the genus *Rhizophora*, and the species *Rhizophora conjugata* and *R. mucronata* are the first to be seen from the sea, at first like outposts cut off by the flood tide and later as a continuous fringe. They form an almost impenetrable obstacle with their stems supported on stilt-roots and aerial roots that stream down from the main branches. Their seedlings, which are developed on the tree itself, shoot like darts into the blue-black mud and send out their roots into it in a few hours—a peculiarity which led Schimper to qualify the species as viviparous. The leaves are of a fine glossy green and are adapted to rapid transpiration.

Farther back from the sea appear other species of *Rhizophora* and also, as the soil is often more sandy and mixed with coral limestone, representatives of the genera *Bruguiera*, *Avicennia*, and *Sonneratia*.

[1] Van Steenis (56), p. 40.

Stilt-roots become less common and in the end disappear from the bottom of the stem; but the roots form an inextricable tangle from whence issue curious outgrowths, called pneumatophores, that have quite different functions than of assisting respiration. The trees sometimes reach a height of 100 or 120 feet, when their growth is not checked. But the mangrove belt has generally been the object of brisk exploitation because it is situated right on navigable water and furnishes various products like timber suitable for making sunken piles: hard, heavy, woody matter excellent for making charcoal, tannin, and so on. On the coasts of densely populated lowlands, like the plain around Manila Bay, the natives have long been systematically exploiting the mangrove belt. The requirements of European enterprise have brought great destruction on coastal forests; but today felling is very strictly regulated almost everywhere and is sometimes offset by afforestation.

Among the species of true mangroves a palm which grows in clumps or belts of varying width is often to be seen. On the banks of muddy, strongly tidal rivers it is found higher upstream than the mangrove and indeed right up to where the water is scarcely brackish. This is *Nipa fruticans*, a deep-rooted tree whose huge rosette of light green leaves stands out against the dark hue of the mangrove and seems to issue from the very ground, so short is its stem. *Nipa* is sometimes cultivated, for it too serves many purposes, its leaves being used for roofing huts and for making wickerwork and household utensils.

In eastern Sumatra and in Borneo a *Myrtacea* (*Melaleuca leucadendron*) forms almost pure stands behind the mangrove belt, its stem with its ragged bark rising white from the black, marshy soil.

Sandy coasts with dunes and spits are clothed in stiff, bluish grass (*Spinifex squarrosus*) or are dotted with black *filaos* (*Casuarina equisetifolia*) that look like cypresses from afar. These graceful trees are often associated with Pandanaceæ and *Barringtonia asiatica*. But this type of coastal forest has often been replaced by coconut groves.

Lowland Forest. The real equatorial forest extends from the fairly narrow coastal vegetation-strip up to a height of about 5000 feet above the sea. It is the type most often described by travellers, who have dwelt upon its monotonous and bewildering lack of order, its overwhelming mass, its long diurnal silences punctuated, however, especially in the morning, by the short calls or prolonged shrieks of monkeys and by the fall of heavy drops of dew, and rustling with the flight of pigeons, parrots, and hornbills. The forest is evergreen, but varies in shade of colour. It knows neither the deep stillness of our woods nor the seasonal and simultaneous fall of the leaves, and it covers vast expanses from the north of the Malay Peninsula to New Guinea, where it has connexions with the forests in Queensland. The adaptation of forms to the hot, damp climate is often exaggerated or at any rate oversimplified. Of course, the foliage in its eagerness for light generally spreads out in a kind of parasol at the top of the boles that are devoid of branches over much of their length. But the leaves differ greatly, some being large, others small, some simple or pinnate, or deeply indented, others dull or glossy. South-eastwards along the Sunda arc and also towards the north of the archipelago the decrease in rainfall, and especially the lengthening of the dry season, is reflected in a higher percentage of deciduous species; but western Flores still presents patches of evergreen forest. The fact is, a minute adaptation to local conditions may be observed, and very varied associations have been described by botanists. There are, for example, associations proper to marsh, peat-bogs, the margins of winding streams, dry ridges, and slopes. Around sheets of water in the peat-bogs covered with white and yellow Nympheaceæ the roots develop in such a way as in some degree to resemble mangrove. Sometimes the parasols of foliage on the tops of the smooth, lofty columns let through the sun's rays, and in their light the vivid colours—scarlet or bright yellow—of some flower flashes out in the confusion of the undergrowth. Or else the parasols of the big trees form a continuous mass impenetrable to light, under which there is an unchanging greenish gloom. The soil certainly affects the vegetation and is being more and more intensively studied in this connexion.

Bare soil, in which the humus decays very rapidly under the action of climatic factors, is a fairly common feature. Such spots have little grass and are merely dotted here and there with shade-loving plants like the Commelinaceæ, Rubiaceæ, Selaginellæ, Scitamineæ (the best known of which is ginger), and Araceæ with their long leaf-stalks and broad leaves. Above these grow shrubs (Strobilanthæ, Zingiberaceæ, Marantaceæ, and other Rubiaceæ), then one, two, or more storeys of trees, whose tiers seem more marked here than in any other equatorial forest. The impression of utter confusion of plant life is due less to the great variety of trees than to the abundance of epiphytes and parasites and to the tangle of lianas, some of which, like the rattan palm, may be more than 220 yards long and may cast over the other foliage crowns of light green, each with a spike standing up like a lightning conductor. It is mainly their flowers that at certain seasons sprinkle a few bright splashes of colour over the pervading green, for the tree-blossoms are often invisible through being very small or else dull in colour or because they open in the light above the foliage. Flowers are on the whole less common

than in temperate forests. Even the orchid blooms are often small
and dull. Notable exceptions are the big yellow bunches of
Coelogyne and the red or orange clusters of *Vanda Lowii* with their
bright purple spots. The flowers are often unscented, and none of
their wild fruit is comparable in taste with the raspberries and
strawberries of the European woodland.

In the main forests of Malaya, Sumatra, Borneo, and the Philippines dipterocarps occupy a prominent place owing to the space
they cover as well as to their height. In no part of the world is this
family better represented than in this region, where it includes about
four hundred species. Several of them, or closely related species,
figured in the flora of the region as early as the end of the Tertiary
period. Dipterocarps often form the top storey of the forest.
Seen from an aircraft and especially in a stereoscopic air photograph, they are recognisable by the colonnades formed by their
white trunks, which rise straight and branchless up to 100 or 130
feet, where they open out their foliage parasol-wise. The total
height may be as much as 200 feet. The trunk measures between
$2\frac{1}{4}$ and 5 feet in diameter above the base which is strengthened by
strong buttresses. Among these giants there are in particular
various species of *Shorea*, *Kompassia*, and *Dryobalanops aromatica*
(or Sumatran camphor tree). Some individual trees which have
been spared by the axe in the huge clearings on the east coast of
Sumatra make a very impressive sight, standing alone as they do.
The aircraft has enabled the dipterocarp forests to be surveyed
approximately. Measurements and tallies of their number have
given a fair idea of their extent. They are said to represent 50 per
cent. of the wooded area below an altitude of 2600 feet in Malaya
and 75 per cent. in the Philippines; and the proportions of the total
volume of timber are even more considerable, being 95 per cent. in
the Philippines; 60 per cent. in the south and east of Borneo, and
50 per cent. in Indonesia as a whole. Dipterocarps seem to shun
limestone and are absent, for example, in Nias.[1] Many species do
not blossom annually, but only at longer intervals. The fruit is
extraordinarily plentiful. The seeds require a dark, moist atmosphere for germination and keep their viability only a short time.
The great majority of species grow below the 1600-foot contour. In
Java, however, dipterocarps now occupy a far smaller place in the
surviving areas of primary forest and are scarcely ever found except
between the 1600- and 4000-foot contours. To the east of Macassar
and Lombok Straits they gradually disappear, but they still form a
few fairly dense stands in the Moluccas, whilst they become very rare
in the Lesser Sunda Islands and eastern New Guinea. Like many

[1] Steenis (56), p. 385.

other Malayan families, they do not reach Australia or the Pacific Islands.

Other fine species in the equatorial lowland forest are often strictly localised; for instance, *Pisonia grandis*, a tree with an enormous trunk, grows all over the Bancoran Islands in the Sulu Sea. Fig-trees are plentiful in the forests, where their innumerable fruit attract small mammals and birds. Some like *Urostigma Benjaminum* have a single bole. Several other species, which are not easily distinguished from each other by the layman, send out aerial roots which hang like ropes and take root on reaching the ground, thus making a whole grove out of a single tree. This is the *warangin*, or sacred tree of the natives, the most famous of which—at Bongkasa in Bali—covers an area of more than an acre and a half.

Palms are very numerous, at least 150 species being found in Indonesia. They rarely form stands by themselves, but are usually scattered. In western Java a species of *Corypha*, or *gebang*, is associated with bamboos, and *Phoenix* palms occur as often in the mangrove belt as in the forests inland. Several palms are cultivated or at any rate protected by man. These include the *latania*; *Areca catechu* (which is especially plentiful in Achin and bears a nut that with the betel leaf forms the traditional 'chew' in Malay countries); various sugar-palms, like *Arenga saccharifera* and a species of *Borassus*, or '*lontar*', which abounds in Bali and has a leaf that is used for several purposes, even for writing on; and the coconut tree, which, as Thomson has happily said, has the habit of leaning over the sea so that its fruit may be drifted by the currents to make oceanic islands habitable. It is by no means certain that the coconut tree is a native of the East Indies, for it is always found in cultivation there. A sandy shore with a saturated stratum underneath seems in fact to be its favourite position, and it is particularly plentiful below the 1000-foot contour; but it is also found above 3000 feet and far from the sea. Other useful palms are the sago (*Metroxylon*), which abounds in New Guinea and whose pith provides the natives of the Moluccas with their chief food. It is found also in western Indonesia, in the plains of eastern Borneo and in the islands to the south of Singapore. It generally favours a marshy district.

Graminaceæ occur in the form of large numbers of species of bamboos with leaves ranging from a bright green to a dull yellow. In exceptional cases they may reach a height of 130 feet, but as a rule are between 30 and 40 feet high. They love light and often cover fairly steep slopes, as they do in the mountains in Java and on the eastern side of Barisan in Sumatra, and they abound in central Flores and on the dry alluvial stretches in south-eastern Borneo.

They extract enormous quantities of water from the soil and grow very fast. The throwing out of suckers enables them to spread very rapidly, and in this dissemination they are assisted by man. They often form dense, unmixed stands which to the homesick European look from afar like fields of giant wheat.

Upland Forest. The composition of the forest is gradually modified by altitude. Certain families give way to others. Between the contours for 1500 and 3000 feet the stands of Dipterocarpeæ, Leguminosæ, Burseraceæ, Sapotaceæ, etc., fall away, whilst on the other hand there is an increase in Lauraceæ, Tricaceæ, Fagaceæ, and conifers.

Among the Fagaceæ *Castanopsis* and *Quercus*, which are plentiful in south China and north Indo-China, play an important part also in the mountain forests throughout the East Indies, except in the Lesser Sunda Islands. The genus *Quercus* alone is represented in the islands by more than a hundred species which differ from our western oaks in general appearance and in not having denticulate leaves.

Less common are species of conifers which originated in the Himalayas and have advanced into the East Indies to meet the casuarinas from Australia. *Pinus insularis* and *Pinus Merkusii*, which abound in Indo-China, occur in the Philippines and northern Sumatra even at sea level, but their most extensive stands are found above the 1500-foot contour, and scattered individuals are to be seen nearly as high up as the 9000-foot contour. *Pinus Merkusii* even crosses the Equator in Sumatra, its greatest advance having been observed on Kerinchi about lat. 2° 6' S. Like another conifer, *Agathis*, this tree sometimes reaches a height of 230 feet.

Agathis is the famous *damar*, which yields one of the best forms of copal gum. Unlike the pines, it grows mainly in the eastern part of the archipelago; but like them it prefers the mountains. It appears even in eastern Borneo, but becomes a characteristic feature of the mountain scenery in Celebes, the Moluccas, and western New Guinea, where it lifts its conical foliage above the forest on its massive trunk. In Celebes, for instance, it forms a storey 160 to 180 feet above a second of 100 to 115 feet and, like the dipterocarps in the lowlands of Sumatra and Borneo, it comprises more than 50 per cent. of the forest. The araucaria occurs in New Guinea only.

The tallest tree in the mountains of Sumatra and western Java is not a conifer, but one of the Hamamelidaceæ, the famous *rasamala* (*Altingia excelsa*). This giant tree advances eastwards in Java as far as Garut, to the east of Bandung. It is especially frequent at altitudes between 3000 and 5500 feet and is sometimes associated with a few species of Podocarpus, e.g. *Podocarpus imbricata*.

1. Equatorial forest in Johore, Malaya, seen through the cutting of a road. Note the straightness of the tree trunks and the stoutness of the displaced lianas.

2. The water-lily pond at Buitenzorg (now Bogor). Like many other things in Java, the famous Botanical Gardens were started by Sir Stamford Raffles during the short period of British rule at the beginning of the 19th century.

3. Mount Bromo, one of Java's complex volcanoes. Note the auxiliary craters and the slopes fluted by erosion.

On the lower slopes in western Indonesia the forest also contains the curious pitcher-plant with its creeping roots and leaves that grow into big lidded urns. As one goes up, herbaceous plants (Compositæ, Gentianaceæ, Graminaceæ, and Cyperaceæ) become more numerous, and many of the flowers, like buttercups, scentless violets, and valerian, remind one of their counterparts in temperate lands.

However, as one climbs towards the summits, one is struck by the general appearance which climatic modifications impose on the forest rather than by the predominance of new species. Between 5000 and 6000 feet up on the average one reaches the vegetation-type called moss-forest—the *mosbosch* or *nevelbosch* of Dutch writers.[1] In fact, it appears at very varying altitudes on mountains of volcanic origin as well as on others. Thus, on Pangerango (9900 feet) in western Java it occurs only above the 8000-foot contour, whilst on Mt. Maros in Banka it is found at a height of 2000 feet; in Buru at 2300 feet; below 3300 feet in some parts of New Guinea; and in the Philippines it is often typical at 4000 feet; but on Mt. Pulog it occurs between 7300 and 8300 feet. These heights correspond to the belt of most persistent fog and appear to vary with the dimensions of the hill-mass and the topography of the surroundings.[2] Moss covers the ground and trees with a thick, damp, fleece-like coating which is constantly imbibing water and makes boles and branches seem to be two or three times stouter than they are. Moss-forest abounds in epiphytes, Lycopodiaceæ, Orchidaceæ, and ferns. Of these one species, *Asplenium nidus*, crowds the boles, branches, and even the attached lianas with huge rosettes of undivided fronds. The long green threads of Usneæ stream down on all sides. Off the paths it is difficult to make one's way through.

Higher up the moss becomes less widespread, but the trees are smaller and more gnarled. In places certain species of *Pandanus* form impenetrable thickets; for instance, on Mt. Loku to the south of Manado in Celebes and on Mt. Sibayak in Sumatra. Dominated by a few taller individuals which gradually become rarer, a belt of shrubs begins on an average at an altitude of about 8000 feet. *Anaphelis Javanica*, a shrub with white flowers of a velvety appearance, like edelweiss, is particularly characteristic of upper slopes in Java, where it often forms almost unmixed clumps. The height of the tree-line varies on volcanoes, that is, on most peaks in Sumatra and Java. On these islands, which have been more closely studied than the rest, the tree-line has been more or less pushed

[1] See Van Steenis (56), pp. 54 and 379; and, for western Java, Schimper (55), p. 759.
[2] Cp. above, p. 36.

down by eruptions. Thus, the arrangement of belts of vegetation may properly be compared with those in temperate regions only on the highest non-volcanic mountains, like Kinabalu in northern Borneo or, better still, the central ranges of New Guinea.[1]

Mountain vegetation here raises some interesting problems. It comprises representatives of typically tropical families and species which have become adapted to the elevated climate; but it also has other plants related to species that are found only in the temperate belts of the northern and southern hemispheres. That in an equatorial climate they should have taken refuge in the mountains is easily understood; but the possibility of their crossing from one

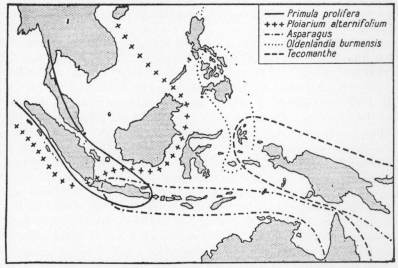

FIG. 8.—DISTRIBUTION OF CERTAIN PLANTS (after Van Steenis)

island to the other can only be examined in the light of palæogeography. Three main lines of approach converge on the East Indies: one bringing Chinese flora by way of the Philippines, another Himalayan flora along the Malay Peninsula, and the third starting from Australia (see Fig. 8).

[1] According to H. J. Lam, the trees in this island sometimes grow as high up as the 12,800-foot contour in places where they are sheltered from the wind; and even tree-ferns climb to 12,000 feet. Above 12,850 feet the ground is carpeted with small plants, like ferns, Ericaceæ (rhododendrons which begin far lower down, Vaccinium), and, in swampy soil, *Cladium* and *Euphrasia*. Above 13,000 feet the foot treads on nothing but grass and even humbler mosses until the snow line is reached at about 15,500 feet. From the 5000-foot contour upwards the fewness of cultivated fields and the absence of herds have modified the vegetation far less than in mountains in the temperate belt. (Van Steenis (56), p. 55.)

Another fascinating subject is plant colonisation on volcanoes after an eruption. This has attracted many botanists, and much observation was carried out on Krakatoa after the catastrophe of 1883, thanks to periodical excursions organised by Melchior Treub. At the approaches to the crater the flora shows signs of the gradual selection of mountain plants according to altitude and becomes poorer and poorer. Only a few species or pioneer varieties venture near the crater, which is still vomiting lava or belching out fumaroles, viz. those able to adapt themselves to high temperatures and the instability of the soil, to send their roots into cracks in the hard and still undecomposed lava, and to resist asphyxiation by the sulphurous emanations. The softest and most friable tuffs permit the growth of richer flora, and the soil in *lahars* is spontaneously reforested far more quickly than the lava. This modification of the vegetation through the influence of vulcanism is not unlike that resulting from burning and affects enormous areas below the 5000-foot contour.

Forest Degradation into Open Forest, secondary Forest, and Savana. In 1920 the area of soil completely transformed by man's action in the Philippines was assessed by an expert at two-thirds of the total. This is only an order of magnitude, a very approximate figure, when applied to the whole region dealt with in this book; and it would certainly have to be increased if none but really virgin forest was excluded from the proportion.

The collection of some natural products, like leaves, fruit, gum, and resin, usually has but little effect on the appearance of the forest. Felling for the requirements of building, joinery, pit-props, charcoal-burning, etc., is far more destructive. European plantations have often been established on forest soil after the trees have been cut down to the roots. But, as in the whole of the Hot Belt, the most general cause of forest degradation is the burning of the bush by native cultivators. The ground permanently in use by these people covers a very small part of the area tilled. Outside the irrigated fields and gardens the practice of *ladang*[1] is in full swing. It consists of cutting down the wild vegetation, burning it at the end of the dry season, and then sowing or planting in the ashes. The field thus cleared is abandoned after being cultivated for a short time, usually one to three years, and is used again after nature has reconstituted the substances which make the soil sufficiently fertile for another crop.

The recuperation of the abandoned *ladang* takes some time and will be attained only if the fallow lasts long enough and if the density of population is still low enough for the native to have a large area

[1] *Caingin* in the Philippines.

at his disposal and for him not to return to the space he had previously burnt and cultivated till after the lapse of scores of years.
As a rule the cycle is too short to ensure a return to the primitive
state. The appearance of the forest is changed; it becomes a
'secondary' growth, what is called a *blukar* in western Indonesia,
Fast growing, light-loving plants multiply at the expense of others,
and species which had been merely sporadic become dominant, as
for instance, the *seru* (*Schima*) in southern Sumatra, *Lantana* in many
other places, and *Melastoma* with its large, violet-red blossoms.
Secondary forest is usually dense and often more difficult to pass
through than virgin forest. The trees are only between 15 and 65
feet high, and there is less variety. *Blukar* is particularly extensive
in Sumatra, Borneo, Celebes, and the Philippines. In Java, owing
to the widespread permanent cultivation, it has succeeded in developing in the south-west of the island only.

Clearing *ladangs* by burning is less devastating than what are
termed 'bush fires' in British colonies. These are due to various
causes, of which one may be lightning; but usually they are started
by someone who wishes either to clear away the forest around his
dwelling, or make it easier for himself to move about, or allow the
grass to shoot up again for the benefit of the cattle which have been
thinned by the dry season, or else to track down wild animals more
easily. Fires are often lit for sheer fun or through carelessness by
people camping out in the open air.

Bush fires are far from unknown in the Malay Peninsula and
western Indonesia, where at the end of an exceptionally dry season
they sometimes even burn swamp forests and destroy peat bogs in
Sumatra and Borneo. The longer and more regular the dry season,
the more frequent and more extensively destructive they are. For
this reason the Philippines as a whole suffer more in the west than
they do in the east. In eastern Indonesia damage by fire increases
with the duration of the Australian monsoon. Even in central and
eastern Java annual bush fires formerly swept over the great volcanoes, whose tops remained shrouded in smoke for days and weeks.
They still occur every dry season in Celebes, the Moluccas, the
Lesser Sunda Islands (especially Flores and Timor), and New
Guinea. The governments have issued severe regulations to check
the practice of clearing by fire and of starting bush fires, but, except
in Java, their enforcement is as a rule difficult.

Besides the effects of fires there are those of droughts. Adaptations due to the latter have certainly modified the forest, which now
comprises a large number of species which regularly drop their
leaves at every dry season. Hence, the appearance of the forest
changes during the course of the year, as in the temperate regions;

and in the dipterocarp forests in the Philippines there is a difference between those in the east, which are evergreen, and those in the centre and west, which are deciduous. However, the trees are seldom quite bare, for the new leaves shoot out before the withered leaves have all fallen.[1] Rattan palms have disappeared, but epiphytes remain and show up curiously green against the brown trees. The foliage is usually thinner; but the parasol-like spread of the tallest trees may still form a continuous top storey. Many species which belong to the normal forest occur here too, but drop their leaves before blossoming. The nearer one goes to Australia along the Sunda arc, the better represented are some families, like Rhamnaceæ, Tiliaceæ, Rutaceæ, and especially Leguminoseæ. *Acacia leucophlea* ('*pilang*'), *Butea monosperma* ('*plosso*') with its flaming yellow blossoms, and the parasol-like *Leptospermum*, which is characteristic of many a district in Celebes, are common species. Trees become twisted and stunted, and thorny species become more common, especially acacias and albizzias which have Australian affinities. Another forest with a well-marked seasonal life and often termed 'monsoon forest' occurs in the Philippines below the 500-foot contour, especially on limestone soils, with *Vitex parviflora Jussieu* ('*molave*') as its dominant species.[2]

These forests are even more rarely original than those in regions with no dry season. Their reconstitution is all the more difficult because the drier climate greatly favours the frequent occurrence and spread of fires. In fact, over a large part of Indonesia the vegetation is not directly related to natural conditions, but represents an adaptation to burning, a 'brand-climax', as Dutch botanists say. By a gradual process of selection a large number of species have been eliminated, and those that were equipped to resist the fires have survived, have adapted themselves to the conditions, and even profited from them in the struggle for life. The vegetation has gradually become impoverished. In this way there have come about stretches of relatively homogeneous open forest, often with very clearly defined limits, in which grass is associated with trees and which are very different from the original selva.

According to recent opinion, the pinewoods in the Philippines and Sumatra are of secondary formation and not relics of a once-dry climate, as was thought by A. Volz. In natural conditions the pine occupied the least fertile soil in the forest and as a rule steep rocky slopes. Bush fires have favoured it at the expense of other species, for its seeds germinate very readily in the light, and the bark,

[1] In the Philippines there is only one dipterocarp *Anisoptera thurifera* that becomes quite bare and then only for a day or two. (Kolb (175), p. 54.)
[2] Kolb (175), p. 53.

which soon becomes thick, quickly enables the young plant to resist the flames. Since the pines grow in fairly open stands with tall grass and ferns between them, the appearance of the vegetation is often that of savana rather than true forest.

In the eastern half of Java the mountain forest is quite different from the woodland that has survived the process of clearing on the western hill-masses. It is a forest of casuarinas, a family resembling the conifers in general appearance and bearing, but distinguished from them by the disappearance of needles and the presence of leafless branches like those of the horsetail. Casuarinaceæ originated in Australia, advanced across the East Indies to meet the pines from Eurasia, and have even mingled with them. One species, the pyramidal *filao* (*Casuarina equisetifolia*), still grows spontaneously on the coasts of Sumatra, the Malay Peninsula, and the Philippines and has been acclimatised even farther west in Indo-China and Madagascar for fixing dunes. Another species (*C. Sumatrana*) is found growing with broad-leaved trees not only in Sumatra, but also in Celebes, Borneo, and the Philippines. In the eastern part of Java there is the *chemara* (*C. Junghuhniana* or *montana*),[1] which is in fact a mountain tree, but grows at lower levels in the east as the drought increases. It is always found above 6000 feet on Mt. Lawu to the east of Surakarta in Java, but it descends to 1000 feet in Timor. Like the Sumatran pine, the *chemara* has profited by the bush fires, since it is well protected against the flames and has a great capacity for reproduction in the open, thanks to the lightness and abundance of its seeds. The *chemara* forest is dark, monotonous, and almost free from admixture with other trees. It forms on the ground a coating of coarse humus which with the tall, dry grass feeds the annual bush fire. The fires often stop short at the very edge of the stands of *chemara*, sparing the primary forests of broad-leaved trees which have survived in the valley bottoms.

Teak, or *jati* (*Tectona grandis*), which covers about one-third of the wooded area in Java,[2] also profits from the bush fires. The teak forests in Indonesia are nearly all situated in the central and eastern parts of that island, and especially on the plains and Tertiary hills extending north from the range of volcanoes. Like other deciduous forest species, the Javanese teak is separated from its Asiatic congeners by a wide gap, for the most southerly natural stands in the northern hemisphere are not to be found nearer than Siam. This isolation has even suggested the theory that the teak was formerly brought from Indo-China to Java by Indian colonists. In any case, up to about the end of last century the teak forests were

[1] Van Steenis, (56), pp. 50 and 197: Allouard (43), p. 772.
[2] Van Steenis (56), p. 372: Reinhard (54).

annually swept in August, September, and October by bush fires
which must have helped towards the progressive elimination of most
other species. In the stands said to be 'wild', teak already figures
in a proportion perhaps exceeding 90 per cent. But the value of the
timber has given rise to one of the finest feats of forest exploitation
achieved in tropical lands. Since 1897 the wild stands have been
gradually cut down and replaced by artificial stands of pure teak,
and the spread of bush fires has been prevented by a system of
propaganda and effective supervision. Teak forests are extensive,
open, monotonous, with few epiphytes, and poor in fauna.

To the east of Java the vegetation assumes a more and more
xerophilous character along the Sunda Islands. The primitive
deciduous forest survives only in remnants of small extent. Owing
to bush fires, it often develops into open woodland almost wholly
composed of species with Australian affinities, particularly of
Myrtaceæ like the *Melaleuca leucadendron*, or eucalyptus. The
eucalyptus is found here on dry soils, whilst in eastern Sumatra,
Borneo, and even in Cochin China it grows on marshy ground
behind the mangrove belt. The area over which the eucalyptus
has spread spontaneously is far more restricted. Its western
boundary passes through Macassar Strait and across the western
end of Timor (see Fig. 7).

The transition from primitive to secondary forest and then to
savana is gradual, and the appearance of the vegetation very varied.
The outcome of repeated burning is the grass-clad savana; and on
large areas tall tropical grasses wave in every breeze. They include
alangalang (*Imperata exalta*), *glagla* (*Saccharum spontaneum*),
Themeda gigantea, etc., which all form wonderful food for the
flames, but, thanks to their deep root-system, remake a sea of green
6 feet high every year in the rainy season. At the end of the dry
season it all turns yellow and is devoured by the fires, whilst large
flights of birds of prey circle over the black expanses of ashes in
search of the charred bodies of animals.

The area covered by savana is estimated at 20 to 30 per cent. in
the East Indies and at nearly 40 per cent. in the Philippines. It is
impossible to say what proportion of the savana is original and
how much is the outcome of fire. One special type common in
high ground in Sumatra is moorland covered with the fern *Eupteris*.

The trees constituting the open forest grow in lines along the
watercourses or in the bottoms of ravines, forming clumps or
scattered more or less regularly over the savana. They contribute
greatly to its character. In northern Sumatra pine savana is
common. In eastern Java the *chemaras* on the mountains and the
teaks on the plains are sometimes widely enough spaced out for the

word 'forest' to become misleading. In the eastern part of the
Sunda arc eucalyptus trees most frequently play the same part.
But here savanas with *lontar* palms (*Borassus flabelliformis*) often
remind one of scenery in Africa. They are seen even at the east end
of Java and in north-western Bali, but are much more extensive in
Sumba and Timor. Another very special type is the savana with
succulents, in which grow opuntias, which came originally from
America, and euphorbias, which occur in Lombok, central Celebes,
and elsewhere.

Fauna. The important contribution made by zoology to the
history of the formation of the archipelago has been described in a
previous chapter. It now remains to give a brief review of the
wealth and variety of the fauna, the distribution of which raises
problems that will always fascinate a great number of those engaged
on research.

The boundary between the eastern and Australian zoological
regions does not possess the linear precision imagined by Wallace
and asserted even more strongly by others whose conclusions went
further than those of the great naturalist. Macassar and Lombok
Straits are, in truth, a boundary which a certain number of species
have not crossed. This holds good for freshwater fish[1] rather than
for mammals, and for the latter rather than for birds, although,
according to Wallace himself, these last are far less capable of
spreading than is generally supposed, and only a few species, like
the Nicobar pigeon and some birds of prey, are found all over the
archipelago. But the line has no existence so far as insects are
concerned. The possibility of passive displacement must be
considered in addition to spontaneous migration: as, for instance,
when a creature clings to some flotsam or is carried by chance in a
boat or taken through human agency.[2] Seemingly, the spread of
species with local adaptations and very sedentary habits should lead
to stronger conclusions; but the theory of a connexion between
islands which today are separate is not wholly satisfactory and may
call for a further assumption, namely, a modification in climate.
Today scientists agree more generally that there exists a transitional
belt comprising Celebes, the Moluccas, and the islands of the Sunda
arc from Lombok to the Kei group inclusive.

The Malay Peninsula, Sumatra, Java, Borneo, and the adjacent
islands—in short, the land on the Sunda shelf—show in their fauna

---

[1] The cyprinids do not go beyond Borneo, but are found in the Sunda arc as
far as and including Sumbawa.

[2] Thus, Wallace (63) notes that the monkey (*Cynopithecus nigrescens*), which is
the only mammal in Celebes that is also found in Bachan in the Moluccas, may
quite easily have been taken there by man. *Malay Archipelago*, p. 259.

and flora an undisputed preponderance of Asiatic affinities, and this is further emphasised by the exuberance due to the equatorial climate. Several large animals from the neighbouring continent, none of which are found farther east, occur in them, including the tiger, rhinoceros, Malayan bison (*seladang*), and the elephant. This last animal was domesticated by the sultans of Achin, used for transport by the Dutch East Indian army up to 1929, and is still employed in Malaya for moving timber. A large proportion of the little forest animals, like the squirrel, are identical with or closely related to those in Indo-China. The insect life is probably the richest in species in the whole world, with 250,000 in Malaya alone, and is remarkable for the gigantic beetle *Buprestes*, the elegant longicorn, and an abundance of butterflies (*Ornithoptera*); but it comprises few new genera. The same may be said of the bird life.

Nevertheless, this region is not perfectly homogeneous. Many species found in Malaya, Sumatra, and Borneo do not occur in Java. The orang-utan, for example, is found only in the two big islands and especially in Borneo. This ape is admirably adapted to life in a great swampy forest, since it lives on fruit and moves about from tree to tree in the upper storeys with an ease due to its long arms. The domain of the tiger extends through Sumatra and Java as far as western Bali, but does not include Borneo. This last island together with Sumatra and Malaya harbour the two-horned rhinoceros (*R. Sumatrensis* Cuv.), whilst only the one-horned species (*R. Sundaicus* Desm.) occurs in Java. The Indian elephant (*Elephas maximus*) did not go beyond Sumatra and seems to have been taken to northern Borneo by man. The tapir, which resembles the corresponding animal in South America and is a curious representative of a group which formerly occupied a large part of temperate Eurasia, no longer figures in the fauna in Java. On the other hand, the Malayan bison (*seladang*), whose massive head is a most magnificent trophy, is known in Java and Borneo as well as Malaya, but not in Sumatra. Wallace explained the survival in Java of certain mammals of Indian provenance that have disappeared from Sumatra as due to the relatively early separation of the two islands. The species driven southwards by the increasing cold of the Ice Ages were able to return later from Sumatra to the mainland, but were cut off in Java.

Indian types clearly become rarer from Borneo to the Philippines, where, for instance, there are no anthropoid apes, elephants, rhinoceroses, or tapirs. The tendency increases in Celebes, which contains only eight families of mammals in common with the lands on the Sunda shelf, as compared with thirteen in the Philippines. To the east of Lombok Strait the Lesser Sunda Islands, which were early severed from Java, have nevertheless been reached by some isolated representatives of Indian fauna. Thus, Cervidæ, Viverridæ, and Soricidæ[1] are found as far east as Timor, and the pig as far as New Guinea. The last named may have been introduced by man, though Wallace stresses its ability to swim across the sea.

To the east of the Wallace Line, starting from Celebes and Timor, approach towards Australia is marked by the appearance of typical groups such as marsupials. Lemurs, which occur as far west as Sumatra and Madagascar, take the place of monkeys; but most of the species have their own peculiarities and bear witness to isolation from the Australian mainland since very early times. Though the ant-eating Echidnæ are also found in Timor, true kangaroos as well as the ornithorrhyncus, that queer Australian monotreme adapted to amphibious life by having webbed forefeet, do not go beyond

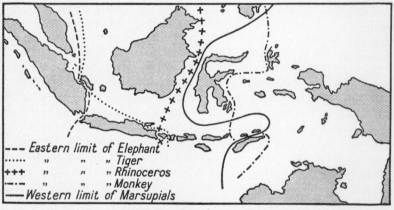

--- Eastern limit of Elephant
......   "   "   " Tiger
+++   "   "   " Rhinoceros
-.-.- "   "   " Monkey
—— Western limit of Marsupials

FIG. 9.—DISTRIBUTION OF CERTAIN ANIMALS

New Guinea. Celebes is famous for its endemic species, the most curious of which are a dwarf buffalo called the *anoa* and the babiroussa, which is a kind of boar with tusks like the horns of a stag. In the little island of Komodo between Sumbawa and Flores there is a giant monitor which is sometimes nearly 10 feet long and looks just like a huge prehistoric lizard.

Whatever interest these extraordinary types of mammals may have for the zoologist and palæogeographer, they are far less important in the country than the swarms of birds and insects. The abundance, variety, beauty, and richness of colouring of these creatures surprise the traveller and have always astonished the naturalist. In two months in a forest area not greater than a square mile on the island of Singapore Wallace collected 700 species of

[1] Stag, civet, and mouse families.

beetles, many of which had been unknown till then and among which were 130 of those beautiful longicorns that are so greatly valued by collectors.[1] At certain times flights of innumerable butterflies are met. Birds swarm, but most of them have well-marked habitats.[2] Some live among the food-crops, and others feed off the parasites on cattle. Among these are the boatbill heron, egret, and tick-bird whose white wings haunt the buffaloes and zebras. Others again belong to dry districts or to the forest, among the latter being the hornbill, the flapping of whose wings can be heard hundreds of yards off. Kingfishers abound on the streams. The huge Argus pheasant, whose ocellated plumage and rapid flight through the thickest part of the forest make its capture impossible, except by trapping, is restricted to western Indonesia. Several species of Asiatic birds do not cross the Wallace Line, but owing to the frequency of endemic types and the spread of Australian forms, eastern Indonesia has for long been famous. For many years the export of birds' feathers was the staple trade in Manado and Macassar.

Asiatic affinities do not regularly fall off towards the east. Lombok, for instance, is far poorer in bird life than Bali, but it is also poorer than Sumbawa. Birds of paradise with their rich and wonderfully ornamental plumage reach as far west as Halmahera and are found in large numbers in New Guinea and the islands near by.[3] These easterly islands are also the homes of parakeets and metallic-coloured cockatoos. Among them are the crimson Moluccan parakeet and the big, black cockatoo which lives in New Guinea and its islands. Though less numerous in species than on the Sunda shelf, butterflies still swarm and are even more striking on account of their brilliant colours, strange forms, and great size. Wallace noticed that the size and brilliance of birds and insects increased in the little islands and particularly that the butterflies in Amboina were larger and more beautiful than those in New Guinea. This, he used to say, echoing the Darwinian theory, resulted from the greater poverty of the fauna and the consequent less bitter struggle for existence on these restricted areas.

[1] A. R. Wallace (63), p. 19.   [2] Berlioz (60).
[3] Wallace (63), pp. 419–39.

CHAPTER 5

THE PEOPLES AND THEIR CIVILISATION

Pithecanthropus affords a disputed, but convenient transition from the study of the fauna to that of man.[1] The East Indies, which were already famous for botanical and zoological reasons, came to be accepted later as one of the cradles of the human race, and Trinil, to the north-west of Surakarta in central Java and situated in the dry yellow plain through which the Solo winds its way, is, as it were, the Mecca of prehistory. In 1891 Dubois, a Dutch scientist, discovered in the bank of the river some remains of bones which proved 'the existence of a being morphologically intermediate between the most archaic human (Neanderthal man) and the chimpanzee and other most highly developed existing types of anthropoid apes'.[2] Is Pithecanthropus really man's ancestor, or must we rather see in him a more or less distant cousin sprung from the same stock, like a branch of the same bough or a bough of the same tree? Can this being have used the two-faced stones of Chellean or Acheulean type which have been found in the same district and elsewhere in the East Indies?[3] Von Königswald believes this and dates Pithecanthropus in the mid-Quaternary, though previously it had been placed at the end of the Tertiary, whilst Van Bemmelen[4] states emphatically that in the Pliocene and at the beginning of the Quaternary, as Java was still joined to Asia, the elephant, rhinoceros, tiger, boar, and bear as well as the most ancient human types could have entered it from the mainland. There is obvious likeness between Pithecanthropus and Sinanthropus, whose remains were found near Peking and who was acquainted with the use of fire.

In Java tools and animal remains seemingly of Indian origin have also been excavated along with several skulls that are clearly related to Neanderthal man. But no Quaternary representative of *Homo Sapiens* has yet been found in the East Indies. It is still impossible to establish a reliable connexion between these fossils and existing man, and impossible also to fix the absolute or even the relative

[1] Königswald (74); Teilhard de Chardin (87); Boule (64).
[2] Vayson de Pradenne, *La Préhistoire*, Paris, 1938, pp. 21 and 203; Leroi-Gourhan, *L'Homme et la Matière*, Paris, 1943, pp. 9 and 64.
[3] In Sumatra and the Philippines as well as in Indo-China.
[4] Van Bemmelen (131). At Mojokerto to the south-west of Surabaya bones have been found which are of a type perhaps older even than Pithecanthropus. The most up-to-date restatement of prehistory in the East Indies is by A. N. J. Thomassen to Thuessink van der Hoop in Stapel (83), I, pp. 8–111.

chronology of prehistory in the archipelago, as indeed it is in all Southeast Asia.

Anthropological Types. The study of existing peoples in Malaya and the East Indies has given rise to innumerable and in some cases substantial books, but has not succeeded in clearing up the mystery of their origin. This, however, could be said of any country, even of those of western Europe.

Anyhow, the human population confirms the contact that has occurred between the Eurasian and Australian or, rather, Australo-Melanesian, worlds; and this great fact has been repeated like a *leit-motif* since Wallace's time in descriptions of the vegetation and fauna. On one side are the Malays (in the widest sense), on the other the Papuans. Wallace drew a line separating them to the east of his zoological boundary. Giving the Philippines to the Malays, it crossed the Moluccas through Obi and Buru and left Flores, Sumba, and Timor to the Papuans. In fact, the limits of human groups are even more difficult to fix than those of plants and animals, as is also the determination of the paths of migration by which the groups reached the situations they occupy today.

What are the characteristics of the Malay and Papuan? If the latter is defined as being tall and having a dark skin, curly locks, a fairly hairy body, a long face, a broad, but prominent nose, and very beetling brows (which are his least variable features) he will be seen to the west of the line drawn by Wallace. But it would be nearer the truth to say that the eastern limit of the Malay type is not found before reaching New Guinea or the little islands to the west of it and that the Malays gradually shade off north-eastwards into the Polynesian type.

In fact under this didactic classification anthropological observations and measurements reveal great complications resulting from intermixture which began in very ancient times and still continues. This might well have been suspected, for it is a fairly general occurrence and was encouraged here by the general position of the archipelago and the ease of communication between the islands.

Nevertheless, scientists think they can recognise elements termed 'primitive' and comprising relatively pure racial types which, it is probable, formerly occupied far more extensive areas than now. These are the Negritoes and Veddas.

The Negritoes have been studied particularly in Malaya. Especially outstanding in this category are the Semangs who wander among the central mountains in the Peninsula within the territories of the States of Perak, Kedah, and Kelantan. Like the Aëtas of the Philippines, they seem to be related to the Negritoes of the Andaman Islands and those found here and there in the forests of

Indo-China. Low stature is recognised as one of the chief characteristics of the Negrito, apart from features that are merely those of the negro. The Semang men who have been examined had an average height of just under 5 feet, and the Aëtas of only 4 feet 10 inches.[1] It must be noticed furthermore that this type can be followed right across the archipelago and even among the Papuans, for certain groups in New Guinea are also noticeably short in stature.

In their descriptions of the Toalas of southern Celebes the brothers Sarasin[2] often speak of the Veddas as a very ancient element in the population of Malaya and Indonesia. The Vedda is described as being slightly taller than the Negrito and as having a lighter skin and long, wavy hair. The root of the nose is flattened, but the face narrows towards the lower end. Long-headedness is far more frequent than among the Negritoes. According to some anthropologists,[3] the Vedda type is thought to be more widespread in Celebes than the Sarasins believed. It occurs also in Malaya in the Senois and Sakais, who live to the south of the Semangs and are to be distinguished from them. Kleiweg de Zwaan has often recognised the type in the Philippines, Borneo, and all the Sunda arc from Madura to New Guinea.

Lastly, putting aside the Papuan, Negrito, and Vedda types, whose distribution is far from being exactly known or generally agreed, there remain in addition to the Malays the also very heterogeneous stock of those designated Pre-Malays, Proto-Malays, or even Old Malays, names which are convenient, but do not hide our ignorance.

We must now pass on from this very obscure anthropological topic, for the more substantial study of the various types of civilisation and modes of life is better suited to the purpose of this work.

Ancient Migrations. Relations with the Pacific. The preponderance of Asiatic influence on the various types of civilisation in the archipelago is generally accepted and outside the innumerable controversies. It is not refuted by anthropological and ethnological data, and scientists have, on the contrary, for long been pointing out emphatically the affinities between the human groups in southeastern Asia and the East Indies, beginning with the Negritoes and Veddas and continuing with the Pre-Malays, who present rather striking likenesses to the little tribes of Mois in southern Annam (often said to be Indonesian) and even to the Mundas of Chota

---

[1] Some well-formed Aëtas measure only 3 feet 10 inches.
[2] Sarasin (157).
[3] For the situation as regards these problems in 1930, see Kleiweg de Zwaan in Rutten (19), pp. 192–206.

Nagpur in India. The term 'Indonesian' has the drawback of rashly prejudging the direction of migration. Many scientists represent the settlement of Indonesians on the contrary as being the outcome of a series of waves of migration from Asia. This view agrees with the progressive lessening in size of the islands towards the south-east and with the fact that the Sunda shelf was not drowned until a comparatively recent date and was able to afford prehistoric man a solid land-bridge across which to reach Borneo, Sumatra, and Java. The impression that the currents of migration flowed from Monsoon Asia and died away as they approached Australia comes from a whole collection of convergent investigations rather than from a study of the flora and fauna. The exuberant life fostered in early times by the tropical portion of the continent spread across the East Indies in waves which gradually died away.

It is, however, impossible to be precise about the date, origin, or size of most of the migrations which led to the existing population of the East Indies. They were prehistoric movements about which Indian, Chinese, and Arab documents leave us completely in the dark. Likenesses or relationships between languages, beliefs, and material manifestations of human life are not incontestable evidence of real displacement or of the migration of individuals or groups of men, for they are certainly more often caused by the mere spread of cultural or commercial ideas and of customs, manners, and commodities.

In the region here considered there are certainly plenty of traces of a civilisation which may be termed Oceanic or Pacific.[1] The relationship between the Malay and Polynesian languages is not disputed. With the Malay-Polynesian family are connected not only the languages of Easter Island and Madagascar, but also certain Moi dialects in southern Annam.[2] Ethnologists, and Graebner in particular, have shown that many cultural elements are common to Polynesia, Melanesia, the East Indies, and the mainland of south-eastern Asia. Beliefs and religious rites and the technique of art reveal curious likenesses between islands as far apart as Nias and

[1] Frobenius (71); Rivet (81).
[2] Kern pointed this out as early as 1917. For the linguistic problems, see the article by van Ronkel in *Science in the Netherlands East Indies*, 1930, pp. 329–48. The Malay-Polynesian, or Austronesian, family of languages remains one of the least known. It is indeed curious that the dialects spoken in Nias should be very different in phonetics and vocabulary from those in Sumatra and closer in likeness to those in Madagascar or even Samoa. See Dupont, according to Steinhart (*B.E.F.E.O.*, 1937, p. 537). The dialects of northern Halmahera are aberrant (cp. map 9b by S. J. Esser in *Atlas* (13)). See also Dahl (68). Folklore affords many tales similar in substance and often even in form in western Indonesia, Malaya, Cambodia, Laos, and even in distant Japan. See M. Colani after Cardon (*B.E.F.E.O.*, 1937, p. 530).

the Marquesas. In the form of the bow and shield, in the use of throwing weapons like the boomerang and also in the architecture of houses and boats, ethnologists have found traces of former relations between the lands bounding the Great Ocean and the islands scattered about in it. There is no need to imagine, as is done by some who follow Cook, Vancouver, and Dumont d'Urville, the existence of a foundered continent whose remnants form the island groups of today. The theory will hardly hold water. Maritime relations sufficiently explain trade between lands thousands of miles apart. At Ratak in 1816 Kotzebue met a native from the Carolines who had drifted nearly 1700 miles. Similar distances might be covered deliberately in stages by the single or double outrigger boats which were invented and perfected by the Pacific peoples. Such craft and the navigational practice they permitted must have spread at an early age in the East Indies. On their arrival the Portuguese were surprised at the skilful seamanship of certain groups of Malay sailors.[1] We know it was good enough to enable settlements to be made in Madagascar by immigrants who probably came from the Sunda Islands and reached Madagascar in small bodies at intervals from a remote time right up to a date near the arrival of the Europeans. Thus, the affinities noticed between the peoples of the western fringe of the Pacific from the East Indies to Japan are clearly intelligible. Among them there is as it were a common cultural foundation, later more or less strongly influenced by the most brilliant and solid types of civilisation, which were themselves evolved in Eurasia.

Indian Influence. The Malay is generally described as a man of moderate height and girth, well proportioned, with a complexion ranging from light yellow to copper colour, with straight black hair, slightly oblique eyes, and rather prominent cheek-bones. This average type is fairly widespread, especially in the western part of the archipelago; but it has many obvious variants. Keeping to our own standard of human beauty, we can, here as in Japan, distinguish a refined and a coarse type by facial features, build of limbs, and general posture.

The linguist has a far narrower definition of the Malay and regards him as a man whose mother tongue is pure Malay. In that case he is restricted to the Malay Peninsula, the little islands of Rhio, Lingga, and Singkep which prolong it southwards, and to certain groups in Sumatra, especially in the district round Palembang.[2]

---

[1] Ferrand (69). In a letter to the King of Portugal (1512) Albuquerque praises a map by a pilot in Java. The map included Southeast Asia, the Persian Gulf, Red Sea, Portugal, and Brazil.
[2] See von Ronkel in Rutten (19), p. 337.

4. A Senoi family. These people are not negroid. They live farther south than the Semangs. Note the bamboo vessel from which a man is drinking.

. Three Semangs (negritoes) in the mountains of Pahang. Note the blowgun.

6. A Dyak head-hunter with his trophies in Sarawak.

7. Dyak girls in their best dresses, Sarawak.

8.
Pile-dwellings on the Telian River in the
Mukah district, Sarawak

9.
Minangkabau houses at Lawang near Fort
de Kock

10.
A Toraja house in Celebes. Made of bamboo, it has a gable lavishly decorated with
geometrical figures and cocks.

11.
A peasant's house in Java, with its
garden

12.
A European house in Java. It
formerly belonged to the manager
of one of the big Dutch tea estates.

In the more generally accepted sense which will be followed here the Malay is distinguished by his mode of life. He lives on the coast and tills the land, and, though formerly often a pirate, he has now taken to planting and fishing. His enterprising spirit and superior organisation, his possession of the river mouths and of tools and weapons which he buys from other countries, give him an ascendancy over the inland tribes. His native character has been developed and transformed by immigrants and cultural influence from overseas; from Eurasia he has been influenced by the Indian, the Chinese, the Arab, and, lastly, the European.[1]

About the beginning of the Christian era India was stirred by an outburst of energy strong enough to carry out in the Far East a remarkable feat of colonisation with apparently ineradicable effects. The importance of the part she played has been shown up by the work of European scholars.[2] The first Indian settlements in the East Indies certainly go back several centuries before our era. The oldest Sanscrit inscriptions, confirmed by Chinese texts, reveal that in the 4th and 5th centuries of the Christian era communities of immigrants from Bengal, Orissa, and the Coromandel coast had settled at certain points on the Malay Peninsula, the north-west coast of Java, and the east coast of Borneo. When the Chinese pilgrim Fa Hien reached Java (or Malaya) in A.D. 413, he found a 'Hinduised' society which ten years later was to be subjected to intense Buddhist evangelisation. The 7th century—the period of the Pallavas dynasty—was a time of considerable trade with India. It was carried on in boats which skirted the coasts of the Bay of Bengal or went directly from Negapatam or Ceylon to Kedah and Ligor on the Malay Peninsula.

The Indian colonies must have been very like those established in Indo-China on the delta of the Mekong and in the district of Champa on the coast of what is now southern Annam. Probably the immigrants were few in number compared with the natives and formed a minority comprising administrators, priests, and traders, and their civilisation was most likely spread mainly by those who married into the local aristocracy or else by 'Hinduised' Malays.

The contribution of India to the material civilisation of the East Indies is not easily recognised. At the arrival of these conquerors the natives seem to have been already fairly good sailors, to have known how to work metals, and to have cultivated rice on level, flooded fields. The degree of improvement added to their skill as seamen, craftsmen, or farmers is unknown.

[1] For the series of Western influences which have affected the Malay language in turn, see Drewes in Schrieke (20), pp. 126–37.

[2] See Krom's article in Rutten (19), pp. 200 ff., 305 ff.; and G. Coedès (67 *ter*).

India contributed the great religions which had grown up in her own confines. Buddhism or Brahmanism, the latter mainly in the form of Mahayana, prevailed according to place and time and were combined with each other and with earlier faiths in complex syncretism. On the walls of the *chandi* Mendout, next door to the Borobudur, are carved Brahmanic patterns, whilst the famous teaching Buddha sits enthroned in the half-light within. The spread of the Indian religions was helped not only by their tenets, which were imbued with moving poetry and fixed in writing, but also by the high reputation of their forms of worship and their art. Even in the Philippines Indian influence is appreciable in the language of the people, the place-names, and the decoration of the houses and bush knives.[1] Sanscrit literature is accessible to only a small number of experts, but yet, owing to this superior position, many Sanscrit words have penetrated into the Indonesian languages.[2]

The immigrants set up new political systems. Under their action the particularism of the clans and tribes began to be swallowed up in centralised states, which were principalities with a territorial basis and governed by rajahs or maharajahs. But for a few temples, nothing remains of their capitals, which were built entirely of wood, but the regular village plan in Java and Bali is perhaps due to Indian influence.

According to G. Ferrand and G. Coedès[3] the first great Indo-Malay kingdom had its centre in the Palembang district, which, however, is very poor in archeological remains. Sanscrit inscriptions and Chinese and Arab writings describe this kingdom of Sri Vijaya as a rich and powerful state. The territory under its rule had shifting boundaries, but between the 8th and 12th centuries extended, temporarily at least, not only over the Minangkabau and Batak districts of Sumatra, but also went far beyond the island to reach Cambodia, Siam, and Ceylon, to cover the greater part of Java and the coastal districts of Borneo, and thence to stretch out through

[1] A long knife with a broad blade like the West Indian negro's 'cutlass' and the *machete* of Spanish America. It is used for hacking one's way through the bush.

[2] Indonesian languages have also adopted a fairly large number of Tamil words through the influence of Muslim traders from India. At the beginning of the 18th century it was impossible to conclude an important transaction in the Straits or Sumatra without a knowledge of Tamil, all measurements and calculations being made in that tongue.

[3] See G. Ferrand (90) and G. Coedès (67 *bis*). For the objections to the localisation of a great centre of Hindu influence at Palembang, see J. Sion, *Sur l'ethnographie de l'Indochine et de l'Insulinde* in *Annales de Géographie*, 1924, p. 391. Traces of Indian, or rather Indo-Sumatran, art have been found not in the district of Palembang, but in the upper basins of the Batanghari and Kampar and in Padang Lawas, i.e. the eastern border of the Minangkabau district. These are sanctuaries that seem to date from the 10th to the 15th centuries. See also Middendorp in Schrieke (20), pp. 34–7; and F. M. Schnitzer (82).

Banjermasin and Brunei to the Philippines. The Cailendra dynasty had relations with Bengal and southern India. The Chinese pilgrim I Tsing spent seven years at the end of the 7th century in their capital, which was a centre of Buddhist teaching and missionary activity and to which men came from very great distances to study the sacred volumes.

The material foundation of this power must surely be sought less in the resources of the forest and of the soil than in maritime activity. From the coast of Sumatra it was possible to control the Straits of Malacca and Sunda, the two main passages from the Indian Ocean into the China and East Indian seas. Loot from piracy added to the gains of commerce, for in the 8th century Malay vessels raided as far as the delta of the Tongking and in the 12th century they attacked foreign ships with slings, throwing-weapons, and poisoned arrows.

The silting up of the east coast of Sumatra was probably a factor in the decay of Sri Vijaya. The empire gradually broke up, and pre-eminence passed to Java. This island seems from early times to have been put to best use and to have been the most densely populated in the archipelago. By the 8th century the princes reigning in central Java—related by blood, moreover, to those of Sri Vijaya—were displaying a certain degree of independence and in the 11th century Javanese overseas trade became very great, as is shown by inscriptions,[1] and Indo-Javanese civilisation reached its zenith between A.D. 800 and 1200. It was during the first half of the 8th century that the first stone Sivaite sanctuaries were erected on the Dieng plateau. Later, but still in the centre of the island, there were built the famous temples of Borobudur (772) and Prambanan (910–19), in which, as in Cambodia, Indian architecture cast off its ornateness in this foreign land and moved towards greater simplicity and purity. Then there followed a great outburst of epic and mystic literature whose chief themes, borrowed from the Ramayana and Mahabharata, were mingled with native subjects both in folklore and in the princely and popular dramas.

The decline of Indian influence was accompanied by the gradual removal of supremacy towards the east.[3] In 1292 Sri Vijaya succumbed to the blows of the peoples it had subjugated. The predominance of eastern Java, which was firmly established with the kingdom of Majapahit whose centre lay at Majakerto to the south-west of Surabaya, was to last until the 15th century. The *kratons*, or court poets, no longer servilely imitated the prosody, style, and

---

[1] Krom, in Schrieke (20), p. 307. According to Stutterheim, Java and Sumatra alternately held the supremacy as early as the 8th century, kings of the same family reigning in both islands and those of Java ultimately gaining the upper hand. Confusion of the two islands is general in the texts.

[2] Eastern Java and Bali seem to have escaped Sumatran domination. See Coedès (67b), pp. 244–68.

[3] Hall (72a), pp. 58–72.

subjects of Sanscrit literature. An Indo-Javanese background came forward again. Sculpture reproduced the grimacing faces of the *wayang*, and decoration with its accumulation of human and animal forms, flowers, and conventional clouds, reflected the influence of native animism on imported religions. The supremacy of Majapahit spread even beyond the limits reached by Sri Vijaya, for tracts of it are still perceptible in southern Formosa, western New Guinea, and there were perhaps traces of trading contact in the Marianas. The zenith of the political and commercial predominance of Java is placed about 1400. But after the 12th century settlements of Malays from that island and Sumatra swarmed on the Malay Peninsula and throughout the archipelago. Naval expeditions went out to punish rebellious peoples. A prosperous colony of Javanese merchants was found by the Portuguese at Malacca, and others existed in the ports on the Indian Ocean. In spite of the Islamic conquest, the glory of Majapahit and its princes is celebrated in epic poems, and their names remain as symbols of national greatness among the people of Java.

Islam. However rapid may have been the success of Islam in Malaya and the East Indies, it was none the less the final act of a long, continued process of development. As so often happens, the conquest was both economic and religious. Ships coming to take in a cargo of produce and especially of precious spices from the archipelago, brought the new faith with them. Before the Great Discoveries the part played by the Arabs in acting as intermediaries between Europe and the Far East is well known. These people had for many years been frequenting the markets along the coast of India, where they were in permanent touch with the Malays. At an early period they even took part in the trade between China and the East Indies and from the 7th century onwards they had in their service large Chinese junks manned by 150 or 200 men. In A.D. 982 an Arab vessel reached Canton with cargo taken on board at Mindoro. Muslim merchants were probably already established there in certain ports in Sumatra, Java, Borneo, and the Philippines, particularly at Sulu, which was the great pearl market.

However, it must be noticed that these Muslim colonies contained more Gujeratis than true Arabs. Islam reached the archipelago through India, a fact which no doubt helped to explain its success, since it was a Hinduised Islam, to which the natives acceded more readily. There is not much information about the details of Muslim evangelisation, but it certainly had a great effect on political geography. Events seem to have moved on the following pattern.[1] From the 13th century onwards there came a stream of Muslims,

[1] Krom in Schrieke (20), p. 309.

who acquired strength and prestige from Tamerlane's victories in India (1398) and who used peaceful means alternately with force. Little Muslim states appeared in northern Sumatra about 1250, but the new religion did not spread to the ports of Java until the beginning of the 15th century. Ternate was reached about 1440; Holo in the Sulu Islands was conquered by the Sultan of Brunei about 1480; and the rulers of Malacca were converted to Islam in the first half of the 15th century. This last port was a stronghold of Muslim Indian and Arab traders, and an important centre of religious propaganda.[1] Jean Parmentier, a Frenchman despatched by the Ango family of Dieppe, had a disputation with Muslim doctors in Sumatra in 1529, and a Muslim sultan was reigning in Bantam when the Portuguese arrived in 1526. The new comers often succeeded in worming their way into the courts of the princes, in marrying the daughters of highly placed Malays, and in acquiring influence in the government. This is how little Muslim kingdoms and large sultanates were founded. The conversion to Islam was assisted by the natives themselves.

Luzón had already been penetrated when the Spaniards reached the Philippines, but they succeeded in pushing back Islam to the south-east of the group, thus checking its other advancing wing thirty years after the taking of Granada. But in Java the progress of the new faith had brought on the decay of Majapahit, which fell about 1520,[2] and the island was almost wholly converted to Islam by the end of the 16th century. Hinduism resisted only at the eastern end around the Ijen hill-mass in Balambanggang and ended by taking refuge in Bali, where it still persists, grafted on to the vigorous stock of popular religions.

Islam not only failed to root out Hindu beliefs and worship, but also compromised with the indigenous faiths. Its rules of conduct are very badly observed, especially by the Javanese. Pork is often eaten, women are never veiled, and fasting and daily prayers are neglected.[3]

Animism remains the basic religion for many natives, who not only believe in the power of the dead, but also venerate a thousand secret deities residing in certain animals (tigers and crocodiles), large trees, and curiously formed cliffs. Offerings are made to the genii of streams, springs, caves, and craters. Nor are practices of genuine Hindu origin eradicated either. They are, for instance, very much alive in the principalities in central Java. Peasants, and even *hadjis* returned from Mecca, still often worship the Buddhist or

[1] Coedès (67b), p. 408–11.

[2] The last document which mentions the existence of an Indo-Javanese prince was dated in 1513. In 1546 the Muslim state of Demak replaced Majapahit. See Krom, *op. cit.*, p. 310.   [3] Bosquet (65).

Hindu idols displayed in museums or kept in sanctuaries restored by Dutch archeologists.

It would be wrong, however, to conclude that there is no loyalty to Islam. The incontestable fact remains that five-sixths of the inhabitants of Indonesia, that is, nearly two-thirds of the people of the Malay lands dealt with here, declare themselves to be Muslims and are generally proud of it. They represent about one-fifth of the world's Muslims. Separated from the great centres of Islamic thought by the Hindu or Buddhist territories of India and Indo-China, they nevertheless continue to submit to its effulgence. The attempts made since the 17th century by Arabs from the Hadhramaut to sweep away the parasitic creeds and lead the faithful to orthodoxy have had only meagre results. Meanwhile, many missionary organisations, the best known of which is the Mohammadiyah, have continued to distribute tracts and pamphlets containing exegesis and apologetics, to try to spread the use of Arabic characters, and to increase the reading of the Koran with learned commentaries.[1] Fanatical Muslims exist in the archipelago; for instance, among the Moros[2] in the southern Philippines, where conversion to Islam is still pursued in the interior of Mindanao; in south-western Java; in Sumatra in the district of Minangkabau and especially in Achin which is famous for the fierce resistance it offered to Dutch occupation right up to the beginning of the 20th century. Every year pilgrims set out for Mecca. In 1927 there were 123,000 and in 1936, after the great sugar slump, 36,000. Those who have visited Mecca are held in great respect. The others often appoint a representative from among the Indonesian colony in the holy city, where in 1937 there were Dutch subjects numbering 3100, including 1400 students. In addition there were about a hundred at the University of El Azhar in Cairo. In 1860 Wallace was told in the islands to the east of Serang that, after having beaten Russia and converted her to Islam, Turkey had become the most powerful nation in the world.[3] But news and slogans issuing from the chief Muslim centres are spread far more quickly today.

Though the attachment to Islam is not disputed and is of vital importance in the development of contemporary Indonesian politics, yet Mohammedanism has, when all is said and done, been but a rather feeble civilising factor. Its influence on the arts has been negative, if anything. The mosque is not a major element in the landscape in the country as a whole or even in urban architecture. The rule against representations of the human figure has killed

[1] Drewes in Schrieke (20), p. 134.
[2] The Moros (i.e. Moors) were so called by the Spaniards because they were Muslims. They are a religious, not a racial, group.
[3] Wallace (63), p. 283.

sculpture, though it has not succeeded in the suppression of *wayang*, a dramatic art which is very characteristic of Javanese civilisation and saturated with Hinduism. Indian writing has remained, except in the Malay language and dialects of Minangkabau and Achin, which are written in Arabic script, and except too in the southern Philippines, where the calendar and the law itself are Arab.[1] In the Indonesian languages and especially in Malay, Arabic words are numerous, the oldest having been introduced by Indian converts to Islam and others having come later directly from the Hadhramaut. New terms expressing religious or moral ideas and statements of dogma or law continue to enter the language slowly.

The social structure has been but slightly modified by Islam. Since the end of the last century Dutch scholars, and especially Snouck Hargronje and C. van Vollenhoven, have proved that the *adat*, or old Indonesian law, survives in native villages. In one patriarchal, in another matriarchal, rule prevails. It is significant that the latter system should have been kept in the midst of one of the most thoroughly Mohammedan parts of Indonesia, namely, the Minangkabau district. Polygamy is rare. According to the census in 1930, out of 7,116,000 married Muslims in Java there were only 105,000 cases of polygamy; and in the Outer Provinces 73,000 out of 2,208,000.

The immigration of foreign Muslims has gone on for centuries, but has never amounted to a large total. Today there are two sources from which they come, one Indian and the other Arab. The great majority of Indian immigrants to Malay-speaking lands consist of the Tamil labourers in Malaya, most of whom are Hindus. The Muslims, who come mainly from the Coromandel and Malabar coasts and from Sind, are more varied in occupation. The richest are money changers or cloth traders, and the magnificently bearded Sikhs from the Punjab are often night-watchmen, policemen, or dairymen.

In 1930 there were 71,000 Arabs in the Dutch East Indies, the majority of whom came from the Hadhramaut. Most of them were shopkeepers, a few were free-lance teachers, but the wealthiest were shippers, jewellers, landlords, cinema proprietors, bankers, and moneylenders who took advantage of their reputation for orthodoxy to cheat the local people. They often marry women of the country. But neither in number nor in commercial activity can they compare with the Chinese.

China and Malay World.[2] Whilst Indian colonisation is an

---

[1] This is not exceptional. The Muslim calendar is in alternative use to the Western, or Gregorian, throughout Malaya and Indonesia and is especially common in those sectors of the community which are not directly linked with Western economic enterprises and central governments.

[2] See the recent work of V. Purcell (80a).

event of the past and Islam is almost restricted to the field of religion, the Chinese still play a very active part as middlemen. Chinese relations with the Malay lands date from time immemorial. Some fine ceramics in the museum at Jakarta prove the existence of trade between South China and Indonesia even before the Christian era in the time of the Han dynasty. They come from rifled tombs in western Java, western Borneo, and several places in Sumatra and they seem to afford evidence that Chinese colonies had already been established in the islands.

Later, Chinese pilgrims, who had gone to visit the holy places of Buddhism and been driven out of their way by storms, brought back details about the Malay lands, which they called 'The South Sea Islands'. China does not afford the epigraphist and archeologist, the prizes offered by the Hindu remains. But there are many references in the Official Annals to the reception of tribute and other diplomatic contacts in this area. However, vassalage was only temporary and never ended in direct rule.

In fact, in this matter China lacked the organising power inspired by the political aims of India and Islam. In 1292 Kublai Khan despatched a punitive expedition against Java. At other periods various emperors received tribute from Malay princes. Thus, tribute was brought by an embassy from the Philippines for the first time in 1372. But such vassalage was only temporary and never ended in direct rule, except in the Philippines during the first half of the 15th century. Nor did the Chinese make religious converts, as did the Indians and Arabs.

So it is that Chinese contribution to Malay civilisation is often underestimated. But in fact the influence on the development of technique has been great. The first Chinese to come were traders and sailors who on their way from South China to the Indian Ocean put in at ports on the coasts of Malay lands and there exchanged their porcelain, bronze vases, silks, and cottons for local produce. The Chinese were the first to prospect seriously for mineral wealth, and there are few deposits now worked by Europeans that were not known and worked by them. They taught the natives how to manufacture and use firearms. Their influence appears not only in dress, boats, and the shapes of sails, but also in certain patterns in the plastic arts featuring dragons, clouds, etc. The native dialects were enriched with many words borrowed from Chinese, mainly connected with trade, but also with agriculture, fishing, and various handicrafts. Ancestor-worship, which was deeply rooted in the local animistic beliefs, must often have been systematised by contact with Chinese immigrants.

Whilst it is difficult to estimate exactly the proportion of Chinese in the population today, the infusion of Chinese blood in the native communities is certainly not negligible. Some anthropologists, like the Sarasins, see in the Malay type the outcome of crossing between the autochthones and immigrants with mongoloid features, these features being less and less apparent towards the east.

The Chinese have certainly long held an important place in the economy of the Malay lands, and their absence would have deprived the latter of their most active leaven. About 4,000,000 of those living outside China work in Malaya and the East Indies. Their number has certainly increased during the last 300 years, for they have thriven wonderfully under European colonial rule. As early as 1632 the Dutch East India Company congratulated itself on finding these industrious people already well-established in Java and recommended its factors to treat them in a friendly manner for the greater benefit of its trade. It employed Chinese in its ships, offices, and warehouses and it did so all the more willingly because trade with China was bringing in great profits. Thanks to the Chinese, the cultivation of sugar-cane increased, and in 1710 it was they who worked most of the 130 sugar-mills between Bantam and Cheribon. At the end of the 18th century large estates were handed over to them by local chiefs and worked by means of forced native labour.[1] In 1796, of the 8535 villages belonging to the Company 1134 were let out to Chinese. Further, they took up a lease for the collection of various dues and taxes, and all trade was dominated by them. Raffles estimated their number in Java at 100,000 and their power at ten times that of all the Europeans. As early as the end of the 18th century they were very numerous in the gold-bearing districts of western Borneo, where their methods of working showed a great advance on native processes, thanks to the engineering of a water-supply for the placers. The troubles and wars in China during the 19th century encouraged an exodus which increased after the revolution of 1911. In 1850 the Chinese in Java numbered 150,000, and in 1900 there were 277,000 in that island and 250,000 in the *Buitengewesten*.[2] In 1930 about 1,233,000 were counted in the whole of the Dutch East Indies, 582,000 of whom were in Java and 651,000 in the Outer Provinces. Purcell estimates their total number in Indonesia at 1,900,000 in 1949. That is two per cent. of the total population. In British Borneo, where there are about 150,000, the proportion rises to 17 per cent.

Their increase is still more striking in Malaya. Even in the 18th century a Malay news-sheet in Perak complained of the free-and-easy ways of the Chinese and compared their music at the royal

[1] Furnivall (15), p. 41.
[2] The Outer Provinces, that is, the Dutch East Indies outside Java and Madura.

festivals to 'the croaking of frogs in a swamp after rain'. By 1854 Singapore was a Chinese town, whose immigrant population amazed Wallace by its industry and the variety of its occupations.[1] In the 20th century Chinese labour streamed in when European capital and technical knowledge began to avail itself of the possibilities of planting, mining, and commerce in a land till then scarcely touched. Chinese immigrants arrived every year in tens of thousands at Singapore, in which place alone 359,000 landed in 1927. In 1937 there were more than 2,000,000 in the country as a whole; and in 1947 this number had risen to 2,615,000, of whom 730,000 were in Singapore. How complete was the change in the composition of the population may be realised from the fact that the number of Chinese was only a few thousand less than that of the Malays.

In the Philippines the Chinese are certainly more numerous than the figure of 70,000 published by the Bureau of Health in 1933, and the total number of Filipinos who have in their veins the blood of comparatively recent Chinese immigrants is estimated at about a million.[2]

The great majority of these immigrants come from South China and especially from the over-populated coastal districts of Kwangtung and Fukien.[3] Kwangsi and the island of Hainan furnish smaller contingents. Relations between these provinces and Malaya are encouraged by the rhythm of the monsoons. On going abroad the Chinese tend to associate in groups consisting of persons from the same districts in China and differing scarcely less than the Europeans in language, temperament, mode of life, and period of emigration.

Their occupations are various. Nearly all of them have fled from a life of misery and crushing debt[4] and have been attracted by the fame of these southern lands (*Nan Yang*). They have come packed on transports or even sailing junks without a farthing and with perseverance, ingenuity, and adaptability as their only capital. These qualities have enabled them greatly to outstrip the indolent natives, who are without initiative, less keen on gain, and attached to the traditional ways of growing their food, however poor the

[1] Wallace (63), p. 16.

[2] A. Kolb (175), pp. 405 ff. Philippine statistics reckon only 'Chinese citizens' as Chinese, whilst Malaya and the Dutch East Indies include in the category all those of Chinese descent. Among the latter are many who no longer have ties with their native land and do not even speak Chinese. Cp. L. Unger (88), pp. 197 ff. The census of 1947 reported 100,971 Chinese in the Philippines. Cp. V. Purcell (80a, p. 569 ff.).

[3] See Purcell (80a), pp. 6–10 in the map showing principal places of origin in China of the Chinese in south-east Asia.

[4] On the causes of Chinese emigration, see Ta Chen (86)

harvest may be. The Chinese respond to every call for labour and readily work at all the new industries. They often display extraordinary endurance, toiling for long hours without a stop and sleeping in an *atap* hut or curled up at the bottom of a sampan. To earn a frugal meal they clear the bush or tap plantation trees, work in the mines or docks, turning their hands to fishing or to cutting and sawing wood in the forestry business in the interior, or burning charcoal in the fever-stricken mangrove swamps on whose edge the Malay population ends with the solid ground. For many this is only a beginning. From the mass of labourers skilled men will emerge more or less quickly owing to chance or personal aptitude. The ordinary tasks will be left to the Malays or to less ambitious or less efficient immigrants like the Indians in Malaya or the Javanese in Sumatra. Chinese will be preferred for the work of timbering the galleries of mines, as machine-minders, or else as book-keepers or clerks.

But our immigrant has a persistent desire to rise to an independent position which will bring him not a wage, but profits which may be increased indefinitely in proportion to his industry and skill. As soon as he has put by sufficiently large savings, he will give up the business by which he has hitherto earned his living. Often he will, in partnership with a few of his likes, go and work, say, alluvial tin or a gold vein. Scorning rice-cultivation as a rule,[1] because the profits are too small owing to the difficulty of securing land enough and to native competition, he will direct his efforts towards crops for export, such as pepper, gambier, copra, and, more recently, rubber. Or else he will take to market gardening or pig farming on the outskirts of a big town.

The Chinese finds that his gifts and astuteness are best used in trade. He often begins as a pedlar, penetrating into the remotest villages to exchange his stock for local produce. Before roads and railways were built, he it was who was mainly responsible for bringing down to the coast the produce to be shipped to China and Europe; but as soon as the new means of transport were placed at his disposal, he took full advantage of them. He excels in business detail. A skilful craftsman, he often makes goods himself, becoming a tailor, shoemaker, glass-blower, smelter, blacksmith, or jeweller. But he also retails all kinds of imported goods, owning most of the groceries, hardware shops, and bazaars in the towns; and he has a wonderful knowledge of the tastes of every race and is able to anticipate them, readily adapting himself to the whims of his

[1] Chinese rice cultivators are, however, fairly numerous in western Borneo, in the 'Chinese districts' of the former Dutch territory and the south of Sarawak.

customers.   He may be found keeping a shop at the cross-roads of
newly built highways or travelling by boat up the rivers in Sumatra
or Borneo, and alive to all the resources of the district.

Solidarity is one of the chief Chinese means of success.   The
tendency is already well developed in his original surroundings, but
becomes stronger abroad.   In great cities like Singapore, Chinese
societies abound, some bringing together persons originally from
the same district, others for recreation or sport, some aiming at
perfecting their members in the use of the English language, the
study of Chinese and English literature, the encouragement of a
moral life, of philosophic discussion, etc.   Most of them are
business associations, however.   The miners, especially those in
Borneo, form *kongsis,* in which each member shares in the profits in
proportion to his contribution of capital.   The partners employ
paid workmen and elect the manager.   The unity of the business is
reflected in the grouping of the buildings, including a dormitory and
a canteen, round a courtyard.   Each association has its own
kitchen garden, arrack distillery, and piggery.

The tendency to form associations is, moreover, encouraged by
the Protecting Power, which finds it far more convenient to deal with
communities than with individuals.   Untroubled as a rule by
politics and missionaries and profiting from the incompetence of the
natives, the Chinese has been able not only to become an indispensable middleman, but also to create complex organisations
which dominate the whole economy of large areas and even overstep
intercolonial boundaries.

The Chinese has an instinct for big business.   In his own way he
realises what our economists call vertical and horizontal integration.
From peddling and petty shopkeeping he rises to high commerce.
He plans closely meshed networks of sale and purchase from which
the native producer has little chance of escape.   He combines trade
with money-lending and, speculating on the peasant's casualness, he
advances cash on the security of the coming harvest.   Since repay-
ment is never complete, he has the debtor at his mercy and thus
controls not only a great deal of agricultural production, but
frequently also the output of the crafts.   In 1911 an anti-Chinese
movement occurred owing to the exploitation of *batik* craftsmen[1]
by Chinese business men.[2]

The path to fortune is never a class privilege among the Chinese,
but is open to the poorest labourer.   The successful man leaves the
noisy, bustling quarter with its narrow streets draped with drying
cloth, where he made his impecunious start, and takes up his
residence in a villa of hybrid architecture, often of florid decoration

[1] See footnote below, p. 102.
[2] This was the origin of the first mass nationalist movement in Indonesia,
Sarekat Islam.

and not infrequently situated in extensive grounds. Many are said to be millionaires—in Straits dollars or 1939 florins. According to an article on the distribution of incomes in Java about 1925, the wealthiest of the Chinese seemed to be richer than the wealthiest Europeans in the island.[1] The Chinese bowling along in luxurious cars in Singapore, Medan, Jakarta, or Manila are bankers, proprietors of large stores, or owners of town property and plantations. Some are industrialists or shippers handling coastwise trade or even owning big steamship lines. Another passable source of profit for the Chinese was to acquire the lease, often by tender, of businesses which bored the European or required too detailed a knowledge of or a too continuous contact with native surroundings. It was, for instance, almost inevitably he who had the privilege of selling opium in Java and of running the ferries and refilling stations on the roads, and who kept the pawnshops and gambling dens. It was he too who collected certain taxes—for example, the dues for slaughter-houses and markets—whose collection by European officials would have been too difficult or too onerous. Rich Chinese are often both very vain and very generous, constructing public gardens, founding and maintaining schools and hospitals, and undertaking at their own expense great operations like the provision of water-works.

The power of the Chinese has not failed to rouse the animosity of both the people of the country and Europeans as well as to cause administrative uneasiness. The Chinese had long been engaged in piracy in the China Seas. In 1570 under the leadership of Limahon they attacked the Spanish settlement at Manila. Even about the middle of the 19th century ships were plundered and crews massacred in Singapore harbour by Chinese pirates.[2] Today, the Chinese are usually charged with usurious practices, want of scruple, and ruthlessness in business. Their communities, obeying instructions issued by elusive leaders, are regarded as dissidents constituting a threat to public order. The spread of certain Communist doctrines seems to give substance to this charge. It was among the emigrants to Malaya and Indonesia that the Chinese Revolution found many of its prime movers and strongest supporters. Owing to the large sums sent back to their native land by postal order or cheque and the even greater amounts entrusted to persons returning thither, the Chinese are abused as parasites.

The Chinese problem is one of the most difficult that face the Malay countries and Indo-China. Various opinions have been expressed ever since Europeans first came into contact with colonies of these people. Whilst the Dutch East India Company instructed

[1] Meyer Ranneft in Schrieke (20), p. 76.
[2] Yet the preponderance of piracy in these waters was Malay or Dyak.

its clerks to deal tactfully with them, Gabriel de San Antonio stated bitterly in his report at Valladolid in 1604 that 'they never go to sterile or poor land, but always live and trade in districts flowing with milk and honey, where they can make a profit'.

Hence, the history of the Philippines has been a long series of violent quarrels between Spaniards and Chinese. The latter were met for the first time in Mindoro in 1571.[1] The murder of governors and officials, which once started a panic in the Spanish colony in Manila, was followed by great massacres of Chinese, like the one that lasted eighteen days and the still more bloody one in 1639. But after these hecatombs the most necessary commodities were no longer to be had, even at exorbitant prices. So Chinese trade soon prospered once more. De Comyn (in Laufer) estimates that between 1571 and 1821 some $400,000,000 worth of silver was exported from Spanish America to Manila and that perhaps half of it passed to China. Since 1580 the Chinese had been relegated to a special quarter in Manila, the Alcaycería, to which they used to flock in spring and where many lived permanently. The merchandise carried by the galleons to Acapulco was mainly of Chinese origin. Similar contradictions appear in the variable policy followed by the Netherlands. After the foundation of Batavia, Governor Coen made raids on the Chinese coast in order to people his capital more rapidly.[2] The Company tried to make use of the Chinese to its own advantage, but these Asians did not willingly give up the positions they had acquired in the archipelago and which they had extended after the economic stagnation of the Philippines from the 17th century onwards had diverted them to the Dutch East Indies. Their desire to check European expansion made them support the resistance of the native princes and weave plots against the Dutch. Competition grew desperate at times, and Dutch power seemed threatened. Consequently, the Company tried to weed out the Chinese population and in 1740 began to deport bad elements to Ceylon. A large number of Chinese then assembled from different parts of the island and attacked Batavia. The Dutch colony called in sailors from ships anchored in the roadstead, and several thousand Chinese were killed.

Since the beginning of the 19th century relations between the Dutch administration and the Chinese mining associations in Borneo had been strained. The Chinese had succeeded in forming some small, practically self-governing republics in the western portion of the island and claimed political authority. After many ineffective operations by small bodies of troops, a strong military

---

[1] Laufer (77), p. 258.
[2] H. Bernard (245), p. 199.

expedition had to be sent in 1850. Even this took four years of hard fighting to subdue the Chinese.[1]

But in fact, the Chinese have gained a great deal of economic power through European rule in the region. Though criticised bitterly, they were made use of. Their influence, which the Europeans wished to reduce, was on the contrary increased owing to the fresh opportunities afforded by the achievements of the Europeans, the resources of their technical knowledge, and the expansion of their rule.[2] There is talk of uprooting them; but their roots go deep. They sometimes snap off and the plant grows again with incredible persistence and renewed vigour.

The Chinese is not a harmful weed. Even usury is not peculiar to him, though he has organised it in an expert manner. Most observers agree in recognising his good qualities as well as his defects. He has undertaken tasks which no one else was prepared to do, neither the Malays nor the Europeans. The success of the great material enterprises in these Far Eastern colonies, which becomes evident when these are compared with Africa south of the Sahara is due to the Chinese for having had a share in the work which it would be unjust to deny them. After numerous experiments in various directions wisdom required not that they should be expelled or persecuted, but that efforts should be made to do without them. This is what was in fact being done in ways that varied with the place, and the fits and starts of the movement corresponded to the slumps and booms of trade.

On the eve of the war in 1941 the situation of the Chinese seemed less attractive than formerly. The world slump had affected them as much as it had affected the Europeans. Their immigration was restricted by law. The American Chinese Exclusion Act had been extended in 1902 to cover the Philippines; though in fact its enforcement was difficult because of the long coastline, and many Chinese were smuggled in. Americans opposed to the independence of the Philippines claimed that the islands would become a Chinese colony. An agrarian law forbade the employment of Chinese farm hands, whilst in the old days Spain would on the contrary have accepted farm hands only.

Until 1928 the entry of Chinese into Malaya was practically unrestricted, but in that year the British administration had to institute a quota system so as to reduce unemployment. In 1937 when this

[1] T. Posewitz (151), p. 242; Kolb (175), p. 406 ff.

[2] The development of the Outer Provinces in the Dutch East Indies is reflected in the rapid increase in the percentage of Chinese in the population. In 1930 this was 3·4 as against only 1·4 in Java. In the Outer Provinces only 21 per cent. of the Chinese lived by trade and transport (as against 61 per cent. in Java), whilst 45 per cent. were engaged in producing raw materials.

restriction was removed, Chinese immigration was vigorously resumed.

The imposition of an admission tax in 1928 in the Dutch East Indies had also brought on a considerable slowing down of immigration.

On the other hand, the actual monopolies held by the Chinese seemed to crumble at times in face of harder competition. The governments took under State supervision the services which had previously been entrusted to the Chinese, such as the manufacture of opium, keeping of pawnshops, and the collection of certain taxes. The official organisation of loans to the people, though laborious and still imperfect, was beginning to sap the Chinese commercial system which was based on lending at high rates of interest. European business was succeeding more easily in doing without the Chinese. Recent generations of natives, being better educated for the new jobs, themselves supplied skilled labour and established little industries or commercial houses. Japanese competition in the crafts and more particularly in trade was becoming keener and keener, especially in the Philippines, but also in the Dutch possessions.

Although their economic function seemed to be declining, the Chinese had succeeded in reaching a more profitable position than before. They claimed the same rights as the Japanese, who were treated the same or nearly the same as the Europeans. Many of the legal restrictions to which they had been subject had been abrogated; and their movements which had previously depended on permits and vexatious controls, had become freer. They had their schools and their press, which was often very influential. They claimed to be allowed to play a constructive part and demanded a greater share in the administration of the districts in which they worked.[1] These demands seemed particularly legitimate in places where the Chinese were most closely mingled with the native population. In this connexion, there was a great difference on the one hand between countries like Malaya or the Oostkust of Sumatra, which had only recently risen to economic prominence and in which the Chinese colonies were as unstable as the wind, and, on the other hand, Java, where long-standing prosperity had on the contrary permitted many Chinese to settle down, often with native wives, after losing all desire to go home and having become more influential in the island than more recent immigrants.[2] In the Philippines and especially in

[1] They were already represented in various assemblies together with the local people and the Europeans: e.g. in the Volksraad of the Dutch Indies.

[2] In 1930 about 86 per cent. of the Chinese in Java had been born in the Dutch East Indies. Whilst in Java and Madura there were 821 Chinese women to every 1000 men, in the Outer Provinces the proportion was only 517 to 1000.

Manila the latter have come into conflict with a body of naturalised half-castes. In the British and American territories as in Indonesia the Chinese were far from constituting a homogeneous mass ready as a whole to make the same demands.

The Europeans. Above the native masses and the intermediate layers of foreign Asiatics the Europeans represent only a thin veneer of population; but their function has been of the greatest importance. In 1930–31, the latest date on which comparisons may be made between the Dutch, British, and American possessions, the Europeans numbered 17,800 in Malaya (31,400 in 1942), 240,200 in the Dutch East Indies as a whole, and about 36,000 (in 1933) in the Philippines. These figures must be accepted with reserve. First, it should be said that the term 'European' in this connexion has a juridical, not a purely ethnical, meaning and is not everywhere applied to the same categories. It always includes Americans. But whilst the Japanese were counted separately in Malaya, they were by reason of their status included with the Europeans in the censuses of the Dutch East Indies and the Philippines, which gave the numbers as 7195 and 19,500 respectively. Lastly, Malaya excluded from the European category the 16,000 Eurasians (19,200 in 1942), or crosses between West and East, a class which on the contrary was partly mingled with the Europeans in the censuses in the Dutch East Indies and the Philippines.

Cross-breeding of Europeans and Asiatics,[1] which gives rise to serious problems, began with the arrival of the Europeans in Southeast Asia. The union of Portuguese and Spaniards with women of local race was very frequent, and missionaries like St. Francis Xavier were soon seen trying to regularise or break them off, according to whether or not they conformed with the canons of the Church. Thus, from the 16th century Eurasians increased in number in the trading centres in Malaya and Indonesia. The infusion of European blood seems to have been particularly great in the Philippines, which remained for nearly three hundred years under Spanish rule. But the Dutch too showed no repugnance to mixed marriages, which until recently were encouraged by the scarcity of their own women in these tropical possessions. British contribution to the Eurasian population in Malaya still seems less than that of the Portuguese, because the occupation by the English was relatively late here. But yet in Padang and Benkulen, for example, one finds Townsends and Farquhars, who correspond to the Albuquerques and Souzas in Malacca and the Moluccas, and to the Reebs and Nessmarks in Jakarta and Surabaya.[2] Consequently, the place occupied by Eurasians in the count of Europeans differs greatly from

[1] Vu van Quang (90); Fuchs (212). [2] J. Chailley-Bert (133), p. 194.

one group of colonies to another and so lessens the value of the statistics and invalidates any comparisons made from them. It is estimated that the Eurasians, or *Indos*, of the Dutch East Indies accounted for about two-thirds of the total number of 'Europeans'. Many others, who are not acknowledged by their fathers, have remained or fallen back into the native masses. Among the latter, who often form a real *élite*, but are not distinguished by the censuses, are most of the Philippine *mestizos*, numbering about 200,000 as against some 5000 full-blooded Spaniards.[1]

Whatever may be thought of the value of former censuses, it is certain that before 1939 the European population had increased more rapidly than the native. In the Dutch East Indies, which formed the largest territorial area and contain the most reliable statistics, Europeans remained few until about the middle of the 19th century. Right from the beginning of the Dutch occupation Coen had advocated the formation of a free European settlement; but the powerful Company did not wish to share out the profits from exploitation among too many hands and, being afraid of losing control of the islands, was unwilling to send out any but clerks in its own service. Even after the downfall of the Company the European population increased but slowly. In 1860 it amounted to only 44,000 persons, including troops; and there were only a few hundred who were not officials. It was mainly from 1870 onwards that the Europeans multiplied along with the development of private enterprises, the encouragement given by the abolition of the *Cultuurstelsel*, and the extension of effective Dutch administration to the whole territory. The number of Europeans rose to 91,000 in 1900 and to 240,000 in 1930. The increase in the European population had been most rapid since 1905, reaching a mean annual rate of 3·91 per cent. between 1905 and 1920, and 3·64 per cent. between 1920 and 1930. Meyer Ranneft shows how this corresponds to the increase in foreign trade, budget expenditure, and note circulation.[2] Between 1920 and 1930 the Chinese had increased at a rate of 4·31 per cent., but the natives by only 2·04 per cent.

Family life was made easier by refrigerators and hill-stations. Formerly, Europeans in the Indies had preferred local *rijstafel* to preserved food and other imported products, which were often rancid or sour. Later the diet had become more like that at home. Fresh milk was often not to be had; but the slaughter of cattle was carefully controlled, and European vegetables were cultivated by the

---

[1] About 1840 Mallat (177), II, p. 131, distinguished true creoles, called 'children of the country' (*Hijos del país*) from the *criollos*, who are in fact crosses between Europeans and local races.

[2] Meyer Ranneft in Schrieke (20), p. 73.

Chinese, Japanese, and even the native hill-folk. Not only were more immigrants arriving from Europe, but, whether officials or settlers, they often went out married to young women of their own race, and mixed marriages were becoming rare. Thus, the proportion of Eurasians was decreasing. In Malaya where the census returns distinguished between Eurasians and Europeans, the latter have had a greater increase than the former since the beginning of the century. In the Dutch East Indies, where half-castes were merged in the category of 'Europeans', this group was on the whole less coloured and whiter than before. Americans in the Philippines are more averse to cross-breeding than the Spaniards were.

Besides, the European and Eurasian elements were in different proportions according to the age of the colony. In the former Dutch East Indies[1] Java, where pure-blooded Dutch, or *Totok*, comprised scarcely one-quarter of the total, has more 'Indos' than the other islands. In the Philippines most of the *mestizos* are in Luzón and especially in Manila and its surroundings. But Java also affords the best conditions for acclimatisation, because of the successful struggle against endemic tropical diseases, the progress of hygiene and comfort, and the facilities for educating children. The more stable, less 'colonial', nature of the European population in Java as compared with the Outer Provinces was reflected in the greater percentage of persons born locally, of young people between the ages of 15 and 20, and of Europeans of over 50 years of age. The age-pyramid in the 'European' category indicated a degree of stability remarkable in a tropical colony. It must be emphasised, however, that this was due mainly to the greater proportion of half-castes. In Indonesia as in Malaya and the Philippines the numerical inequality of the sexes among pure-blooded Europeans remained very marked, although it had decreased almost regularly since the beginning of the century. The number of females was scarcely more than half that of the males.

Europeans are very unevenly distributed in Malaya and Indonesia. In 1937 about half of those in Malaya were on the islands of Singapore and Penang. In the Dutch East Indies in 1930 more than 80 per cent. were in Java, more than 10 per cent. in Sumatra. They were mainly town-dwellers, especially in Java, where 70 per cent. of the Europeans dwelt in big towns, as against 40 per cent. in the Outer Provinces. The European communities in the big towns in Java were among the largest in Monsoon Asia. Batavia, including Meester Cornelis, had 37,000 Europeans, Surabaya 26,000, Bandung 20,000, and Semarang 12,000, as did also

[1] Lehmann (97); Meyer Ranneft, in Schrieke (20).

Singapore, where there were in addition 7000 Eurasians. Manila contained about half the Westerners in the Philippines.

The functions and way of life of the Europeans were very various. The Eurasians have sometimes been able to rise to a high social or intellectual position; as, for instance, Wilken, the great ethnologist, did in the Dutch East Indies, and Quezón, the first President of the Commonwealth, and Rizal, the chief national poet, have done in the Philippines. But most of them were humble clerks and officials or petty farmers. This often seemed due rather to want of education and concentration than to any deep-seated lack of aptitude. Anyhow, the average income of Eurasians in Java was assessed in 1925 at only ten times that of a native, whilst that of the pure-blooded Dutchman was twenty or thirty times as great. The 'hundred per cent.' Europeans shared among themselves the functions that were theirs in all administered colonies.

In 1930, 24·3 per cent. of the Europeans in the Dutch East Indies were administrators, soldiers, or police; 5·5 per cent. were in industry; 12·8 per cent. in the post office and transport services; 13·4 per cent. in commerce; 13·2 per cent. in the liberal professions (including missionaries), and, finally, 22·3 per cent. in production properly so-called, especially in work on plantations and mines. The last figure, being relatively high, emphasises the value of the capital invested in the soil and the underlying rock and the importance of these tropical possessions in the world-supply of raw materials. Europeans engaged in private enterprises had as a rule seen their social status improved relatively to that of officials since the beginning of the century.

Another feature to be mentioned, which bears some relation to the remarks above, is the comparatively large number of 'Europeans' who were not nationals of the Protecting Power. Considering the Dutch East Indies in particular, the figure of 208,000 Dutch in a 'European' total of 240,000 included nearly all the Eurasians. After the Dutch came the Germans and Austrians with 7381, Japanese with 7195, English with 2414, Swiss with 790, Americans with 643, Belgians with 625, French with 414, etc.

The Europeans (or those ranking as such) were, however, a mere handful compared with local peoples. In Indonesia the average proportion was 1000 local-born people to 4 Europeans, of whom only one or two were pure-blooded Europeans according to the estimate of the number of Eurasians. In Malaya the Europeans, who are in this case nearly all of pure blood, number 4 to every 1000 Asians, owing to the intense and varied activity in Singapore. The ratio falls to less than 1·5 per 1000 in the Philippines. By our reckoning the pure-blooded Europeans in Malaya, Indonesia, and the Philippines in 1930 numbered at most 120,000 out of a total of 75,000,000 souls. That is a fairly normal figure for tropical lands and is higher than that for other possessions in Monsoon Asia, including French Indo-China. The complexity of these colonial populations is evident. It must be emphasised that the different racial groups were not distinguished from each other merely by their origin, language, civilisation, and mode of life. Among the foreign elements, European and Chinese, a distinction was often made between sojourners, or *trekkers*, on the one hand and, on the other, the *blijvers*, or those who no longer expected to return one day to their native land.

After the various parts of the region have been dealt with, we shall return later to the recent development of Malay lands, a development which had made steady progress under the control, or at least guidance, of Europeans for varying lengths of time and in different degrees.

From the spiritual point of view the influence of the Europeans may seem slight. Certainly, the great majority of natives continue to hold their traditional beliefs. Islam has spread itself like varnish over the old superstitions, over the ancient syncretism of the Hindu tenets and immemorial animism. The social organisation has its roots in a distant past, and Indonesian communities are still often regulated by the very ancient customs or *adat*. All the same, since the arrival of the Europeans these old beliefs and venerable institutions have certainly been shaken and more or less seriously affected.

The material contributions of colonial expansion have stirred the mind and social organisation of the local races more deeply and generally than education has done. Christian missions have had only moderate results, except in the Philippines. In spite of the great progress made recently by education, only a minority is affected. But the technical knowledge and skill brought in by the Europeans, the industrial organisation instituted by them, and the transfers of population they have caused have had an effect on the Asian masses as a whole. To the fleeting tourist the life of bygone days may seem to continue unchanged in the Malay *kampong* or Philippine *barrio*. A little knowledge of the past and a moment's thought soon show the attentive observer the multiplicity of changes that have come about. No doubt the influence dies away like a ripple as it leaves the towns, railway stations, and main roads; but the work of the last decades had hastened its penetration. Certain writers insist on the slow pace of the changes; but there are few native communities which do not to some extent feel and show by their conduct and reactions the effect of the new order of things.

The import of manufactured goods has gradually disorganised

the crafts. Exotic plants, in particular those from America, have come into favour with the local cultivators. Domestic animals, to which imported species have been added, have been put to new uses. Other agricultural systems—government monopolies of certain commodities, forced labour, and large privately owned plantations— have changed the conditions of life, caused the transfer of labour, and in some cases made a complete change in the population of vast areas. Money has universally replaced barter in trade. Roads and railways permit rapid movement. The population has increased in many places, and a portion of it has gone to settle in town, where more than anywhere else the new habits are spreading. These include the use of detachable collars and leather shoes, meat and white bread, coffee, aerated or iced drinks, visits to the cinema, and the reading of newspapers. In the towns, too, have occurred strikes and seditious agitation.

CHAPTER 6

DISTRIBUTION OF POPULATION; MODES OF LIFE

Density of Population. In spite of the progress of European penetration, the Malay lands are still very unevenly populated. Here and there immigration has caused a very rapid increase in the number of inhabitants. The best example of this is furnished by the Oostkust of Sumatra, where the population rose from 116,000 to 1,674,000 between 1880 and 1930. In Malaya it was more than doubled between 1901 and 1931 in the States of Perak, Negri Sembilan, and Pahang, whilst in Selangor, the great rubber-planting district, it was trebled during the same period. This was due to the recent establishment of plantations on land that had been largely uncultivated and to the sudden demand for labour resulting from it. But astoundingly great differences in density of population still persist (see Fig. 11).

The mean density, which was 83 to the square mile in Malaya (1931) and Indonesia (1930) and 116 to the square mile in the Philippines (1939), is the mean of very different extremes.[1] In Malaya, putting aside the essentially urban districts, the population varied between 13 to the square mile in Pahang and 168 to the square mile in Selangor. In Indonesia the mean density ranged from about 5 to the square mile in the Moluccas to 816 to the square mile in Java and Madura, after passing through the intermediate figures of 10 in Borneo, 46 in Sumatra, and 443 in Bali and Lombok. In the Philippines in 1939 Palawan and Mindoro supported respectively only 15 and 34 persons to the square mile, whilst Luzón had 186, Negros 248, Panay 303, Leyte 326, and Sebu 630.

The regional treatment below[2] will explain these differences, at least to some extent, but it is not easy to master the laws governing the distribution of population, for the factors are very complex. The fertility of the soil clearly plays an important part, as does the climate, but other things being equal, recent volcanic soils derived from basic lava-flows, i.e. well supplied with lime, magnesia, iron, potash, and phosphoric acid, are the most densely peopled. Well-watered land having the advantage of a dry season seems better off than districts in which rain falls all through the year. This perhaps explains the relatively high densities in the Banjermasin district in

[1] In 1951 the density was estimated to be 106 to the square mile in Malaya, 132 in Indonesia, and 176 in the Philippines. For more recent figures, see below, p. 439.   [2] See pp. 113–296.

south-eastern Borneo and in the south of the Macassar peninsula in Celebes. The effects of altitude are various. The degree of ease with which the cultivable land and irrigated fields, or *sawahs*, are worked depends on the relief. Yet the contrasts between lowland and mountain, which are so striking in Indo-China, are far less marked here. In eastern Sumatra the wide plains remained thinly populated in spite of the great fertility of the soil in places, until the fertile areas were brought into use by Europeans. But the density is far lower on the east coast than in the backland of the west coast State of Padang, which consists of volcanic plateaus nearly 3500 feet above the sea. As far as we know, there has been no attempt to take a census of the population by zones of altitude, and, indeed, such a distribution could scarcely be accurate, except in Java and other areas already properly mapped. The highest villages in Java are situated above 9600 feet in the Tengger district in the east of the island and above the 5000-foot contour on the plateau of Dieng, where the ruins of Hindu temples bear witness to the existence of a dense and relatively sedentary population as early as the 8th century.

The relation between the natural conditions and the density of population is certainly not simple. The diversity of aptitudes in the racial groups must be taken into account, and for this it would be necessary to know the prehistoric and historical circumstances which ended in placing those groups in their present position, the less skilful and weaker being pushed back into the most difficult districts and there more or less quickly assimilated by successive invaders. This assimilation is very advanced in Java. The island, which is privileged in so many ways, seems to have afforded the most convenient dimensions for the development of Malay civilisation and the exercise of its skill, and to have been long the most favourable also to the efforts of European colonisation. Sumatra and Borneo were too big, too difficult to exploit by means of the agricultural methods then known, and too difficult of penetration and control by States whose power was based on the mastery of the seas. Piracy, which was no negligible factor in the prosperity of those States, helped to drive the land folk into the interior and to increase or maintain their political separatism. The high density of population in Bali and Lombok is not explained merely by the fertility of the volcanic soil and the relatively short duration of the dry season. The two islands were refuges for parties fleeing from Islam when that religion got control of Java and tried to bring into subjection the Sasak survivals. The Muslim conquest seems on the other hand to have been responsible for at least a share in thinning out the population of the southern Philippines.

The map showing population density (Fig. 10) thus presents a very complex mosaic of different values, a mosaic that is not related to the physical conditions alone, but reflects the clash, the more or less complete superposition or fusion of cultures, of peoples who have succeeded each other in these islands. The least densely populated districts are not merely those to which nature has been unfavourable, but also those that have not had time to be affected by the most intensive types of exploitation. Some places are intrinsically poor, but many others have remained as it were in the backwaters of the streams of human migration and in particular have benefited only to a small extent by civilising influence from Eurasia.

Modes of Life. (*a*) *Collecting and Hunting.* The region contains human groups, which are often termed 'primitive' or 'savage' by ethnologists, and which have been accurately described. They live mainly by collecting, hunting, or fishing; activities that may be pursued concurrently in one and the same community and which furnish part of the food-supply, this varying with place and season.

These backward folk nearly all seem to belong to the oldest layers of population, the Negritoes and Veddas. They include, for instance, the Aëtas of the Philippines, who wander about in Mindanao, Mindoro, and, in even greater numbers, in Luzón; and also the Kubus, Bassaps, and Toalas, who are described as wandering about in eastern Sumatra, the central parts of Borneo, and in Celebes. Their peculiar civilisation is typically of the forest, their tools being not of stone, but of wood and bamboo. The Kubus, for instance, are out of their element away from the forest. They say that they cannot live in the sunshine. Collecting is the chief method of obtaining food, and after one of them has passed a spot, the earth seems as much turned up by his digging-stick as it might be by a boar's snout. Van Dongen, whose observations go back to 1906, describes the silent, almost creeping glide, now fast, now slow, of the Kubu through the forest.[1]

The most closely studied of these primitive peoples have been the Semang and Senoi,[2] who live in the hilly districts of Malaya, the former even overflowing into Siamese territory. The Semang live mainly by collecting food, searching for it almost constantly over rather large areas and moving at a rate of five or six miles a day at most. Their diet consists mainly of young shoots, pith, sap, fruit, tubers, rhizomes, and yams dug up with long sticks whose ends are sharpened in the fire. All the same, the Semang always regards himself as living in a definite district belonging to his community and named after a brook, mountain, or other geographical feature.

[1] B. Hagen (118), p. 111.
[2] Sakai (the common term) means 'slave' and is now being generally changed to the correct Senoi.

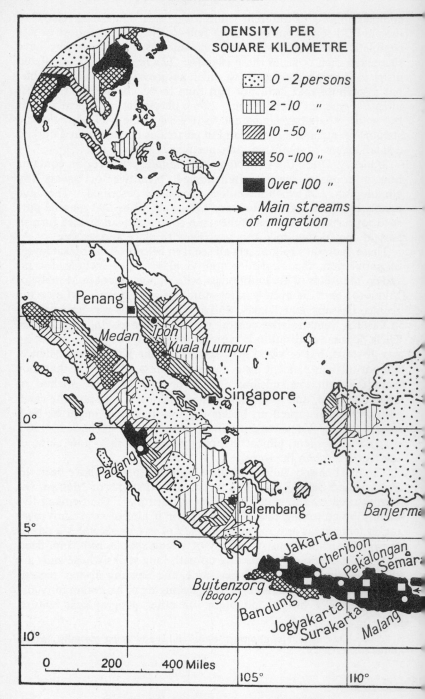

DENSITY PER
SQUARE KILOMETRE

[∷∷] 0 - 2 persons
[||||] 2 - 10   "
[////] 10 - 50   "
[▨▨] 50 - 100 "
[██] Over 100 "
⟶ Main streams
   of migration

Penang

Medan   Ipoh
         Kuala Lumpur

                    Singapore

0°

Padang

                    Palembang   Banjerma

5°
                              Jakarta   Cheribon
                                        Pekalongan
                                              Semar
                    Buitenzorg
                    (Bogor)   Bandung
                              Jogyakarta Malang
                                 Surakarta
10°

0   200   400 Miles

105°   110°

FIG. 10—DENSITY OF POPULATION, *circa* 1950

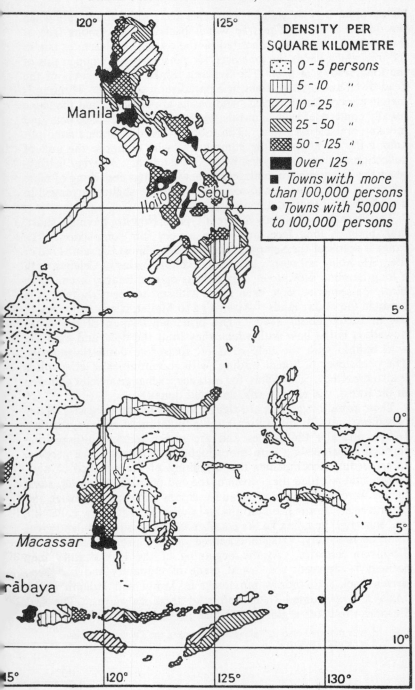

DENSITY PER
SQUARE KILOMETRE

0 - 5 persons
5 - 10   "
10 - 25   "
25 - 50   "
50 - 125   "
Over 125   "
■ Towns with more
than 100,000 persons
● Towns with 50,000
to 100,000 persons

Manila

Hoilo Sebu

Macassar

rábaya

However far he may wander, he comes back to it, at any rate when the durian is ripe. The tree which bears this enormous fruit is owned individually and inherited by the owner's children, as is also the tree which yields the *ipoh* used for poisoning the wooden tips of the long arrows in use. The Semang thinks that the souls of the dead dwell among fruit trees in a paradise in the west. Hunting is merely a secondary business, wild beasts are avoided, and the game usually consists of rats, squirrels, birds, and lizards. The boar and monkey are seldom eaten. The food gathered is often shared out among the members of the community, who comprise the unit of collection and are usually led by the oldest man. At every halting-place the Semangs soon make ready new lodgings consisting of mere screens of palm leaves or of somewhat stronger shelters arranged in a circle or oval around a central space.

The Senoi is a physically different type of Negrito, having a short, lank body, a long face, and often a very fair complexion. His range is south of the Semangs, and he leads almost the same kind of life. He hunts not with a bow, but, like the Toalas in Celebes, with a long bamboo blowpipe. His sight is extraordinarily keen. The blowpipe seems to have been more widespread formerly than it is today in the Malay lands. According to Mallat, it was still much in use in Luzón about 1840.[1] The principal weapon of the Aëtas nowadays is the bow with which they hunt the boar and even the wild buffalo with the help of dogs, their sole domestic animals. The persistence of 'silent trading' with communities of other races is also reported. The Aëtas, for instance, exchange articles gathered in the forest, viz. rattan, wax, and wild honey.[2]

These primitive groups are rightly valued by ethnologists. They constitute only tiny minorities in the population of Malaya, the East Indies, and the Philippines and are rather quickly disappearing through interbreeding with more highly developed native peoples. Interbreeding accompanies the beginning of the practice of agriculture and a settled life. Even at the end of the 19th century some Senois were using metal tools and weapons and planting maize and upland rice. In the little groups still living exclusively by collecting and hunting, the nomadic life entails a very low birth-rate and great infantile mortality. Hagen observed definite progress among the Kubus in Sumatra. At the beginning of the 19th century they seemed to represent the lowest grade of humanity and had been driven back into the swamp forest in Jambi and Palembang by Malays, who hunted them and sold them as slaves. The first European to catch a glimpse of them (about 1820) 'as one sees the

[1] It is reported also in Palawan and among the Dyaks of Borneo.
[2] A. Kolb (175), 108.

hindquarters of a fleeing stag' merely speak of them as nomads.
In 1838 they had already formed twenty-five permanent settlements
on the banks of streams; and they had adopted the Malay mode of
life at the same time as the Mohammedan religion. Cotton *sarongs*
had replaced bark loincloths, and huts built on piles had taken the
place of shelters made of branches and leaves. Collecting had been
followed by cultivation, at first timid and stealthy in clearings, but
later permanent and irrigated. Rice boiled in earthenware pots is
certainly a better food than the produce of collecting or hunting
eaten raw, often half-rotten, or slightly softened by fire. In 1906
there were hardly more than 7000 Kubus, about thirty of whom
were regarded as 'wild'. The census in 1930 did not include more
than 1463, many of whom were employed on European plantations
and in the mines.

A change has also been observed in certain groups that live almost
exclusively by fishing and display a higher culture than the primitive
forest folk. These are the Orang Laut, 'the Sea Gipsies'. Some of
them have escaped the ravages of piracy and are still met with hiding
in out-of-the-way bays made inaccessible by currents to sailing boats.
These survivals occur particularly in the Rhio group, on the east and
south coasts of Borneo, and around Celebes. The Sibutu Islands
to the north-east of Borneo in the Sulu group form the main assembly point of people known as Bajaos, who are born, live, and die
in their solidly built and often ornamented twin-outrigger boats.
These house-boats are usually moored under a sheltering roof, and
a lighter craft is used for moving about and fishing. The Bajaos
make neither cloth nor pottery. They sell part of their catch to the
Chinese to buy cassava and tapioca.[1]

Ladang and Sawah Methods of Cultivation. The supply of food
derived from collecting and hunting does not by itself support more
than a very sparse population. Even in the mountains agriculture
is far and away the principal food-producing activity. In the subsistence of the Ifugaos in the Philippines the part played by hunting
is estimated to average only one per cent. But the cultivator continues to eke out his food by collecting. Population density
increases with the practice of agriculture, but varies greatly with
technical knowledge, the kinds of plants cultivated, and the place in
the diet still occupied by the produce from collecting. The search
for wild sago palms[2] causes frequent journeys into the interior of
certain islands in eastern Indonesia, whilst the coconut tree helps to
feed communities in the coastal districts near areas most favourable
to its growth. In Indonesia most of the cultivation is done on the

[1] A. W. Herre (95).
[2] These are cut down to get the parts required for food.

ladang system, that is to say, the most widespread system in all the hot belt, the system based on burning the natural vegetation. The trees are cut down to within a foot or two of the ground—all except the biggest, the felling of which would involve too much trouble, but which are sometimes ring-barked. The wood and foliage are burnt before the first rains fall; but fire has sometimes to be set two or three times. Seeds or slips are then planted in the ash-fertilised soil. The fertility of such land is short-lived, however, for no further manure is applied. At the end of two or three years the patch is usually abandoned and not touched again until after a long period of fallow during which it returns to the forest. The burning of this vegetation renews the fertility of the patch. In the *ladang* system, which is known as *caingin* in the Philippines, neither plough, nor irrigation, nor domestic animals are used.[1] The implements employed are the cutlass and hoe wielded by men or women. In some places, as among the Karo-Bataks in central Sumatra and also many of the hill-folk in the Philippines, the soil is merely turned over by means of stout sticks. These are sometimes shod with metal and often decorated, and have a bunch of feathers at the upper end. The sods are broken up and the seed buried in holes which are then closed with the foot. The workers move forward or backward together in line and often cheer themselves on with singing. Between the sowing and harvesting a little weeding is done. But the main business is to keep watch on the field so as to protect the crop from thieving animals. The watchman's shelter, perched on long stilts in the middle of a clearing in which food plants are ripening amidst charred tree-stumps, is a picturesque feature of this extensive system of agriculture. The beginning and end of the main operations are occasions of great collective rejoicing and the fulfilment of complicated rites to procure the goodwill of the gods and spirits.

The *ladang* system is not utterly primitive. It bears evidence of patient adaptation to natural surroundings, though this is often unrecognised by the foreign traveller. The succession of crops is not left to chance. Several kinds of plants are often mingled in the same patch in order to preserve the soil from the risk of insolation or of being washed away. On the other hand, the staggering of crops shortens the time between harvests, during which supplies in the storehouses are sometimes exhausted, and then collecting may become once more the main source of food.

The *ladang* system is generally used for the cultivation of roots, tubers, and rhizomes (cassava, sweet potatoes, and yams), the planting and harvesting of which can be carried on during a great part of the year. From it are also obtained certain products, like

---

[1] Kolb (175), p. 109 ff.; Pendleton (179), p. 195.

cotton, and various kinds of hemp or chinagrass needed for local industries; and it sometimes carries valuable crops like tobacco and sugar-cane. The working period of the *ladang* can be lengthened by planting certain shrub crops which require only slight care. These may be traditional plants like the banana-tree and useful palms or else export crops like coffee or rubber introduced by Europeans.

Even cereals, whose period of growth is more strictly limited, are cultivated on the *ladangs*. Maize, which was brought from America, is often so grown. As early as 1699 Dampier noticed that maize was the chief food on the coastal plains in Timor; but its cultivation has been greatly extended during the past fifty years not only in the eastern islands of the Sunda arc, but also in western Indonesia and the Philippines. As for rice, that typical cereal of Monsoon Asia, many varieties of it need no planting out, require only such moisture as comes from the rainfall, and grow readily on very steep patches wrested temporarily from the forest. Rice is frequently followed by tubers or rhizomes which go deeper into the soil to get the plant-food.

In the Malay lands, as in all Southeast Asia, elaborate cultivation of rice is the basis of the areas of most advanced civilisation and greatest density of population. Communities living mainly by *ladangs* are forced to live a semi-nomadic life at any rate within the limits prescribed by tradition. The use of different patches in turn entails instability in the people and their dwelling-places. Every year a part of the community spends a few weeks in huts near cultivated patches more or less remote from main villages. Life becomes more sedentary as permanent fields, and especially *sawahs*, increase in proportion to the whole area under cultivation.

The *sawah* is a flat field enclosed by little embankments that prevent water from running off. It is essentially a swamp-rice plantation. In it the soil suffers neither from the run-off of surface drainage, which washes away the humus from the *ladangs*, nor from the effects of the sun's heat which hastens the lateritisation of bare surfaces. Irrigation adds its fertilising virtues to those of the rain. As cultivation becomes permanent, so the area under fallow is reduced and the potentialities of human settlement increased. M. B. Smits estimates the area needed to support a peasant family at between fifteen and twenty acres under the *ladang* system, but at only one or two under the *sawah* system in similar conditions of soil and climate.[1] If there is water enough and the temperature is sufficiently high, the *sawah* even gives a second crop of rice in the year, though this is exceptional to the east of Celebes and Sumbawa.

It has by no means been proved that the *sawah* originated in India.

---

[1] Smits (228), p. 502.

Most ethnologists agree in recognising its continental origin, probably Indo-China. Of course, it is found in Sumatra, Java, and Bali, where traces of Hindu civilisation are most marked; but it occurs elsewhere, far from the main centres of Indian settlement, and especially in Luzón among the Ifugaos, where the system reaches a high degree of perfection, flooded terraces climbing the steep slopes well above the 3000-foot contour. It is rather surprising to see them in this isolated district in the heart of the island. Neither in Formosa, Borneo, nor the southern Philippines does such impressive terracing exist.[1]

In the mountains the *sawah* demands the most ingenious care in its construction and maintenance, and the cultivated terraces, whose rise from the one below is at times greater than their own width and which follow the contours of the slopes, make a deep impression on the traveller. But *sawahs* cannot really cover large areas except at points where streams enter the plains. Here the differences in level are slighter and the fields larger; the work of levelling has been easier, but the catching and supply of the water need wider collaboration. In the East Indies, as elsewhere, irrigation has certainly been a powerful factor in social development and political cohesion on account of the effort it has required and the increase in population it has permitted. It has developed especially in districts that have a dry season or in which the control of the streams does not require too much effort. But it was far from having covered the whole area of the cultivable lowlands or from having employed all the potentialities of the streams. Today, many *sawahs* still use nothing but rain-water.

Sawah rice calls for more trouble and more delicate care than does the cultivation of upland rice. First of all, it is sown in a seed-bed and then planted out in the fields to grow. Direct sowing is used only for certain early varieties in the lowlands which are flooded by the first rains. In mountain *sawahs* the soil has often merely been turned up with a pointed stick or hoe. The Ifugaos use a wooden pick. In some places the earth is churned up into liquid mud by the hoofs of oxen and buffaloes. In other places, and usually on the lowlands, the animals are yoked to little ploughs or primitive harrows. Even then man's share of work is far greater than the animals'.[2] The *sawah* must be weeded, and the sheet of water necessary to the life of the plants must be kept on the soil inside the embankments. The field dries only a few days before the harvest. The stalks are cut one by one with a little knife.

Ladangs and *sawahs* are very often found together in the same agricultural unit. This is especially true in the mountains, but less

1 Kolb (175), p. 122 ff.   2 W. Bally (203), p. 101.

so on the plains. The *ladang* very probably represents an older form of cultivation than the *sawah*. However, an increase in the population and the difficulty of extending the irrigable area sometimes renders a greater number of forest clearings necessary and reduces the proportion of *sawahs*. This has happened, for instance, in the Batak district in the uplands of Sumatra. In Java, on the other hand, the *ladang* was banned in 1874 and is rarely used. Dutch irrigation systems in the island have greatly increased the area of *sawah*. The Javanese also use a system called *tegal*. It differs from the *ladang* in the absence of burning and the relatively short period of fallow. It is used on slopes from which the forest has long been removed and has a rotation consisting of directly sown upland rice, tuberous or rhizomous crops, groundnuts, and various vegetables. The yield is often very poor. However, by improving the rotation and the agricultural practice by adding manure and especially by burying green crops, the *tegal* may continue to be worked and may become a permanent field. In central and eastern Java it is no rare sight to see hills cultivated without irrigation almost to the top. In Luzón too the hills and mountains have patches here and there in which unirrigated crops of sweet potatoes, rice, etc., are interrupted only by short periods of fallow.

Rice holds first place among all the crops in the Malay lands. In the Philippines there are more than a thousand varieties of the plant about a hundred of which are found everywhere. Rice is the favourite dish and nearly everywhere forms the basis of the diet. According to Smith,[1] it represents forty to forty-five per cent. of the daily food in Java. In some Malay dialects, as in Indo-Chinese, the word for 'boiled rice' is the same as that for 'food'. Sago is often more important in most of the Moluccas, the Rhio Islands, and in that part of the lowlands of Sumatra that looks towards Singapore. But as it is the pith of a palm seldom cultivated and as it is got by collecting, its predominance in the diet must be accompanied by a low density of population. Maize, on the other hand, is as important as rice in some densely populated districts where, because the climate is too dry or the soil too permeable, *sawah* cultivation is impossible. Maize may be boiled like rice in a little water, or else the ear may be boiled and sold whole in the market ready to eat, or again it may be ground into flour. As maize is more resistant to drought, it sometimes even forms a more important part of the diet than rice; as it does, for instance, in Madura, the Lesser Sunda Islands to the east of Lombok, in Sebu, and eastern Negros.[2]

[1] *Riz et Riziculture*, V. 1931, p. 278.
[2] In the Philippines as a whole the ratio of rice to maize in the diet is thought to be three to one, see Kolb (175), p. 185.

In some places in the mountains of Luzón more sweet potato is eaten than rice.

As in all Monsoon Asia, the Malay diet is essentially vegetarian. The list of main elements is completed when to rice, maize, and sweet potatoes are added tapioca, beans, fruits (that ripen all the year round), and various vegetables fermented or seasoned with pepper and capsicum. Fats are supplied chiefly by the coconut-tree, but in the preparation of food the soya bean is competing more and more with the coconut, though the latter is still valuable owing to its many uses. With these food-plants must be mentioned the betel and areca palm, which are even more characteristic of Malay civilisation, although they are commonly found also in India and Indo-China and have spread even to Melanesia and the islands of Oceania. The betel is a climbing liana closely related to the pepper bush. Its leaf is added to the nut of the areca palm to form the traditional 'chew'. A little powdered lime, often got from oyster shells, is thrown in, and sometimes tobacco and gambier are added. The 'chew' is astringent and refreshing and reddens the lips and saliva. From time immemorial it has played a great part in social life and necessarily makes its appearance during visits and at conferences, festivals, and ceremonies as a pledge of peace and goodwill, friendship and love. The tobacco habit, which was introduced by the Europeans, has often become a craze, especially in the Philippines, where Mallat observed in about 1840 that the men and women nearly always had *cigarillos* in their mouths, whilst *mestiza* women smoked enormous cigars.[1]

Domestic Animals. The function of domestic animals in agriculture varies with the region. The use of cattle—oxen and buffaloes —seems to have been affected by influences from India and is greater than in countries like Annam which are permeated with Chinese civilisation. The animals are indeed used for draught purposes on field and road and also for milk, meat, and for making manure. But, as is the case throughout Monsoon Asia, full use is not made of them. The plough seems to have been known in the East Indies from very early times.[2] The type used in the Philippines is of Chinese origin and differs from the one employed in other Malay lands. But the implement is little used except in the *sawahs*. The ox-drawn cart does not seem to have reached the islands east of Java before the arrival of the Europeans, nor did it appear in Borneo or the Philippines either. The natives in the last-named islands were certainly acquainted only with the ox- or buffalo-drawn sledge which is still found in some districts.

The proportion of horned cattle and bubalins to population

---

[1] Mallat (177), I. p. 384; II. p. 75.   [2] Werth (91); Kolb (175), p. 159.

remains small. According to the latest count (which is very approximate), for every 1000 persons there were only 121 animals in Malaya, 125 in Indonesia (where it varied from 16 in the province of western Borneo to 346 in Madura), and 240 in the Philippines. And it must be emphasised that the yield of milk is very poor and the beasts themselves small, a full grown Javanese bull weighing on an average 550 lb.

In the districts in which *ladang* cultivation is considerable the animals remain out-of-doors day and night and are driven into a pen in the evening only. This is true in a large part of Celebes, some districts in Sumatra, and in Timor and the islands nearby. Where permanent *tegals* or *sawahs* are prevalent, as in Java, Madura, Bali, Lombok, and the lowlands of Luzón, the buffaloes and horned cattle are sheltered in byres. Buffaloes are the more numerous in districts that have a short dry season and heavy, swampy soil, as in Malaya and western Java, where it is a common sight to see a buffalo happily buried in mud up to its shoulders to escape the bites of insects. Cattle outnumber them by far in districts which are at all arid and have a lighter and more easily worked soil, as is the case in most of Java, in Bali and Lombok, and above all in Madura. Generally speaking, buffaloes are giving way to cattle because, though they are stronger, they are less resistant to disease and less adaptable, and their meat is less popular.[1]

The relative abundance of goats seems to be another Indian touch. The animals are reared for mutton rather than milk. In the mountains of Luzón they sometimes carry small loads. On the other hand, sheep are rare, and their mutton less esteemed.

The small number of pigs is due to the spread of Islam, and the animals are few, except in non-Muslim districts. These include Bali and Lombok especially, as well as Flores, the Batak district in Sumatra, the Toraja country in Celebes, and the mountains in the Philippines. Many Bontoc families in Luzón have a score of pigs lodged in peculiar styes hollowed out of the ground and lined with stones at the sides. Elsewhere, the animals are reared exclusively by European settlers and, to an even greater extent, by Chinese, who are wonderfully skilful in fattening them.[2]

The horse is scarcely used except for riding or carrying a pack and is less often used in Malaya than in the East Indies and Philippines. In towns particularly it is harnessed to light carriages called *sados* in Jakarta and *carromatas* in Manila. The animal now used in the Philippines is a cross between the Andalucian and Chinese horses, with some Arab blood thrown in. The rearing of local breeds— small, very hardy, and enduring—is still carried on in Timor and the

[1] Ormeling (156a) emphasises the unwise nature of pastoralism in Timor, where cattle and buffaloes are regarded as a measure of social standing, over-graze the country by their excessive numbers, and are used neither for draught nor for the supply of manure. Sometimes their dung is used as fuel, as it is in India.

[2] Kolb (175), p. 312.

neighbouring islands, which export several thousand animals to Java every year.

Poultry is kept everywhere. The birds run loose in the day and are shut up at night in baskets hanging up in the house or under the floor to keep them from being devoured by rats. Like the Philippine *tao*, the men in Bali pet their fighting cocks. They clean and smarten them up, carrying them under their arms or feeding them with tit-bits in front of their doors. In every Philippine *pueblo* there is a building, called the *gallera*, in which cock-fights are held, and these give rise to keen betting.

European influence has developed the trade in livestock in the main plantation areas and big urban centres. Local supplies do not meet demands in Java, particularly for the transport of sugarcane in the centre and east of the island, or in Sumatra and especially in the East Coast Province. Oxen and buffaloes have therefore to be imported. Animals for draught purposes or slaughter are imported into Malaya mainly through Singapore. Many of the beasts are sent from Indonesia, Bali being the chief source. Timor, Flores, Sumbawa, Sumba, and Madura also export livestock. Some degree of specialisation in breeding animals is becoming noticeable in certain families and districts in these islands. In Masbate in the Philippines and especially in the district of Bukidnon in Mindanao the rearing of livestock is the business of large enterprises, each with several hundred beasts, to meet the needs of the towns and sugar areas in the group.[1] The cattle strain is being improved by crossing with imported breeds many of which come from India. They are either the Ongole (imported since 1912 into Indonesia) or the Nellore (imported into the Philippines).

So far as meat is concerned, the Malay countries are nearly self-supporting, for native consumption is still very small. Apart from pork and poultry, it amounts to $2\frac{1}{5}$ lb. a year for each person in the Philippines; but it has increased rapidly in the towns and is about 60 lb. in Manila. In Indonesia milk and its by-products are supplied almost exclusively by a few Europeans or Chinese who have dairy farms in the mountains or near the towns. In Malaya the business is carried on mainly by Sikhs or Tamils. The quantity of imported condensed or sterilised milk, cheese, and butter to supply the European settlers continues to be considerable. The Philippines also get eggs from China, but some maize-growing islands like Sebu are beginning to export eggs to the large towns.

Fishing. Fish is a far more common food than meat and is eaten fresh, dried, salted, smoked, or even pickled. There are between 1500 and 2000 species in Philippine coastal waters, and some of

[1] Kolb (175), p. 317.

them, which are related to the pilchards, anchovies, and mackerel of our Western seas, arrive in countless schools at certain seasons. Fishing is particularly profitable on the sand and mud shallows which are very extensive owing to the last positive movement of the ocean and which lie off the shores within the local seas. The industry is far less active off the coasts facing the Indian and Pacific Oceans, i.e. the south coast of the Sunda arc and the east coast of the Philippines. Some villages live entirely by it; but it is often associated with agriculture, one or other activity predominating. In the district of Malabon to the north of Manila four-fifths of the population live mainly by fishing or the cognate occupations of boat-building, net-making, the preparation and marketing of fish, etc. The Navotas who live in this district man their boats with crews of about fifty men, an unusual number for native craft. They stay at sea for a few hours only and fish near the coast with a variety of means, including lines, nets, bow-nets, and fish-pots; and they often work at night with lights. Fishing villages generally consist of wretched huts on piles and are pervaded by the strong smell of fish drying on the sand or roofs. Life in them is often squalid, especially when there is no agriculture; and it frequently happens that the men work for an employer, who advances money and supplies the outfit. The greatest catches are got by Asian immigrants, who have better equipment than the local people. Thus, the Chinese exploit the coastal waters of the Straits of Malacca, working along the Peninsula and especially off the coast of Sumatra. The Japanese with their motor trawlers used to be the only deep-sea fishermen, were generally organised in co-operative associations, and supplied big towns like Singapore and Manila. A rather skilful form of fish-breeding is carried on by the local people near the large centres of population on the north coast of Java and around Manila Bay, and also in freshwater fishponds. Yet fish continues to be one of the main imports into the Malay lands.

Traditional Industries. Besides agriculture, livestock breeding, and fishing, the basic occupations include craft industries. These are mainly rural and are carried on by specialists whose only source of income they are, or by peasants who get from them the wherewithal to eke out the returns from agriculture and use them to fill up the slack intervals between the busy times when agriculture calls on all hands. The tools are very simple, even crude, and machines are not used. The distribution of the industries is not always determined by the presence of raw material, but often by the available labour. The intensity of the work varies with the season, two peak times being noticeable in the *batik* industry in central Java: just before the rice harvest and then in the reaping of the secondary crops.

Timber industries depend on transport by *prahu*, which is far easiest in Java during the south-east monsoon.   Pottery, which is one of the most concentrated manufactures, is carried on in the Brantas valley mainly during the dry season, for the workshops are not sheltered, and the clay beds are flooded by the river when it is swollen.

On the other hand, basket-making goes on everywhere.   Bamboo, rattan, palm leaves, and various fibres are used to produce all kinds of domestic articles, like receptacles, hats, matting, light walls for native huts, and also implements for irrigation and sails for boats. The ornamental patterns differ slightly from one island to another and in the same island from one community to the next.   Certain articles are widely known.   Thus, the mats made in the upper valley of the Kotabató in Mindanao are found as far away as the markets on the south coast of the island.   It is thought that influences which have spread from the Philippines *via* north-western Borneo to Sumatra can be seen in the style in which the fibres are plaited.   Cotton weaving has passed eastwards from India and China through the southern East Indies right to Melanesia, where, like pottery, its practice is exceptional.   Roti Island to the south-west of Timor still produces very fine cloth, but on the other hand garments of bark cloth, or *tapa*, persist in some corners of Celebes and the Moluccas.   The line of distinction between plaiting and weaving is not easily drawn.   The filaments of certain plants, particularly of pine-apple leaves are extremely fine.   Mallat records that Filipino craftsmen when making the cloth called *piña*, used to place themselves under a mosquito net to avoid draughts.[1]

Silk has for a long time been imported from China.   Cloth is dyed and decorated by ingenious and very skilful processes, like *ikatten* and *batik*,[2] the latter flourishing mainly in the central principalities in Java.   Trengganu in Malaya is famous for its cloth of gold.   The chief centres of the textile industries in the Philippines were the province of Ilocos in north-western Luzón, the neighbour-

[1] Mallat (175), II, p. 284.

[2] BATIK—a Javanese word meaning wax painting—the application of a wax 'resist' to various materials which are afterwards dyed, and certain portions of which are protected by the wax so that they do not absorb the dye, leaving as a result a pattern or design on them.   The resist is usually composed of bees-wax, paraffin, and sometimes a little resin, which makes it adhere more securely to the material.   This resist is applied hot so that it flows easily and sinks into the material, protecting from the dye that part which it covers . . . the designs . . . consist of conventionalised objects of nature, such as flowers, butterflies, birds, fruits, foliage, cuttlefish, and shells and occasionally of a conventionalised Malay kris or knife.   These designs are passed from generation to generation and taught by each mother to her daughter, for it is the women who draw them whilst the men do the dyeing.

Encyclopædia Britannica, 14th edit. s.v.

hood of Manila, and the lowlands of Panay.   The fine quality of the produce was extraordinary at one time, the designs were very varied, and the colours generally bright; but these traditional manufactures have suffered from the effects of fashions and commodities imported from the United States and Japan.

The industries connected with the working of metals are less widespread than basketry and weaving.   The art of forging iron is known as far as the north-west coast of New Guinea.   Throughout the Malay lands it is, like the casting of bronze, the special business of a special few villages, some of which are famous for the quality of their produce.[1]   The technique of making *kris* blades is particularly remarkable.   The jewellers of Brunei are the most famous in the East Indies; and filigree-work is a well-known speciality of the Minangkabau district in Sumatra.

Dwellings.   The native house in Malaya and the East Indies affords a topic of great interest, but very difficult to study.   It displays an extraordinary variety in shape, dimensions, structure, and plan, and neither the physical environment nor the necessities of material life are an adequate explanation of them all.   Man's dwelling no doubt corresponds to a definite economic system; but the latter is subject to psychological and social factors which find their expression in buildings and the grouping of them.   The great number and complexity of the facts make analysis very difficult and often misleading.   Our information, though by now very copious, is still insufficient, however.   This cannot be surprising, considering on the one hand the various influences which have acted on Indonesia and on the other the local phenomena resulting from insularity.

The native dwelling (see Fig. 11) is often perched up on piles.[2] Possibly the practice is a development of the primitive shelter on a tree, such as existed at one time in Sumba and New Guinea, and among the Senois on the Peninsula.[3]   The height of the piles varies a great deal.   For example, in Borneo it may be more than 16 feet; or, as is often the case in western Java, it may not exceed a foot or two.   The most usual height seems to be between 3 and 6 feet.   It is often asserted, and not without reason, that the pile-dwelling is well adapted to the environment, that it protects its occupants from damp, vermin, and harmful beasts of all kinds; that furthermore it is fairly economical, since it shelters under a single roof not only man, but also the harvest which can be piled up in the attic, and the domestic animals that are driven for the night at least into the pen

[1] Paravicini (139), p. 461.
[2] Nguyen-van-Huyen (99).
[3] The shelter on a tree is still occasionally found in the interior of Luzón and Mindanao, but is becoming less and less common.   (Kolb (175), p. 119.)

formed by the piles. The space under the house is also frequently used for storing agricultural implements together with certain feminine appliances, such as a loom and the mortar and pestle used for husking rice. It should be said, however, that these advantages have not seemed decisive to the people of the Dark Continent, who live in a similar climate and among whom the pile-dwelling is comparatively rare. Indo-China and the East Indies are its true home. It is found not only among the fishing folk on the coasts, river banks, lake shores, and periodically flooded alluvial plains, but also indeed on hills and well-drained slopes. The practice of sheltering domestic animals under the huts is far from being general. The piles may be absent without any apparent reason both in the East Indies and on the peninsula of Indo-China. Such is the case, for instance, in Buru in the Moluccas, in Bali and Lombok, among most of the hill-folk in Luzón (apart from the Ifugaos), and in the greater part of Java. This last island, however, exhibits every stage of transition from the house built flat on the ground to the pile-dwelling which is still common in the west, where types like those in Sumatra are found. It is possible that the former may be a response to the already very advanced civilisation of the country, the high density of population, and the scarcity of timber.

In fact, the Javanese are often obliged to get the main pieces of the framework of their dwellings from a tree planted near their villages, *Hibiscus teleatus*. In other places, as for instance in the mountains of Luzón, Timor, and Flores, and on coral islands, walls or at any rate formations of mortarless stones may be seen. The use of laterite is very restricted, although when broken up into blocks it hardens quickly. In some districts it is used for the foundations of huts without piles. In sodden earth in Malaya the piles themselves are sometimes placed on blocks of laterite. But wild vegetation is nearly always the source of building materials. The bamboo, when whole, split and flattened, or cut into strips and plaited, often forms the floor and walls of the dwelling. Savana grass, wooden shingles, bark, leaves of palms like the *arenga* (*atap*), the *nipa* on the coast, and the *latania*, are used for roofing, when they soon turn to a dull greyish colour.

Dwellings are usually square or oblong. The ends are occasionally rounded, as among the Belus in Timor. Octagonal or hexagonal form is seen in the Tobelo district in north-eastern Halmahera, and a circular plan in western Timor and Flores. Fifty years ago a very peculiar dwelling, made like a kind of round beehive raised up between 10 and 15 feet above the ground, was used in Enggano Island (to the south of Benkulen in Sumatra) (see Fig. 11c, no. 3).

The silhouettes of the different kinds of roofs greatly help to bring out the peculiarities of the native house. Sometimes, as among the Torajas in Celebes or the Toba-Bataks in Sumatra, the ridge describes a graceful curve like a saddle or keel. In Sumatra the Minangkabau remain faithful to multiple overlapping roofs whose ends are raised vertically to form *tanduk,* or sharp-pointed horns. Among these tribes and also among the Moros in the southern Philippines the pile-dwelling reaches its highest development with strong, harmonious types. Within, it is dark, dirty, and blackened by smoke from the hearth. Outside, the walls are adorned with carved and painted decorations. These are sometimes plain, but at other times complex, and they have a magical significance which is heightened among the Minangkabau by the flash of unsilvered glass meant to drive away evil spirits. The whole process of building demands the fulfilment of certain rites together with offerings that no doubt formerly entailed human sacrifice.

The dimensions of the interior plan depend not only on the owner's wealth, but also on the organisation of the family and community. At times the house may shelter not merely a couple and their children, but several households related by blood and forming one large family. This is a fairly general custom among the Dyaks of Borneo, whose dwellings are more than 650 feet long and are occupied by anything up to 600 persons. The house may thus be by itself the whole village; or else there may be two or more of these long constructions built on piles from 3 to 15 feet high. Each household has its own compartment, which in many cases opens on to a corridor running the whole length of the building. This type of communal hut, which is also found among the tribes in Mindanao,[1] is curiously like those used by some of the Mois in southern Annam. Certain scholars have claimed to see in it the result of a matriarchal system in which sons-in-law live with their wives in the house of their parents-in-law and thenceforth work with the economic unit directed by the eldest male in the maternal group. But in fact the Dyaks' social organisation rarely exhibits an absolutely pure matriarchal system, even when the wife's family exercises great influence.

Lack of published observation prevents exact description of the changes in the form of dwelling due to social developments. Yet it seems clear that the break-up of the big family, be it patriarchal, matriarchal, or a mixture of the two, involves that of the house. The East Indies certainly exhibit every stage of transition towards the dwelling occupied by a single married couple and their children and towards the village that no longer contains a single family, but is merely a territorial unit. The house tenanted by several households

[1] Kolb (175), p. 118.

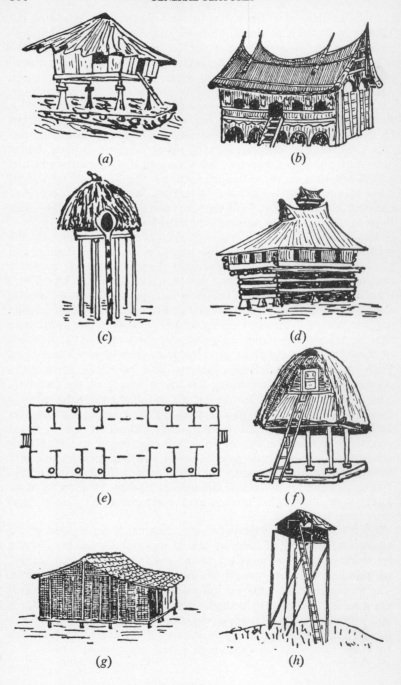

(a)

(b)

(c)

(d)

(e)

(f)

(g)

(h)

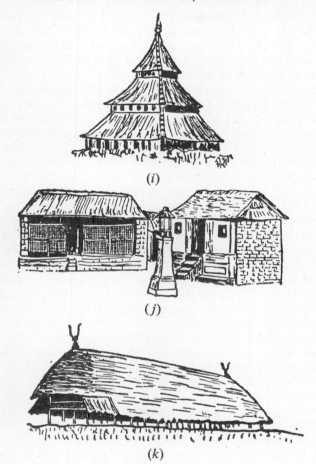

FIG. 11.— BUILDING STYLES IN THE EAST INDIES

(a) An Ifugao House in North Luzón. Note the piles resting on a platform of stones (after Kolb)

(b) A Minangkabau House in Sumatra. (After a model in the Colonial Institute in Amsterdam.)

(c) An Enganno House. (After a model in the Colonial Institute in Amsterdam.)

(d) A Batak House at Simalungun to the North of Lake Toba. (From a photograph by the author.)

(e) Plan of a Murut Dayak House in north-west Borneo. Note the rooms each occupied by a separate family with doors opening on to a central corridor (after Owen Rutter)

(f) A Barn in Bali. (From a photograph by the author.)

(g) A House in western Java. (From a photograph by the author.)

(h) A Lookout Post in a *ladang* in Sumatra. (From a photograph by the author.)

(i) A Mosque in the Minangkabau Country

(j) Domestic Houses and Pagoda in Bali. (From a photograph by the author.)

(k) A Communal House in Flores. (From a model in the Colonial Institute in Amsterdam.)

exists among many racial groups, as for instance among the Minangkabau, Gayos, and Bataks in Sumatra, the Torajas in Celebes, and the Mangarais in Flores; and it is found in eastern Serang, in the Mentawai Islands, and in the plank houses of the Sibutus in the Sulu Islands.

But the little home intended for a single married couple is already common in Malaya and the East Indies, and is the only type now found in the districts of Bugi and Macassar in Celebes, in Bali and Lombok, and, lastly, in Java. It is interesting to notice that these are districts with a high density of population and where consequently individual property rights are most strongly asserted at the expense of collective ownership.

The dwelling, large or small, whether on piles or fixed to the ground, is in its various forms and places an answer to certain constant requirements. First, there is the desire to define the space reserved for privacy. The dwelling almost always consists of one room that is common to the members of the family or the households of the community and in which strangers are received; then, as a rule, behind this there are the private apartments where the women live. The separation of the sexes, which was no doubt more marked once, was also reflected at times in the separate shelter to which women went for their confinement, as is still done at Lomblen in eastern Flores. When the weather is not too bad, the veranda, which is a platform sometimes under shelter of the overhanging roof, permits escape from the dark and at times stifling interior and forms a drying-room for clothes and food. It is often built on the main front, but sometimes runs like a gallery right round the house, an arrangement frequently adopted in European bungalows.

Domestic animals do not always have a separate, covered shelter. If the larger animals are not driven at night into the enclosure formed by the piles, they may be penned in a primitive, unroofed paddock. The store-rooms containing not only food-supplies, but sometimes also valuables such as ceremonial dress, are usually special buildings, as for instance among the Toba-Bataks or in Bali. They are built in a different style from that of the dwelling. Often the body of the building rests on piles fitted with wooden discs to prevent rodents from climbing up. At times, as is the case in the mountains in Luzón, the store-houses are placed together a little way from the village so as to lessen the risk of fire.

. *Concentration and Dispersal of Population.* Regard for security, convenience, and rational cultivation is revealed in the clustering of houses. Absolute dispersal is very rare. Kruyt states that the To-Wanas, a backward people in eastern Celebes, are divided into four clans whose members assemble only for feasts and live in isolated houses near the land they cultivate. Even so, their houses are common to several families. A rural concentration may have only a few dwellings, but it may also run to several hundred. The last case is of frequent occurrence only in densely populated districts like Java and Bali, but it is not rare in Luzón among some of the hill-folk like the Lepanto-Tinggian. Clusters of from 10 to 50 households may be said to be normal. According to the census taken at the beginning of the century, a quarter of the population of the Philippines lived in *barrios* of fewer than 400 souls and three-fifths in *barrios* of less than 1000 souls. Isolation did not suit a system in which war between clans, head-hunting, and piracy were current practices. Not only did the families cluster together, but the cluster took steps for its defence. Hence, the village is often surrounded by a stout palisade, as for example among the Bataks, who occupy the flood plain south of Lake Toba. It shuns the sea-shore and sometimes favours hill-tops, as is the case in central Celebes, among the Mangarais in Flores, and in the north of Nias. For this reason water must at times be fetched from rather long distances.

Even on marshy ground drinking water is often hard to come by, for the water-table, being very variable and diluted in the gluey density of lateritic clays, does not encourage the digging of wells. Hence, nearness to running water often takes precedence of considerations of defence. Many villages are placed near the stream which irrigates their fields and supplies water for various uses. They often take their names from this stream and may form a very compact cluster.

Not only does the concentration of households help to protect the community from hostile clans, but it also fits in with an economic system in which mutual assistance and co-operation are still practised; in which property, if not the tilling of the soil, is often a collective matter; and in which the shifting of cultivation from one patch to another involves merely the removal of temporary dwellings —or indeed just mere watchmen's shelters—within a more or less lengthy radius around a fixed, or at any rate relatively permanent, village. Where most of the fields are in permanent cultivation, concentration is encouraged by the requirements of irrigation, the desire to occupy as little space as possible at the expense of cultivable land, and, lastly, by the dispersal of the family patches over the whole of the communal area. Thus, in the river plains in Java, Luzón, and the north of Malaya, the villages with houses scattered about among the gardens look like wooded islands in the expanse of cultivation. In coconut groves the houses are more dispersed, because there is no communal work or agricultural constraint, the harvest being gathered in all the year round on property that is usually all in one block.

Village layouts are very varied. The Karo-Bataks build their houses in no very apparent order, whilst the Tobas and Nias folk, like the forest tribes in central Africa, place theirs in two rows facing each other across a medial path blocked at each end. The social and religious life is marked by the presence of communal buildings. Thus, the *balë* of the Karo-Bataks is a meeting-house in which the young men spend the night, where strangers are received, and where councils drink fermented beverages as they discuss communal business. In the mountains of Luzón bachelors and widowers have a dormitory in common. Ceremonies and feasts are held in the *ato*. In Java the family dwellings are often unmethodically placed at varying intervals among the gardens. Around the *alun-alun*, or rectangular 'square', which is adorned with a *waringin* tree, stand the mosque, the communal house in which *wayang* performances take place and passing guests sleep, and, in big villages, the *passan-grahan* which is reserved for officials on their rounds.

European influence has already brought fairly great changes in the form of the dwellings in the districts in which it has penetrated most. The church or temple is often the only stone building in Christian villages in the Batak district in Minahassa and in the Philippines where its white mass rises above a crowd of huts made of vegetable matter. Tiles, bricks, sheet-iron, and other new building materials have come into use and make the house more watertight and better protected against fire, but shatter the harmony of the countryside with their vulgar flashiness.

Settled security, a widened economic horizon, and new means of transport that encourage communication have made towns spring up and grow. Some are local markets, but others are large towns with populations of more than 50,000 souls. The Malay himself is unaccustomed to town development. Towns seem to have been created by the Indians as strongholds and administrative centres. Today, they are mainly European and Chinese. Though the people of the country form the majority of the inhabitants, they still live in quarters that have a countrified appearance, the most typical being the *kampong* in Javanese towns, which is hidden among bamboos, banana trees, and other garden plants and crossed by canals.

On the other hand, a falling-off in rural villages is noticeable. Formerly, the policy of the Roman Catholic missionaries succeeded in encouraging the concentration of native families in the Philippines, as they had done in Mexico.   Ease of communication, the change-over to the system of individual property, the break-up of the big family, and the maintenance of security help to scatter communities. People are moving nearer to the roads and railway stations.   The tendency towards dispersal is most general in rural districts today and is very apparent in recently colonised lands like Malaya or Mindanao.

PART II

THE REGIONS

CHAPTER 7

MALAYA

The Malay Peninsula thins out near Kra and once again seems about to tail off at the isthmus of Ligor, but widens out southwards to a breadth of 220 miles, thus prolonging the mainland of Asia as far as 1° north of the Equator. On this narrow appendage of the continent European colonisation has had the most surprising results and the most revolutionary effects that it has had on any tropical country. Within seventy-five years a thinly peopled land has attracted hundreds of thousands of immigrants and has become the world's chief producer of tin and rubber. At its southern end an island almost uninhabited in 1819 has seen the growth of one of the busiest ports in the Far East.

A Worn, but Varied Relief. Appearances suggest that the Peninsula forms a single mountain range rising between the two relative depressions of the Irrawaddy syncline and the basin of the lower Menam. But the structure is far more complex than that.[1] To the north of the Siamese boundary there is a series of at least eleven ridges. To the south of it six or seven are still recognisable running parallel with each other, but less oblique to the meridian than is the axis of the Peninsula. The material of which these little ranges are formed is fairly varied, but the predominant rocks are granites, which generally appear in the anticlinal axes, Palæozoic limestones[2] lying on top of the granites, and above that quartzites of the Trias. Among the rocks covering the crystalline core in Pahang and Singapore Island appear sandstones, conglomerates, and shales.[3] The main folds, which in any case are the best known, are post-Triassic and probably contemporary with the intrusions of tin-bearing granites. Sedimentaries later than the Trias are unknown, except for a few Tertiary survivals and the Quaternary and recent alluvia.

[1] Scrivenor (109, 110). See Fig. 1, p. 11.
[2] Very widespread in Indo-China.
[3] Dobby (102), p. 84.

The Korbu. or Mountain, Range, which is the best marked and most continuous, rises to a height of 7160 feet in the State of Perak and, dying away towards the south, disappears north of Malacca, to reappear in the island of Banka. To the east of Kerbau is a series of two or three other ridges, one of which contains the culminating peak of Tahan 7186 feet. The last of them, the most easterly, seems to continue into the island of Singapore. Only fifteen per cent. of the Peninsula rises above the 2000-foot contour, and the southern part forming the plateau of Johore and crossed by slow, winding streams does not exceed 1200 feet, except in a few *bukits*, or isolated residual hills with sides as steep as those of the ranges themselves.

In fact, the high ground rises sharply from the lowlands all over the Peninsula. The granite rocks give rise as usual to relatively gentle and regular features still covered with a thick layer of soil due to decomposition. From this layer the run-off of rainwater often washes huge boulders. But the quartzites and limestones stand up in veritable walls. This is especially true of the latter, whose cliff-faces—still compact or looking like great ruins—present picturesque, jagged, and often fantastic silhouettes. There is a strong contrast between these escarpments and the valleys spreading out between them, though the latter's thin mantle of alluvium is pierced by rocky stumps and relict hills. The breadth of these valleys seems disproportionate to the existing rivers Scrivenor, the geologist, thinks them to have been formed by marine erosion following on a positive movement which brought the sea to 500 feet above its present level. This hypothesis is ill founded, considering the absence of marine deposits above the 80-foot contour, the gradients of the valleys, and their penetration deep into the mountains to reach the upper courses of the streams. To explain the breadth of the valleys, it seems sufficient to appeal to the character of fluvial erosion in a tropical climate.

However this may be, the relief places no continuous barriers between the two coasts. Grik on the upper Perak is only 380 feet above sea level, and between the headwaters of this stream and those of the Patani, which flows in the opposite direction and empties into the Gulf of Siam, the watershed rises very little above 1000 feet. Farther south the Pahang, which at first runs from north to south suddenly turns at right angles and, crossing the two outer ridges, reaches the east coast. This is perhaps the result of capture, before which the upper Pahang flowed into the present Muar, a stream that reaches the sea on the west coast to the south of Malacca. To go from the basin of the Muar into that of the Serting (Bera), a feeder of the Pahang, it is only necessary to climb up 180 feet, and the ridge is crossed without much difficulty by natives carrying their canoes.

The road from Kuala Lumpur to Kuala Lipis on the Pahang leaves the valleys and crosses the gap at a height of 2800 feet just below the hill-station of Fraser's Hill (4264 feet).

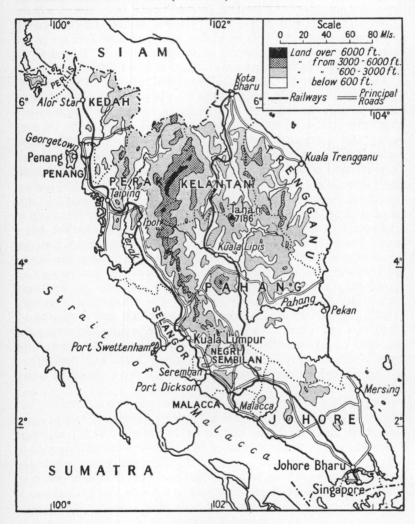

FIG. 12.—MALAYA

But a more serious obstacle than the relief exists in the dense forest, whose character is due to the climate.

Equatorial Climate and Vegetation. The territory under British rule passes northwards slightly beyond lat. 6° N. The fact that the long narrow peninsula, which is almost an island, lies between two warm seas strengthens the equatorial influences. At Singapore there is a range of only 2·7° F. between the warmest month (May) and the coolest (January). At Penang, farther north, but better sheltered from east winds, it is only 2·3° F. (between March and November). In inhabited districts, that is, valleys less than 1000 feet above sea level the thermometer generally oscillates between 70° F. and 88° F. in the shade, and it never seems to have reached 100° F.

Only in the north of Kedah and Perlis and in Siamese territory does one begin to notice the beginnings of a dry season. But yet even south of this the influence of alternating winds is reflected by appreciable shades of difference in the rainfall system. On the east coast the north-east monsoon blows strongly from November onwards and, after crossing the Gulf of Siam, causes the heaviest precipitation of the year. At Singapore, too, the wettest months are November, December, and January, with a total of 30·1 inches; but from February to July, which is the least rainy period, there is a total of at least 6 inches a month. At Kuala Lipis (Pahang), in the interior, the maximum occurs in October and November, but a second rainy spell comes in April and May. This is the equatorial rhythm; and it is still better marked on the west coast of the Peninsula, since it is less windy there. Between the two periods of April–May and September–October, June and July are relatively dry at Kuala Lumpur as at Penang. The south-west monsoon, broken by Sumatra's mass, is often scarcely felt and is masked by land and sea breezes. At very irregular intervals, however, gales brought on no doubt by barometric depressions that have become very noticeable over Indo-China between April and September, sweep through the Straits raising storms that are a danger to native shipping.

Dry spells that cause tall grass to wither may last a fortnight, but there are few places that do not get at least 3 inches of rain in every month in the year. The station at Jelebu (lat. 3° N.) in Negri Sembilan owes its annual total of 64 inches—the lowest recorded in Malaya—to its sheltered position. In the country as a whole the annual totals vary from 80 to 160 inches. The maximum occurs in the Larut Hills near Taiping in Perak at a height of 4900 feet and is 250 inches. This is exceptional, and other stations at the same altitude get little more than 120 inches. It is enough, however, to bring on frequent disastrous floods, that destroy the harvests and cut the roads and railways.

In such a climate the natural vegetation consists of tall, luxuriant, dense forest with trees often exceeding a height of 130 feet and with soil almost bare owing to the very rapid decomposition of the dead portions that fall. Dipterocarps are very numerous (*Shorea, Dryobalanops*, etc.) and outnumber other families nearly everywhere in the stands, though these comprise a large variety of species.[1] Forest appears in its magnificent vigour even on the east coast behind sandy beaches which break the somewhat thin mangrove fringe. It covers a great part of the States of Kelantan, Trengganu, and Pahang, that is, the eastern and central districts of the Peninsula. A few bare, elevated spots give a view over the sea of closely packed foliage covering the plains and hills. Above 5000 feet the forest is still dense, but is composed of smaller trees, including *Podocarpus* and *Dacrydium*, which have twisted trunks and branch out right to the bottom. The ground is covered with a continuous carpet of small plants. On slopes like the buttresses of Tahan the force of the north-east monsoon may check the growth of the trees. The dry spells are too short to allow forest fires to spread, and the ravages caused by fire are further restricted owing to the sparseness of the native population and the rather small part that agriculture plays in their life.

But the penetration of roads and railways already threatens the primitive forest in the districts in which it grows best. Its destruction has been carried to an advanced stage especially in the west. Since the end of the last century rubber plantations have increased at the expense of the forest and the extraordinary scaffolding used in tin mines worked by Chinese has swallowed up a great deal of the timber. Wood has been needed, too, for the various requirements of a rapidly increasing population largely concentrated in the towns, for smoking latex, and as fuel for locomotives. Since the beginning of the century a forestry service with the advantage of experience gained in India has exercised an effective control over utilisation. Reserved forests cover about one-fifth of the total area of Malaya. There methodical felling is carried out in places to eliminate secondary species and establish stands that can give a large and regular yield of timber. The reserves are specially designed to lessen the violence of the floods and the damage caused by torrential erosion, the vigour of which is illustrated by the swamps and mud-flats densely overgrown with mangrove on the west coast. The mangrove itself is systematically utilised.

In spite of the extent of its forest, Malaya buys far more wood than it exports. Its chief source of supply is Sumatra, from which timber comes across the Straits more cheaply than it travels from the interior to the points at which it is used, particularly the big saw-mills in Singapore. Malaya has depended on Siam for teak and on the United Kingdom and various foreign countries, notably Japan before

1 Allouard (43), p. 779.

1942, for crates for the export of rubber and pine-apples. It even imported large quantities of firewood and charcoal from Siam and even more from Sumatra to meet the needs of large towns.

The New Population: Natives and Immigrants. Submerged by a flood of immigrants, Malaya is less than fifty per cent. Malay in population and even less by far in the workers who co-operate in producing her exports. The great island-city on the Straits is mainly a Chinese town. The tin mines and rubber estates are worked by swarms of more or less settled Chinese and Indian labourers. To the passing visitor the Malay in his light fishing skiff or on the veranda of his hut in the shelter of a clump of graceful coconut palms looks like a background figure, a picturesque and passive supernumerary in a prodigiously busy scene.

Most of the Malays themselves are not really natives of the country. According to Chinese chronicles, emigrants from Sumatra in the 7th and 8th centuries—at the time when Sri Vijaya flourished —began to settle on the coast of the Peninsula, over which the ancestors of the Semang and Senoi were wont to roam. They did not penetrate far inland, but formed a series of principalities on the coast near the river mouths. The power of the rajahs was confined to a narrow coastal strip and did not begin to spread until the 13th century, when Moslem enthusiasm rapidly ousted the Indian religions. Here and there complexion and hair betray inter-breeding with the aborigines, and in the northern States there is evidence of an infusion of Siamese blood.

Though in British statistics all Malays are classed as 'natives' without distinction, they are in fact fairly various in origin and their settlement on the Peninsula is often recent. Thus, Selangor shows traces of a Malay aristocracy that was set up several hundred years ago; but the existing nobility is composed mainly of Bugis from South Celebes. Immigrants have come from Borneo and other parts of the East Indies, the largest contingents being from Sumatra and Java. Immigration from Sumatra is the oldest in standing and the easiest, too, as it merely meant crossing the Straits. After 1910 there was a rush owing to the high price of rubber and the very liberal grant of little concessions by the Government. The Malays on the Peninsula and on the big island opposite are much alike in physical features and language. The princes of Negri Sembilan trace their descent from the monarchs of Sri Vijaya through their ancestors who came from Minangkabau. The people of Java and the other islands do not so quickly fuse into the population, although mixed marriages are encouraged by the common religion. The Javanese, being born in an overpopulated country, are the most amenable of the Malays to the discipline on the estates.

As their labour was sought after at the beginning by the rubber plantations, especially in Johore State, many have settled there as free peasants.

Malaya is a no man's land by population, said the commentator on the Census of 1931. In fact, the Malays in the widest sense, who are the least foreign of all after the few aborigines, represented only 44·7 per cent. of the total population, as compared with 49·2 per cent. in 1921. The percentages fell in 1937 to 42·2, but in 1947 the Malays and other 'Malaysians' numbered 43·5 per cent. And it might be estimated that half of those composing this percentage were born outside the Peninsula.

Numerically, Malaya is almost as much Chinese as Malay. In 1931 the Chinese formed 37 per cent. of the total population, and in 1947 this percentage had risen to 45.[1] Malaya is far more Chinese than Malay if the share of each people in economic effort is considered, and it is difficult to accuse Sir Frank Swettenham, a Governor of the Straits Settlements, of exaggeration when he asserted that the transformation of the country would have been impossible but for Chinese co-operation.

Chinese[2] had been visiting the Peninsula from time immemorial and had begun to settle long before the coming of the Europeans. They worked not only in the ports as tradesmen, artisans, and fishermen, but also inland, exploiting the tin deposits and clearing the forests in order to cultivate gambier, cassava, and pepper. The British soon grasped the importance of Chinese immigration, which seemed to them necessary to the development of the country in view of the small number of the natives and their aversion to work. Shortly after Raffles had taken possession of Singapore, the place had a population of 5000, mostly Chinese. In 1824 there were more than 10,000 of them, and in 1840 nearly 40,000. Junks continued to arrive with the north-east monsoon, overcrowded with a poverty-stricken human cargo.[3]

The 'credit ticket' system was the most widespread means of recruiting. The labourers were engaged in South China by agents of the same race and received an advance. On arrival they were taken charge of, either directly by the employers or more probably by brokers who specialised in this trade in human merchandise. Before their departure from China a contract had often been signed binding the labourer for a definite time, usually 300 days. After this period the coolie was regarded as free from his engagement and could receive full wages and choose another master.

---

[1] In 1953 the Chinese in the newly created Federation numbered 2,153,000, or 40 per cent. of the population.

[2] Dennery (191), pp. 159–80; Pelzer (197); Purcell (80a).

[3] The Chinese did not all come directly from South China. A certain number had spent some time in Manila, Brunei, Malacca, etc.

This system of recruitment, known in China, as 'pig business' lent itself to constant abuse. In Malaya itself the employers, who were mostly the Chinese owners of mines or plantations, formed rival associations which intrigued with the Malay rajahs, organised parties of immigrants into armed bodyguards, spread disorder and anarchy everywhere, and stirred up cruel acts of vengeance against themselves. As late as 1880 the Governor of the Straits Settlements wrote: 'The fact is, Malays think no more of killing a Chinese than a tiger does.' It was only shortly after 1870 and after British intervention in Perak that Chinese immigration was put under effective official control and the contracts inspected on arrival by British officials. In 1877 the Chinese Protectorate was established. On landing, the labourer was now kept in a lodging-house before being signed on. The contract system itself was abolished in 1914, and the immigrant left free to hire out his services where he would.

The fact is, the development of Malaya demanded an ever increasing abundance of labour. The journey from South Chinese ports, which took about ten days in a sailing junk, was now done more quickly in English, German, Norwegian, or Japanese steamers. Between 1840 and 1853 the mean annual number of Chinese immigrants landing at the two large ports on the Straits, Singapore and Penang, was estimated at 9000 or 10,000. In 1880 there were 78,000. From this year on, the great majority of coolies landed at Singapore, where some were kept and others distributed among the mines and plantations in Malaya and the Dutch East Indies. Rubber estates took many of these from 1895 onwards. In 1911 Chinese arrivals in Singapore alone amounted to 270,000. The war of 1914–18 caused a great falling off, and only 58,000 landed in 1918. But the flow began again in 1920 and went on fairly regularly until 1925, when there was a sharp rise in Malaya as a whole, giving a total of 360,000 in 1927, during the application of the Stevenson plan. After another drop in 1931–33, the figures rose again, and in 1937 403,000 Chinese landed in Malaya. Singapore was then certainly one of the world's leading immigration ports. This last number represented nearly a fifth of the Chinese population in the country. Clearly, immigration was final for a minority only. Between 1928 and 1937 nearly 2,800,000 Chinese landed in Malaya, but nearly 2,400,000 left the Peninsula, some for other non-Chinese lands like Siam or the Dutch East Indies, though most of them went home again. In the three years 1931–32–33 the excess of departures over arrivals was 241,000.[1]

[1] After 1937 Chinese immigration greatly decreased, and in 1940 there were 113,000 arrivals as against 112,000 departures.

Yet, since the beginning of the century the net balance of immigration has caused the Chinese to increase more rapidly than the Malays.

In Malaya the Chinese do not form a homogenous, solid body. Differences of sentiment and interests depend on whether they have entered the country recently or long ago. Those who have been in the country a long time and have only occasional relations with their homeland naturally settle down most easily in the country. In 1931, 31 per cent. and in 1947 62 per cent. of the Chinese in Malaya were born in the territory and so were 'British-born Chinese' or '*Baba*'.[1]

On the other hand, provincial differences are very slow in disappearing, for the Chinese remain officially grouped according to the provinces whence they came. This origin itself entails a certain occupational specialisation. Thus, the Hokkiens, who come from Fukien, are very often tradesmen in the old Settlements and former Federated States. They comprise the majority of the British-born Chinese, are hostile to revolutionary nationalist propaganda, and some of them no longer even speak Chinese. They have often been plantation labourers at first, but fairly quickly reached a position of independence as small planters or suburban gardeners. The Cantonese become artisans and tradesmen, but are more numerous in agriculture and even more in the mines. The Teochiu (Tiechew), who sail from Swatow in northern Kwangtung, engage in a great variety of work. The Hakkas from Kwangtung and the Hailams from Hainan are found on plantations, especially in Johore; but the former prefer to work in the mines and are particularly numerous in the tin-mining district of Kinta, whilst the Hailam is often a domestic servant in a Chinese or European family.

The remarkable adaptability of the Chinese is perhaps seen at its best in Malaya, where it has taken advantage of the very liberal regulations dictated by British policy. There are few parts of the economic system into which he does not enter and in which he does not work patiently and hard, and often prosperously. He may be seen on every rung of fortune's ladder: as a humble coolie on a plantation or on a mining venture, or even as the wealthy owner of a rubber or pine-apple estate or a tin-mining concern; as a stevedore in a port, a rickshaw man, or a hawker in the streets of the big towns, or else as a secretary or typist in the office of a big broker in Singapore; as a broker even, and not one of the least, a wholesale merchant, shipper, public works contractor, big business man, or the owner of cinemas, large shops, and real estate in the towns. Tan Kah Kee, the richest man in Malaya about 1928, employed thousands of people in his shops and factories. Ten years later the publicity given to

[1] This percentage must be far greater today.

'Tiger Balm' on the hoardings in Singapore revealed one of the profitable activities of another Chinese Straits-dollar millionaire.

The Chinaman's very varied aptitudes made him a wonderful colonising instrument in a new and almost uninhabited land whose position and natural resources had since the end of the century been attracting an enormous amount of capital. As may well be imagined, after the economic crisis of 1931 an increase in the Chinese population seemed less desirable to the administration. Disturbances in the Chinese Republic and the Sino-Japanese War had far-reaching repercussions on immigrants in Malaya. Unemployment, strikes, and boycotts seemed equally dangerous. The British Government, therefore, established a system of administrative decentralisation which favoured the Malays, but displeased the Chinese, who were already opposed to the measures that had reduced immigration from 1928 onwards.

The restrictions also affected the Indians, who comprise the other main section of non-Malay immigrants in the Peninsula. In 1932 they numbered 624,000, or 14 per cent. of the total population; in 1937 they were 755,000, or 14·7 per cent. Their immigration was far more passive than that of the Chinese, their aptitudes and activities far less varied, and their social rise and prosperity in business far more rare.[1]

Indian immigration began in the Straits before 1850. The English East India Company had deported criminals to the Settlements there after Benkulen was handed over to the Dutch. After being employed in public works yards, many of the deportees had settled in Singapore as shopkeepers, cattlemen, carriers, etc. A stream of slave labour had also begun to flow in to the little plantations of sugarcane, spices, cassava, and copra, in Penang and Wellesley Province in 1800. Slavery was abolished in 1833 and replaced by the equally inhuman system of indentured labour. The demand for Indian labourers increased with the extension of British rule in the Peninsula. It was encouraged by the Government, because the Straits Settlements remained politically dependent on Calcutta till 1867, and the Presidency of Madras provided their garrison. Many European planters came from Ceylon. Tamils and Sinhalese supplied the agricultural labour, and their immigration, like that of the Chinese, increased from 1880 onwards. But the immigrants engaged mainly in rubber-planting, whilst the destination of the Chinese newcomers was very varied.

A small fraction (31,000 in 1931) of the Indians in Malaya are Muslims from the Indus valley, Punjabis or Sikhs. They function as caretakers, herdsmen, moneylenders, or policemen. Six feet

[1] Dennery, *op. cit.*, pp. 184–229.

tall, with black or grey beards, turbaned heads, and hairy legs protruding from a khaki uniform, the Sikh police have distinguished themselves when called upon to suppress the revolts of Malay chieftains; for instance, in Pahang in 1894.[1] But the great majority, amounting to 88·5 per cent. in 1931, are Tamils from the Madras Presidency. Some of these work as secretaries, railway clerks, and building hands, but most of them land at Penang and become plantation coolies.

Owing to pressure from the Government of India and to the claims of political leaders in that country, Indian immigration was placed under official control earlier than Chinese. Recruitment by contract, whereby the labourer was kept in ignorance of the conditions in which he was to live for several years in a strange land, was fairly soon regulated and finally suppressed in 1910. Nowadays, the *kangani* system prevails. The Indian sails at the instance of a *kangani*, that is, a recruiter from his village, who has usually worked on the plantations he recommends to his fellow-villagers and who is the agent of his manager or a planters' association. Unlike the indentured coolie, the immigrant may at the end of a month leave the firm to which he is at first sent. He scarcely ever exercises this option and during his stay in Malaya usually remains a member of the gang under his *kangani*. In spite of the wretched conditions in which he lives in his native land, he leaves it without enthusiasm and even with apprehension. The sight of a colony at the peak of progress offers little temptation to his uncomplaining heart and his untutored mind. As a rule, he returns home a coolie as he left it, the average length of his stay being three years—less, it would appear, than that of the Chinese.

Indian immigration into Malaya is as irregular as that of the Chinese. More than the latter it depends on the demands of the plantations. For instance, between 1930 and 1933, a period of great slump in rubber, the number of those who returned home was nearly 200,000 more than those who landed.[2]

Yet there are also Indians settled in Malaya, 'Malay-born Indians', who form a group apart, despise the crowd of unsettled ignorant labourers, have forgotten the Tamil language, and care nothing for

---

[1] The Chettiars, who come from southern India, form separate communities in Malaya as they do in Burma, Siam, the Dutch East Indies, and Cochin China (South Vietnam). They are tradesmen, estate agents at times, but mainly money-lenders connected with big capitalists in India. Some of their firms are a hundred years old, and their Hindu temples are richly endowed with real estate and jewellery and with silver chairs on which on certain days the idols are paraded.

[2] Since 1937 departures have greatly exceeded arrivals. In 1948 the total number of Indians did not reach 600,000, and Indian labour often had to be replaced by Chinese on the plantations. Yet in 1953 the Indians and Pakistanis numbered some 665,000, or 12 per cent. of the population, whilst the Chinese numbered about 40 per cent. Singapore is not included in these figures.

caste. Efforts have been made to develop in the Indians in Malaya a sense of belonging to the same community. They have been visited by leading fellow-Indians, like Rabindranath Tagore. The first All-Malayan Indian Conference was held at Kuala Lumpur in 1927, and in 1928 the Federal Council included its first Indian member.[1]

The unsettled character of the people living in Malaya and the demographic incompleteness of the Peninsula are evidenced by the considerable relative importance of migration. Between 1928 and 1937 nearly 5,000,000 persons from abroad landed at ports in Malaya, and nearly 4,500,000 left Malaya for a foreign destination.

The relation between the sexes is still more significant. Though among the Malays women are nearly as numerous as men, among the Chinese and Indians as well as the Europeans they are only about half as numerous. In Malaya in 1931 out of a total population of 4,350,000 there were 800,000 more men than women. Yet the disproportion was less than it had been ten years before, for the Chinese had been showing a tendency to bring their wives. Before 1914 women formed only 10 or 11 per cent. of all Chinese arrivals, whilst between the wars the percentage rose to 30. On the other hand, the efforts of the planters and the Government to import Indian couples has not been unsuccessful.

The Malays and other races are far from being uniformly distributed over the territory under British rule or protection.[2] The Chinese are the most numerous in the old Straits Settlements, where in 1931 they formed 59·6 per cent. of the population and reached the high figure of 74·9 per cent. in Singapore Island.[3] Their percentage, like that of Europeans and Eurasians, decreased to 44·5 in the old Federated Malay States and still more to 21·4 in the old Unfederated States.[4] Indians were numerous in the Malay States in consequence of their relative absence from the towns and preponderance, on the other hand, on rubber estates. They occurred in large numbers on the relatively narrow strip of country occupied by those plantations on the west coast of the Peninsula between Penang and Malacca. The distribution of Malays is exactly the opposite to that of Europeans and Chinese. They formed more than two-thirds of the population in the Unfederated States, but were only slightly more than one-third (34·7 per cent.) in the Federated States and hardly

[1] The Indian and Sinhalese Ladies Club, called the Lotus Club, was founded in Singapore shortly before the war began in 1941 and included Indians of every language and religion and even other Orientals, such as Persians and Malays.

[2] Dobby (103), pp. 211–18; Vlieland (112).

[3] 77·5 per cent. in 1947.

[4] The distinction between the Federated and Unfederated States was abolished in 1948, and now, with the exception of Singapore, the whole of Malaya forms a Federation.

one-fourth in the Straits Settlements.[1] This uneven racial distribution reflects rather faithfully the economic development and
utilisation of the land.

The World's Leading Producer of Tin. Tin has played an outstanding part in Malayan history. Before the coming of the
Europeans the ore was worked by Malays, Siamese, and, since the

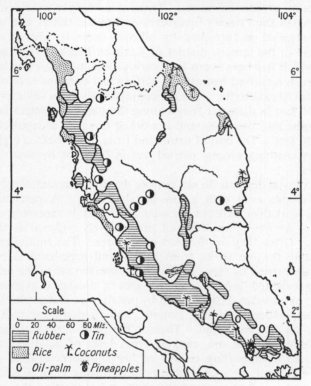

FIG. 13.—PRODUCTS OF MALAYA

beginning of the 18th century, by Chinese. Since Malacca was
taken by Albuquerque in 1511, many travellers have spoken of the
tin trade in that port. The discovery of rich deposits in the State
of Perak and the bloody rivalries which ensued among the Chinese
led to the first English intervention in the interior of the Peninsula.
European technique and capital greatly increased production. Until
it was ousted by rubber at the beginning of this century, tin held its
ground as the most paying Malayan export and the chief source of

[1] Only 11·8 per cent. on Singapore Island in 1937 and 12·3 per cent. in the
Colony of Singapore in 1947.

both private incomes and Government revenue. Even today the old Federated States—the others count for little in production—supply more than one-third of the world's exports of the metal.

The original deposits are found in the granite rocks in most of the ridges forming the skeleton of the Peninsula, but especially in the longest, the Korbu range. The western slopes of this ridge contain the world's richest tin-mines. These seldom touch the veins that run through the Primary limestones or Triassic shales, and most of the production is furnished by alluvial deposits. About half is extracted in the famous district of Kinta in Perak. The limestone rock, which has been worn into curiously picturesque scenery, has been much dissolved beneath the surface and contains hollows filled with alluvial cassiterite. The ore comes largely from veins, or pipes, 30 or 40 feet in diameter found along the plane of contact between the granite and limestone and is worked down to a depth of more than 330 feet. The cost of extraction from these rocks is high, as is also the crushing process carried out in factories by rows of ore-crushers.

The alluvial deposits do not require the same amount of work and are profitable even with a low metal content. A percentage of 0·015 is workable, whilst in the veins 2 per cent. is necessary. Huge holes, or *lombangs*, are dug and progressively widened as they go deeper. Often they are flooded with water. The equipment used for raising the ore varies from bailers and rope-handled buckets which are carried by men in relays from one terrace to the next to a counter-weighted lever something like a *shaduf* (Egyptian well sweep); or a bucket-chain worked by pedals; or a water-wheel. But the most modern pumping systems, and in particular centrifugal pumps, are also employed. There is the same variety of means in transporting the tin ore, ranging from lines of male and female coolies, each supporting on his or her shoulders a yoke with a basket balanced on each end, to water-raising engines and huge gravel pumps. For washing the rock and separating the ore the primitive method of the sluice, a simple channel with a stream of water, has been brought to perfection. Powerful pumps, known as 'monitors', send jets of water on to the metalliferous sand. The works are often marked by huge scaffoldings of thin wooden poles, in the construction of which the Chinese excel. But dredgers are always preferred. Mounted on a floating pontoon, they move over the water in the quarry to attack the wall of alluvium with their heavy chain of buckets, emptying the alluvium into a large rotating cylinder in which the first sifting is carried out, and throwing the waste material behind them. The final extraction is carried out in a factory by means of repeated washings and the aid of magnetic separators.

The Chinese have made great efforts to learn modern technique, by which the cost of the ore as it leaves the mine is constantly being lowered. Many gangs of Chinese, sometimes including Malays and aborigines, also work deposits in a primitive way along water-courses or in abandoned quarries, crushing the earth with wooden stamps and separating the ore in wash-troughs as is done with gold-bearing sand. Marks of this gleaning exist everywhere. The practice is called *dulang*. The Government was still issuing more than 9500 licences for it in 1937, though *dulang* no longer yielded much more than 1·5 per cent. of the total production. The share achieved by gravel pumps, dredgers, and other modern machinery in extracting the ore has risen sharply in the last thirty years. The investment of capital, mainly English, but including some French, has enabled large works to be constructed. The Chinese have succeeded in continuing to work deposits that give high yields, like the famous Beatrice mine in Perak, in which a little capital expenditure brought enormous profits within a few years. They do not hesitate to enlist the help of European engineers or other technicians.[1]

In spite of all, a relative decline has been visible in Chinese production. Before 1912 this production represented some four-fifths of the total, but on the eve of the war, it was not much more than one-third. Yet most of the labour in the mines still remains Chinese.[2]

The ore is smelted at Penang and Singapore by two smelting companies which until recently also handled a large part of the ore from Indo-China and Indonesia.

Other mineral products in the Peninsula lag very far behind tin. Reef gold is worked in the State of Pahang alone. The only coal-field is at Batu Arang in Selangor, where lignite is mined; but its yield, which was 630,000 tons in 1937,[3] does not meet half the needs of Malaya. Iron and manganese ores had been worked from 1931 until 1945 by Japanese firms in Johore, Trengganu, and Kelantan and exported directly to Japan.[4]

The Rubber Boom. Up to about the beginning of the 20th century Malaya did not seem destined to become a great land of plantations. In the neighbourhood of the ports the Chinese had long been cultivating manioc, pepper, and gambier, a shrub whose bark is

[1] Ooi Jin Bee (107a). In Kinta by the 18th century the Chinese were already using the noria and were sinking mines and timbered galleries. Modern machinery was first introduced by the British in 1877, and the dredger came into use in 1912. In Kinta about half the total production in 1952 was raised by dredgers. Mines owned by Europeans yielded 59·5 per cent., those worked by Chinese yielded 39·24 per cent., and the remainder came from *dulang* operations.

[2] 81 per cent. in 1937.   [3] 204,000 tons in 1955.

[4] In 1937 the export amounted to 2,500,000 tons of iron and 190,000 tons of manganese ore; in 1953 iron export was down to 1,250,000 tons; the metal content is about 60 per cent.

used for tanning, and these fed a moderate export trade. The first European planters, who came from Ceylon in 1885 and onwards, had set out to produce coffee, mainly in Selangor; but this crop soon ceased to be cultivated.

Heveas were first introduced into Ceylon and Malaya in 1877, but cultivation scarcely began until 1890 and was at first confronted with difficulties. The shares of local firms were not readily bought in England, and it was only in 1910 that the great boom began. The planters made huge profits owing to the increasing consumption of raw rubber and to the rise in prices; and the smoke of burning forests spread over the western slopes of the Peninsula.

The area planted in *hevea* rubber more than quadrupled between 1910 and 1920, in which latter year it approached 2,500,000 acres and production jumped from a few thousand to nearly 200,000 tons. The German War of 1914–18 increased the demand and enabled firms to pay dividends of from 25 to 50 per cent. Then ensued a great slump with a considerable fall in prices, when vast areas were just beginning to be productive. The application of the Stevenson plan (1922)[1] renewed the possibility of high profits. But prices fell again from 1930 onwards, at a time when *hevea* trees covered 3,000,000 acres in Malaya alone. After this the rate of increase slackened, and at the end of 1937 the area under *heveas* was less than 3,250,000 acres. But production exceeded 500,000 tons.[2]

In fact, the technique of *hevea* cultivation (see below, pp. 342–5 ff) had made great progress during these slumps. The planters were much helped by the Government. The Rubber Research Institute at Kuala Lumpur used the results of experiments already conducted in some small degree elsewhere, devoted itself to scientific research, and published accounts of the best methods. But the application of these was not easy on old plantations, whose ill-used soil became irretrievably sterile. The sowing of leguminous plants between the rows of trees spread slowly and proved less effective than in neighbouring countries, like the Oostkust of Sumatra and French Indo-China, where rubber cultivation is more recent and the soil less impoverished.

The European planters who contributed to these improvements have lost the monopoly of production. Official statistics distinguish plantations of at least 100 acres ('estates') from small holdings. In 1937 the first category represented 61 per cent. of the area planted, three-fourths of them being owned by Europeans, mainly British, and only about one-sixth by Chinese. In 1947 the percentage had fallen to 58. The average size of European plantations is now far greater than that of the Chinese. Of the latter 49 were of more than

[1] See below, p. 354.

[2] At the end of 1947 the total area was 3,350,000 acres, and production amounted to 700,000 tons.

1000 acres, whilst 514 of the European estates exceeded that figure. Dunlop Plantations, Ltd., and the London Asiatic Rubber and Products, Co., Ltd., each owned about 100,000 acres in 1935.

Large plantations are sometimes established on peaty swamp-soil, but often on more or less undulating country rising to about 1300 feet above the sea, on the site of fairly dense forest. The clearing away of the bush was usually entrusted to Chinese contractors. A large number of Chinese are still to be found among the labourers, but the great majority are Indians landed at Penang, Singapore, and Port Swettenham.

Between the large estates owned by joint stock companies and small holdings there is the average plantation measuring from 100 to 500 acres. Whilst ranking as estates, they belong mostly to Chinese, though some are held by Europeans or even Indians, who are former employees of the joint stock companies and have invested their savings in rubber cultivation, sometimes going into partnerships to which they contribute capital and service.

More than a third of the area planted in *hevea* trees and of the total amount of latex produced is due to little plantations of 100 acres or less. Their multiplication, unsuspected at first, became evident under the system instituted by the Stevenson plan. Here and there one belongs to a European and less frequently to an Indian, but most are owned by Chinese or Malays, and these have become far more numerous since the end of the war in 1945. Most of these holdings are on flat land near the coast.

The *hevea* tree occupies nearly two-thirds of the 5,000,000 acres under cultivation in Malaya. This is close on 10 per cent. of the total area of the country. The rest is also used for various export crops, the chief of which are palm-oil and pine-apples, and for food-crops, rice and coconut especially, which occupy respectively 17 and 12 per cent. of the cultivated land. In spite of the efforts of the Government to increase the acreage and yield of the rice-fields, these as a rule scarcely supply 40 per cent. of the demand, which, it is true, is the highest per head in the world. Few rice-fields give two crops a year. About one-third of the coconut plantations are of more than 100 acres and belong to Chinese or Europeans, who used to find in the export of copra a stabilising factor in their economic system, which compensated for losses suffered on other produce, such as coffee and rubber. This led to the coconut being termed 'the Consols of the East'. The other two-thirds of the plantations are owned by Malays. These are nearly all on the coast and have by-crops growing between the palms.

The oil palm (*Elaeis*) was brought from Africa to Selangor in 1917 and became widespread mainly after 1926. Big companies prefer it to the coconut palm, since by careful selection of the trees and by improved processes of extraction it gives a high yield of oil of good quality.[1]

The cultivation of pine-apples,[2] begun by Europeans on Singapore Island about 1888, has spread in southern Johore, which supplies two-thirds of the production, and to a less extent in Selangor. Often planted at first between young *hevea* trees, the pine-apple enables the rubber planter to get a return before tapping can begin. The first harvest is ready 18 months after planting and the following ones every six months. After the sixth year the plants must be replaced. This crop has been grown mainly by Chinese, each working 12 or 15 acres. About one in six of the canning factories has its own plantation, and many others have invested capital in the crop so as to ensure control. Before 1941 Malaya became, after Hawaii, the world's second largest exporter of pine-apples and is now fast regaining its pre-war position. Cassava is cultivated and made into tapioca mainly by Chinese.

Regional Variety. The economic system, described above and founded on the predominance of produce for export, is not uniformly spread over the whole Peninsula. It is still restricted to a rather narrow strip along and behind the south and west coasts close to the great ocean route through the Straits, by which people from overseas have brought their vitalising influence. In 1931, 56 per cent. of the population of Malaya were crowded into a strip 350 miles long and seldom more than 50 miles wide, with a density of about 150 persons to the square mile. Even on this coast the soil, natural resources, ease of access, historical circumstances, and type of settlement cause a fairly wide variety of scenery. Between the more or less old ports of Singapore, Malacca, and Penang other centres of activity have sprung up and increased, but the development has not taken place everywhere on the same basis or with the same steady rhythm.

The State of Johore in the south of the Peninsula alone stretches from sea to sea. In spite of the nearness of Singapore Island, its princes in their capital of Johore Bahru showed a strong spirit of independence. Johore could not escape, however, from the economic influences of the great city, and its increase in population of nearly 181 per cent. between 1911 and 1931 was greater than that of any other State. A large number of Malays from the islands work in it as wage-earners or have settled as independent peasants. Its Chinese are four times as numerous as its Indians and equal them in number on the rubber plantations. Although rubber comes at the head of its agricultural produce with 19 per cent. of the total area, the products remain very varied, and Johore also exports a great deal of copra, pine-apples, tapioca, and areca nuts. In the north and east of the State vast expanses are still covered with jungle that is swampy in places or carpeted with *alang* savanas which often have the appearance of parkland owing to the presence of clumps of trees.

Between the mouth of the Muar to the south of Malacca and that of the Selangor to the north of Port Swettenham the railway from Singapore to Bangkok passes through the great rubber-growing district of Malaya and the area which is the world's leading producer of the commodity. In the Settlement of Malacca and the States of Negri Sembilan and Selangor rubber-trees covered 26 per cent. of the total area. North of the rather monotonous plateau of Johore the relief becomes broken. In Negri Sembilan the skyline is raised by wooded ridges with jagged crests. Rice-fields run like streaks along little, densely populated valleys which are fringed on either side with villages. The scenery is pleasant and bright with flashes of water divided up by little dykes and with seedbeds of vivid green. Clumps of coconut palms shelter pile-dwellings with slightly concave roofs often strengthened with sheet-metal angle-irons. Buffaloes wallow in the mud. But these pictures of traditional Malay life are but fleeting glimpses. The traveller is beset by lines of trees with slender, greyish trunks and pyramidal foliage. It is the well-trained *hevea* lacking in majesty and gracefulness, but speaking of human effort. Yielding to the normal growth of the forest covering, some plantations seem to have been recaptured by wild vegetation. Others are well weeded and show only short grass between the rows of trees. Young *heveas* shoot up vigorously among the fallen boles and stumps. From the tops of the ridges on which the manager's comfortable bungalow in some cases stands, the view extends across the alluvial plain and the sea and, eastwards, over a landscape of wooded hills among which rise a few bold features. Here and there yellow patches betray recent clearing. The covering of vegetation which might be thought to be virgin consists merely of legions of *heveas* spreading up as far as the cloud-veiled ridges. In places a practised eye recognises by a different shade of green a stand of oil palms and then in the background the wall of the virgin forest retreating before the exotic, domesticated trees.

Amid this verdure, red roofs betray the characteristic building of all large estates, viz. the offices in which Tamil clerks work, workers are paid, and the walls are adorned with graphs and maps showing details of the progress and life of the plantation, the extensions planned, the nature of the soil, the yields, the unavailability of coolies, etc. Then there is the factory in which for some hours every day crêpe and leaf rubber are rolled out from coagulated latex in the compartments before being smoked, packed, and pressed into cases.

The coolie village collects its hutments or individual hovels into a clearing whose hygiene is improved by a network of cement gutters and by a film of oil which covers every puddle for hundreds of yards around. After the day's work on the plantation the Tamils assemble there. They have the advantage of more plentiful and regular food than at home, an infirmary, and in many cases a school taught by one of their own race. Women are among them, and the bright colours of their pink or yellow clothes stand out against the dark green of the vegetation. The little Hindu temple, with its tiled roof and white walls adorned with brightly coloured portraiture, generally stands by itself in the plantation. Of all the States in the Peninsula Selangor has the greatest number of Indians, though they are nevertheless outnumbered by the Chinese. They were there even at the beginning when about 1870 In Kuala Lumpur the shops supplying the little mineral workings in the neighbourhood stood in lines along two streets at a river confluence. Today they form the majority of the population of the town, which numbered 110,000 in 1931.[1] On the left of the River Klang, which flows towards Port Swettenham, the hills are adorned with magnificent gardens. Near the railway station the strange, neo-mauresque style of the buildings with cupolas and white or ochre minarets emphasise rather than hide the youth and triumphant progress of the federal capital. Capital it is too of rubber cultivation, and its business quarters are developing mainly on the right bank.

The slender trellis-work of scaffoldings, the spoil-heaps, and the quarries abandoned and full of water indicate tin-workings even on the outskirts of Kuala Lumpur. But rubber continues to predominate. The two great sources of Malayan wealth are found together to the north of Selangor in Perak. Perak, however, is the chief mining State on the Peninsula, and Ipoh in the heart of the Kinta district is the leading tin town. The River Kinta separates the modern quarters from the old town, which at the end of the last century was still merely a sordid cluster of coolie huts. The villages scattered about in the rubber plantations are in contrast with the compact mining centres. The miners are nearly all Chinese, as are the shopkeepers whose one-storied houses stand side by side along the roads. The Chinese are more than twice as numerous as the Indians in Perak, and the proportion of Malays is greater than in Selangor.

Malays are still more numerous in Kedah, which, like the tiny State of Perlis, did not pass from Siamese suzerainty to British protection until 1909. They form two-thirds of the total population in Kedah and four-fifths in Perlis. This majority is reflected in the

---

[1] Kuala Lumpur owes to its central situation its status as capital of the Federation of Malaya. In 1954 it had a population of 300,000 persons.

kinds of exploitation.   The undulations rising eastwards and crossed by some of the ridges are still mostly covered with *hevea* trees. Farther north rice becomes the chief crop and occupies the wide valleys and the coast plain.   Elliptical villages often mark the line of contact between the hills and the alluvial lowland.   Kedah is the greatest rice producer among the Malay States.

Kedah is thus transitional to the States on the east coast, where the country and mode of life have been far less affected by external influences.   Population is concentrated mainly in the extreme north-east, on the coast plain of Kelantan, where rice-fields and coconut groves spread out behind a low, sandy shore.   The inland parts of Trengganu are more mountainous and far less civilised besides. Malay traditions are maintained in the courts of the sultans.   There is an inscription which seems to bear witness to the existence of a Muslim kingdom in Trengganu as early as the 15th century.   The schools in Kelantan are attended by Muslims from Siam and even French Indo-China.   In Kelantan and Trengganu British administration deviated less than elsewhere from the true idea of the protectorate, a fact which was greatly helped by the persistence of the old agricultural economic system.   Many Government appointments are held by Malays, who form 90 per cent. of the total population in these two former Unfederated States.   There is a strong contrast between the capitals of Kelantan and Selangor, for the population of Kota Bahru is 70 per cent. Malay, whilst that of Kuala Lumpur is only 10 per cent.[1]

Pahang too is 60 per cent. Malay.   It is the largest and wildest State on the Peninsula, with great stretches of forest swampy in places, waiting to be cleared away.   Rubber cultivation has spread, however, around Kuala Lipis, which is connected by motor road with Kuala Lumpur.   Along the River Pahang, as along the Perak on the west, villages line the river banks, where there are also little native plantations of *hevea* trees.   The hollows behind are flooded for several months in the year and are cultivated with rice.   The coast, beaten for six months in the year by the violent north-east monsoon, displays a series of granite spurs pointing south-east. These are connected by very straight sandspits which block the mouths of many of the streams, thus forming freshwater lakes. One small delta, that of the Pahang, juts out into the sea.

The slowness of the colonisation of the eastern side of the Peninsula is also marked by a lower density of population, 62 to the square mile in Kelantan, 36 in Trengganu, and 13 in Pahang (in 1951). Most of the towns are still isolated.   Only two roads run right across the Peninsula, one ending at the little port of Kuantan in Pahang and the other at Mersing in Johore.   The East Coast

1 Emerson (251), p. 249.

Railway which leaves the main line at Gemas and crosses the States
of Pahang and Kelantan was only finished in 1931. In the three
States of Kelantan, Trengganu, and Pahang the *hevea* covers
scarcely 2 per cent. of the whole area.

The Ports. The economic progress of Malaya has increased the
number of urban centres. Internal trade was greatly stimulated by
the relative decline of the traditional mode of life in favour of
production for export. At the same time roads and railways
encouraged the birth of permanent commercial settlements to replace
or overshadow the periodical rural markets. In 1951 there were in
Malaya 120 towns with populations exceeding 1000. These contained more than 30 per cent. of the total population of the Peninsula, which is a considerable figure for a tropical colony.

This urban population does not seem to be more unstable than its
rural counterpart; on the contrary, it changes less. Fluctuations
due to emigration mainly affect the gangs of coolies distributed
among the plantations and mines. Family life is easier in a town,
the number of women is relatively greater and immigrants stay
longer.

These immigrants are mainly Chinese and most of those who
have settled permanently live in the towns. They already form the
majority in inland centres which in many cases, including Kuala
Lumpur and Ipoh, have grown up on the sites of old mining camps.
Their majority is even greater in the large coastal towns, the former
Straits Settlements, in which 15 per cent. of the total population
of Malaya was living in 1951.

Each of these cities has its own peculiarity and has experienced
turns of fortune. The most glorious is now in decay, whilst the
most recent has become one of the busiest of the world's nodal
points where the globe-trotter may always meet a friend who is also
there by chance.

Malacca (pop. 37,000 in 1951) still bears stirring traces of the
rulers who have succeeded each other on the shores of its open
roadstead. On St. Paul's Hill, which marks and shelters the river
mouth, stand the imposing ruins of the church that Albuquerque
built to the glory of *Nossa Senhora da Annunciada* and which lodged
the body of St. Francis Xavier before its removal to Goa in 1553.
On the gravestones clustering in the shade of its walls Dutch epitaphs
surmounted by proud coats-of-arms cover the obliterated Portuguese
inscriptions. Standing amid cool English lawns, majestic red-
fronted edifices like the Town Hall and Clock Tower recall the
power of the great Amsterdam Company. And near the walls of
the Portuguese fort in a graveyard scented with frangipani trees the
graves of British officers killed during the expeditions into the

interior about 1825 are mingled with those of the Dutch. Malacca is no longer the great trading centre for the produce of India, Indo-China, China, Java, and the Moluccas, as it was when at the end of the 16th century Linschoten, the traveller, described the bustle there and the attraction it had for the sailors and traders of every nation, in spite of its unhealthiness. The energetic and astute Dampier, who landed opium there at the end of the 17th century, mentions the decline of the town, which had begun even in his day.[1] In 1854 Wallace remarked that the port was almost deserted and that its trade was reduced to a few forest products and to the fruit from orchards planted by the Portuguese, whose wretched half-breed descendants still spoke the language of their Iberian ancestors.[2] But even then the Chinese seemed to Wallace to be the most numerous people. Their one-storied houses roofed with round tiles have replaced the Dutch residences which were formerly situated in the business quarter on the right bank of the river along Jonker and Heeren Streets; and they have the lion's share in the new stir of business due to the progress of rubber cultivation in the backland.

Penang. Other ports which are better situated, better equipped, and better adapted to the requirements of modern shipping, ousted Malacca in the 19th century, and today it is limited to a strictly local function owing to the growth of Singapore and Penang. It was in 1786 that Captain Francis Light, a British merchant seaman, took possession of Penang Island. Singled out by Sir James Lancaster as early as 1592 and ceded by the Sultan of Kedah to the Honourable East India Company, it already had a larger population than Malacca by 1795. When the future Duke of Wellington visited it in 1797, he foretold that it would dominate the Far East commercially. The territory on the mainland opposite which became Province Wellesley was acquired from the same prince for a pension of £10,000 and was annexed to Penang in 1800. Penang was not supplanted by Singapore as capital of the Straits until 1837.

The port of Penang lies at the north-east point under shelter of the island itself, which rises to a height of 2700 feet. The completion of the Singapore–Bangkok Railway has made Penang the nearest port of call to the Siamese capital on the way through the Straits. It also gives the quickest approach to the chief mining and plantation area from the east coast of India. So it remained the leading port for the arrival and departure of Tamil coolies. It has benefited too from the recent development of the east coast of Sumatra, which is only a few hours away by boat. As in Malacca, the old trade in native produce consisting of areca nuts, spices, and

[1] Dampier (3), III, p. 181.　　　　[2] Wallace (63), p. 21.

copra has disappeared in face of the tin and rubber boom. It was here that the Chinese set up the first large tin-smelting works, which afterwards came into the possession of an English firm, Eastern Smelters, Ltd. The tonnage of vessels entered and cleared rose in 1837 to more than one-third of that of Singapore. The streets in the business quarter run on to the docks facing the railway station at Prai, about four miles away on the mainland and connected by ferry to the island. Behind these the residences of the Europeans and wealthy Chinese are spread about among gardens, sports grounds, and lines of coconut trees running up the slopes. The hills here are climbed by a funicular railway. In 1951 the population of the town was 155,000.

Singapore. It was in Penang that Stamford Raffles, who had been appointed Assistant Secretary to the Penang Government, made the acquaintance of the Malay world, a world he was destined to know better while he was Governor of Java. He dreamed of securing for Great Britain the commercial domination of the Far East, which seemed to him to be threatened by the ambition of other Powers; and, inspired by zeal for his country and by puritanical sentiments, he proclaimed that Great Britain's mission was to protect the natives against the pernicious enterprises of European adventurers. In 1824 he obtained from the Sultan of Johore the cession of Singapore Island, which had already been offered in 1703 to Captain Hamilton, a Scot.[1] Finally, his energy triumphed over the hesitation of the Government, which feared difficulties with foreign nations. Combining, as great colonisers have frequently done, a keen sense of reality with a lofty idealism, he established his country in spite of herself on the land he had marked out,[2] at once encouraged Chinese immigration, and drew up a plan for the education of the local peoples. He aimed at making the little island a model of peaceful ways and sound morality, at putting an end to the *kris* custom, at forbidding gambling and cock-fighting, at suppressing slavery, and controlling the consumption of alcohol and opium. He wished this 'shop', as he called it, which was so near to the Dutch 'shop', to be open to all. The principle of free trade was maintained steadily in spite of all opposition. For some time navigation was unsafe among the islands owing to the pirates who infested them. Despite this, in 1825 fifteen ships sailed with cargoes for Europe, most of them bound for London or Liverpool, the rest for Hamburg, Bordeaux, or Stockholm. The goods destined

---

[1] By 1819 the right to establish a settlement in the island had been secured.

[2] Cp. Raffles' words as quoted by Pelzer in *Die Arbeiterwanderungen in Südöstasien*, p. 68: 'You may take my word for it, Singapore is by far the most important station in the East; and as far as naval superiority and commercial interests are concerned, of much higher value than whole continents of territory'.

for Europe were at first bought by auction with the aid of many Chinese. But the latter mainly carried on a trade in commodities imported from China. The arrival of big junks, eyed by a pirate sampan stationed out to sea, caused great excitement in the town shortly before Christmas, and the coming of the Buginese fleet was another leading event.

In 1837, about ten years after Raffles had died in retirement in England, Singapore became the capital of the Straits Settlements. The colonies did not escape from the authority of the India Office and pass to the Colonial Office till 1867. Meanwhile European ambition was increasing in the Far East. The Suez Canal made the Straits of Malacca, rather than the Sunda passage, the great ocean route from Europe to the seas of China and Japan, and Singapore became one of the world's chief nodal points. Amid the amazing racial mixture of Malays, Portuguese Eurasians, 'Klings' from southern India, Arabs, Bengalis, Parsees, Javanese, and Bugis from Celebes, the activity of the Chinese had already struck Wallace, who stayed in the island several times between 1854 and 1862. He remarked on the good nature and astuteness of the wealthy Celestial, who was already established here as if at home. With his plait adorned with a red ribbon and hanging down to his heels and with his body comfortably dressed in ample garments, he was out every evening enjoying the cool breeze in a gig drawn by a spirited horse. He had shops in the town, ships in the harbour, and plantations of pepper and gambier in the neighbourhood. He exploited the forest which still covered the tops of the hills and in which the naturalist, though troubled by the abundance of tigers, made wonderful collections of insects in areas where the trees had been felled.[1]

In the south the Malay Peninsula breaks up into a group of rocky humps which form islands that guard all the passages between Sumatra and the extreme end of Asia. Singapore Island[2] is scarcely separated from the mainland. The intervening water, which is crossed by a causeway 3465 feet long carrying a railway, a road, and a large pipe line, widens out and deepens towards the east. Until 1819 this strait had been the main passage from India to China, in spite of the attacks of pirates. The plateau of Johore is continued in the island at a mean height of about 200 feet, and this is dominated by hills which reach their culmination in Bukit Tima (tin hill; 560 feet approximately). The crystalline core, now covered with brightly coloured light-red and yellow laterites, was formerly capped with sedimentaries. Traces of these are recognised in the sandstone which still crowns some of the hills, like the hog's-backed Mt. Faber, and also in shales

[1] Wallace (63), p. 18.   [2] Dobby (102).

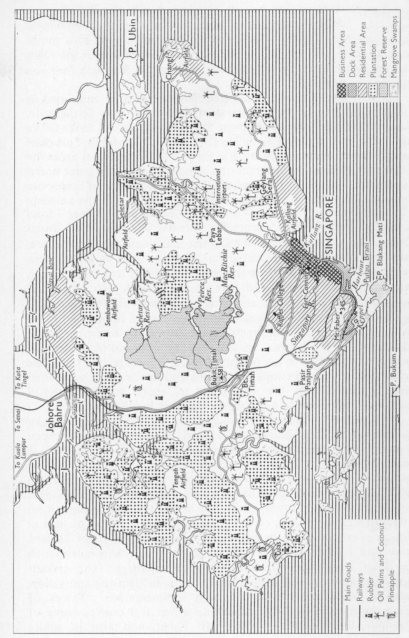

FIG. 14.—SINGAPORE ISLAND

gashed by the little streams that empty into mud-choked estuaries. These last are now cut off from the sea by sluice gates to check malaria, lessen the deposit of salt, and benefit the cultivation of copra. On the south of the island at the mouth of the Singapore River and on the nearby hills there has grown up the largest town in the Malay world. It runs about 10 miles from Keppel Harbour to beyond the River Kallang. The Singapore River, which divides it into two equal parts, is still a great centre of activity. Round Raffles Square on the south side of its mouth the city gathers its banks, Indian money-changers' booths, company offices, and some of its European shops. This is the 'business area' and is almost deserted at night. On the other bank Government buildings, large hotels, and churches stand less closely together behind gardens and recreation grounds. The bold, white sea-front is not so imposing as the Bund at Shanghai, but it has been raised during the past few years because the high price of land has led to the construction of taller buildings.

The further spread of these central quarters is in fact prevented by the Asiatic town which hems them in closely on both banks. The European on his first trip to the Far East is surprised at the sudden change from the European to the Chinese world with its swarming streets, vertical shop-signs bearing mysterious characters, and the noises and smells rising from commodities overflowing on to the pavements in picturesque disorder. Innumerable little craftsmen are housed in tiny shops. Above, cloths of many colours drying on poles give the continuous impression of a dressing of flags to mark some public rejoicing. On the carriageway trishaws, bicycles, motor-cars (of which there are many thousands on the island), and trolleybuses, mingled even now with slow ox-carts, call to each other as they pass. Malay police, dressed in white, pivot round like automata to control the traffic. The bustle goes on far into the night under the harsh glare of electric lights. Long before the wooden shutters are closed, the streets are filled with the smell of food stewing or frying and being guzzled by men naked to the waist, with the cries of hawkers, and the music of gramophones.

There is great overcrowding in the Chinese quarters. New streets have been cut through the blocks of houses and their tiny interior yards. The main thoroughfares run dead straight for miles, passing between hills which maps made in the middle of the last century showed as uninhabited. Several of the hills have not been encroached upon, and streets run round their sides. To the north of Singapore River, Mt. Canning with its green lawns is still a military area, but is wholly shut in by the town, which southwards has reached the modern harbour and northwards has swept across the River Kallang. Beyond it, Paya Lebar is reserved for Malays. These people remain faithful to their pile-dwellings and form a compact island-community. Elsewhere the Malays and Indians are often mixed with Chinese. In the suburban belt Indian labourers are housed in large buildings; but the Chinese, many of whom are market-gardeners, are in the majority here too.

More than three-fourths of the island population live within the town boundaries. In 1950 the total for the whole island was estimated at nearly 1,032,000 souls, 80 per cent. of whom were Chinese, 12 per cent. Malays, and 7 per cent. Indians. Eurasians (mainly clerks) numbered more than 10,000 and the Europeans 10,271.

The cosmopolitan nature of the population calls for a strong police force. In 1935 this numbered 2315 men, of whom 135 were detectives. The plots of many Chinese societies, the most dangerous of which are those of the Cantonese, sometimes involve murder; and in 1926–7 Singapore rivalled Chicago in the exploits of its gangsters.

The town has grown with the harbour, which is still its essential organ and the reason for its existence. The mouth of the river, in which Raffles' ship glided amongst the mangroves in 1819, has long been too small for the traffic. Farther south at the foot of Mt. Faber a series of moles and docks taking the largest ships form Keppel Harbour, which occupies the site of a former valley now drowned and which is sheltered from wind and swell by the islets of Pulau Brani and Blakang Mati. Between the modern harbour and the river docks also cover large areas reclaimed from the sea and on to which the Chinese town has extended. To save the fees for entry and berthing many ships still anchor some way from the shore. In front of the town the water is always full of ships and of lighters and motor-boats passing to and fro between them and the land. Outside the modern docks a good deal of merchandise is stored in warehouses by the riverside. On the river itself there is never-ending movement of a picturesque swarm of Chinese sampans. Farther north a large part of the wood and charcoal needed for use in the town is landed on the banks of the River Rochor.

The business of the port is not restricted to the needs of the town or its backland or even of Malaya as a whole, for owing to its geographical position and its free-trade policy, it is one of the greatest seaports in the Far East. Its functions are mainly to warehouse and distribute goods. Certainly statistics show the predominance of Malaya's two great products: tin and rubber, arriving by rail, road, and coastal boats. But goods also come from abroad, especially from Siam, North Borneo, Sarawak, and Indonesia; and

the port collects from over a wide radius and re-exports copra,
areca nuts, and various spices. In exchange it imports and distributes manufactured goods from Europe, the United States, and
Japan, mineral oil from Indonesia, and bunker coal from South
Africa. This is a very varied trade, its most salient feature being
imports from Indonesia (which before the war amounted to nearly
half the total imports), the export of tin and rubber to the United
States,[1] and the import of manufactured goods from the United
States, Great Britain, and Japan. A fairly large part of the trade

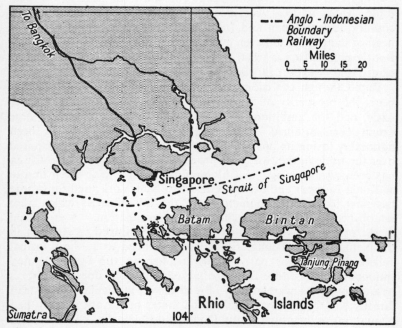

FIG. 15.—SINGAPORE AND THE RHIO ISLANDS

between Europe and the Far East and between India and China
used also to pass through Singapore. Big exporting and importing
firms, usually with European capital and management, used to
operate through Chinese and Indian merchants.

It is perhaps surprising that this trade has not given rise to the
establishment of industry, which compared with commerce is still
on a small scale. A passenger on a liner reaching Singapore sees
the smoke of large tin-smelting works on the island of Pulau Brani;
but on the main island itself there are no large manufactures. All

[1] And recently to the U.S.S.R. (101,000 tons in 1948).

that is done is to effect certain preliminary operations, such as the sawing up of wood, cleaning and smoking native-grown rubber, and soap-making, before despatching the produce to be exported or used locally. Of course, many little establishments make foodstuffs, rubber goods, pottery, metal containers, etc., for Malaya or the neighbouring countries. But for industry to grow up in the face of Japanese competition would, before the war, have called for protective duties and would therefore have meant the suppression of free trade.

Singapore used to handle about two-thirds of Malaya's foreign trade, which in 1937 was greater than that of any other Asiatic country, except Japan and India, and in some years its value per head of the population even exceeded that of the United Kingdom.[1] But the comparison is greatly vitiated by the immense part played by transit and re-export in Malayan ports and especially in Singapore.

Rapid though the economic development of the Peninsula has been, the prosperity of Singapore has been placed on a far wider basis, and the ambition of its far-seeing founder has to a large extent been attained. For some years, however, it has been noticeably losing its position, for gradually the monopoly acquired over the trade in the two great products of Malaya and Indo-China has been disappearing. A Chinese firm had begun to smelt tin ore at Kuala Lumpur and export it direct to New York; and Singapore has now to face the competition of the tin refineries which were established in Texas during the Japanese occupation. A great deal of the ore in Banka was smelted locally or shipped to Arnhem in the Netherlands. Though Singapore continued to be the principal collecting centre for native-grown rubber on the Peninsula and Indonesia, the produce from the large plantations does not always pass through its warehouses. Big firms in particular often dealt directly with buyers from the United States or Europe or even had plantations of their own, as did Dunlop and Michelin. Hence, there is less profit for the merchants who warehouse the goods and whose stocks form as it were a reserve between the producer and the consumer; for the brokers who, knowing prices, bring together sellers and buyers without seeing the goods, the specification for which, however, is clearly defined and determined by the principal taker, the United States: and for the speculators who gamble on an extremely sensitive commodity which is constantly exposed to sudden changes in price. Furthermore, the proportion of rubber dealt with in the famous auctions has tended to decline.

Apart from tin and rubber, Singapore's essential function of

[1] In 1937 the value per head was £37·49 in Malaya and £34·35 in the United Kingdom.

distributing the very varied kinds of goods imported and exported has come up against the competition of other ports, British or otherwise, which are progressively better equipped and nearer to the areas of production or consumption. There are, for instance, Hongkong, which is well placed to profit from the huge Chinese and Japanese markets, though it is often handicapped by Chinese boycotts; Jakarta with its modern docks at Tanjong Priok; and Surabaya, Macassar, and even Saigon. The tightening up of protection among the nations, the support given by home countries to their shipping companies, and the conclusion of compensation agreements all did harm to a port whose prosperity was based on free trade and the absence of customs duties. The progress of transpacific relations and especially of the trade between the United States and Indonesia has caused Singapore's remoteness from the centre of the whole Malay world to be more of a disadvantage than before.[1]

In spite of all the decline has been slow, and there is no certainty that it will continue. Now that England has withdrawn from India and Burma, Singapore seems more than ever to be the main British stronghold in Southeast Asia. Besides being the link between the Indian and Chinese worlds and standing on the chief passage from the Indian Ocean to the Pacific, it is also the key to a country which earns more United States dollars than any other part of the Commonwealth and Empire. Furthermore, Singapore's excellent geographical position cannot be taken from it. There was, indeed, one project which threatened to lessen its importance, viz. the proposal to cut off the Malay Peninsula by making a canal some 44 miles long across the isthmus of Kra, using the valleys of the rivers Pakchan and Tayun in Siamese territory. The first exploration of the project was carried out by an Englishman in 1861 and the years following. But the prosperity of Singapore naturally made the British Government oppose the scheme. It was taken up quite seriously by the French after 1880 and especially by Léon Dru. Kra was one of the bones of contention between Great Britain and France up to the *Entente Cordiale.* Some years ago Japan seemed to want to resume the project herself at a time when she was trying, not unsuccessfully, to extend her trade with India, the Near East, and East Africa. But in fact, a Kra canal would have far less commercial and strategic importance than the Suez or Panama Canals, with which it has often been compared. Fast liners sailing from Europe for the Far East would save hardly more than two days on the journey through the Straits. This difference would be

[1] In 1914 17 per cent. of the imports of the Dutch East Indies passed through Singapore; between 1928 and 1930 only 12·8 per cent. and in 1940 only 7 or 8 per cent. (Broek (187), p. 88.)

really important only to communication between the Bay of Bengal and the Gulf of Martaban, between Calcutta and Rangoon on the one hand and the ports of eastern Indo-China, especially Bangkok and Saigon, on the other. Besides, the tolls would have to be relatively high to ensure remuneration for the capital invested. Its strategic importance is not obvious, and the operations of the Japanese army in 1941–42 demonstrated that in certain conditions Singapore was not impregnable. The Anglo-Siamese Treaty of Singapore signed on January 1, 1946, forbids the cutting of a canal across the Isthmus of Kra.[1]

[1] For the situation in 1957 see below, p. 421.

CHAPTER 8

SUMATRA

The island of Sumatra on the other side of the Straits looks like an elder, grown-up sister of the Malay Peninsula. The resemblance is not only in shape and general direction of axis. We have seen that the continental Malays have often come from Sumatra; and trade across the Straits is of very long standing and continues to be very busy. Like Malaya, Sumatra was late in being penetrated by European settlers. It must have appealed to non-Sumatrans in a less degree than Malaya, for in 1930 the number of inhabitants born outside the island formed only 10·8 per cent. of the total population, though it was more than 50 per cent. in some districts. Besides this, fairly large currents of internal migration are noticeable. As in Malaya, a map showing density of population in Sumatra indicates a relatively dense western half in contrast with a far more sparsely peopled eastern half.

But differences between the island and the Peninsula are nearly as great as the likenesses, nor do they depend merely on the accident of having been under the different colonial systems of the English and Dutch.

Sumatra has had a more brilliant past. While Sri Vijaya lasted (A.D. 650–1350 *circa*), it had a glorious period, whose splendour is attested by history and archaeology. This westernmost island of the East Indies has not been influenced by India alone. In it Islam has found its warmest partisans and supporters, whose faith sometimes reaches fanaticism; following closely on Muslims from the Hadhramaut and Sind, Europeans established agencies on its north and west coasts to trade in spices, and Christian missionaries achieved one of their most conspicuous successes on the Batak plateau. More than any other peoples Sumatrans are often of a restless disposition and of an inquiring mind open to novelties. Yet, under all the foreign borrowings, they keep their original characteristics, their peculiar social structure, and their very varied *adats*, or ancient customs and traditions. In the work of their craftsmen in making jewellery, weapons, and cloth, as in the construction and decoration of their houses, they reveal an artistic temperament which, far from owing everything to the foreigner, smacks strongly of the soil.

Another characteristic feature is that the centres of Sumatran civilisation are not situated on the coast itself, but lie inland and preferably on the western highlands. There, in spite of emigration and recent changes, are still found today the most densely populated areas as well as the most unmixed and firmly established people. It contains the cradle of the Minangkabau and Batak peoples, who form compact groups that are otherwise very different from each other and have no counterparts on the Peninsula. The cultural preponderance of the highlands over the lowlands is rare enough in tropical Asia for it to deserve special mention.

True, it might be objected that scholars usually locate the capital of Sri Vijaya near Palembang, that is, on the eastern plain. But it is doubtful whether this town was anything more than a port near the great seaways and the chief seat of Indian rule. There is no evidence that it was the centre of a densely populated district.[1] In any case, the Europeans found on these low-lying plains, just as they did on the coast of Malaya opposite, only little principalities narrowly restricted to the river mouths and lying amid vast expanses of swamp forest in which wandering communities lived mainly by collecting and hunting. Until the middle of the 19th century these marshy and unhealthy lowlands were avoided by European settlers. The prosperous trading settlements, long disputed by British and Dutch, were situated on the west coast in spite of the heavy surf and frequent attacks of malaria. Even now eastern Sumatra is on the whole far less densely peopled than the highlands. But the eastern lowlands were the scene of the greatest European achievements in the fifty years immediately before the war in 1941, and especially since 1910, when the area had been in process of complete change. The Oostkust plantations around Medan display perhaps the most successful attempt at agriculture in the tropics. Oil wells have been increasing in the lowlands, and the islands of Banka and Belitong contain enormous tin-mining works. Immigrants have streamed in from China and Java.

Thus, Sumatra seems to be both older and younger than Malaya. It is a land of old traditions, but has been from early times receptive of external influence; an island which contains strong native communities, but still has uncivilised features. After repulsing the Europeans for a long time and restricting them to a few trading centres on the coast, it has given them on almost virgin soil even ampler means than did Malaya to invest their capital, apply their technique, and exert their energy.

The island differs still more from Java, where the great density of population, after having brought gains to commercial enterprises, no longer allows of such solid achievements and imposes stricter limits and more tactful methods on exploitation by oversea peoples.

Over and above a great variety of land-forms and people there

[1] Cp. above, p. 66 n. 3.

remains the fundamental distinction between the highlands in the west and the lowlands in the east.

The Highlands.. The Sunda Shelf, on which the ridge-and-groove relief of the Malay Peninsula dies away and disappears, continues under the film of sea-water in the Straits and under the recent alluvium on the wide plains of Sumatra as far as beyond Medan and Palembang, where the first Tertiary hills rise.

Along the whole of the west coast runs a lofty backbone parallel with the shore, but varying in breadth and of widely different appearance. There are little ranges with gentle features, jagged ridges, plateaus of tuff whose wild and gloomy monotony is suddenly broken by the yawning gashes of canyons, volcanoes of unspoilt shape rising to more than 11,000 feet above the sea, and deep trenches that in some cases contain lakes whose bottoms go down to sea level.

This is the outcome of a very complex and still not well understood geological evolution. The Sunda Shelf was here bordered by a geosyncline which was a continuation of the one in western Burma. Sediment continually accumulated in it from at least the Permo-Carboniferous epoch. Geologists recognise a great variety of material in the island. There are mica-schists and gneiss, quartzites, greywackés, diabases, shales, and limestones, all usually arranged in narrow beds and showing signs of having been intensely folded about the middle of the Cretaceous epoch. It was at this time that must have occurred the intrusion of most of the granite masses, which pierce the sedimentary beds here and there and make the hills in Sibolga, for instance, so broken and picturesque.

After a period of erosion which is revealed by an almost constant discordance between the Secondary and Eocene beds, Tertiary sedimentaries were spread over the sites of mountain ranges that had been worn level and along which a geosynclinal trough deepened the surface again at the beginning of Neogene times. Then orogenic activity awoke once more, and the beds assumed a gradually increasing continental appearance. The end of the Tertiary epoch was marked by more folding accompanied by fracturing and violent volcanic phenomena.

This young relief was attacked by the forces of erosion, and the Tertiary folds often appear worn down in their turn, the removal of the anticlines leaving the oldest beds bare. The processes of construction and destruction have continued up to the present day. Rutten insists on the impossibility of understanding the relief of Sumatra without taking into account very recent movements in opposite directions. A further discordance is often recognised between the Neogene and Quaternary systems. The importance of the last uplifts is shown by the height of the Tertiary marine beds observed more than 3000 feet above the sea, whilst the pre-Tertiary beds go up to more than 10,000 feet in the Gayo district north of Lake Toba. But they are all dominated by the lofty volcanoes which must date from the middle of the Quaternary epoch. Earthquakes are very frequent along the longitudinal fractures in the Barisan Mountains, where they destroy houses and cause landslides. In 1926 subsidence measuring 33 feet was observed on the shores of Lake Singkarak, and a similar occurrence was noticed on the south-west side of Lake Toba in 1921.

The whole subject is still confused. Geologists are far from agreed on the structural plan or on the number and direction of the main axes of folding, these having often been cut across by extensive faulting. The granite usually forms very dissected domes, whilst the ancient volcanic rocks (diorites and diabases) stand up sharply like walls. Small areas of limestone, jagged and riddled with caves, rise boldly on the soft shales. The tuff plateaus are dissected by valleys with flat bottoms and very steep sides.

These broad mountain areas form a serious obstacle to communications between the lowlands on the east and those on the west, where the coastal plain, which in places is reduced to a narrow strip, is seldom wider than 12 miles. The mountains are, however, grooved by a longitudinal trough which can be followed on a map from one end of the island to the other. It is in fact very complex and is drained by many streams, some flowing into the Straits, others into the Indian Ocean. Its altitude varies greatly. Often it is interrupted by more or less bulky volcanoes, like the Batak hill-mass, which contains Lake Toba, whilst farther south Lake Sing-karak goes down to little more than 300 feet above sea level. This trench has naturally played its part in the history of the island. Along it the various communities have come into contact, foreign influence has been able to spread inland, and nowadays the main road from Padang passes along it between Lake Toba and Fort de Kock on its way to Medan.

The recent volcanoes near by all stand in this trench or on its edges and do not overlook the sea. There are about a hundred of them. A dozen huge cones are still smoking and form a novel sight for people coming from the mainland. But they have not played such an important rôle as their counterparts have done in Java either in the benefits they have conferred or the damage they have done.

The island is long and the Equator passes across it somewhere near the middle, but differences in latitude cause no great climatic changes. Relief and aspect, however, introduce slight regional modifications.[1] Slopes exposed to the south-west winds which prevail nearly all through the year generally get more than 120 inches of rain annually, distributed fairly evenly, though with two maxima. The peaks of the mountains are seldom visible from the coast, as they are nearly always veiled in greyish mist or capped with clouds. At an altitude of 9400 feet on Mt. Singgalang—almost on the Equator and close to Fort de Kock—there are 320 days of rain a year and a mean relative humidity of 93 per cent.; and this never

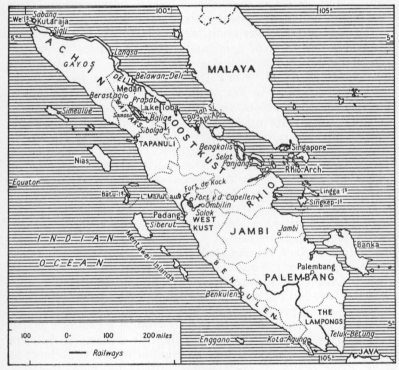

FIG. 16—SUMATRA

falls below 89 per cent. in the driest month. A fine drizzle descends on the forest nearly every night. The sky usually clears in the morning, but becomes overcast again in the afternoon. The warm, moist air and the almost continuous vapour-bath are wholly favour- able to dense forests with many species, among which flourish certain varieties of giant orchids. One of these, *Rafflesia Arnoldii*, has a fleshy, purplish-blue corolla sometimes as much as two feet in diameter.

[1] C. Braak (38), p. 75.

Dense forest does not, however, cover the whole area of the high-lands; far from it. After crossing the western slopes, the south-west winds often blow violently, but have been robbed of some of their moisture. Seribudolok (4600 feet) to the north of Lake Toba gets only 70 inches of rain a year; and over inland valleys the sky is far more often clear and sunny than on the coast. The permeable soil, especially volcanic ash and tuff, has often facilitated man's destruc-tion of the forest. Vast expanses above the 1600-foot contour are covered with open forests of *Pinus Merkusii*, *alang* savanas, dense fern moors, and other consequences of bush fires.

The natives themselves contribute a great deal to the regional diversity. The flood of immigrants which inundates the western side of the Malay Peninsula does not flow here. But many little districts which would be described separately in a more detailed work than this must be dealt with as coming under the heads of three human communities, viz. the Achinese, Bataks, and Minang-kabaus. None of these peoples definitely predominates in the south, which, moreover, is less densely populated and less well known.

Achin. Achin covers the northern end of Sumatra. The Tertiary hills straddle out here and even reach the east coast, off which the continental shelf becomes very narrow. The ancient folds splay out northwards, and the highlands are not pushed over to the west as in the rest of the island, but occupy the centre more or less. Pre-Tertiary sedimentary beds rise to 10,000 feet on Bandahara in the south of Gayo district. There are few recent volcanoes, though one on Pulo We and Gudberg (6000 feet) on the main island are the first parts of the East Indies seen by ships entering the Straits. Inland, Lake Laut Tawar, which is in process of drying up, lies behind a lava-flow damming a valley cut in Primary limestone beds.

This outlying portion of the archipelago was naturally the first district in the East Indies to be seen by Western travellers. Marco Polo and Ibn Batuta both landed there. At the end of the 17th century Dampier[1] wrote a long description of the brisk business done in the capital of the kingdom. There European traders—English, Dutch, Danish, and Portuguese—came into contact with Gujerati Indians, whose shops were doing a most thriving business, and with Chinese. Many of the latter stayed only between June and September, but they carried on a most considerable trade. The backland is rich in gold.

However, though the natives benefited at an early date from their trade with the West, they manifested keen hostility to domination by Europeans. The Achinese princes used the rivalry of the Powers to keep their effective independence and protect their

[1] Dampier (3) III, pp. 145 ff.

traditional piracy. In 1869, in order to escape from the Dutch, who were becoming more pressing, they offered to recognise the overlordship of the Sultan of Turkey. The opening of the Suez Canal gave Achin greatly increased importance, and, by the Treaty of 1871, England gave up all objection to Dutch occupation.[1] In 1873 the native rulers were negotiating with the American and Italian consuls at Singapore, and diplomatic conversations were begun with France. The Dutch experienced a series of rebuffs owing to their ignorance of the country and to their hesitation. Not until 1896 did they lay aside half-measures and undertake the methodical occupation of the country under the guidance of the great Islamic scholar Snouck Hurgronje and with van Heutsz in command of the forces. Resistance, however, was not crushed by the Dutch troops until the beginning of the present century and then only after several bloody campaigns. The resistance of the Achinese was based on religious fanaticism, and before 1940 the flame was still sufficient to cause an occasional fanatic to attack a police post in an attempt to merit admission to the paradise of Allah. The Achinese, who have been studied by Snouck Hurgronje, are like the Arabs in their energy and love of freedom. But though they show signs of much racial admixture, they seem to have only a slight infusion of Semitic blood.

The Achinese is a gambler, a capricious worker, and sometimes an opium addict, but clever and adaptable and one of the most capable of the Malay peoples of competing with the Chinese. He lives mainly on the lowland strip which borders the coast and penetrates fairly deeply inland, especially in the valley of the River Achin. Thanks to the large area of *sawah*, the density of population exceeds 260 to the square mile in the subdivisions of Kutaraja, the capital, and of Sigli on the north-east coast. Next to rice the chief native crops are coconut and pepper, for which Achin was famous of old, but which are rather falling off. Then come cloves and nutmeg, to which rubber has lately been added. The large European rubber and oil palm plantations are situated for the most part on the east coast in the district of Langsa[2] and are included in the extensive Oostkust group centring round Medan, whence a railway, constructed for strategic reasons, runs to Kutaraja.

Achin is ahead of all the other provinces in Sumatra and of most of the former Outer Provinces in the number of horned cattle and goats. The hills and mountains seem to afford rather extensive opportunities of rearing livestock. If the Achinese scarcely ever leave the lowlands, this does not mean that forest covers the whole of the inland areas. Passengers on liners rounding Pulo We in clear

[1] Emerson (251), p. 378.
[2] The west coast ports of Melaboh and Susoh also export palm oil.

weather may see light-coloured slopes indicating large clearings on the north coast. These are the *blangs*, or savanas. *Alang* is seldom predominant on them, but other grasses (*Pogonatherum paniceum*, *Saccharum spontaneum*, and *Themeda gigantea*) grow along with ferns (*Eupteris aquilina*) and orchids; but in places the soil is left bare. The *blangs* are often clothed in pine trees (*Pinus Merkusii*) that grow in thickets scattered about on the ridges and on steep and crumbling slopes. They sometimes cover moderately large areas and are mixed with broad-leaved species. This tropical conifer, *Pinus Merkusii*, seems more plentiful here than anywhere else in the East Indies. Bush fires have probably greatly helped it to spread.[1] Though the Achinese do not engage in *ladang*, this method of cultivation is still common among the hill-folk, especially the Gayos, who in their type of dwelling and mode of life are transitional to the Bataks.[2]

The Batak Districts. Between lat. 2° and 4° N. the highlands spread out more widely than anywhere else in Sumatra. From the little port of Sibolga on the west coast the road starts to climb a slope covered with extensive forest that has already suffered from the attacks of *ladang* cultivators. Cuttings show big, rounded boulders buried in reddish sand. Once the ridge has been scaled, the high-road winds through a maze of valleys among countless hillocks whose fairly regular slopes have been carved out of partly metamorphosed Primary and Triassic rocks—limestone, sandstone, and shale. Towards the north the horizon is closed by the heavy mass of the bare and dismal Batak plateaus which are topped here and there with extinct volcanoes. Beyond these the relief drops suddenly down into the Toba trench.

Vulcanism has been particularly active here.[3] At the end of the Tertiary period and the beginning of the Quaternary great emissions of andesite occurred along a line cutting the ancient folds obliquely, and a couple of thousand feet of lava and scoriæ were piled on the pre-Tertiary rocks. At the same time the whole area was uplifted, the highest part of the bulge and the main outlets of magma being apparently on the site of the existing lake. During the period of upheaval—the middle Quaternary for certain—the discharge of dacitic and liparitic lavas was followed by a gaseous phase during which an enormous mass of acid tuff and pumice stone was emitted. Van Bemmelen reckons their volume at 2000 cubic kilometres. They were carried partly by the wind, but even more by running water to great distances and were thus spread over an area of 12,000 to 18,000 square miles. Around the lake their depth may be as much as

[1] Van Steenis: (56), p. 200.   [2] Volz (130), II.
[3] R. W. van Bemmelen (115); Volz (130), pp. 253 ff.; Umbgrove (36a), p. 29.

2000 feet. They occur also on the other side of the Straits on the coast of Malacca, where they are still 15 or 20 feet deep and cover pebble beds in which stone axes have been found. The Toba depression came into being during these gigantic eruptions, either through an explosion or, more probably, owing to the collapse of the roof of the magma chamber.

The water in the lake thus formed found an outlet eastwards through the valley of the Asahan. A few miles downstream from Porsea the river cuts a trench through an alluvial terrace mainly composed of tuff. Its altitude of 3700 feet above the sea must be that of the original level of the lake surface, which has now been lowered to 3100 feet. Meanwhile, another bulge had formed at the bottom of the lake and collapsed in its turn, leaving the island of Samosir to mark the western part of its arch. The greatest known depth (1700 feet) lies in the narrows between Samosir and Prapat. Finally, the latest phase (in the lower Quaternary and Holocene) may even now be traced by emissions of andesite like those forming the still active volcanoes of Sinabung and Sibayak to the north of the Lake (see Fig. 19).

The Toba subsidence has an area of about 1150 square miles. The Lake still covers more than 435 square miles, the difference consisting of the large island of Samosir and the alluvial plains, which are most extensive in the south. The immaturity of the depression is proved by the smallness of the area draining directly into the Lake, for the river systems radiate outwards towards the Straits and the ocean. All round the basin steep and at times precipitous slopes down which fall cascades rise to more than 5600 feet above the sea; shelves of ancient rocks appear among the lava and tuff; and recent plantations of pine trees here and there mark an effort to retain the crumbling soil.

Lake Toba is the heart of the Batak country and long remained unknown to Europeans. It was only in 1863 that Dr. A. Neubronner van der Tuuk succeeded in reaching its shores; but he soon had to beat a retreat owing to the threatening attitude of the natives. Christian missionaries then began their successful work of preaching the gospel, but the last districts, Samosir and the peninsula of Habinsaran to the south-east of the Lake, were not finally brought under Dutch rule until 1908.

There are about 1,200,000 Bataks in Sumatra, two-thirds of whom are concentrated in the Residency of Tapanuli around the Lake. They are divided into several tribes, the most compact and unmixed being the Tobas, who live to the west and south-west of the Lake and on Samosir Island, and the Karos, who dwell to the north of the Lake. Each tribe is composed of a large number of genealogical units called *marga*, which still exist as exogamous patrilineal clans. Every Batak traces his descent very far back, at times as much as four hundred years.   But the territorial unit is the *huta*, or village, which does not include only persons related by blood.   The disposition of the houses and the houses themselves differ from tribe to tribe.   The villages which impress most are perhaps those of the Tobas, which dot the rich Balige plain to the south of the Lake or run in a line along the shores of Samosir Island.   Each village is defended by a thick bamboo hedge planted on a bank of earth, in some cases with a ditch running round outside it.   The entrances are narrow openings invisible from the road and barricaded at night. This is a relic of the time not long past when tribal wars and cannibalism were in full swing and women tilled the fields while their brothers and husbands stood armed guard over them.[1]   On either

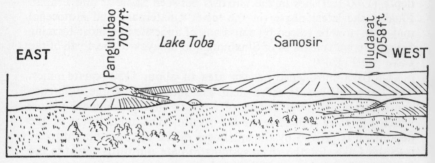

FIG. 17.—LAKE TOBA FROM THE NORTH (from a photograph by the author)

side of a long pathway in the village stands a row of strongly built houses with saddle-backed roofs.   The fronts lean steeply outwards and are decorated with three lines of painted carvings in which traditional subjects are ingenuously mingled with up-to-date ones such as types of Europeans, motor-cars, etc.   One must bend low to pass through the kind of curtained door leading to the dark, smoke-begrimed interior of the house from which the presence of European objects does not wholly banish the atmosphere of magic and superstition.

The Bataks are making rapid progress, however.[2]   The highroad from Padang to Medan passes right through their country.   Prapat on the shores of the Lake and Berastagi on the plateau farther north have become hill-stations popular with Europeans in Indonesia and even in Malaya.   Motor-boats are seen on Lake Toba together with long native canoes that bring to market the produce of the soil and of the little industries.

[1] Tichelman (127).   [2] Promes (126a).

The Bataks make *sawahs* wherever possible. The Belige plain with its carpet of flooded ricefields and its stippling of big villages surrounded by geometrically arranged plantations is surprisingly reminiscent of the delta of the Tongking. Away from the alluvial flats by the Lake *sawahs* can occupy only a small area. The Batak still terraces the pockets formed by erosion on the hillsides and lays out his ricefields like beautiful green ribbons along the bottoms of the valleys which cut deeply into the tuff. Their narrow gorges have, however, been widened by the ingenuity of the peasants, who turn the meanders of the streams against one or other of the banks and thus undercut them. But as the tuff plateaus themselves are too permeable and as the water table has been lowered by the deepening of the valleys, this higher ground can only be cultivated on the *ladang* system. When the ground has been cleared by burning, men and women stand close together in little groups and keep time as they raise and bring down the hoes which have generally replaced the digging-stick. In other places natives can still be seen dragging a primitive plough. On these uplands the dwellings are more frail, rougher, and less ornamented and the villages smaller than in the valleys.[1]

Up to and somewhat above the contour for 5000 feet the forest has everywhere disappeared, and periodic burning prevents its growing again. It is replaced by scrub consisting of bushy shrubs, then by stretches of grass, and, lastly, by the kind of extensive moorland covered with Eupteris fern mixed with cotoneaster, which in the last phase of degeneration sometimes forms very dense exclusive thickets.[2] Dense forest scarcely exists now except on the upper slopes of the volcanoes or in the bottoms of canyons which cannot be reached by cultivators. The destruction of the forest together with the colour of the volcanic rocks largely helps to give that impression of gloom which the Batak plateaus make on the traveller. Their undulating upland surfaces, russet or olive-green in colour, look ghastly under the overcast sky, whilst here and there are seen the tin-like reflection of a ricefield, a bamboo hedge with roof-corners projecting above, and a picketed goat looking like a white speck.

Lutheran missionaries have played a great part in the progress made by the Bataks. At least a quarter, indeed more than 300,000, have been converted and many given Biblical names like Jacob, Rachel, etc. The little, white-spired churches in which the people gather on Sundays to sing hymns in the Batak language and to listen to a European or native preacher are not among the least curiosities in the district. Schools and infirmaries have increased in number,

[1] Helbig (119), p. 113; (122) p. 144.   [2] Van Steenis (56) p. 187.

and a model leper station has been established south of the Lake. The population is rapidly increasing and is now cramped for room.[1] There is a density of between 700 and 800 persons to the square mile on the Balige plain and 320 even on Samosir Island, where the *sawah* area is far less extensive. Hence, there is a fairly large stream of emigrants. These move for good into the mountains around which little cultivation can be carried on except on the *ladang* system, to the great detriment of the forest; or else they temporarily move even farther off towards the European plantations, for the Bataks have a high reputation throughout Sumatra for the preliminary work of clearing and burning. But when educated, they also make good secretaries, and they are employed as clerks, telephone operators, and overseers in Achin and Oostkust, as well as Jakarta, and as 'house boys' in European residences in Singapore. Some are graduates of Dutch universities, and some doctors. The son of a chief who made his fortune in the old days of trading in opium and slaves was sent to study law at Leiden. A very considerable factor in social change has been the introduction of export crops, and these are gradually being extended. There is little rubber, of course, owing to the height above the sea, but coffee, incense-trees (*benzu*), and, above all, vegetables (cabbages, onions, beans, potatoes, etc.) are grown, and the produce sent for sale to the lowland towns and even Malaya.

The Minangkabau District. To the south of the great volcanic plateaus of the Batak district the Tertiary beds widen out on both sides of the ancient rocks and cover them almost completely. The country is relatively low; the *bohorok* wind has a drying effect on it; and *alang* savanas dotted with stunted and twisted trees and moors covered with *Backea frutescens* clothe the gulley-incised ridges. Typical instances occur in Padang Lawas quite near to the Equator. Here survive traces of 12th and 13th century Hindu temples, which were built of brick without mortar and are crumbling beneath the wild vegetation. South of Padangsidimpuan the longitudinal trench is well marked and is occupied by the Rivers Angkola and Gadis, whose waters flow to the west coast, and by the Sumpur (or Rokan), which runs down towards the Straits. Here the Bataks have been affected by influences from the south and have become Mandailings, a Muslim people who are unwilling to accept the gospel of Christianity. More than a century ago the revolt of the *Padri* began here. It was a rising led by fanatical Wahabites and was not suppressed by the Dutch until 1879. Thus, these Bataks are transitional to the great Muslim community of the Minangkabaus.

[1] Lehmann (126) p. 7.

The Minangkabaus are the most numerous people in Sumatra, forming 25·6 per cent. of the total population. They are the most advanced, too, and have assimilated foreign influence better than most other Indonesians, whilst they keep their own well-marked character. They are already thronging the coast strip of the Westkust, especially to the north of Padang, where a wonderful tropical region of *sawahs* and coconut trees stretches over the alluvium which has been torn from the volcanic highlands by steady, well-fed streams. These highlands are nearer the sea than are the Batak plateaus, and the rugged, picturesque coastal slopes south of Padang have been carved out of lava and tuff. The railway and motor-car have soon climbed the wooded escarpment to a height of 3000 feet above the sea, where the drier countryside is reached around Fort de Kock. This town is the centre of the Padang Highlands and the real cradle of the Minangkabau people.

The volcanic relief, though more varied and less austere than in the Batak district, is of real majesty here. Tall, typical cones like Singgalang (9400 feet) and Merapi (9480 feet) merge their long concave slopes into the tuff plateaus which spread out around Fort de Kock at a height of about 3000 feet above the sea. The plateaus are cut by *ngarai*, or broad flat-bottomed valleys, the bareness of whose steep sides is incessantly maintained by slides of soft rock falling in vertical sheets. The surface shows great yellowish-white scars. In places the high ground has collapsed to form lacustrine trenches, whose origin is either volcanic or tectonic. From Punchak Bukit to the west of Fort de Kock the traveller suddenly beholds the calm face of Lake Maninjau (1500 feet) and, through the valley cut by its outlet, the Antokan, the dim, misty expanses of the Indian Ocean. The plateau on which Fort de Kock stands is also drained by the River Masang, which flows down to the west coast. But only a dozen miles south of the town the water runs off towards Lake Singkarak and then through the Ombilin and the Inderagiri into the South China Sea. The surface of the Singkarak is only 1200 feet and its bottom 320 feet above sea level. It is only after crossing this impressive and contrasting relief that the Palæozoic and Secondary ranges are seen again with their thin, jagged, knife-edged, limestone ridges rising from softer beds. Among these remain the folded Tertiary sedimentaries of the Ombilin basin which contain the seams of coal worked near Sawahlunto. This is the most important coalfield in the East Indies, but its working is greatly handicapped by the cost of transport to the sea; and the annual production scarcely reached 500,000 tons in 1938 and was much less in 1955.

Here as almost everywhere in the East Indies the *sawahs* determine the distribution of population. They lie at the bottom of canyons cut in the tuff and on alluvial flats near the lakes, like for instance the Solok plain to the south of Lake Singkarak, spread out on the shoulders which break the sloping sides of the big valleys and the escarpments of the trenches, and climb as high as 5000 feet on the slopes of the volcanoes. At this altitude the relief and rainfall facilitate irrigation. This is practised skilfully enough by means of leats or bucket-chains by the Minangkabaus, who form nearly the whole of the population throughout these highlands. Along with sawah-grown rice, the chief crop is coconut, which is cultivated in the most fertile soil and flourishes at a height of nearly 3000 feet on the plateaus near Fort van der Capellen. Next among food crops come maize, cassava, and ground-nuts. Sugarcane and tobacco also flourish in volcanic soil. It was not long before the peasant began to plant coffee and more recently in the less elevated districts, the *hevea*.

This variety of crops combines with the natural picturesqueness to make the landscape pleasant. It is quite different from the naked and in fact rather distressing wildness of the Batak scenery. The *negari*, or villages, sprawl comfortably among gardens and useful trees. The mosques with their domes, onion towers, and glazed windows lack beauty, but are more imposing than anywhere else in the East Indies and indicate the strength of Islam. Fezzes are often worn. The power of the matriarchal tradition and the artistic sense of the Minangkabaus are reflected in the type of dwelling. This is built on piles rising to the roof and dividing the house into compartments which in days gone by increased with the number of married daughters the head of the family could boast of. From the tops of the overlapping, saddle-backed roofs gracefully rise the sharp horns of the *tanduk*, which are prolonged upwards by galvanised iron sheets. The exterior surfaces of the house are adorned with carving that is often delicately worked. Even the highly raised storehouses placed away from the dwellings are not without this decoration.[1] The richest ornamentation often covers the communal houses or *balë*, where village meetings are held, and the buildings which contain the big drums made of hollow tree-trunks and used for calling the villagers together.

There are few towns, although certain districts have more than 520 persons to the square mile. For instance, Old Agam situated around Fort de Kock had 612, or 570 without the town. The fact is that the soil here has been greatly enriched by the eruptions of Mt. Merapi, which were still very violent a hundred years ago and since then have often thrown out considerable quantities of basic ash. This is a common occurrence in Java, but rare in Sumatra.[2] Fort de

[1] Nguyen van Huyen: (99), p. 64.   [2] Mohr (98) p. 488.

Kock, the administrative capital and main commercial centre of the upper Minangkabau district, grew up around the fort built by Dutch troops in 1825 and at the beginning of the *Padri* war had a population of only 15,000, of whom 550 were Europeans. In the native quarter with its arcaded houses and pediments reminiscent of Holland, the sheet-iron shelters are not enough for the crowd which flows in periodically. On market days, or *pasar*, streams of women with shawls over their hair arrive early carrying bulky loads on their heads. Lively little horses with their harness decorated with red pompons and bright copper discs trot before light carriages, whilst buffaloes with hoofs protected with straw shoes slowly drag carts whose concave tilts are modelled after the fashion of the house-roofs.

There are few Chinese here. Among the Minangkabaus both men and women are expert traders. On the other hand, the men dislike working for wages on large plantations, and they are seldom found on European estates (which, moreover, are fairly rare here) and even less often in the galleries of the mines at Ombilin. They prefer to emigrate and open shops or cultivate farms of their own. Minangkabaus are numerous throughout western Indonesia and in Malaya and may be found even in Ceylon and southern India. These distant adventurers keep in touch with their native villages. The long established practice of emigration is no doubt responsible for the open minds which the Minangkabaus show towards new ideas and for their liking for education, all of which features are harmoniously blended with a very marked individuality.

Padang, the outlet for the Minangkabau district and the chief town on the whole of the west coast, is situated on the River Arau under shelter of the andesitic hill of Apenberg. It had a population of 52,000, of whom 2600 were Europeans. The quiet of this rather sleepy city of long avenues and residences surrounded by magnificent gardens surprises the traveller acquainted with the great Javanese towns. The port is at Emmahaven 6 miles to the south of the town on the inner end of a bay fairly well protected from the south-west winds. A railway, part of which is run on a rack, connects it with Fort de Kock and Sawahlunto, the chief town on the coal-field.

The Southern Highlands. The Minangkabaus are still the dominant people southwards as far as the last big areas of tuff which lie around Lake Kerinchi. Beyond this the highlands become far narrower and the great eastern plain much wider. The complex system of basement rocks, which is still imperfectly understood, supports several dozen volcanoes, the highest of which, Dempo (10,400 feet) to the south-east of Benkulen, is still active. A line of streams, nearly all of which are parts of rivers flowing to the Java

Sea, follow each other in the longitudinal trench, whose drowned end forms Semangka Bay at the southern extremity of the island.

The population is not so dense here, being for instance 31 to the square mile in the Benkulen district; and it is divided into several tribal groups none of which clearly outnumbers the others, as do the Minangkabaus, Bataks, and Achinese in the north. Indian influence in the Sri Vijaya period came from the east coast up the River Musi and the Klingi and others of its feeders to reach these highlands. Traces have also been found here of an older megalithic civilisation. River navigation and the railways are now spreading the influence of Palembang far into the west. The west coast ports do only a small amount of trade, since they afford little shelter from the violent surf. Coffee-growing began to spread in 1847 by a system of forced cultivation introduced from Java, and in 1939 the berry still held first place among the exports. Benkulen is the only place which is at all busy. It was formerly a centre for the English settlements in Malay lands, a fact still marked by the fort with its little bronze cannon pointing out to sea and the graves of many Englishmen who 'died in the Lord', which lie in the cemetery under the twisted branches of frangipani trees. The European plantations, which increased after the success of the Oostkust, and the most productive gold mines in the Indies[1] led to the immigration of Javanese, who already formed more than a quarter of the population in the districts of Lebong and Rejang behind Benkulen. This is a foretaste of demographic movements like those which have been characteristic of eastern Sumatra in recent years.

Separated from Sumatra by a channel averaging more than 60 miles in width, the western islands are still very isolated and have scarcely been affected by colonisation. Nias,[2] the best known owing to its pre-Malay peoples and its megaliths, has a relatively dense population of 85 to the square mile in the south and 145 in the north, which it supports mainly on rice and cassava.

The Eastern Lowlands. At least half of Sumatra lies below the 700-foot contour. The western mountains slope down to a belt of Tertiary hills which die away eastwards to their junction—often clearly marked—with the Quaternary and recent alluvium of the lowlands. On the Equator and in the latitude of Palembang these lowlands are about 125 miles wide. Here and there the surface is pierced by the short folds and flattened domes of Neogene sedimentaries.[3]

The river basins are separated from each other by undulations which are scarcely perceptible except by the appearance of the

1 Lehmann (126) p. 8; Ter Braake (237) p. 53.   2 Helbig (119).
3 Lehmann (136) p. 112.

13. Singapore, showing the Victoria Memorial Hall in the foreground, the new Supreme Court on the right, and Fort Canning in the background

14. Penang, a view of the town and island

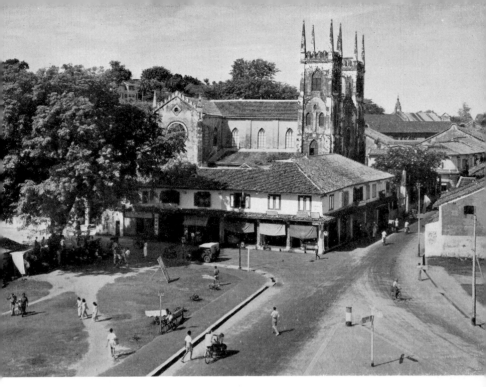

15. A square in the old town of Malacca

16. The Secretariat at Kuala Lumpur, showing a fine mixture of Western and Eastern architecture

vegetation. Big rivers like the Hari and Musi flowing from the Barisan Range are less regular in volume than might be expected in these latitudes. Their water has an oily look and is heavy with vegetable waste and at times with trees torn from the banks by violent spates. They flow in ill-defined beds through a forest which is swampy in many places and grows here and there in a peaty soil. The hills formed of older alluvium and Tertiary beds have a different, yet still very dense, plant cover in which a few species of Dipterocarps predominate in number and height. The lowlands end in large deltas which merge imperceptibly into the shallow waters of the Straits and the South China Sea. The process of silting-up has certainly been going on since early times, but has been checked by a positive movement of the sea and also by the strong tidal currents that sweep the estuaries. The penetration of salt water brings the mangroves with it, and these cover a greater area here than on the west coast. The mangrove fringe is backed by a belt of *nipa* palms, which are also halophytes.

Though still heavy, the rainfall is less regularly distributed than on the narrow west coast strip. At Palembang, where the mean is 104 inches, a well-marked dry season is noticeable in July and August. North of the Equator the *bohorok*, a sort of foehn which blows down from the Karo Mountains, sometimes damages native crops and is particularly feared by tobacco growers in the Medan district.

Still, the dampness of the soil on this almost level ground and the density of a half-drowned forest that is difficult to clear away have been great obstacles to settlement and exploitation. The recent developments are therefore all the more striking. They have not affected the lowlands uniformly, for the two ends of the island are favoured owing to the contraction of the plain and also to the fertility of the volcanic soil. But regional differences from north to south are mainly due to the methods of exploitation and the diversity of natural wealth.

The Lampong Districts. Sunda Strait is strewn with islands and narrows to less than 16 miles between Java and the southernmost point of Sumatra. An easy crossing has made communication between the islands immemorial. The Bantam and Lampong districts, which lie on either side of this once much used Strait, were long under a common rule, even after the decline of Sri Vijaya.

In the Lampong districts the soil has been enriched not only by volcanic alluvium brought down by the streams from the Barisan Range, but also by æolian contributions from Krakatoa. Since the great eruption in 1883 falls of ash have several times added fertility. Like Achin, the districts were formerly reckoned among the chief producers of pepper in the East Indies. But lately the number of coffee plantations has increased, and, though still far behind the Oostkust, the districts take second place in degree of European exploitation.

Interesting experiments in settling small-holders on the land have been tried here with varying results. The Indo-European Association founded a settlement at Giesting between 1500 and 2000 feet above the sea near Kota Agung by means of voluntary subscriptions mainly for Eurasians from Java. But just when the coffee bushes were beginning to bear, the peasants were struck by the slump and got into debt to Chinese moneylenders. In 1938 the settlement contained only 200 persons.

The transfer of natives from overpopulated districts in central and eastern Java has had greater success. The first experiment took place in 1905. The immigrants were established in the southern part of Teluk Betung and Kota Agung. The Government spent large sums to help them, and by 1927 their number had already risen to nearly 25,000. In 1931 the settlers began appealing for more labour to be sent to them, and a new and less expensive scheme was started, based on mutual assistance. New areas were prepared in the island near Sukadana and Menggala. These official attempts at settlement have had their most substantial results in the Lampong districts. In 1937 out of a total of 80,000 Javanese settled in the former Outer Provinces and cultivating 64,000 acres, nearly 63,000 were cultivating 52,000 acres in these districts. The rest were in Benkulen or the Oostkust. Recent immigrants, Javanese and Sundanese, already amounted to more than a third of the population of the Lampong districts.[1] which with only 32 persons to the square mile were still below the mean density in Sumatra.

The local capital and chief port is Teluk Betung (pop. 25,000), whose trade was gradually improving before the war. It is connected by shipping services with the port of Merak in Java and by rail with Palembang.

The Great Plains from Palembang to the River Rokan. In the very south of Palembang Residency the plains attain something like their greatest width. The rivers have long remained the only means of communication through the great forest, and most of the villages are situated on their levées. However, upstream from Palembang town the population is denser and more evenly distributed. The presence of a large area of secondary forest even degraded in many places to scrub points to clearings having been repeatedly made in the long past.

[1] In 1930 Javanese properly so-called formed 25 per cent. of the population of the Lampong districts and the Sundanese 11·2 per cent.

Palembang[1] is the largest town in Sumatra and all the former Outer Provinces. In 1930 it had a population of 108,000, of whom nearly 2000 were Europeans and 16,000 Chinese. It is situated 50 miles up from the mouth of the River Musi, which is here about a quarter of a mile wide. The river is still tidal at this point and enables ocean-going ships of moderate size to reach the town easily. Downstream even the levées do not afford dry ground for human habitation on the swampy plain; but upstream the Musi and its feeders fan out into a number of navigable ways reaching right up to the foot of the mountains. Palembang (see Fig. 18) stretches out along both banks of the river, but especially on the left on each side of the *kraton*, or residence of the princes. The Chinese, who have been trading here at least since the 10th century, live farther down-stream in a very busy quarter with narrow, winding streets. For two or three miles along the river there is a succession of pile-dwellings and floating shops built of bamboo rafts. This gives a picturesque appearance which was described as early as A.D. 950 by an Arab sailor, Bozorg bin Shabriar, and which is to be seen also in Bangkok. Canals enable boats to move about the *kampong*, which widens out behind the business quarter. A ferry runs from the town centre to Kertapati, the terminus of the railway to Teluk Betung and Lahat.

Only below the town is European influence strongly marked in the buildings erected at Plaju around the refineries of the Royal Batavian Petroleum Company. These deal with the oil extracted from the Tertiary anticlines in the backland. Petroleum has contributed greatly to Palembang's recent development. In 1937 38 per cent. of the production of crude oil in Indonesia came from the Residency. In 1937 coal deposits worked at Bukitasem yielded 433,000 tons, which is nearly as much as was raised in the Ombilin field.

Nevertheless, agriculture is still the main occupation. European plantations are far outdone by native production, particularly rubber. Upstream from Palembang town rubber-trees are increasing in number in the gardens and *ladangs*. But in certain districts in the Jambi Residency it often becomes the main business, one-fifth of the population taking part in it exclusively and the greater part of the *kampong* having a collective plantation as well. This is probably the effect of the proximity of Singapore, from which came the prime movers and the incentive to profit. The first *hevea* trees were planted by natives at Jambi in 1904. In 1928 the Stevenson plan had to be given up owing to the rapid and unexpected increase in native production. Most of the latex, which at first was sent to the big ports on the Peninsula, is smoked locally now by large Chinese firms. Native rubber cultivation could only be

[1] Lehmann (96) pp. 136–9.

extended with the help of the temporary labour of fugitive coolies from the plantations or unemployed from Malaya or Java, who came in during a boom and worked on a métayer system. Fabulous profits have been made at times. These were at once used partly for buying goods and partly for planting more rubber.[1]

Rubber cultivation has spread very little north of the Jambi Residency between the Rivers Kampar and Rokan, for here stretches the most marshy and inhospitable portion of the great forest. The transition from land to sea is more indefinite than anywhere else. Between the wide estuaries river silt spreads out in huge muddy islands, and mangrove swamps are certainly nowhere else so extensive.[2] But the area disputed by mud and water is, surprisingly

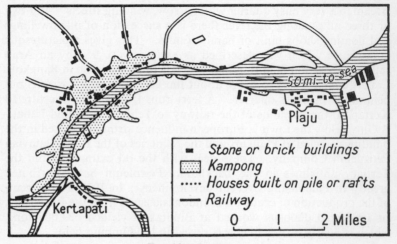

FIG. 18.—PALEMBANG

enough, the wealthiest and most densely populated today, thanks to Chinese firms. Their mobile sawmills, or *panglong*, exploit the mangrove belt under official control, especially between the Kampar and Siak, and make it a plentiful source of timber and charcoal, both of which are shipped to Singapore. The Chinese also supply most of the fishermen on the rivers. These streams are well stocked with fish owing to the abundance of organic matter in them. Bagan si Api Api is the little chief town of one of the busiest and most productive fishing centres in the world. Bamboo fences and lanes ingeniously arranged to lead fish into traps are to be seen sticking out of the dirty water; but methods of fishing vary a great deal, as

1 See Le Fèvre's picturesque account in *L'épopée du caoutchouc* (222) p. 114.
2 Van Steenis (56) p. 2.

they do on the Great Lake in Cambodia. Every year some 40,000 or 50,000 tons of dried or salted fish used to be shipped to Malaya and Java.[1]

Besides this, the natives engage in rubber cultivation, especially in Bengkalis,[2] whilst the other islands are large producers of sago. Selat Panjang on the island of Tebing Tinggi is after Sarawak the second largest exporter in the whole of the East Indies.

This variety of natural wealth explains the astonishing growth of the population. Between 1920 and 1934 it increased by 56 per cent. in the sub-district of Bagan si Api Api and by 75·7 per cent. in Bengkalis. Between the sea and the western mountains the average density does not reach 25 to the square mile, but goes well above that figure on certain parts of the coast.

The Oostkust. Developments on the Oostkust have been the most striking and best known and have been of a kind and on a scale quite different from those of the districts mentioned above. North of the River Bila and as far as beyond the Achin boundary and the River Tamiang the great forest gives way to a group of plantations which was one of the most important in the world owing to its size, the vigour and speed of its development, and the value of its production in international trade (see Fig. 19).[3]

The geological map is of great help in explaining the remarkable growth of the area. Volcanic matter ejected from the Toba hill-mass is carried by the very violence of the eruptions, by the wind, by mud-flows in *lahars*,[4] and finally by the action of the run-off and of erosion, to fertilise the soil on the plains over areas far larger than those in the Lampong districts at the other end of the island.

These advantages began to be exploited after the middle of last century. The cutting of the Suez Canal was destined to make the Straits of Malacca take the place of Sunda Strait as the best route from Europe to the Far East. The ports of Penang and Singapore on the opposite coast were expanding owing to the incoming stream of Chinese immigrants. On May 5, 1863, Jacobus Nienhuys, the son of a tobacco broker, embarked at Amsterdam for the Indies. He set up as a planter on the outskirts of Medan, the little capital of the sultanate of Deli, where the fine, rich soil resulting from the decomposition of dacite and andesite proved to be excellent for tobacco cultivation. The climate itself was very favourable. The mean monthly temperature ranged throughout the year between 75° F.

---

[1] Delsman (93). Unfortunately, fishing is being made more and more difficult by the silt brought down by the River Rokan.
[2] Tideman (128).
[3] Tideman (129); Dootjes (117); Robequain (200) pp. 50–57.
[4] See p. 24.

and 79° F.; the rainfall exceeds 80 inches a year and is nearly 4 inches in the driest month. Though the *bohorok* does not continue for very long, the decrease in humidity in June and July helps to dry the leaves, whilst afterwards fermentation is promoted by the return of the rains, whose maximum fall occurs in October. After initial set-backs came success. Nienhuys was copied by others, and soon the plantations came into the control of large Dutch firms. Strong commercial organisation and constant improvements in methods enabled the plantations to surmount every crisis and to keep for Deli tobacco a reputation which in fact rivals that of Havana for high class cigars. This, however, was at the cost of drastic reduction in the area cultivated; which after unwise extension, has been restricted once more around Medan to the most favourable soil. In 1928 tobacco covered 50,000 acres, but in 1937 the area had shrunk to barely 30,000 acres. However, the total area of the concessions, which had originally been easily acquired from the native princes, exceeded 540,000 acres. Indeed, not only was the best land reserved for tobacco, but the crop was not repeated on the same ground until after allowing it to revert to forest for seven years, though this treatment was often replaced by growing a leguminous crop (*Mimosa invisa*) on the land. Parcels of one *bouw* (about 1¾ acre) were grouped in bigger lots of from 18 to 25 acres and entrusted to coolie leaders (formerly all Chinese, but now often Javanese) who engaged gangs for the very difficult work of cultivation. As they mature, the leaves are picked, one or two from each plant, beginning at the bottom. They are then delivered to the Company at the big teak sheds, in which they are placed to ferment. Every three or four years these, together with the coolie quarters, are moved so as to follow the rotational use of the fields.

Though tobacco was the pioneer crop in the Oostkust, the area under it and the total value produced were in 1940 far less than for other crops. These consist of plants which occupy the soil for several years, indeed for decades, and have been introduced far more recently. The first was the *hevea* which, though already widespread in Java, did not reach the Oostkust till 1907; and the last of these exotic new-comers was sisal, which was not cultivated until 1917. Coffee, which was the last resort of many planters at the time of the great tobacco slump in 1890, has fallen mainly into the hands of the Indonesians.

Contrary to the development mentioned in Palembang and Jambi, European rubber plantations were responsible for far more of the production than were the native cultivators. In 1937 the estates produced 113,000 tons of raw rubber as against 28,000 tons produced by natives. Around the central area still reserved for tobacco it has often ousted the latter and has rapidly spread northwards as far as the Achin boundary and southwards to beyond the River Asahan on the liparitic tuff.   In 1937 it covered 638,000 acres and had the largest value of all the exports from the country.[1]

Palm oil production was greater in weight.   The same plantation often intermingles the *hevea* and the *elæis*, for the latter is considered by the firms to be an excellent offset during rubber slumps.   Owing to

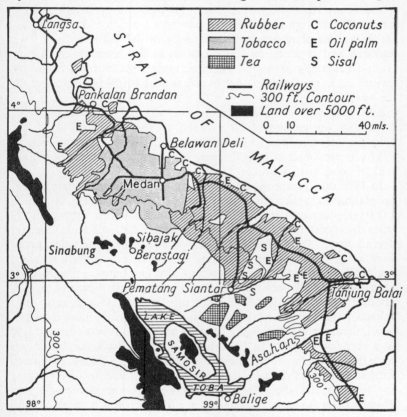

FIG. 19.—SUMATRA: OOSTKUST PLANTATIONS

selection and constant improvements in cultivation the two trees have given increasingly higher yields.   In 1937 palm oil from Indonesia— mainly from the East Coast Province—already formed 20 per cent. of world export, and there were 173,000 acres under oil palms.[2]

[1] It yielded 11·3 per cent. of the world's rubber production in 1937.

[2] The export of the nuts is relatively far less than from Africa, for selection has aimed chiefly at increasing the yield of oil.   Note too that the oil is not used locally.

Preparation for the market is carried out in separate factories on the plantation itself. The latex is generally brought up in lorries, whilst the *elæis* nuts, which are much more bulky, arrive in narrow-gauge rail trucks drawn by engines using nutshells as fuel.

Tobacco plants, rubber trees, and oil palms extend to within about six miles of the coast, with a belt of coconut plantations cultivated by natives separating them from the mangroves; but they are seldom found above the 600-foot contour. Higher, and up to about 3000 feet, on the eastern slopes of the plateau on which Lake Toba lies, the Assam tea plant was acclimatised by British planters from 1911 onwards and it yields excellent brands in the Simalungen district around Pematang Siantar. The area under this crop cultivated by Europeans in the East Coast Province was about 50,000 acres before the war.

Sisal (*Agave rigida*) also flourished on the Simalungen hills, preferably on ground much exposed to the drying effect of the *bohorok*, which is fatal to other crops. The area under the crop in 1937 was reckoned at 50,000 acres, which gave an export of 53,000 tons of good quality fibre.

In 1937 the European concessions in the Oostkust *Cultuurgebied*, or plantation area, comprised about 2,500,000 acres, of which 1,000,000 were cultivated. This area has been won almost wholly from the great forest which had preserved the soil from lateritic degradation. Only a few Dipterocarps with their white boles spread wide at the base by huge buttresses remain here and there as giant remnants of the forest which was cut down and burnt. The formidable task was only possible by means of a huge investment of capital, about 57 per cent. of which went into rubber, 15 per cent. into tobacco, and the same into palm oil.[1] Only slightly more than half was Dutch, the rest belonging to other nations. It was concentrated in a very few hands. In 1937 there were only five sisal plantations and four tobacco companies—the 'big four'. Firms combined further in powerful associations, viz. the *Deli Planters Vereeniging* for tobacco and the *Algemeene Vereeniging van Rubber-Planters Oostkust van Sumatra*, the famous *Avros*, which was a union of firms connected with nearly all the other crops.

To these products of the soil has been added mineral oil from the underlying rocks. In 1884 the Royal Batavian Petroleum Co. made its first successful borings round Aru Bay in the north of the territory. Extraction has been extended to the bordering districts of Achin and it rose in 1937 to more than 800,000 tons of crude oil.

In the great forest which was almost uninhabited except where Malay villages were situated at the mouths of the rivers the labour

[1] The figures are those for 1935.

problem was very difficult. The Chinese coolies, at first regarded as indispensable, were replaced by Javanese, who outnumbered them first in 1910 and by 1913 were already twice as numerous. In 1937 the total number of imported coolies on the plantations in the *Cultuurgebied* of the Oostkust amounted to 225,000 out of 330,000 in the whole of Sumatra and perhaps 350,000 in all the Outer Provinces. By far the great majority were Javanese, the Chinese numbering only 10,500.

Many temporary labourers return and end by settling in the territory, either on the European concessions or on their own property, where they combine the cultivation of food plants with crops for export. Others settle in the towns and work as artisans, tradesmen, unskilled labourers, or clerks in big firms.

The population of the Oostkust rose from 116,000 persons in 1880 to 1,675,000 in 1930. The increase was certainly greater than in any other province in Indonesia. It would still be very great even if temporary immigrants could be ignored and only settled elements counted. If the Europeans (numbering 11,000, of whom three-quarters were pure or half-caste Dutch) and the Chinese (193,000) are put aside, the mixture is still great and shows an astounding variety of elements. True natives, called 'Malays' in the statistics, were little more than 22 per cent. in 1930 and were outnumbered by the Bataks (26 per cent.), animists from the Karo district, Toba Christians, Mandailing Muslims, and, above all, by Javanese, who comprised 44 per cent., 3 per cent. of whom were Sundanese. Two far less numerous groups were the Minangkabaus (5·5 per cent.) and the Banjarese, who come from south-eastern Borneo and have settled on the coast. There were also 2 per cent. under the heading of miscellaneous.

The Chinese in the Oostkust, who formed 43 per cent. of the Chinese population of Sumatra, are very different in origin and occupation. The Cantonese are in the lead and work as goldsmiths, cabinet makers, or tailors. Many of the Hakkas are cobblers, tin-smiths, or basket makers. The Hokkiens from Fukien work on plantations as do the people from the Swatow district, most of whom work on tobacco estates, though some of them are market gardeners or pig breeders. The few Japanese were antiquaries, dentists, or photographers.

Such a population called for a complex administrative organisation. The sovereignty of the native petty princes was greatly restricted by the powers granted to larger firms, and communities foreign to the country had the advantage of extra-territorial law.[1]

The density of population in the Oostkust in 1930 was 46 to the

[1] Emerson (251), p. 55.

square mile, which is about the average for Sumatra and the greatest
in all the eastern Residencies.   But it is far higher in the plantation
area itself, the *Cultuurgebied*, and, including the town of Medan, it
reached its maximum of 538 to the square mile in the district of the
same name.

The town of Medan [1] bears marks of the sudden, mighty development of the Oostkust.   The Malay element, which occupies some
kampongs along the River Deli, plays a very unimportant part.
The Sultan's palace and the big mosque are not on the central square,
but stand away from the town.   Europeans, Chinese, Indians, and
Arabs formed nearly half the total population, which in 1930
amounted to 76,500 persons.   Around the shopping centre, which is
mainly Chinese, the quarters containing the big business offices,
administrative buildings, banks, headquarters of the associations,
hospitals, and private villas spread out comfortably and are inter-
sected by wide, shady streets.   The clubs and hotels where people
from overseas foregather used to be the scenes of memorable
banquets in the days of prosperity.   The quarter occupied by the
tobacco associations is distinguished by its tall wooden buildings in
the old Colonial style standing in huge gardens.   Additions due to
the development of rubber and other crops from 1907 onwards are
marked on the other hand by luxurious stone edifices built closer
together owing to the increased value of land.

The capital of the Oostkust is crossed by the road and railway
leading to the neighbouring port of Belawan Deli, an artificial
construction right out on the marshy coast.   Its exports place it
among the chief ports in Indonesia.   But part of the wealth of the
Oostkust flows out through the little ports of Pankalan Brandan
at the entrance to Aru Bay and Tanjung Balai at the mouth of the
Asahan.

The Islands off the East Coast.   The islands off the east coast of
Sumatra differ much from those off the west coast in structure and
in the development of their resources.   In them reappear the type
of soil and the features marking the relief of the Malay Peninsula.
From a gently undulating surface ridges and lone hills suddenly rise
to a height of nearly 4000 feet in Pulo Lingga, 2300 feet in Banka,
and some 1600 feet in Belitong.   Palæozoic rocks, mainly sandstones
and shales, are far commoner in them than granite.   Mangroves
still fringe the shores in many places, particularly in the Rhio and
Lingga groups.   Except in Singkep and Pulo Lingga, which still
contain some virgin forest, the interior of the islands is almost wholly
bare of woods.   The soil is in fact poor and the possibilities of
irrigation are limited.   The *ladang* system with its long period of

[1] Lehmann (96), p. 13.

fallow would allow of but a low density of population, did other resources not come into play. The mean density in the administrative district of Rhio-Lingga is 33 to the square mile. In the Rhio group only 44 per cent. of the people live by cultivation on native lines. Many families engage in inshore fishing and, like the Orang Laut, never leave their boats, or else they have a pile-dwelling on land. The Chinese are already numerous in the Rhio and Lingga groups, which are near Singapore. Like the few Europeans in the islands, they grow gambier and rubber.

But on Singkep an occupation which is widespread on the Malay Peninsula and which, as will be seen, is very active in Banka and Belitong again makes its appearance,[1] for cassiterite abounds in the alluvium in the valleys and even in their continuations under the sea. On Banka its working was at first left to the natives and brought in great profit to the East India Company, which required the tin to be delivered to it as tribute from the native chief.[2] The mining itself began to be controlled by Europeans at the beginning of the 19th century under British rule and became a State enterprise. Dutch capitalists took no interest in Belitong until 1852. After initial difficulties the discovery of very rich deposits gave unexpected returns to the Belitong Company, which undertook methodical mining on Singkep in 1887. In 1924 five-eighths of the company's shares passed into the hands of the State.

The technique of production has been greatly improved. About 1860 an ingenious drill was perfected on Banka for ascertaining the metal content in the deposits of cassiterite, which generally lie at a depth of some 20 to 30 feet, but in places are more than 100 feet below the barren soil. The first steam-driven machines appeared in Banka in 1890. After gravel pumps and, later, monitors had been used, powerful chain-bucket dredgers mounted on pontoons were introduced in 1920. They were able to work to a depth of 100 feet and to dredge nearly four million cubic yards a year. The Belitong Company had recently begun in addition to work veins of ore at a depth of 1000 feet, and this deep mining already represents one-fifth of the production in the island. The tin deposits gave Indonesia third place after Malaya and Bolivia in world production of the metal. Smelting used to be done largely on Banka itself or at Arnhem in the Netherlands, but the profits arising from it have been steadily slipping away to Singapore and Penang. The metal found in the island was considered to be some of the best in the world.

Mechanisation has greatly lowered costs and enables the amount of ore raised to be more easily equated with the demand. A large

[1] Van den Broek (231); ter Braake (237), p. 36; Helbig (123).
[2] Lord Macartney (8), II, p. 107.

dredger manned by 150 workers organised in three gangs working in eight-hour shifts handles as much material as 4000 or 5000 men did previously. In 1937 the mines employed about 26,000 workers, nearly all Chinese and mostly on a yearly contract. The Chinese population is far greater than this and, including women and children, comprised about 125,000 persons in Banka and Belitong alone. This is nearly half the total population of 279,000. Besides working in the mines, the Chinese are, here as everywhere, tradesmen or artisans. Many of them, especially those from the Hakka country, have even taken to cultivating pepper, etc., particularly on Belitong. Banka specialises in the production of white pepper, the yield from which is sometimes as much as 1·2 tons to the acre.

So at the outbreak of war in 1941 Sumatra was in the midst of changes. Colonisation had by no means removed local differences due to nature and history. On the contrary, since it had found conditions more favourable to its progress on the eastern plains, it had created fresh differences by introducing hitherto unknown forms of capitalist exploitation, by attracting a swarm of outside labour, and by inspiring the natives with an irresistible craze for growing crops for export. The mean density of population on the main island probably did not at the beginning of the war exceed 50 persons to the square mile. This is slight compared with Java. But the increase has been faster. Between 1920 and 1930 the population rose by 31·1 per cent. as against 19·3 in Java. Between sparsely populated expanses of forest or savana, there are dense concentrations, those on the west being of long standing and others mainly on the eastern plains being of recent growth. Sumatra contains scarcely one-sixth of the population of Indonesia, but its world importance is indicated by the value of its exports, which in 1937 exceeded half the total for Indonesia.

CHAPTER 9

JAVA

Java is the best known of the East Indian islands. Among Western people, whether poet or factory-hand, its name evokes more or less unreal visions of exotic brilliance and tropical luxuriance, of a Nature at once prodigal and dangerous. We may, for instance, recall the somewhat frenzied pages in which Michelet describes '*la mortelle, la féconde, la divine Java*' with its cinnamon-coloured volcanoes belching smoke to heaven from their fiery summits, its poisonous orchids, its terrible black tigers, and every kind of food in the five continents, including all the stimulating ones: rum, tobacco, coffee, and strong spices.[1] The historian, geographer, archæologist, and economist agree in recognising it as the heart of the East Indies. For a very long time past Java above all other countries has seemed to favour man, and he has multiplied in it extraordinarily. Though it forms only one-fourteenth of the area of Indonesia, it feeds about two-thirds of the population. In it nearly 55,000,000 people, peasants for the most part, are closely packed on an area equal to that of England. Such enormous density in an agricultural community is probably unparalleled in so large an area in any other part of the world.

This leading position in Indonesia seems at first view to be difficult of explanation, and an opponent of geographical determinism might use it as an instance in support of his ideas. Yet, whatever share history, chance, and imponderable factors may have had in Java's good fortune, nature has certainly contributed a number of causes favourable to its development.

First, there is its slight width relatively to the massive islands of Borneo and Sumatra. It stretches from east to west for rather more than 600 miles, but at Surakarta it is little more than 120 miles wide, and this breadth decreases to about 60 miles in the central waist between Cheribon and Semarang.

[1] See *La Montagne*, pp. 169 ff. This should be compared with Raynal's idyllic description in his *Histoire philosophique et politique des établissements et du commerce des Européens dans les deux Indes*, vol. I, p. 156: 'A mild, healthy climate cooled by wind and rains . . ., a land prodigal of delicious fruit . . ., flowers blooming beside others that fade . . ., sweet, penetrating odours exhaled from every plant in a perfumed land, kindle a voluptuous fire in one. Nature had done everything for the Malays, but society had done everything against them . . . Feudal laws conceived among the cliffs and oaks of the North had driven their roots right down to the Equator.' Etc.

The ease with which the interior is reached depends not only on nearness to the sea, but also on the arrangement of the relief. Unlike Sumatra, it has no large, compact hill-masses to divide the island into distinct highland and lowland regions. The 12,000 feet of Mt. Semeru in the Tengger Mountains are but little less than the 12,400 feet of Mt. Kerinchi, the culminating peak of Sumatra; and several other volcanoes in Java exceed 10,000 feet. But, unlike those in the neighbouring island, they do not stand on a high plinth or broad, elevated surface which they help to increase with their ash. On the contrary, they often rise up straight from the lowlands into which they merge by long, regularly decreasing concave slopes. They do not form an unbroken barrier, but stand separately; and between them are gaps affording an easy way from north to south across the island. Even in the west, where they are often placed on Tertiary sedimentaries and are most compact, modern roads and railways from Jakarta have no great difficulty in reaching the inland districts of Sukabumi and Bandung.

Java is not without its contrasts; but highlands and lowlands mingle and are interspersed instead of standing separately. One of the great charms of the island consists of the varied relief in the scenery. Single landscapes include valleys carpeted with flooded ricefields and dotted with villages, hills with dry *tegal* cultivation climbing up their sides above the zone of *sawahs*, and the steep, ravined, and often dark-wooded slopes of volcanoes with their bare tops plumed at times with greyish steam from fumaroles.

The great number of volcanoes, of which there are one hundred and twenty-one in the island, largely contributes to the fertility of the soil and so to the density of population. The neighbourhood of the extinct or active craters is not the only area thus fertilised, for the ash is often carried long distances. Soil formed by eruptions long past is certainly much impoverished on the whole by now. But the proportion of active volcanoes is greater than in Sumatra, and most of the matter ejected in recent times has been basic in character and hence suitable for making fertile soil.

Nor has the climate been without effect on the fortunes of Java. The island is a transitional area between Sumatra and Borneo on the one hand and the eastern isles on the other. Very heavy rain falls on the mountain slopes and the lowlands below. But towards Australia the dry season becomes longer owing to the influence of the south-easterly winds. The discontinuity of the highlands further increases the number of shades of climate due to differences of aspect. In the lowlands there is often a deep, black soil which has been leached by the rain less than usual in an equatorial climate. Irrigation is possible because the slopes of the nearby mountains are

of permeable material,
like lava, ash, and tuff,
and thus retain moisture.
On Mts. Kelud and
Merapi, for instance, the
water which rushes down
after rain along the upper
courses of the torrents
quickly sinks into the
ground to issue again
lower down in a number
of springs.

Ease of communica-
tion, the variety and mixture of relief features, the
fertility of the soil, the
abundant (yet not exces-
sive) supply of rain, and
the opportunities for irrigation — these are the
geographical causes of
Java's long-standing pre-
eminence. To them must
be added the island's position between straits that
until the opening of the
Suez Canal were much
used by ships passing from
the Indian Ocean to the
China Seas. More than
any other part of the East
Indies, Java has attracted
immigrants and retained
them. Owing to the very
fertility of the soil new-
comers from abroad have
fused one after another
with the native masses.
Local peculiarities have
died away also, because
of the easy communica-
tions. The juxtaposition
of areas of very different
altitudes and conse-

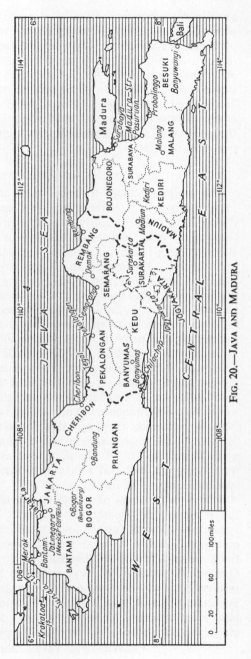

Fig. 20.—Java and Madura

quently of various types of cultivation have naturally fostered complementary modes of life everywhere, and, thanks to this, racial differences have died out. In spite of the distinctions noticed between the natives of Sunda, Java proper, and Madura, these three large groups are far more like each other than are the tribes in Sumatra, Borneo, or Celebes. In short, the 'savage' has almost completely disappeared from Java. The critical traveller might certainly reproach Java for being too civilised and too uniformly so. Nevertheless, shades of difference exist from north to south and even more from east to west.

THE SURFACE RELIEF AND ITS HISTORY

The geological map[1] at once shows the 'youthful' character of Java, for it reveals nothing but Tertiary, Quaternary, and recent rocks. The oldest strata, very probably cretaceous, appear only in three small spots: one in the south-west of the island near Whale Bay; the other two in the central area to the south of Banjar Negara and Klaten. Cretaceous and Eocene strata with a few granite intrusions form only about one per cent. of the area of Java and Madura, and it has been said that the morphological history of Java really did not begin until the Pliocene period.

At the beginning of the Miocene the Java Sea was occupied by Sundaland, that peninsula of the continent of Eurasia whose easternmost remnant consists of the Karimun Jawa Islands to the north of Semarang. On the site of northern Java ran a strait formed by a geosyncline in which sediment eroded from Sundaland and the lands to the south were later to accumulate. In fact, southern Java was foreshadowed then by an archipelago of volcanoes and limestone islets, no doubt like those now dotted about farther east. Eruptions produced huge quantities of breccias and conglomerates formed of andesite and basalt. At the same time as these islands to the south were being uplifted and joined together, the deposits in the geosyncline began to be folded.

After a pause a new phase of intense vulcanism marked the end of the Pliocene and Quaternary periods. The deposits in the geosyncline underwent further folding and ended by emerging. This emergence became more and more recent towards the east, where the Strait of Madura still persists today. Thus, in the Pliocene and Quaternary periods Java was joined to Asia, whence doubtless it received a variety of fauna and the first human types. Meanwhile, Sundaland had suffered from erosion and had perhaps also undergone subsidence and so became a lower area than the land formed out of the geosyncline. In the Pliocene period the drainage still ran

[1] Rutten (33) pp. 139 ff.; Lehmann (136).

17.
The mosque at Alor Star,
the capital of Kedah

18.
A Chinese woman and her children looking at a travelling shoe-seller's wares. Note the mode of carrying an infant.

19. A street scene in Medan, showing the old head offices of Avros

20. The Minangkabau market at Fort de Kock, Sumatra

southwards, as is proved by the oil-bearing strata which represent an ancient delta to the west of Bojo Negoro near Chepu.[1] In the Quaternary the drainage was reversed and in Java the rivers flowed in the opposite direction towards the north. Owing to the submergence of Sundaland at the end of the Quaternary, Java became an island and acquired its present outline and relief through local subsidence, changes in sea level, coral formation, and, above all, through volcanic action and erosion. Sedimentary rocks which had been folded since the very beginning of the Tertiary period were attacked by the forces of erosion and planed down to the surfaces now forming the platform for Quaternary and recent volcanoes. The history of the Quaternary period was also very eventful, for many volcanoes were destroyed and new ones built up. Alluvium filled the lake basins and extended the island out into the sea, especially on the north coast.

In spite of these developments three longitudinal belts are clearly recognisable in Java running parallel to the long axis of the island. One on the shores of the Indian Ocean is formed mainly of Miocene plateaus and hills. The second which is in the middle is essentially volcanic; and lastly, in the north there are the Pliocene and Quaternary lowlands.

(a) The southern belt is certainly the remains of a land that must have stretched much farther southwards until the end of the Tertiary period. In it are found the least recent sedimentaries in the island, and in particular Eocene and Oligocene conglomerates with granitic elements. But most of the area is covered with Miocene deposits. The breccias and andesitic tuffs, which are the remains of the volcanoes of this period, are generally very dissected. Limestones of globigerina ooze or coral formation often present the appearance of little karstic plateaus whose folded strata are cut by an erosional surface which has been warped into a kind of vault running east–west and is itself affected by many secondary undulations. The altitude does not often exceed 3300 feet. The coast is generally rocky and cut into by deep inlets, which points to a recent positive movement along fault scarps already much worn by erosion. At the end of the Miocene the emergence of the southern belt was no doubt nearly complete, for no marine deposits of the Pliocene have been recognised in it.

(b) On the other hand, the Miocene beds in the central belt remained submerged till the end of the Pliocene, when Java's huge volcanoes were built up on the southern edge of the geosyncline, which was deepened at the same time as the southern belt of the island was uplifted. According to van Bemmelen, the side of the

[1] East of Semarang.

geosyncline was stretched by folding and even broke in places. On these lines of weakness rose the great volcanoes of Java to form huge superimposed mountains which masked the Mio-Pliocene deposits and caused them to sink still further under the weight. Volcanic activity has been recognised as having recurred in various places several times at this period (the end of the Pliocene and during the Quaternary). The volcanoes themselves, whose weight presses on an unstable mass, show a tendency to sink and slip, displacing their craters along west-to-east as well as south-to-north lines.

Eruptions piled up enormous quantities alternately of lava and other ejected matter, which were spread out at long distances from the craters on gently inclined surfaces by *lahar* flows and the run-off of rainwater. The volcanic hill-masses often enclose high plains, some of which (e.g. the one at Bandung) were formerly occupied by lakes and so remain more or less marshy. Fourteen of the volcanoes rise above the 10,000-foot contour, and most of them are situated in the central belt.

(c) Northern Java corresponds to the bottom of the uplifted geosyncline. None the less, the Mio-Pliocene sedimentary beds removed erosionally from Sundaland and the volcanoes in the south bear marks of very complex evolution. This has been studied in the east of the island by H. Lehmann. Folding has taken place several times: as early as the Miocene and especially in the middle of that period; but mainly during the volcanic period at the end of the Pliocene and in the Quaternary. In the Upper Pliocene a few ridges had already emerged with lagoons between them. One of the lagoons ran through the present site of Surabaya and was bounded on the north by the Kendeng Hills. Emergence continued during the Quaternary, but was very slow and irregular and was connected with eustatic movements as well as continental displacements associated with the volcanic and seismic activity. In places marine deposits of the Neogene period, as much as 23,000 feet thick, were uplifted to a height of 3000 and even 4000 feet above the sea. The lines of gently sloping hills are interrupted by wide valleys which end in coastal plains fringed with mangrove. Here and there a delta forms a projection.

This northern belt is an extension of the great plains of Sumatra and does not occur farther eastwards in the Lesser Sunda Islands. According to recent researches by Dutch geologists, it reappears probably in eastern Borneo. The greater part of this island was a portion of Sundaland and formed the resistant block against which the Neogene syncline was moulded round in a curve to the north. The belt may possibly occur also in south-western Celebes.

Such are the three structural belts of Java. It must be repeated

that they do not form clearly separate regions. The plains and hills
in the north merge into the long slopes of the volcanoes. Recent
tectonic movements, and also no doubt the slighter resistance offered
by the rock to the agents of erosion, have favoured the streams
flowing towards the Java Sea. As a result of capture, these often
rise not far from the Indian Ocean and, like the Solo and Brantas,
pass right across the volcanic belt. Thus, the northern ports have
an advantage and benefit not only from their position on seas with
a great deal of traffic, but also from their easy communications with
the backland.

MAIN NATURAL REGIONS OF JAVA

Climate rather than structure is the basis of a threefold division of
Java which is visible on the ethnographical map, in the forms of
colonisation, and in the administrative subdivisions. Under the
Dutch the island was indeed divided into three provinces, each
containing elements of the three structural belts described above.
But the treatment here will not bind itself slavishly to observe their
boundaries.

The West. The western division runs from Sunda Strait eastwards to a line joining the Kinderzee on the south coast to a point
just east of Cheribon on the north coast. This part of Java resembles Sumatra in its massive structure and the contrast between
its wide lowlands and compact highlands. East of the worn
volcanoes which, corresponding to those in Lampong and with them
forming something like a ring of satellites round the terrible
Krakatoa, command Sunda Strait, the northern lowlands stretch for
about 160 miles from Bantam Bay to Cheribon and maintain a
fairly constant width of 30 miles. The land is being added to
relatively quickly by the silting up of the sea. Rivers flowing down
from the mountains in the south prolong their courses by means of
the mud which they transport and deposit; and they project into the
sea a whole series of deltas to form Bantam, Jakarta, and Chasem
Bays. The old harbour at Jakarta, which was still on the sea in
1610, is now separated from it by a mile-wide fringe of mud, the
mangrove swamps on which have been turned into fishponds. The
Tanjung Priok docks have been constructed somewhat farther east
in this same belt of mud.

The coast is closest here to the mainland of Eurasia and is reached
by visitors coming from the west through the Straits of Malacca or
Sunda or from the north across the South China Sea. Bantam Bay
is the first haven sighted by ships on doubling Cape St. Nicholas and
the volcanic cone of Salak Gedeh at the northern exit of Sunda
Strait. Up to the 17th century and the rise of Batavia the port at

the mouth of the river was more frequented by European ships than any other in the island and was one of the best known in the East Indies. Bantam was then another name for Java, as Achin was for Sumatra, and the port was the great entrepôt for pepper and other spices. There Portuguese, and, later, English and Dutch, merchants matched their astuteness with Arab, Indian, and Chinese traders. These foreigners were all jealously protected by the local rulers, who got fat profits from the trade.[1] But the creation of other trading stations at Benkulen by the English and at Batavia by their Dutch rivals brought on the decline of Bantam. Furthermore, the bay was rapidly becoming silted up and at the end of the 18th century the harbour had become inaccessible to laden ships.[2]

Batavia then supplanted Bantam, and the fortified trading station built amidst swamps prospered in spite of its unhealthiness. 'Half the Europeans of all classes who go and settle in Batavia are thought to die before the year is out', says the editor of Lord Macartney's *Journal of the Embassy to China* (1793). 'Hence, Batavia is like a battlefield or besieged town'. 'Batavian ladies, whether creoles or half-castes, seldom go out until evening', and 'the colour of the rose never adorns their cheeks'.[3] But the Company had made this post the headquarters of its stations and its very prosperous trade. The produce of the Moluccas and other Spice Islands as well as coffee, pepper, sugar, and areca nuts from Java itself were piled up in its spacious warehouses. Indeed the wide lowland area of which Batavia rather than Bantam was the natural outlet soon saw its export crops increase. These were often cultivated under Chinese management, especially sugarcane, which was no doubt introduced in the 14th and 15th centuries when the Majapahit period was at its zenith. This delegation of duties left the Company's agents free meanwhile to concentrate their attention on the sumptuous gardens which surround the houses they had built some distance from the town.

After the Company's downfall in 1796 export crops continued to be cultivated on the area left to the natives on the lowlands and even more so on the estates which had passed into government ownership or were alienated to individuals. Recently, before the war, the latter used still to act as veritable feudal lords towards the villagers

1 On trade in Bantam in 1639, see Olearius (9) II, pp. 358 ff.
2 Macartney (8) II, p. 95.
3 Macartney (8) II, pp. 23 and 43. See also Raynal (198) I, p. 393: 'From 1714 to 1776 87,000 soldiers or sailors died in hospital alone. . . . A statement that a citizen who was perfectly well had died caused no surprise, so usual was the occurrence. Avarice restricted itself to the remark: "He owed me nothing".' These two authors give many details about life in Batavia at the end of the 18th century. For the middle of the 17th century, see J. B. Tavernier (11) II, pp. 506–66; III, pp. 348–70.

dwelling within the bounds of the seignorial landed properties. On the few private estates that remained in the lowlands after the government purchases, the chief products were often those that ensure a supply of food for the natives, viz. sawah rice, cassava, sweet potatoes, ground-nuts, soya beans, and coconuts. The cultivation of sugarcane began in the west in the neighbourhood of Cheribon. Here, as in the centre of the island, the plant is grown on the lowlands, but was cultivated on land rented from native villages by sugar companies. The other European plantations have mostly spread over land leased from the Government and are situated mainly in the central and southern highlands, which are far less densely peopled and include large areas that remain uncultivated.

Owing to the Tertiary rocks in which the volcanic areas are embedded, West Java is the least accessible and has more difficult communications than any other part of the island. Though the density of population is still very high, it falls far below the general average, being 630 to the square mile as against 816 in Java as a whole.

Tertiary beds cover the whole of the northern part of the Residencies of Buitenzorg and Bantam, which latter is the westernmost division in Java; but south of the volcanoes in the Preanger Mountains the beds form a narrower belt. Sometimes they consist of Eocene sandstones, but are mainly of Miocene volcanic breccia, the folds in which seem to have been truncated by erosional agency. The surface has been studied particularly in the Jampang Hills to the east of Whale Bay. It reaches an altitude of about 2600 feet in the north and somewhat gradually becomes lower towards the south, ending at the bay in imposing cliffs. Farther east a similar structure gives almost identical relief in a plateau covered by extensive *alang* savanas dotted with small shrubs. The soil is often full of volcanic matter, but is too old, leached, and exhausted; and, in spite of the heavy rainfall of between 100 and 200 inches, a year, the relief is not very favourable to irrigation because of the frequent occurrence of convex slopes.[1]

The Bantam Residency, with 334 persons to the square mile, is by far the least densely populated in Java. The district of Chibaliung at the extreme south-west of the island has the exceptionally low figure of 52 persons to the square mile. The population, which is weakened by malaria, lives mainly by *ladang* cultivation, and the steady advance of the clearings is causing the almost complete ruin of the forest. Nowhere else in Java does collecting and hunting play so large a part in supplying food.[2] The southern districts are isolated from the life of the island, and only three roads reach the

[1] Mohr (98), p. 484.   [2] Lekkerkerker (137), p. 872.

shores of the Indian Ocean. For transport buffalo carts are exclusively used. A peculiar community, the Badujese, persists in south Bantam. The people are very backward and are scarcely affected by Islamic or Malay influence. Irrigation works have been undertaken on the shores of Sunda Strait in Pepper Bay. But a large part of the district of Chibaliung together with Prince's Island has been made into a *natuurmonument*, or reservation, for the protection of specimens of the fauna—wild oxen and rhinoceroses—which was threatened with complete extinction. Farther north on Sunda Strait the natives have found compensation for the rare occurrence of *sawahs* by cultivating the coconut, an occupation which was very extensive between 1906 and 1915.[1]

The area occupied by recently extinct and active volcanoes is far greater in the Residencies of Buitenzorg and Priangan. They seldom stand as separate cones, but rather as huge collections of volcanic pipes still not quite rising above the Tertiary beds and often already worn by erosion. Some of them still show intermittent, but seldom catastrophic, activity. In the Buitenzorg group the highest peaks are Salak, Gede, and Pangerango (9900 feet) and in the Bandung group Papandayan and Chikurai (9250 feet), whilst Chareme stands in splendid isolation to the south of Cheribon. The Bandung volcanoes form the largest and most varied hill-mass and are among the most closely studied in the East Indies. The headquarters of the island's geological department and its associated volcanological section is situated at Bandung itself. Stehn, Taverne, and van Bemmelen have carefully followed up the complex history of Mt. Tangkuban Prahu (= the upturned boat; see Fig. 3) which rises north of Bandung. The oldest volcanic episodes cannot be deciphered under the pile of matter ejected more recently to fill a vast caldera. The details of the summits and twin craters of Kawah Ratu and Kawah Upas are due to the latest eruptions, which were accompanied by a slipping of the craters along an east–west fault and caused ejections of ash and tuff. At an older phase the ejected matter had consisted mainly of basalt with olivine, and this rock can be traced in some of the valleys for a distance of 12 or 13 miles. Still earlier, huge masses of ash, *lapilli*, bombs, and rocks torn from the base had been spread widely over the neighbourhood, forming screes of tuff on the lower slopes. One of these screes dammed the Chitarum and turned the whole Bandung plain into a lake. This lake was certainly still in existence in prehistoric times and is even now but imperfectly drained by the Chitarum, which has lately dug itself a new course

---

[1] The district of Anger in the north-west of the island has the lowest density of population, 515 persons to the square mile of cultivable area (Kuperus (135), p. 475).

farther south through the tuff barrier. Extensive areas of alluvial soil, still swampy in places, but very fertile, spread out here in the heart of the mountains at an altitude of about 2300 feet. The high plain of Garut lying between Mts. Papandayan and Chikorai to the east of Bandung may also have passed through a lacustrine phase.

The interior basins enjoy a drier atmosphere and often a sunnier sky than the plains they overlook or the hill-masses above. There is a great difference in climate between Bandung, 2300 feet above the sea, and Buitenzorg, which is situated at an altitude of 870 feet among hills, and also between the volcanic highlands and the plain around Jakàrta. Buitenzorg gets more than 160 inches of rain a year, and rain falls on 216 days. At Bandung rain falls on 144 days with a mean total of 77 inches. In the months of July and August the average is only 4½ inches. However, in the western mountains rain is sufficiently plentiful and regular to maintain the great evergreen forest. In the middle of last century Junghuhn and Wallace were struck with wonder at the abundance of tall tree-ferns which filled the gorges above the 2600-foot contour, at the splendid foliage of the Musaceæ, and at the elegant and varied shapes of plants related to the Begonias and Melastoma. At an altitude of 6500 feet the raspberry becomes plentiful, and higher up still are other species which remind one of western Europe. Among these is a primrose (*Primula Imperialis*) whose stem is sometimes more than three feet tall. South of Buitenzorg in the forest reservation of Chibodas, which a hundred years ago was still the haunt of many rhinoceroses, the primitive flora may still be seen, though much of it has been destroyed in the past century.[1] But as the climate is remarkably favourable to certain valuable crops, these have ousted the forest in many places. The forest has protected and enriched with humus volcanic soils of quite recent date, which are very permeable, yet retentive of moisture, fertile, and easily worked. On its site is found one of the most prosperous plantation areas in the Indies.

The Preanger Mountains—the name often applied to the volcanic highlands in the Residencies of Buitenzorg and Priangan—form the leading tea-producing district in Indonesia and one of the most important in the world.[2] Seed was imported from China as early as 1826, and the first shipment was despatched from Batavia in 1835. About 1880, varieties which are most commonly cultivated today

---

[1] C. J. Bernard (204).

[2] Robequain (200), pp. 47 ff.: In 1937 out of a total European plantation acreage of 630,000 under crops in western Java and 1,450,000 in the whole island, the Residencies of Buitenzorg and Priangan together had 460,000 acres or nearly one-third of the total for Java as a whole. The production of tea, like that of other plantation crops, has greatly decreased during the past twenty years. See below, pp. 429-30.

were introduced from Assam, and Java tea was regularly quoted on the London market. From 1900 onwards large areas above the 3000-foot contour were cleared by joint stock companies. The highest yields and best qualities are obtained at an altitude of between 4000 and 6000 feet. In some places the shrub is cultivated on very steep slopes which are terraced and on which the soil is protected by little banks against the run-off of rain-water. The leaves are picked throughout the year and are treated in factories built on the plantations. The most modern ones look like big glass cages. The leaves are dried on the top floor, put through the various processes of rolling, sifting, and fermentation which ultimately produce the tea of commerce. The leaves are then packed on the ground floor in tin-lined cases. In 1940 about a third of the output of the factories came from native cultivation.

Although the cinchona tree provides less of Java's exports than does the tea plant, it is the special and best-known crop in the Preanger Mountains.[1] It does not grow well except above the 4000-foot contour, and plantations go up to 6500 feet, the optimum being between 4300 and 5000 feet, where the temperature never falls below freezing-point. The bark produced on 35,000 acres in the Preangers is the result of most careful and scientific cultivation and before the war furnished more than three-fourths of the world's consumption of quinine.

The *hevea* is grown on a wider area. In West Java, as elsewhere, it is scarcely ever found above the 2000-foot contour and thus forms a belt around the tea and quinine region. Its whitish bole is seen right down to the south coast.

West Java has been more favourable to the high altitude crops of tea and quinine than any other part of Indonesia. It is to this fact, as well as to the presence of the Indonesian capital, that it owed its relatively high proportion of Europeans. In a house with a veranda giving shelter from the sun, but opening wide to the breeze, life is less oppressive on a well chosen hillside position than on the plains. In the garden attached to the house flourish casuarinas (*chemaras*) together with magnificent tropical flowers and shrubs, like the hibiscus, thorn-apple, palm, and tree-fern. But even there the European could not without risk work on the land with his own hands.

The labour problem is certainly less complex than in the Oostkust of Sumatra, and displacement of workers is far less. They have for the most part, however, to climb up from the lowlands and stay away from their native villages for a more or less considerable time. They nearly all belong to the Sundanese community which inhabits

[1] And especially in the Pengalengan district. See below, p. 347.

the western part of the island, except the north coast, where Javanese properly so-called are already more numerous. The Sundanese are stocky of body, broad of face, and have straight black hair. Rough of speech and untutored of mind, they are yet frank and quick to learn; more demonstrative and less silent and restrained than the Javanese. They are said to be more hardworking and thrifty, but their Mohammedan faith is also more fanatical and less tolerant. The pile-dwelling affords another feature of likeness between the Sundanese district and Sumatra. Lastly, big villages are rarer here in the west than elsewhere in the island, for the people prefer to live in little hamlets scattered among the ricefields.

Mid Java. Between Cheribon and Semarang the breadth of the island falls to about 60 miles, but increases again eastward of the latter owing to the recent welding on to it of the volcano Muryo on the north and to the reappearance of the Miocene plateaus in the south of the Principalities. The mountains, which in other parts of the island run along the south coast, are here central and form a fairly continuous range as far as Surakarta, but are much narrower than in the west. First of all, there are the Pembarisan Hills, which are of very dissected Tertiary shales and nowhere rise as high as 3000 feet. Farther east the sedimentary base is again surmounted by volcanoes, most of them active. Mt. Slamat raises its isolated cone to 11,200 feet. Then come the uplands of the plateau of Dieng, averaging about 6500 feet above the sea, but with some volcanic peaks rising somewhat higher. According to Umbgrove, these peaks were formed during several phases of volcanic activity. Lastly, there are the twin volcanoes of Sumbing and Sindoro and of Merbabu and Merapi, three of which rise to about 10,000 feet. Merapi has been one of the most active volcanoes in the archipelago in recent years. Its great eruption in 1934 caused a downrush of incandescent matter and enormous clouds of burning gas which poured down more slowly than those from Morne Pelée in 1902, but repeatedly exploded sideways. Thanks, however, to a warning system and a well-executed plan of evacuation, there were no casualties. In Java the rate of erosion is seen to be greatest on the slopes of these central mountains, which are far less compact than those on the west and are very bare of woods. The ash and tuff on the slopes are deeply cut into by gullies, and large quantities of rock waste are carried seawards to fertilise the still narrow coast strip between Cheribon and Semarang. To the east of the latter port and south of Muryo there still remain vast brackish swampy wastes barely rising above sea level.

Again to the south of the backbone of mountains Quaternary and alluvial deposits cover nearly all the surface in the Presidencies of

Banyumas and Kedu. North-west of Chilachap a large inlet of the sea is in process of sedimentation, and the limestone island of Kambangan has been joined to the mainland by a complex isthmus. The margins of the surviving lagoon, the Kinderzee, are being silted up at a rate of 20 or 30 yards a year. East of Chilachap the coast cycle is more advanced: the lagoons have already been dried up behind their sand spits, which form long, nearly straight arcs and are supported here and there by islands of sedimentary or coralline limestone.

It is only beyond the River Opak in the south of the Principalities that Tertiary beds again form plateaus reaching the ocean, as in the west of the island. The district of Gunung Sewu (Thousand Hills) stands up over the sea in a steep face between 75 and 300 feet high and rises northwards to some 2300 feet. The relief here is carved in a bed of Miocene limestone which has a maximum thickness of 330 feet, dips gently southwards, and rests discordantly on a folded series below. Escarpments clearly appear south of Jogyakarta. The yellowish-white, but seldom naked, rock has been carved into a series of closely packed beehive-shaped hills between 150 and 225 feet above their bases and having low slopes which are in places vertical. This relief has aroused the interest of many observers since the time of Junghuhn. Lehmann attributes it to the karstification in a tropical climate of a fairly thin limestone layer of average compactness which was formerly drained by a normal river system and was later dried in consequence of uplift.[1]

The plains and hills of the Principalities between the central volcanoes and these rugged limestone plateaus form the heart of Java. The soil is very fertile and communications easy from sea to sea. During recent complex earth movements the streams draining into the Java Sea have captured nearly the whole country. By annexing the basin of the Baturetno in southern Surakarta the Solo, the longest river in the island, has carried the boundaries of its drainage area to within 20 miles of the Indian Ocean.[2] Farther east the karstification of the limestone has also facilitated an inversion of drainage.

For long ages the climate itself seems to have favoured a variety of crops with a good yield and thus encouraged the concentration of population. More recently it has allowed the Europeans to develop the use of the country by a peculiar intensive method of cultivation.

Owing to their narrow character the lowlands have the benefit of

---

[1] Lehmann (136) p. 25.

[2] Besides, the lower Solo has been able to keep its course through the slowly rising Kendeng ridge to the north of Ngawi. On this case of antecedent drainage, see Lehmann, *op. cit.*, p. 110.

plenty of rain everywhere, since the high relief of the central range causes condensation to take place. At Yasareja (5000 feet) to the south-east of Pekalongan on the north slopes of the range there is a mean annual total of 270 inches. In the south at Kranggan (1000 feet) near Chilachap one of 266 inches; and farther east at an altitude of only 60 feet at Gombong one of 135 inches. Cheribon and Semarang on the north coast and Surakarta and Jogyakarta, the capitals of the Principalities, have totals of about 86 inches a year, as against 71 inches at Jakarta. But the rainfall is not so evenly distributed as in the west. There is a well marked dry season from June to September, and whilst Jakarta has nearly 19 per cent. of its annual total during those four months, Semarang gets only 13 per cent. and Jogyakarta 8 per cent. At that time, indeed, the lowlands between Cheribon and Tegal fairly often experience the drying effort of the south-east wind which, after crossing the Pembarisan Hills, becomes a foehn known as the *kumbang*.[1] Teak forest becomes more frequent here and with man's aid covers all the poor land east of Semarang. The big deciduous leaves make this tree characteristic of the tropical climate with a dry season. Evergreen rain forest with its great mixture of species was less robust here than in the west and has been almost completely destroyed.

The fertile volcanic soil here is given its full value by the climate. It is usually basic in character and has been renewed by ejections continued up to the present time. Wind and run-off have spread it far and wide over the lowlands which separate the volcanoes. Originally more fertile than in the west, the soil has, moreover, been less quickly leached and impoverished and is better preserved owing to the longer dry season. During this time of year irrigation enables the necessary water to be scientifically distributed to the crops on the long concave slopes of the volcanoes and on the plains below them.

The proportion of the soil tilled by natives is greatest in central Java and reaches 68·1 per cent. of the total area of *Midden Java* properly so-called. In the two principalities of Surakarta and Jogyakarta it rises to 76·2 and 81·6 per cent. respectively.[2] There too the percentage of *sawahs* and irrigated ricefields attains its maximum in relation to the total area under cultivation. The so-called secondary crops, which not only occupy land that cannot be irrigated, but are also sandwiched in between rice crops in the *sawahs*, have a far greater place in rural economy than they do in the west; and this is true of maize, tubers like cassava and sweet potato, and leguminous plants like ground-nuts and soya beans.

1 Braak (38), p. 82.
2 Against 50·9 per cent. in West Java and 59 per cent. in East Java in 1937.

Improvements in agriculture had increased as a result of European influence. This influence was far less visible here than in the west where large areas have been handed over to Europeans to grow any crops they like. The plantation area was far less extensive than in the west or east of the island. The tea plant and the cinchona are alike rare, and though the *hevea* and the coffee bush have rather more space, the cacao tree, which was once more plentiful, has been dealt a severe blow by Brazilian and African competition.

The small area available, that is, not used by the natives and available for clearing by Europeans, here narrowly restricted the spread of crops that have had such great success elsewhere. Export crops could not safely monopolise soil which was already in short supply and necessary to the subsistence of a very dense population. The prevailing rule was to alternate domestic food crops and export crops on a given piece of land. Consequently, the export crops cannot be derived from trees or shrubs which occupy the land for several years, but only from fast-growing plants which will be succeeded by food crops according to a strict rotation.

Owing to methodical application and constant improvement of this ingenious system, Mid Java was able to become a great exporter of tobacco and sugar, two commodities which had long been produced in the island, but whose cultivation was much extended after 1870. Their production was carried on mainly by European firms working chiefly with Dutch capital on land which was as a rule rented from native villages. Tobacco is grown about every other year. Sugarcane, which continues to grow for fifteen or eighteen months must give place to domestic food crops at least during the whole of a rainy season. In fact, on every estate a sugar company planted only 10 or 15 per cent. of the area over which it had acquired rights, as the sugarcane took its place in the rotation on the most fertile soil only.

The distribution of these two crops, tobacco and sugarcane, is not the same. The chief sugar districts in Mid Java are the Principalities and the low ground to the east of Cheribon round Tegal and Pekalongan. The intrusive capitalist production of sugarcane, with its high yield, was related to the existence of a dry season and the practice of carefully regulated irrigation. It was said to be most prosperous where there were fewer than twenty days of rain during the four driest months. Tobacco sometimes grows high up on the slopes of volcanoes, whilst, except in seed-beds,[1] sugarcane is confined to the low ground below the 650-foot contour. However,

[1] Seed-beds placed between the altitudes of 1000 and 5000 feet were meant to supply slips immune from *sereh* to the plantations in the lowlands. The progress of selection made them less and less necessary, see below, p. 342.

the two plants are sometimes found together, especially around Klaten in the Principalities.

It was in central Java that the most brilliant success was won by the type of colonial exploitation which calls on the same soil to yield in turn commodities for export and produce for local consumption, whilst it tries to keep the balance between the requirements of Western capital and the raising of the native standard of life, and endeavours to use as scientifically as possible European technical knowledge and money together with a docile and ever increasing supply of labour. Hence the characteristic features of the scenery in the most densely populated parts of Java were the mixture of the lighter green of the canefields with rice and other traditional crops; white-walled sugar-mills with megass heaps beside them and in crop-time with heavily laden ox-carts streaming towards them; huge sheds for drying tobacco leaves; and along the roads villages stretching out for miles amidst coconut palms and other trees, so that the traveller did not realise when he was passing from one *dessa* to another.

Indeed, the development of scientific agriculture which was made possible by the density of population has helped to increase the density still further. In 1930 Mid Java had a mean density of 1050 persons to the square mile. The most densely peopled divisions were the Residency of Pekalongan in the north with 1212 persons to the square mile, the Residency of Kedu with 1184, and the Principality of Jogyakarta in the south with 1270. Naturally, the difference became accentuated in the smaller areas. An amazing swarm of human life was seen in purely rural districts; for instance, Delangu in Jogyakarta had 2310 persons to the square mile, Wiradesa in Pekalongan 2530, Plumbon in Cheribon 2780, and Adiwerno in Pekalongan 4210. The density fell below 650 mainly in the peripheral districts: for instance, in the district of Chilachap, which included large unhealthy swamps; on the karstic plateau of the Sewu Hills in the south-east; and in the north on the poor Tertiary soil in the valleys of the Serang and Lusi to the east of Semarang.[1]

The centre of the island still shows traces of the political and cultural pre-eminence which is known to have followed on the establishment of Indian colonies and was consolidated in the 10th century of our era. The temples on the Dieng plateau and in the Jogyakarta countryside were built during this period. They have been restored piously and scientifically by Dutch archæologists and include the shrines of Mendout and Prambanan among others and, most famous of all, the Borobudur, a gigantic shrine (*stupa*) of blackish andesite, which is perhaps also the tomb of a prince. Its

[1] Kuperus (135), p. 467.

long galleries of mural paintings describe family life in the palace together with the chief episodes in the life of Buddha. Under the Dutch the special status of the Principalities (*Vorstenlanden*) was reminiscent of this glorious period. Dutch occupation met with real resistance here between 1825 and 1830. The Javanese princes of Jogyakarta and Surakarta (Solo) were, however, allowed a mere semblance of power in their *kratons* which still present to tourists a curious mixture of native traditions and European manners. Yet under the veil of Islam the ancient Indo-Javanese civilisation survives best here in the artistic skill displayed in gold and silver work, *batik*, dances, and the *wayang* theatre.

East Java. The two main geographical features, the discontinuity of the relief and the drier climate, which have been mentioned in Mid Java are accentuated still more in the east of the island. The

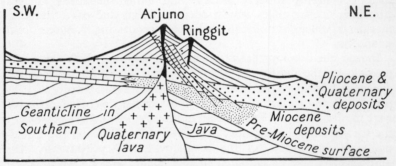

FIG. 21.—SECTION FROM S.W. TO N.E. THROUGH THE VOLCANO ARJUNO
(after Van Bemmelen)

three longitudinal belts are most distinct here. The Tertiary plateaus and hills continue without a break right up to the foot of the Tengger hill-mass and they occur again in the south-eastern peninsula of Blambangan. They are mainly formed of Miocene volcanic deposits and foraminiferal limestone which is more chalky than that in the Sewu Hills and does not weather into such typically karstic relief. These beds covering the south slope of the anticline which emerged at the end of the Miocene become higher from south to north, where they reach a maximum altitude of 2400 feet and fall away abruptly in an escarpment due either to faulting or folding and enhanced by erosion.

In the north indeed the arch and sides of the anticline are hidden. The Miocene beds are masked at the foot of the escarpment by Pliocene and Quaternary strata whose origin is mainly volcanic. On the sunken substratum have been built up huge volcanoes, many of which are still active. As they rest heavily on an unstable mass of sediments whose thickness increases quickly towards the north, the volcanoes themselves tend to slip over in that direction. Hence, there is a frequent movement of the craters, some of which are aligned in a west–east direction parallel with the longitudinal dislocations, whilst others stand in a north–south line.[1]

In the middle region the volcanoes are not so much bunched together as they are in West Java. Here they stand separately or at least form separate groups and appear on a relief map like beads on a rosary. From west to east one after another there are the huge cones of Lawu and Wilis, the less elevated Kelud, and then the complex mass of Arjuno-Welirang, the whole of whose northern part sank while the eruptive centre was displaced. The narrowest portion of the island, measuring only 40 miles across to the east of Prabalinga shows a series of three volcanic masses. The Tengger Hills and Semeru (12,000 feet), their culminating peak, have already been mentioned.[2] Then there follow the groups around Mt. Lamongan, which is dotted with *maares* and ash cones, and those round Mts. Yang and Argapura. Lastly, Mt. Idyen looks on the maps like a lunar volcano. It is an enormous caldera dotted with craters some of which hold lakes and are dominated by volcanoes. One of these, Mt. Raung, rises to a height of 10,000 feet. Long, gullied slopes surround it, falling away eastwards to the Strait of Bali (see Figs. 4, 21, 22).

The isolation of these hill-masses must be emphasised. In the western

1 Van Bemmelen (132).
2 See above, p. 21.

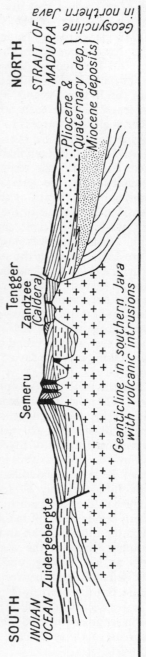

FIG. 22.—SECTION FROM S. TO N. THROUGH THE MASSIF OF TENGGER (after Van Bemmelen)

part of the region they are separated by the broad valleys of the Madiun, a feeder of the Solo, and by the Brantas, whose upper courses curve round behind them. In particular, for about 50 miles downstream from Malang the upper Brantas flows through a typical longitudinal depression between the volcanoes and the Tertiary hills in the south at a distance of only about 18 or 20 miles from the Indian Ocean. The three big hill-masses in the extreme east leave between each other low ridges across which roads and railways give easy access to Madura Strait.

As in the rest of the island, the busy north coast differs from the still wild and almost uninhabited south coast. It is low nearly everywhere and marks the recent and irregular outline of the deposits accumulated in the geosynclinal trough. The folding of these deposits, which began at the end of the Miocene period, became intensified at the end of the Pliocene and beginning of the Quaternary, while the volcanic superstructure was being built up in the south. Emergence was slow, however, and was almost counteracted by erosion. Between the segmental arches of Mt. Rembang in the north and Mt. Kendeng in the south, which are now joined by alluvium deposited by the Solo, lagoons persisted for a long time. Tertiary beds appear only as little inliers in the Surabaya district, rising out of the flood plains of the Solo and Brantas. The Rembang Hills rise again in the nearby Miocene limestones in Madura. But south of this island a broad gulf still persists, and at the mouth of the strait linking it to the Java Sea has grown up the great sugar port of Surabaya.

Over this relief and its contrasts the climate tends to be drier and drier. The volcanic hill-masses are of course islands of heavy rainfall; for instance, Kayuenak (3100 feet) south of Tosari in the Tengger district gets 220 inches a year and Pakudo (2400 feet) in the south-eastern slopes of Idyen more than 160 inches. The lowlands near by benefit from this rainfall; for example, Rogojambi at the foot of the last-named hill-mass about six miles from Bali Strait and at an altitude of only 270 feet totals 75 inches. The foehn effect is stronger in the east than in the centre of the island, for the southeasterly winds from off the Australian desert have a shorter passage across the Indian Ocean and, once their moisture has been spent on the south slopes of the volcanoes, they reach the lowlands in the north as hot, drying, and fairly strong breezes, since they are canalised in the gaps between the hill-masses. Even at Kediri on the middle Brantas scarcely 7 per cent. of the total annual rainfall of 70 inches occurs in the four months from July to October. This dry season lengthens towards the east. Thus, in a five-months' period Pasuruan gets only 4½ inches out of the year's total of 51 inches, and

Asembagus at the foot of Mt. Idyen and on the same coast of Madura Strait gets 2¾ inches out of a total of 36 inches[1] and only 0·2 inch in the months of August and September. The number of days on which rain falls decreases similarly. At Kediri the mean is 103, at Pasuruan 94, and at Asembagus 72. This last station has recorded a total of only 9 days with rain in the month of August over a period of 30 years (1895–1924). The effect of aspect is confirmed by contrasting Asembagus with Rogojambi, which has already been mentioned as being situated on the other side of Mt. Idyen.

Drought makes itself clearly visible in the scenery in the eastern region and especially on the lowlands around Madura Strait. For weeks at a time the sun shines hot and clear for most of the day. At Sarokha on the south coast of Madura insolation reaches 90 per cent. between 9 a.m. and 4 p.m. from June to September, a circumstance very favourable to the salt industry. Passengers by train from Surakarta to Surabaya in September are struck with the red tints of the fields (which are in places hedged with cactus), the monotonous forests of white-boled teak with branches almost bare of leaves, the tiny greyish leaves of the mimosas planted beside the dusty roads, and, now that the harvest has been taken in, the wide cracks in the soil in the ricefields. In the extreme east of the lowlands nothing is seen but savanas whose sun-scorched grass is dotted with borassus (Palmyra) palms. Asembagus with its cane-fields irrigated with water from Mt. Idyen looks like an oasis.

Man's use of nature here is more like that in Mid Java than the latter is like that in the west of the island. But it is more varied owing to the greater contrasts in relief and climate, to which the island of Madura adds its own peculiarities. The original diversity in the physical conditions has been increased still more by the work of the Dutch.

The soil on the Tertiary ridges which run through the lowlands in the north from Semarang to Surabaya is the least fertile in East Java and besides cannot be irrigated. So the district has been given up to teak forests which were gradually improved by the Colonial Government by means of scientific treatment and development. The natives responsible for the maintenance of young plantations were rewarded with the right to grow catch-crops between the trees.[2] Elsewhere the soil is often very fertile. Many basins have a very productive black soil which must be distinguished from the reddish-brown soil found on some of the karstic plateaus, from the yellow

[1] In some years only 15·7 inches. The drought is sometimes absolute for six months and at times even eight. (Mohr (98) p. 485.)

[2] Reinhard (54).

M.I.B.P.—13

soil of recent alluvium,[1] and from the reddish-violet soil in certain volcanic districts. Its type seems to be like that of the *regur* in India, and it is not much affected by the nature of the underlying rock. At any rate, it is found on strata rich in calcium as well as on friable volcanic soil. It seems mainly related to the length of the dry season and is absent wherever the total annual rainfall exceeds 80 inches.

The proportion of the soil cultivated by natives, 59 per cent. of the total area, is lower than in Mid Java, but greater than in the west. The distribution of crops is different. The area devoted to *sawahs* is less than in the centre, and even than in the west. This is due to the greater drought and the smaller quantity of water available for irrigation. On the other hand, since the so-called secondary crops depend as a rule on the rain only, they are far more extensive than in the rest of the island. Less upland rice (*padi gogo*) is grown than maize, and the latter crop is more extensive than any kind of rice in the Residencies of Bojo Negoro, Malang, and Besuki. Cassava, sweet potatoes, and other tubers, groundnuts, soya beans, and various other legumes also occupy a greater proportion of the area under cultivation than is the case elsewhere. Nowhere else is the soil so intensively cultivated or the period of fallow so short.[2]

The quantity of these food crops grown for local consumption and also for export varies with the year. The chief export is cassava, which is prepared for shipment by native and Chinese petty traders.

The natives have also increased the acreage they have under tobacco, a proportion of the leaves being handed over for drying and fermenting to companies like the Anglo-American Tobacco Co., which thus supplemented the yields of their own plantations, as was done in the central region of the island. On the other hand, the sugarcane handled in European mills came, as was also the case in the central region, almost exclusively from crops grown under European management on land rented from native villages. There it was grown alternately with food crops for local use. The growing of canes and the making of sugar has played an even greater part here than in the central region. In 1937 the eastern region had more than half the island's total area under sugarcane and was responsible for more than half the production of sugar.

European plantations were on the whole far more extensive than in the central region. Sugarcane is above all the speciality of the lowlands in the north on both sides of Surabaya and between

---

[1] Lehmann (136), p. 53.

[2] In 1937 the area under cultivation represented 135 per cent. of the area which could be cultivated by the natives, that is, two crops a year were grown in a large number of fields. Secondary crops covered 5,870,000 acres against 2,830,000 acres of rice.

Madiun and Situbondo. Around Majakarta the ruins of the
capital of Majapahit have been used to build sugar-mills. In the
south of the island to the east of the River Brantas the *hevea*, which
had become rare east of Chilachap, reappears above the tobacco on
the slopes of the volcanic hill-masses. Coffee cultivation has
increased at a higher mean altitude, and the bushes are often grown
among the rubber-trees. The eastern end of the island from Mt.
Kelud to Mt. Idyen is the main coffee-producing district in Java.[1]

Madura, which is attached for administrative purposes to the
eastern division of Java, retains a peculiar appearance on the other
side of the two-mile-wide strait which separates it from its larger
sister. As there is no mountain mass and as the maximum altitude
is 1544 feet, irrigation is restricted to a very small area. The island
has, however, been a refuge in troublous times and swarms with
people. The poor soil afforded by Tertiary marls is cultivated to
the utmost. There are no woods, not even an artificial plantation
of teak, and none of the land is rented to Europeans. Out of an
area of 2270 square miles (including the islets near by) 1760 square
miles are under cultivation, but only 285 in *sawahs*. Besides, the
yield from the latter is very poor and falls in some years to fifteen
bushels an acre, which is half the mean in Java. On the other hand,
Madura is the land of maize, a crop which has become the basis of
the local diet, rice being a luxury. In 1937 Madura planted 855,000
acres in maize as against 183,000 in rice. On the other hand, the
island is distinguished from Java by the relative importance assumed
by stock-rearing. In no other province are oxen so numerous in
relation to the population or area. A stream of emigrants has
recently poured into Java from this overpopulated island.

East Java has been through great vicissitudes of population.
Thither the devotees of the Hindu religion who had gathered in the
glorious kingdom of Majapahit fled before the advance of Islam.
Majapahit held out for a long time against the attacks of Mataram,
the kingdom in Mid Java whose princes had become Muslims.
However, in the 17th century Majapahit was invaded, and its people
taken *en masse* westwards. Later, the wars between the Muslims,
supported by the Dutch, and the lords of Bali helped to depopulate
the country, especially the extreme east.

Since 1870 a strong current of immigration has revived the
eastern districts. The new-comers are Javanese who have moved
eastwards from the districts of Madiun, Kediri, Malang, and
Surabaya, and there are even more from Madura.[2] The immigrants

---

[1] In 1937 the plantations, or 'estates', growing both rubber and coffee in
East Java numbered 233.

[2] Lekkerkerker (137), p. 877.

were at first seasonal labourers who worked on the European plantations and in Surabaya and other towns. But temporary immigration often ended in permanent settlement. In 1930 there were 1,950,000 Madurese in Madura and 2,337,000 in eastern Java. They are very numerous, especially south of Madura Strait, and form 37 per cent. of the population in the Residency of Malang, 63 per cent. in Besuki, and 98 per cent. in the Districts of Panarukan and Bandawasa in the last-named Residency. Into this ancient Javanese country they bring their own language and customs, their fierce and melancholy disposition, and their fondness for using the *kris*.

The inflow of Madurese has placed some of the districts here among those with the greatest increase of population in Java. Between 1920 and 1930 the population of the Residency of Besuki increased by 33 per cent., that of Kediri by 21 per cent., that of Malang by about 21 per cent., whilst in Madura it increased by a bare 12 per cent., and in Java and Madura as a whole by 17·4 per cent.

There are, however, well marked differences in the distribution of population. Here again the sugar-producing lowlands in the north are the most densely peopled, with more than 1300 persons to the square mile in the district of Surabaya. Dry and barren Madura was shown by the 1930 census to be overpopulated with 930 persons to the square mile and only 100 men to every 113 women. The density falls to 530 in the Residency of Besuki and to less than 259 at the eastern extremity of Java in the District of Asembagus.

These relatively low figures may nevertheless reveal serious overpopulation in the mountain districts. This is true of the Tengger hill-mass, whose people form the most peculiar community in Java, since they have long remained isolated from the plainsmen. They alone have kept their old religion amidst the rising tide of Islam. Their villages with houses built of casuarina wood are situated as far up as about the 6600-foot contour. Their crops grow still higher up. Fields of upland rice, maize, and sweet potatoes separated by hedges and dotted with trees make a curious wooded landscape. But the Tenggerese, of whom there are about 16,000, are visited by tourists from Tosari and are now moving with the times. Nowadays they roof their houses with corrugated iron and cultivate potatoes, cabbages, and other European vegetables—even strawberries, large quantities of which they sell in the lowlands, mainly in Surabaya.

AGRICULTURE AND IRRIGATION IN JAVA

As Java was under Dutch influence for more than three hundred years, its development presents a most interesting picture to the geographer as well as to the economic historian. Many experiments

were tried, very different systems were applied and often reached a
degree of perfection that made the island into a model setting a
standard for colonial territories.

Its fame was indeed eclipsed at first in European eyes by the Spice
Islands. The attraction of the Moluccas continued for some time
after Coen's victory in 1619. The foundation of Batavia, however,
made Java the centre of Dutch power; but the East India Company,
which was a commercial firm, was less interested in using the soil
than in the business of its trading posts strung out from the Cape of
Good Hope to New Guinea and Japan, and on the coasts of India,
Ceylon, Indo-China, and China.

However, the Company did not fail to take advantage of such
favourable conditions as the high quality of the soil and the teeming
population afforded for the production of certain tropical commodities. It was mainly the wish to develop this production and to
monopolise the trade in these commodities that led it to a policy of
territorial acquisition. At the end of the 18th century its effective
rule spread over the whole island, and Java's agricultural exports—
coffee and sugar in particular—were far more important than the
spices from eastern Indonesia.

Java's leading position was confirmed during the 19th century
after the Company's downfall. Colonial policy underwent pro-
found changes. Liberal ideas took the place of those which led to
forced labour. Until about 1860 or 1870 all Java's exports came
from native smallholdings.[1] But then company-owned plantations
increased in number. European capital began to be interested in
the Outer Provinces, but did not neglect Java, which had been
wholly pacified, enjoyed a long-standing reputation, and was
plentifully supplied with labour whose value had been increased by
the abolition of slavery in the West Indies. In 1894 Java and
Madura produced 82 per cent. of the exports of Indonesia.

It was in the first thirty years of the 20th century that the Outer
Provinces made up their leeway. In 1925 and every year from 1932
to 1940 the value of their agricultural exports exceeded that of Java.
The proportion was 65 to 35 in 1937 and 60 to 40 in 1940.[2]

Another statistical fact strikes one's attention. The share of the
European plantations and of native small holdings in these exports
in Java was very different from that in the other Dutch islands. In
the Outer Provinces native producers accounted for 57 per cent. of
the total exports in 1937; but in Java only 25 per cent., and even so
this latter figure had increased since the sugar crisis.[3] This difference

[1] More or less under European control.
[2] Broek (187), p. 35. But only 20 per cent. in 1948.
[3] It was 19 per cent. in 1928; see Broek (187), p. 42.

is evidently connected with dissimilarities in population-density. In most of the Outer Provinces there was plenty of land on which the native peasant could grow crops for export. In Java and Madura, on the other hand, land was scarce, and it was surprising that the people succeeded in earmarking so large a proportion of their crops for sale abroad.

Land held by Europeans—and a far smaller portion held by foreign Asiatics—amounted in 1937 to about 9 per cent.[1] of the total area of Java and Madura. On land so held the native was only a wage-earner. About 60 per cent. of the total area was cultivated by the peasants without European interference. It is noticeable that the proportion of land under cultivation is very high compared with the Japanese Islands, where it is only 16 per cent.

The average area of native holdings paying land tax was 2·2 acres, and the average number of lots held by each landowner was 2·6 in 1938. But these figures were but an imperfect indication of the truth. Since registration was done village by village, it was difficult to discover the amount of landed wealth of large landowners who had property in several villages. A field might be mortgaged for debt, whilst continuing to figure on the cadastral rolls in the name of the former owner. *Métayage* is widely practised in Java, especially in rice growing. The smallholder rents out his *sawah*, the rent being paid him in advance on condition of his continuing to work the field and handing over a proportion of the crop. It must be added that middlemen, mainly Chinese, who are firmly settled and more active in Java than in the rest of Indonesia, skim off a fat share of the profits from the sale of agricultural produce. Thus, the division of profits from agriculture is carried much farther than appears from a mere examination of cadastral documents. Below the big landowners and traders and under the well-to-do peasants exists a numerous class of cultivators who have at their disposal either a mere patch which is not big enough to feed them or else own nothing but the little garden next their houses. Consequently, they are obliged to seek a living otherwise than by farming.[2]

It is becoming increasingly difficult to get bigger yields from agriculture in Java. Land worked by natives falls into three main classes: *sawahs*, or irrigated fields, *tegals*, or fields without irrigation, and gardens. All three classes had increased in total area owing more or less directly to the Dutch administration.

[1] Of which 5 per cent. was under cultivation.

[2] For this paragraph, see Boeke (186), pp. 40–8. Safe comparisons between Java and other overpopulated areas in Monsoon Asia are desirable; but they are difficult to make, for the statistical bases are not the same and the information published is often inadequate. See, for instance, P. Gourou: *Les paysans du Delta tonkinois*, Paris, 1936, p. 356, for land tenure on the Red River Delta.

The extension and improvement of irrigation was of course the great achievement of the Dutch in Java[1] and is the greatest factor in maintaining a proper balance between food crops and produce for export. Irrigation has been practised from time immemorial, though it is impossible to say how much native methods owe to the Hindus, Chinese, or Arabs. It is almost everywhere indispensable if a regular yield is to be had from the *sawahs*. Even in the west of the island during the rainy season the weather may be fine for two or three weeks and so the crops may be endangered. Such droughts become more and more frequent as one goes east. In 1914, a year of disaster, the monthly rainfall was below 0·2 inches for two or three months in western Java, four months in central Java, and as much as five months in the east.

The problem is not merely one of distributing the water which the rivers drain off naturally. In spite of the permeability of the soil on many of the volcanoes, the river régime is unreliable owing to the short courses and steep upper slopes. Sudden, violent spates, or *banjir*, in which masses of water heavy with boulders and mud sweep down into the valley, are followed by periods of low water, when mere ribbons of foam stream along the bottoms of the beds. In the northern lowlands the normal extremes of discharge from the Brantas, which is the least irregular of the rivers in Java, are 97 and 1480 cubic yards per second, and in exceptional floods 2220 cubic yards. On the Solo, the longest river in the island, the figures for the normal extremes are 30 and 2600 cubic yards, with 3370 cubic yards in exceptionally high floods.

The volcanoes present a fairly simple problem. On the long concave slopes gullied by streams the natives make terraces with horizontal or slightly sloping surfaces and enclosed by the wall supporting the terrace next above and by embankments of earth following the contours. In this way not only is the rainwater retained on the terraces, but the peasant also easily turns on to them streams fed by constant springs. Little canals branch out above a fall or rock sill and follow the crest line in order to serve the *sawahs* on both slopes. The precious liquid reaches the terraces by open dykes or else by coconut or bamboo pipes. The irrigation network is evidence of admirable, long-continued teamwork.

In the lowlands the native method no longer works, in spite of its ingenuity, for the current is more difficult to control and the areas to be irrigated more extensive. Acting together, the villages have built dams of stones without mortar, tree trunks, or bamboos; but these cannot stand up to the floods, which often destroy the banks of the canals as well. Besides, the problem of drainage on gentle

[1] Reinhard (225); F. Bernard (205).

slopes has been very imperfectly solved, and the surfeit of water on the low ground has threatened to damage the crops.

From 1830 onwards strong teak dams were built under Dutch supervision. The first modern irrigation work was constructed about the middle of the last century at Sidoaryo to the south of Surabaya. But permanent networks enabling the use of water from big rivers over wide areas were not made until after 1880. They were all under the care of a special body of engineers, the Waterstaat, whose competence and reputation equalled those of their fellow-countrymen at home. Operations began only after detailed preparations, including the making of large-scale plans (1/5000 or 1/2000),[1] with contours at a vertical interval of 1 metre or 0·5 metre, the study of the nature of the rainfall and river systems, and the examination of the character and yield of existing crops. Close co-operation was indispensable between the engineer, farmer, forester, and administrator for the construction and use of the system. The difficulty was increased by the fact that the work was usually not on virgin soil, but on areas already overpopulated, where former native construction had to be taken into account and cultivation could not be interrupted without risking a catastrophic famine, and where, even in times of low water, the land had to be protected against floods and as far as possible navigation uninterrupted. Hence, the construction of the finest systems was not carried out all at once, but took years of effort and progressive improvement. The process is illustrated on the plains of Demak north-east of Semarang, the delta of the Brantas south of Surabaya, and the valley of the Solo, all districts exposed to disastrous famines.

The typical irrigation system consists of a masonry dam with an overfall or sluice-gates to allow of the escape of flood-water and behind this a regulator carefully protected from the terrific force of the *banjirs*. From the dam issues the main canal, which runs round the upper boundary of the area to be irrigated, and the distribution depends wholly on gravity. Feeders of the river are crossed either by aqueduct or siphon. After the water is used, it is led back to the river or emptied into the sea through special canals. Electric pumps are seldom employed. At first, the material needed for construction —even bricks and concrete—came from the Netherlands as ballast on sailing ships.

At the end of 1938 the fields irrigated by these improved systems covered about 3,000,000 acres (not counting those in the Principalities), i.e. 38 per cent. of the total area of the *sawahs*, whilst the older systems irrigated 3,700,000 acres. Construction had been expensive, averaging 470 florins an acre; but this price was not too

[1] Aerial photography was beginning to be used.

high, considering the results. Rice production was increased and made regular, and the remarkable association of sugarcane and tobacco with the traditional crops in the centre and east of the island was made possible. In districts with these mixed crops, distribution must be most carefully regulated, since drought increases everyone's need for water. It was controlled by distributing stations, the sectors, or *golongan*, being irrigated in turn according to the quantity of water available and the needs of each crop at the successive stages of growth. There was no charge for the water. In principle the cost should be covered by the land tax and by the various dues accruing to the Government from the increase in production (see Fig. 23).

Owing to the activities of the Waterstaat the increase in irrigable area between 1927 and 1938 was about 125,000 acres a year. The area that remains to be dealt with reasonably, i.e. at a cost proportionate to the results, is now very small.

Owing to the use of irrigation the area of *sawahs* had increased in Java since the beginning of the century by about 24 per cent.[1], which is less than the rate of increase in population. The yield itself had not increased proportionately, for the intrinsic fertility of the newly irrigated areas is often less than that of old *sawahs*. On the other hand, in the centre and east the best soil was reserved for sugarcane, rice not being planted there except in the intervals between crops of sugarcane. Since 1927 the average yield per acre had been oscillating gently around 70 bushels of dry unhusked rice,[2] which is equivalent to 35 bushels of husked rice. The planting out of seedlings takes place mainly in December, January, and February; and the principal harvest months are April, May, and June. But no week passes without one or other of these operations taking place in a certain number of fields. Fewer than half the *sawahs* yield a second crop of rice in the dry season, but the yield of such a crop may be better than that of the first, if the irrigation water has been suitably distributed. Recent researches have established the beneficial effects of light, which seems vital especially during the first months of growth. (See *Revue de Botanique appliquée et d'Agriculture tropicale*, Paris, 1943, p. 43.)

After 1936 Java no longer imported rice, but on the contrary exported small quantities to the rest of Indonesia.[3] The bulk of native-grown rice exported, however, came from non-irrigated crops.

Though rice continues to be the chief food, yet the area devoted to so-called secondary crops has increased far more than that on which

[1] About 60 per cent. between 1874 and 1921 according to van der Wærden, (232), p. 608.
[2] Only 46 in Madura, where irrigation is impossible.
[3] Since the end of the war rice is being imported once more.

the prevailing cereal is grown. These crops may be cultivated in *sawahs* during the dry season; but they are grown mainly in *tegals*, the total area of which increased by 350 per cent. between 1874 and 1921, whilst the *sawahs* increased by only 60 per cent. Whilst in 1916 the area of *sawahs* still represented 50·8 per cent. of the cultivable land, in 1936 it was no more than 42·8 per cent. Since 1925 the decrease in the percentage has been very slow, however, owing to the construction of huge irrigation systems. It is estimated that in the average holding of 2·2 acres 0·95 acre is occupied by *sawahs* and 1·25 acres by unirrigated crops.[1]

The main crops on the *tegals* are maize, cassava, sweet potatoes, groundnuts, soya and other beans rather than special varieties of upland rice. This produce is chiefly intended for local consumption, but, apart from the sweet potato, it supplies an export trade which, with the wages earned on European estates, is the main source of funds from which the native pays his taxes and buys imported goods.

Enclosures known in Dutch as *erven*, which are adjacent to the dwellings and are cultivated by horticultural, not agricultural, methods, are to be distinguished from the *tegals* properly so-called, with which, however, they are often confused in official statistics. As the population grew, so these parcels increased in number, even at the expense of the *sawahs*. Many families hold only these enclosures together with the sites of their dwellings. They contain a great mixture of commonly used vegetables. Under fruit trees and others yielding firewood or timber and under bamboos grow tuberiferous and leguminous plants, sesame, millet, maize, gourds, greens and herbs, spices and dye-plants, sugarcane and coffee, tobacco and betel, etc. It is estimated that these enclosures alone form 15 or 16 per cent. of all the land under cultivation and that in proportion to their size they give a bigger yield than the fields. Whilst the *tegal* is mainly worked by men, the garden is the woman's sphere. From it she gathers day by day the produce needed for the family or to be sold in the market.[2]

Unlike the developments noticed in the former Outer Provinces, the increase in the area under cultivation in Java in recent years has been due essentially to the spread of annual plants whose produce is intended both for local consumption and export. This increase was only 3·5 per cent. between 1929 and 1938, which is much less than that of the population. Like the *sawahs* the areas suitable for unirrigated tillage will increase still more slowly in the years to come. The steady bringing under cultivation of steep slopes makes the damage caused by erosion more serious in the highlands. The forests which survive have been reserved and are maintained under

[1] Boeke (186), p. 40.   . [2] Boeke (186), p. 63.

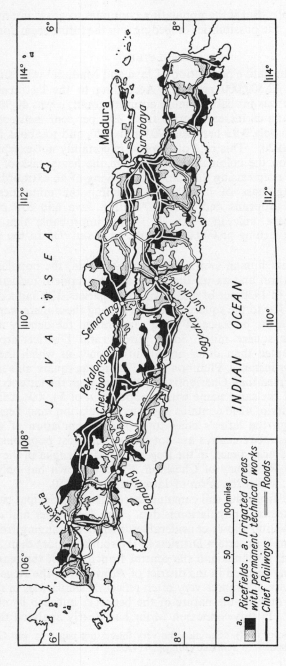

Fig. 23.—Java: Ricefields, Railways, and Roads

strict control.   But if the population continues to grow and to swell like a *banjir*, the possibilities of feeding it in the future seem doubtful.

POPULATION

In 1860 the native population of Java and Madura[1] was estimated to number 12,500,000 persons.   According to the last census in 1930, which was probably a more accurate count, it was 40,900,000. The mean annual increase varied from 2·64 per cent. between 1860 and 1870 to only 0·93 between 1905 and 1920, and to about 1·5 per cent. after 1920.   This rate of increase is certainly not exceptional, but it laid on the colonial administration the heavy task of maintaining and even raising the standard of living of an extraordinarily fast-breeding mass of humanity.   Including the minorities consisting of Europeans and foreign Asiatics, Java had 816 persons to the square mile in 1930.   It is not improbable that today she may be feeding 55,000,000 people, or about 935 to the square mile.

As in other human swarms in Monsoon Asia, the population is essentially rural and as yet little attracted by modern industry and town life.   In 1930 out of a total of 432 Districts, 120 had a density exceeding 1300 to the square mile, and among these there were only ten in which the presence of a big town raised the density to over 2600 to the square mile.   Some purely rural Districts are more densely peopled than other neighbouring ones in which there are towns.   For instance, Plumbon with 2780 to the square mile is more densely peopled than Cheribon with 2450, though the latter contains the town of the same name with a population of 54,000; Adiwerno with a density of 4240 contains a greater population than Tegal with 3800, though the latter's chief town has a population of 43,000. The administrative centres are not always the most populous in the Districts.   For instance, in the Regency of Majalengka in the southwest of the Residency of Cheribon, the chief town has only 8000 inhabitants, whilst the *dessa* of Jatiwangi has 10,250.

The yield from the soil remains therefore the principal cause to which this teeming population is due.   The density per unit of land under cultivation shows considerable differences, ranging from 520 per square mile in certain Districts in the south to more than 2600 in the northern lowlands and the central Principalities, the maximum of 4560 being reached in the district of Adiwerno in the Regency of Tegal.   These differences very often reflect dissimilarities in fertility caused not only by the nature of the bedrock, but also by climatic conditions.   In this connexion Mohr has clearly analysed the part

[1] Lekkerkerker (137).   See also the very interesting pages by van Gelderen and Meyer Renneft in Schrieke (20), pp. 71–102.

played by the eruptions of Mts. Slamat, Merapi, and Kelud in the middle and east of the island, where the rainfall system ensures the preservation of the salts contained in the basic lava.[1] On the other hand, in Bantam the soil feeds a far less numerous population, because it is derived from acid lava which is chemically poorer and since in addition it is heavy, compact, and more quickly exhausted by a heavy and very frequent rainfall.

The possibilities of irrigation are another leading factor in the uneven distribution of population. They depend not only on the quantity of water available, but also on the topography which may make the leading and distribution of the water more or less difficult or even impossible. In this respect Java is particularly favoured by its volcanic structure and the variety of its relief, which almost everywhere mingles highland and lowland. Increase in density of population must long have been closely related to the expansion of the area of *sawahs*, which have been comparatively bigger in the northern lowlands. But it seems clear that Dutch intervention has often acted in the same way by further increasing the resources of densely peopled districts in which irrigation is possible and which afford plenty of water and labour. The part played by the sugar-cane appears to be considerable. The most densely populated districts are mostly those in which the prosperity of sugarcane cultivation has been a triumph for European capital and science.[2] The natives have profited by the rent paid to the villages for land, by the wages for work on the plantations and in the mills and for their help in transporting the canes. The huge irrigation projects carried out for this crop, the fertiliser required, the roads and rail-ways which are due to it or whose completion it has hastened have also enabled the soil to be more intensively used in the intervals of time reserved for food crops by the compulsory rotation. Though the food crops have been left to the care of the natives, the yield has increased in many places, and it has even been possible to export part of the harvest. For instance, cassava, soya beans, and other leguminous produce have been exported from the Residency of Pekalongan and groundnuts from the Residency of Cheribon.

The influence of European plantations, therefore, seems to be greater than appears from the statistics of chief occupations. According to the census of 1930, 69·6 per cent. of the active male population of Java lived mainly by agriculture and stock-rearing on native properties and 6·6 per cent. by working on European planta-tions. But many persons who were classed as fishermen (0·9 per

---

[1] See Mohr's article (98) and the graph accompanying it.
[2] Kuperus (135), p. 470; Robequain (200), p. 44.

cent.), artisans, or workmen (11·5 per cent.) certainly worked for a time on the land.[1]

Industry is mainly a family affair both for doing jobs incidental to an agricultural community or in landless villages for carrying out, as is done in French Indo-China (Vietnam), specialised tasks in some manufacture, the processes of which are handed down more or less secretly from generation to generation. The industries which call for the greatest amount of labour are the food industries, then the textiles, then timber and bamboo. The largest proportion of workmen seem to be employed in the most densely peopled districts; as, for instance, in the neighbourhood of Pekalongan, where *batik* manufacture is widespread.

Indeed, overpopulation favours a variety of small crafts which give whole or part-time work to persons whom the land can no longer employ or feed. Transport workers and middlemen increase in number along with craftsmen. Pedlars jog along the side-paths by the roads with their shoulders bent under the bamboo loaded at each end; or else, in the east, with head high and stiff under the burden. Then there are *prahu* boatmen and car drivers, the latter being especially numerous in the sugar-growing districts. Barter still goes on. But the general use of money, the new roads, and rapid means of transport have helped to foster those petty deals for which women are chiefly responsible. It is the women too that enliven a host of periodical markets, or *pasar*.[2]

The population lives in *kampongs*, or villages, whose sites are determined by relief, water supply, and facilities for agriculture.[3] In the lowlands where there is a risk of flooding the village may run along a contour on a hill, forming a crescent which at times almost closes into a circle. On the coast it may stretch out along the sand ridges marking the successive lines to which the shore has advanced. The average number of inhabitants has no connexion with the density of population in the district. On the slopes of Merapi in Mid Java the population is concentrated in big villages, whilst farther east in the District of Ponorogo, south of Madiun, where the density exceeds 1300 to the square mile, the map shows a sprinkling of smaller villages placed more closely together. Until a closer study is made,

---

[1] Boeke (186), p. 171. In the 69·6 per cent. living by agriculture and stock-rearing on native properties, stock-rearing accounted for only 2·5 per cent. Boeke also included in the total half of the 8·7 per cent. which the 1930 census report classes as 'miscellaneous'. It should be noted that the 69·6 per cent. represents a proportion about three times as great as is found in the Netherlands in 1930 (23·2 per cent.). The low percentage of fishermen is surprising, considering that Java is an overpopulated island with a well-developed coastline.

[2] For significant examples, see Boeke (186), p. 94.

[3] Atlas (13), pp. 6b and 8e.

tradition and racial habits must be called upon to explain the matter. The Javanese properly so-called prefer large concentrations, whilst the Sundanese and Madurese prefer hamlets. The complete dispersal of family holdings is rare, however, and is scarcely ever seen except in cases of recent settlement, as on the south coast of East Java to the south-west of Jember. Irrigation is a potent factor in concentration. In the Middle Province many *kampongs* have populations of more than 5000, but the average lies between 500 and 2000 persons.

The houses are seldom close together, each standing in its own garden under the shade of fruit trees. The building, which is of wood or bamboo lattice-work covered with rough-cast, stands on low wood or cement piles among the Sundanese, but otherwise rests on the ground itself. The pitch of the roof is fairly low, and brown tiles often replace thatch, though instances of the latter persist here and there. The windows are quite often fitted with shutters and at times with glass panes. In the Western Province the few live-stock are sometimes driven at night into a fenced paddock. The oxen and buffaloes usually have a separate shelter close to the house, or else a paddock is made just outside the village and is common to all the inhabitants.[1] Family holdings are often separated from each other by hedges of *lantana*. The changing light throws on the vegetation in the gardens every shade of green from the pale tint of the betel to the sometimes metallic glitter of the palms. Among the common trees are species of exotic origin which have succeeded in flourishing in Java; for example, the kapok, or silk-cotton, tree (*Ceiba pentandra*), which was imported from America and has a straight trunk of a beautiful green and at times is made to support telephone lines on its storied branches; and the African tamarind (*Tamarinda indica*), whose magnificent spread of foliage throws a pale sieve-like shade on the ground. Above the 3000-foot contour the villages are tree-less, hedges become rare, the gardens are smaller, and palms are no longer seen in them.

In the lowlands of the Middle and Eastern Provinces the Javanese village looks like a well-protected organism surrounded by tall bamboos like those in Annam or by low walls of rough-cast built with gates through them. Even when the *kampong* comprises several hamlets, it remains a well-knit social and administrative unit, in spite of the blows struck more or less conscientiously by Europeans at the old *adat* rules. It contains no separate castes, as in India, but nevertheless has a hierarchy based on wealth in land, from the man who owns a large area of *sawah* to the tenant who possesses only a few pieces of furniture. In deliberative assemblies the voting is

[1] Paravicini (139), p. 454.

usually restricted to members of the highest classes. In important matters like the election of executive officers and especially of the mayor, the *lura* or *petingi*, the wishes of the Dutch district commissioner used nearly always to prevail.

Most Javanese villages have grown up on sites occupied from time immemorial. But Dutch influence has led to many new clusters of houses along the roads and near the railway stations. The island has the advantage of a fine network of modern lines of communication. Even in the mid-19th century it was possible to travel from one end of the island to the other in a horse-drawn vehicle at a rate of between 9 and 10 miles an hour, luggage being carried by ox-cart or coolies. The first two railways, built by private enterprise, but taken over by the Colonial Government in 1873, were intended to connect Jakarta and Semarang with the plantations in the Preanger and Vorstenlanden Districts. Up to 1875 the innovation was regarded as utterly rash, and the first train of vehicles was drawn along the rails by buffaloes.. Then the Government took a hand in developing the railway system, which today has 3400 miles of track with a general gauge of 1·067 metres (3 feet 6 inches). In proportion to the area of the two countries this network is denser than that in Spain. Lines across the island to feed the three great ports in the north are joined by two main lines running the length of the island, on one of which the night express in 1939 used to cover in about 12 hours the 530 miles between Jakarta and Surabaya. The lines radiating from Jakarta are electrified (see Fig. 23).

Since motor-bus services increased in number, the railway system has been complemented and rivalled by the roads, about 12,500 miles of which have been surfaced with tarmac or at any rate metalled.[1]

These fast routes have hastened the growth of towns.[2] And yet in 1930 places with a population of more than 20,000 contained only 7 per cent. of the total population.[3] Six of them had populations exceeding 100,000, and one exceeds half a million (see Fig. 10). The three biggest are ports on the north coast and at the same time economic foci, and there is a strong family likeness between them.

By adapting itself extraordinarily well to new conditions Jakarta (see Fig. 24) has kept the pre-eminence at which its founders aimed.

---

[1] Unfortunately, there is little good road-metal in the underlying rocks in Java, apart from certain limestones. The volcanic rocks, which are basalt and andesite, are easily decomposed.

[2] The figures given here are those of the last census. Since the war ended, the towns in Java have grown very much.

[3] As against 50 per cent. in the Netherlands.

The old city is still clearly recognisable at the mouth of the *prahu*-crowded Chiliwung. The abandoned warehouses of the Dutch East India Company still stand within their sheltering ramparts and the green water that fills the moats. The tile-roofed houses closely packed along the canals are now tenanted mainly by Chinese. In this part of the town there still remain the warehouses and offices of a few European firms as well as Government buildings, like the old Stadhuis with its superadded pediment rounded in the Dutch fashion. But the town has expanded far southwards away from the swampy and unhealthy coast. In 1808 Daendels razed the citadel to the ground and during the first twenty-five years of the 19th century the Weltevreden quarter, now the centre of the town, was built according to his plans. This more recent quarter is 2½ miles south of the old town and is now joined to it by a continuously built-over area. Spread out around the enormous Royal Square are the Government Offices, consulates, big hotels, and commercial offices, most of which are built of concrete. On either side of the streets a series of large European shops and *tokos*, or small shops, were usually kept by Chinese or Japanese. The regularly laid-out quarters of Gondangia and Menteng join it to the hills on which Meester Cornelis (Jatinegara) stands. In this aristocratic suburb the older residences with their verandas, bow windows, and splendid gardens are in contrast with the little, three-or-four-roomed cottages which stand close together in rows giving the impression of the new part of a Dutch town. This was a recent development and marked the progress of comfort due to the innumerable domestic uses of electricity, but it also betrayed the impoverishment of many Europeans and Eurasians during the 20th-century economic crises. All around the Javanese population lives in *kampongs* which are not very unlike the country villages. They have the same kind of houses built of vegetable matter and hidden among trees, and the same murmur of running water in which women may be seen doing their laundry.

Owing to the linking up of its nuclei at different dates, Batavia, or Jakarta, as it is again called (pop. 533,000 in 1930),[1] covers 7½ miles from north to south. Besides, the old harbour on the Chiliwung has had to be abandoned and is now used only by small fishing and coastal boats. The river itself has been inaccessible to ocean-going ships since the beginning of the 18th century. The modern harbour at Tanjung Priok was built 6 miles farther east to avoid the river silt. Its four docks are connected with Jakarta by canal, road, and rail. In 1937, 39 per cent. by value of the imports into and 40 per cent. of the exports from Java passed through this port.

[1] This may perhaps have reached two million in 1950. For the population-figures of Indonesian towns, see below, p. 442.

Surabaya (pop. 342,000), on the Kali Mas, a distributary of the
Brantas, clearly developed in much the same way as Jakarta, though
more slowly.　It was only just after 1870 that the town broke out of

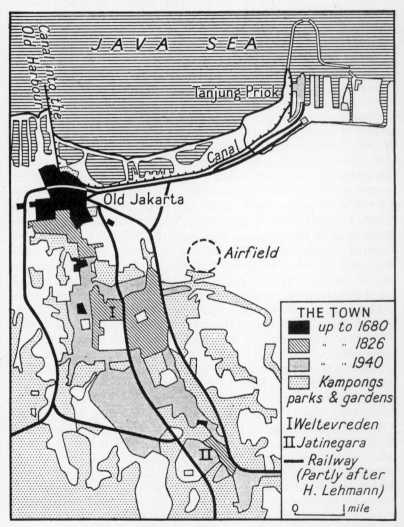

FIG. 24.—GROWTH OF JAKARTA (BATAVIA)

the fortifications of the old trading station and spread southwards
along the river towards Ketabang and Kupang.　Compared with
Jakarta, Surabaya looks rather like an upstart—more ostentatious

perhaps, but less confident. It was hard hit by the economic crisis after 1930. In it too the basins and breakwaters of the new harbour have been reclaimed from the sea and furnished with huge docks, fuel tanks, and ample equipment. It is the terminus of the great Dutch shipping lines. In 1937 it handled 32 per cent. of the island's imports and 23 per cent. of its exports.

Semarang (pop. 218,000; 18 per cent. of the island's imports and 23 per cent. of its exports) supplanted the old port of Japara only at the beginning of the 18th century. The contrast between the old town and the new is even greater than in the two towns mentioned above. Formerly the old town was isolated among fever-stricken marshes which could only be crossed on causeways, whilst the modern part, built in 1920 on the Tertiary hills to the south, contains airy villas and large parks facing the sea and Mt. Muryo and is one of the finest examples of colonial town-planning in the Far East. The construction of the harbour was begun in 1870 beyond the swamps and enabled the town to export sugar, tobacco, cassava, and kapok.

Before the war the other ports, in the north: Cheribon, Tegal, Pekalongan, Pasuruan, Probolinggo, and Panarukan; in the east Banyuwangi; in the south Chilachap (long known as 'the White Man's grave'); and others even smaller, shared between them 10 per cent. of Java's imports and 24 per cent. of its exports.

The large inland towns are of at least two very different types. To one belongs Bandung (pop. 169,000) the capital of the Priangan Residency and situated on a terrace 2400 feet above the sea on the edge of a high plain surrounded by volcanoes. Founded by a Sultan of Cheribon in the 17th century on the banks of the Chi Tarum, the village was moved at the beginning of the 19th century during Daendels' governorship to a site on the longitudinal *Postweg* (=trunk road) built by forced labour. It contained only nine Europeans in 1846 and it did not grow until just after 1880, when it was reached by the railway and when the number of plantations in the Preangers began to increase. It has not succeeded in superseding Jakarta in spite of the relatively cool, dry climate, its picturesque surroundings, and its plentiful supply of pure water. Only a few of the Dutch Government services, like the Ministry for War and the Mines Department, were moved thither. The Governor-General usually resided at Buitenzorg, halfway between the two towns. But Europeans used to be relatively more numerous here than in the ports and formed 12 per cent. of the population, whilst at Jakarta they were only 7 per cent.

Bandung is a new colonial town with no trace of *kraton*, fort, or old European trading station. On the other hand, Jogyakarta (pop. 137,000) and Surakarta (or Solo; pop. 165,000), the capitals of the Principalities, look like the direct descendants of the Indo-Javanese capitals of Mataram. In them the *kraton*, or Prince's palace, has been the centre of growth and, after being greatly modified by Muslim and, later, by European influence, still harbours within its pale a veritable town within a town and a population of several thousand persons, including members of the family, servants, guards, and craftsmen. Outside the belt of commercial quarter and the *pasar*, one soon comes to the *kampongs*, which merge with no precise boundary into the rural *dessa*. In Jogyakarta the natives formed 90 per cent. of the population before the war, whilst the Chinese formed only 6 per cent. and the Europeans 4 per cent.[1] The proportion of the various racial groups corresponded to the type of city: old native capital, or former European trading station, or modern colonial foundation.

Whilst in 1930 the urban population comprised four-fifths of the 'Europeans' and more than half the Chinese, it did not yet include 8 per cent. of the natives. The last group increased by nearly half a million a year, so that the towns received only a small part of the contingents that were regularly added to an already superabundant population. But during the war of 1941–45 there was a considerable influx into the town.[2]

Security has long reigned in Java. Owing to sanitary inspection and mass vaccination epidemics have done far less harm than formerly. Famine has been less deadly and rarer in consequence of transport facilities and modern irrigation works. It is doubtful, however, whether the native standard of living has appreciably risen during the past fifty years, and in particular it is not certain whether the food supply has increased. Java is less of a paradise on earth than many other tropical islands that are commonly given this epithet. Travellers' impressions vary according to temperament and mood, the sights expected from what has been read, the places visited, the weather, and the season. It is surprising, however, that in all this swarm of humanity sordid poverty was seldom seen. This was due to the steady climate and the traditional thrift of the native, and also to the achievements of the Dutch.

Java was the glory and at the same time the problem of the Dutch Government. The increase in supplies must exceed or at least equal that of a population whose average length of life is steadily rising without a corresponding fall in the birth-rate. At the prewar rate, Java would have had a population of 116,000,000 in the year 2000

[1] But only 2 per cent. in Surakarta.
[2] People moving into the towns and European plantations come mainly from the districts in which the proportion of folk not living by agriculture is greatest.

on an area almost exactly that of England. How would it have been fed?

There is no longer a great deal of land available for cultivation. Irrigation works are already well developed and in future can only affect some 1,200,000 acres, and then only at great expense. To increase the resources of the countryside by means of an enhanced yield from the soil, popular co-operation, and the suppression of middlemen will be a long and delicate task. The most ingenious plan for industrialisation seems able to employ only a small fraction of the annual excess of births.

There remains the possibility of emigration to the neighbouring islands, which, unlike Java, appear to be underpopulated, Sumatra having 46 persons to the square mile in 1930, Borneo 10, and Celebes 56. But the Javanese is no adventurer. As in many other peasant swarms in tropical Asia (India and Tongking, for instance) a life of poverty and undernourishment has not developed a taste for taking risks. The Javanese is strongly attached to his family, his village, and the patch he cultivates. Besides, the utter want of capital is often an obstacle to settlement abroad.

Yet the prosperity of export crops in the neighbouring islands, and especially in Sumatra, was bound to attract a certain number of Javanese. The 1930 census showed that more than a million persons born in Java were dwelling in the Outer Provinces, 643,000 being in the Oostkust alone. They were to some extent temporary emigrants: indentured or unindentured wage-earners on European plantations and free *métayers* in districts of native rubber cultivation. Many men had come without their families and had not settled. Thus, between 1930 and 1936 more than 50,000 Javanese had sailed for the Outer Provinces under indenture, but 165,000 had returned owing to the economic crisis.

By promoting little settlements of peasants the Government of the Dutch East Indies had tried to settle emigrants from Java in other islands. This step, which had been mooted by official observers as early as 1889, was begun in 1905. Families from the very over-populated Presidency of Kedu in Middle Java were settled in the Lampongs Residency in southern Sumatra near the port of Teluk Betung.[1] Since then whole train-loads of others have left to take ship at Jakarta, Semarang, or Surabaya. These petty Javanese settlers are most numerous by far in Sumatra, where in 1939 there were about 117,000 of whom 91,000 were in the Lampongs Residency. The despatch of parties to the backland of Banjermasin in southern Borneo and to Celebes (especially to the Mandar and Palopo plains in the west-centre of the island) did not begin till 1938 and by 1939

[1] See above p. 162.

had only succeeded in establishing 670 settlers in the first year and 6300 in the second.[1]

To anyone who knows the difficulties of the problem these figures indicate a remarkable result. But their inadequacy was revealed by the annual excess of about 500,000 births. In the light of past experience far greater effort will have to be made if Java is to be relieved. Official initiative and encouragement are undoubtedly necessary. The Government is responsible for choosing the area, for making the road and irrigation systems and other preliminaries, and for the transport of the settlers. But once the nuclei of the settlements are firmly rooted, they should grow of themselves, thanks to the accounts spread in the home town or district by families already established. Emigration must not look like a charitable deed intended to rid a peasant community of its weakest elements. On the contrary, there is every reason to send to the new lands healthy and energetic persons and to choose recently married couples so that the children may be born in the new country. From rather complicated calculations made by statisticians in Jakarta it is found that an annual emigration of 120,000 young childless couples would be enough to check the growth of population in Java. But this is an enormous figure and is far from being attained. Towards the middle of this century it was hoped at any rate to ship 100,000 emigrants a year. But the war came to upset these plans.

[1] Peekema (140); Broek (1), p. 192; Pelzer, 197 *bis*. The Javanese who went to settle in the Outer Provinces numbered 230,000 from 1935 to 1941 inclusive. Besides, emigration took a few thousand Javanese out of Indonesia every year, but they settled very rarely. Thus, in New Caledonia, where they supplied nearly all the plantation labour, they numbered about 8500 in 1938. On the other hand, they generally stay for good in Malaya and Surinam. In 1950 they numbered about 35,000 in the latter country, where they formed 12 per cent. of the total population and were all Muslims.

CHAPTER 10

BORNEO

Borneo with an area of 284,000 square miles is the largest island in the East Indies and one of the largest in the world. It flanks seas affording the most direct routes from China and Japan to the Indian Ocean. That it should contain so few people—about 3,000,000, or 10 to the square mile [1] and that European settlement should hitherto have remained so backward is really astonishing. Apart from factors which cannot be distinguished, from chance, and from accidents in prehistoric and historical times, the physical environment has an undoubted share of responsibility in this backwardness.

A Large, Massive Equatorial Island. Borneo is more massive than Sumatra, which itself is more compact than Java, and not so narrow. The coastline is relatively short. In Java the greatest distance from the sea is hardly as much as 60 miles; in Sumatra it is 100; but in Borneo it is 220.

The relief does not oppose serious obstacles to the way inland, however. The interior is imperfectly known, because only the western third and the south-east part of the island are covered by accurate or near-accurate maps. But it is sufficiently well known to preclude the idea that the island is very mountainous. In fact, most of it—three-fourths perhaps—is below the 1600-foot contour and about one-fourth below 350 feet (see Fig. 25). In the north and north-east the hills and mountains come almost down to the sea; but elsewhere the coast plain runs far inland, especially in the west and south-west in the valleys of the Kapuas and Barito. To the west of long. 113° E. and to the south of the Equator a few isolated peaks alone reach 3000 feet. In the east the area rising above the 1600-foot contour forms a compact mass which is cut by the Anglo-Dutch boundary and commanded by short ranges or by single hills reaching to 3000 feet above sea level. Only a few peaks exceed an altitude of 6500 feet, and then only by a little. Mt. Kinabalu,[2] the highest point in the Malay world (13,445 feet), is exceptional.

[1] In 1930 the population in the Indonesian portion, known as Kalimantan, is said to have numbered 2,168,000; that of British Borneo was estimated at 953,000 in 1951.

[2] The highest peak after Kinabalu appears to be Murud (about 8000 feet). This mountain is situated in the very mountainous district in which the boundaries of Sarawak, North Borneo, and the Indonesian territory meet. The district was explored during the recent war. See T. Harrisson (146a).

But this mountain is merely the culminating peak of an isolated hill-mass in the extreme north of the island. The ranges are by no means as continuous as was imagined before Borneo was crossed by the few Europeans who have explored it. Bold relief, detached in character, rises steeply from a hilly area or a moderately low plateau. The watershed between the Kapuas and Kutai (or Mahakam) was crossed by Molengraff at an altitude of 2600 feet near the middle of the island. The lines of hills do not join in a big central knot, but seem rather to converge on the north end, as is the case of the Philippines; and it is with them, and not Celebes, that a comparison of structure is appropriate, although recent changes have ended in giving them very dissimilar outlines.

Borneo as a whole still forms part of the Sunda shelf, that is, of the old plinth projecting from the continent of Asia, and, like the east of Sumatra and north of Java, the island represents a remnant which has escaped the most recent positive movements. Its pre-Tertiary geological history is far from being unravelled. Crystalline rocks—granite, gneiss, and schist—outcrop at many points in the little discontinuous ranges which bound the river basins. The most compact granite core has been recognised in the Schwaner Mountains in the south-west of the island between the valleys of the Kapuas and Barito. But crystalline rocks recur elsewhere in smaller outcrops. For instance, on the huge steep-sided cone of Mt. Kinabalu, which rises abruptly from the plain and was long regarded as a volcano. Primary and Secondary sedimentaries are represented by limestones which are pierced with caves where salangane swallows nest and which give a rugged appearance to the coast plain of Brunei; and by the group, called 'Danau formations' by Dutch geologists, which comprises quartzites, shales, sandstones, and lime-stones, mingled with ancient eruptive rocks and has a total thickness of as much as 16,000 feet.[1] Orogenic activity seems to have worked from west to east and thus to have extended the continental area at the expense of the geosyncline which has now shrunk into Macassar Strait. The pre-Tertiary folds in the west and centre of the island run from west to east and gradually curve round to the north-east. The Cretaceous was a period of great folding, and most of the granite probably came into its present position at that time.

The Tertiary deposits are better known owing to the attraction of the coal measures and oil-bearing strata, and they cover about two-thirds of the surface of Borneo, though they are often masked by a

[1] Beds similar to the Danau formations are also found in the south of Annam with a radiolarian appearance. (E. Saurin: *Études géologiques sur l'Indochine du Sud-Est. Bull. Service Géolog. Indochine*, xxii, I, Hanoi, 1935, p. 78.)

relatively thin Quaternary mantle. In the west there are sedimentaries which seem to have originated in lagoons or lakes or to be merely continental and which have remained almost horizontal.

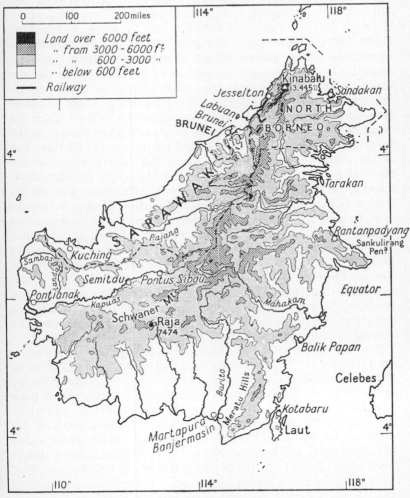

FIG. 25.—BORNEO

In particular they form large expanses of reddish, unfossiliferous sandstone which gives rise to plateaus deeply incised by valleys and which is sometimes, as in the Muller Hills,[1] overlaid with Tertiary or Quaternary lavas and tuffs. The whole of central and western Borneo with its mantle of Tertiary beds tilts down very gently under

[1] To the north of the Schwaner Mountains.

the South China Sea, beneath which Molengraaff recognised at no
great depth the surest traces of the drainage system of the now
largely drowned Sunda shelf.

Eastwards the almost undisturbed continental Tertiary beds pass
into marine deposits of sand, marl, and even limestone along
Macassar Strait. These sedimentaries are in places as much as
26,000 feet thick and prove the great length of time required to
accumulate at the bottom of the geosyncline detritus from lost
lands that must have stood on the site of Malacca Straits and the
South China Sea. The beds have been affected by folding which
continued at least into the Pliocene. The strata, which in places
have been turned into a vertical position, have been given an
orientation nearly parallel with the east coast, in particular to the
north of the lower Kutai and in British territory at the northern end
of the island. According to Rutten[1] the facts essential to the
explanation of the existing relief are: the great erosion which
followed on the Pliocene movements, a relative lowering of the sea
level, a fact attested by the frequency of narrow, steep-sided valleys
in the interior; and, lastly, post-glacial submersion and the deposition
of sediment which followed. The folding was not accompanied
here by volcanic manifestations as intense as those in Sumatra and
Java. The lava which fills the valleys around Mt. Niut in the
Chinese Districts north of Pontianak reveals comparatively recent
eruptions. But Borneo contains no active volcano and does not
have the advantage of that natural enrichment of the soil which is so
important in the other two islands. Earthquakes are rare: an
average of four a year as against 43 in Celebes and 55 in Java.

Between the often scarcely perceptible waterpartings formed by
the Tertiary hills the rivers quickly deposited sediment and silted up
the inlets caused by the post-glacial submersion. Big lakes persisted
in the valleys of the Kapuas and Kutai. In the wide southern plain
drained by the Barito and the Big and Little Dyak Rivers which
converge in the Banjermasin district the straightening-out of the
meanders has left many swamps, called Danau, which spread widely
in time of flood and become sheets of clear, brownish water shut in
by the great forest. In the dry season they are only hollows filled
with black mud and dotted with pools. Long before reaching the
sea the rivers branch out and wind between muddy islands overgrown with nipa palms and mangrove. Some of the deltas already
push right out into the sea, especially that of the Kutai. But the
general appearance remains that of a recently drowned coast.
South of the Kutai many little streams end in steep-sided estuaries
like Balik Papan Bay.

[1] Rutten (32), p. 305.

On this huge, rugged island, in which high mountains are exceptional, the equatorial climate imposes its dull uniformity more than
anywhere else in the East Indies. On the coast and on extensive
lowlands the thermometer oscillates feebly all through the year
round 77° F. and 79° F. The trade wind and monsoons, weak as if
enfeebled by their passage through the belt of calms, penetrate far
inland; yet they often seem to be replaced or masked by land and sea
breezes or valley and mountain winds which are themselves usually
without strength. The Celebes Sea off the north-east coast is
reputed to be one of the calmest in the archipelago. Typhoons are
nearly always mild—and rare too, for in forty years only three
violent cyclones have been recorded and then only on the extreme
north of the island.

Of course, the advance of knowledge will introduce some diversity
into the monotonous picture. Meteorological stations are few and
far between and are nearly all on the coast. As elsewhere in the
tropics, the rainfall system determines the regional shades of
difference. Most of the island gets between 100 and 130 inches
annually, well distributed through the year. The amount increases
from the coast inland because of the greater mean height of the land.
This is clearly seen in the Kapuas valley, where Pontianak (on the
delta) gets 127 inches, Semitau (about 100 miles from the coast)
140 inches, and Putus Sibau (140 miles from the sea) 175 inches. At
most of the stations November, December, and January are the
wettest months, but in the west of the island the driest month still
gets between 4 and 7 per cent. of the total precipitation for the year.

Along the east coast the rainfall is also very evenly distributed
over the whole year, but is less plentiful. The lower Mahakam
valley has only between 65 and 70 inches, the lowest rainfall recorded
in the island. Only in the north and south-east can one speak of a
dry season. In the north this occurs in April, when the north-east
trade wind ceases to blow. In the lower valley of the Barito at
Banjermasin and its backland the driest month (July, August, or
September) gets only between 1 and 3 per cent. of the total rainfall.
The Meratu Hills, a low obstacle indeed, but running parallel with
the coast, no doubt make the south-east trade into a foehn. The
annual means exceed 120 inches, but at times, as in 1914, drought
may last for two whole months, and drinking-water must then be
brought by sea to Banjermasin.

Perhaps two-thirds of Borneo are covered with evergreen forest in
which, and especially in the south-eastern half, Dipterocarps predominate both in number and height. But here again the traveller
who crosses the island brings away not only the impression of
luxuriant forests, but also of stretches of secondary scrub and

savanas covered with ferns or tall, hard grasses. These degenerate forms are here as elsewhere the direct result of human action. Their continued existence is no doubt favoured by the occurrence of a short dry season in the north and south-east of the island; but they are also found in regions of typical equatorial rains like the valley of the Kapuas. On the whole, they occur wherever population is densest.

PEOPLE

Dyak and Malay. Borneo is the home of the Dyak.[1] But this name, which foreigners apply to all the uncivilised people in the island, does not denote a population homogeneous in origin or mode of life. There are no Negritoes or Pygmies as there still are in Malaya and the Philippines. Anthropologists distinguish a type in which the dominant feature is a Mongoloid brachycephalic skull and which includes the Kenyas, Kayans, Bahans, and Ibans; and another consisting of the dolichocephalic Klementans, who inhabit a large part of Sarawak, the Kapuas valley, and the whole area south of the Kutai. The existing population is the result of a series of expulsions and mixtures which ethnologists and linguists are trying to unravel. It was mainly in the south-west and north-west that the most recent waves of Dyaks (Ibans and Klementans), coming no doubt from Indo-China and the Philippines, must have penetrated into the island, driving the older peoples eastwards.

Pure Dyaks may be reckoned as forming one-third of the total population. They occupy the interior, but in fact very unevenly. Extensive areas remain uninhabited. So, in some places in the central mountains and on the boundary between Dutch territory and Sarawak, the streams, though obstructed by rapids and swollen by sudden and dangerous spates, are, together with the tracks made by wild beasts, the only routes by which explorers can pass. The skilful Dyak boatmen have to portage their frail canoes, hollowed out from tree trunks, from one clear stretch of water to the next. Quite recently a German named Helbig with one European companion and four Malays travelled in this way for a week without seeing a habitation and meeting only a few timid Dyaks, many of whom were suffering from goître. They lived by hunting and collecting forest products, and they still regarded White men as strange and superhuman beings. Their dress was in some cases a mere loincloth made by beating bark with a wooden mallet until it became very fine material.

Elsewhere the population is denser, and groups usually live together in dwellings built on tall piles. The length of the houses

[1] Helbig (147, 147a, 147b); Vroklage (89).

depends on the number of families living in them. They are often only some 30 feet long, but may be as much as 1000.[1] The furniture consists of hunting equipment and fishing tackle, basketwork of all kinds, calabashes, and bamboo tubes for drawing water. As among the Mois in French Indo-China, the most valuable things are heavy bronze gongs of Chinese or Japanese origin and large imported earthenware pots in which are kept fruit, pickled vegetables, and alcohol made from rice. Amulets of hens' feathers sprinkled with blood hang on the partitions in evidence of ritual offerings to the household gods. Under the soot-coated roof timbers in some dwellings hang the blackened skulls brought back from a head-hunt by the occupant in his youth or even by his father and long ago stripped of their flesh by vermin.

Dyak hospitality, which years ago was made famous by Wallace, is generally praised by European travellers. Ethnologists indignantly deny the epithet of savage which clings to the name Dyak. Nieuwenhuis[2] describes the people of the upper Kapuas valley and of the upper and middle Mahakam above the 2000-foot contour as well formed, healthy, clean, and living in fine communal houses. The Madangas of the backland of Brunei have bright eyes, are easy of movement, wonderful boatmen, and unsurpassed walkers in the forest. Dyak handicrafts are well known. Dress varies. Above the square of cotton cloth caught up between the thighs many Dyaks put on a kind of vest and a big sun-hat with small ornaments. Tattooing is general, but besides this they wear bracelets, leg rings, and heavy earrings which stretch the lobes. Among the Sea-Dyaks the women enclose their busts in a rattan corset. In the interior head-dresses are adorned with magnificent argus or hornbill plumes. The weapons are a big shield, a lance, a blow-gun which is sometimes 7 feet long, and a sword with a heavy blade and a hilt that is in some cases splendidly carved. Their piston-fitted tinderboxes in which a vigorous compression of the air sets fire to some tow, and the piston-bellows designed to maintain and blow up the spark are remarkable contrivances; but it is uncertain whether they were inventions, imitations, or importations from abroad. The Dyaks in the interior already live mainly by agriculture. They till patches of soil which have been cleared by fire; but often too they cultivate a ricefield which is irrigated by fairly effective methods. The gardens adjoining the dwellings produce allspice, betel and areca nut, sugarcane, vegetables, and various kinds of fruit. When there is a shortage of food, their chief stand-by is often the pith of the sago palm which sometimes grows in dense thickets around the huts. The pith is grated, kneaded in water, and dried in the sun. The

[1] See above, p. 105.   [2] In Schrieke (20), pp. 11 ff.

harvest festival is a time of noisy feasting and singing of traditional songs carried on far into the night to the sound of gongs beaten by men and the tapping of digging-sticks on the floor of the house by women.

Gradual stages of transition from a savage state to civilisation are observed. The development has taken place under the same influences as in the rest of the East Indies. A distinction is often drawn between Sea-Dyaks and Land-Dyaks. Perhaps the practice of irrigation together with many beliefs and customs spread from Indo-China and India. About 1350 the island was under the influence of the Indo-Javanese kingdom of Majapahit. Malay settlement had long been established in coastal districts, and in particular in the lower valleys of the Kapuas and Kutai and along the south coast. On coming into contact with them the Dyak redeemed his reputation by adopting the Malay language and becoming a Muslim. Pigafetta, a companion of Magellan and the historian of his voyage, who in 1521 visited the capital of Brunei, describes the impressive ceremonies which took place at the court of the Sultan, then one of the most powerful in the Malay world. Brunei was destined to give its name to the whole island. In the south the delta of the Barito remains one of the citadels of Islam among the Malay peoples, and with the ports in Java right opposite and the equatorial climate already weakening, Indo-Javanese influence seems greatest there. It is the land of the Banjarese, who are a mixture of Dyak elements with Arabs, Malays from Johore, Javanese, and Bugis from Celebes. They have a ready understanding, live in clean villages, and carry on a prosperous trade. They are fanatical Muslims, and many of them go on pilgrimages to Mecca. They hate Europeans, yet they adopt many Western customs and also cultivate the most paying export crops. In the district of Ulu Sungei the density of population reaches the figure of 121 persons to the square mile, which is quite exceptional in Borneo.[1]

Chinese have been attracted to the west coast by minerals and especially gold mines. To the north of the lower Kapuas they founded the small, but fairly vigorous states of Mandar, Monterado, and Bengkayang which were serious obstacles to European penetration.

EXPLOITATION

European traders were attracted to Borneo mainly by its gold and diamonds as well as the pepper from the Banjermasin district. The

[1] Mohr (98), p. 491. Apart from this district of Ulu Sungei and the subdivision in which mineral oil and coal are worked, the Residency of South and East Borneo had no more than 515,000 souls (1930), or 3 persons to the square mile, and these live only on the banks of the rivers.

first agent of the Dutch East India Company, Gillis Michielszoon,
was murdered in 1606. The rival efforts of the Dutch, English, and
D̶̶̶̶̶ ̶ed with the secret or open hostility of the Banjarese.
ꞓmonotonous and bloody tale of agreements made and
ʿopeans slain, and native ears and noses cut off in
ꞁe Dutch were the most tenacious and at the end of the
ꞁ obtained the cession of the kingdom of Banjermasin
ꞁcognised in 1826. Yet the troubles, murders, and petty
ꞁ on in the interior until the end of last century.
ꞁreat names in the exploration of Borneo are those of
iller, who was murdered by the natives in 1824, and
ꞁ44–47). Methodical exploration was later undertaken
ꞁers of the Dutch Mining Corps which was formed in

ꞁ into the northern portion of the island was carried
out mainly by the English,[1] and the Dutch had to admit English
sovereignty there. After the middle of the 18th century the English
proceeded to acquire the mastery of the Straits of Balabak and
Sibutu between Dutch territory and the Spanish-owned Philippines.
The best harbour in the island is situated here at Sandakan. They
succeeded in thrusting aside the competition of American firms and
of taking advantage of the expeditions of Overbeck, an Austrian,
whom Bismarck would not support. The British North Borneo
Company was formed by charter in London in 1881. English
influence also extended to Sarawak, thanks to the success of a lucky
adventurer, James Brooke, an Englishman born in India in 1803.
Fitting out a ship at his own expense in England, he offered his
services to the Sultan of Brunei, who was being harassed by pirates
and troubled by rivals for his throne. In 1841 as a reward Brooke
was given the territory of Sarawak with the title of rajah. Sarawak
together with Brunei was placed under British protection in 1888.
The island of Labuan had been ceded to England as early as 1846.
Situated at the entrance to the Bay of Brunei, it was important as a
port of call for steamers on the way from Singapore to Hong Kong.
The whole of this northern part of the island was placed under the
supervision of the Governor of the Straits Settlements, who became
High Commissioner of Brunei, but only Agent in Sarawak and
British North Borneo. By holding Hong Kong, Singapore, and
Sandakan, England commanded the main passages leading from the
South China Sea into the Indian and Pacific Oceans. Besides, she
outpaced the Netherlands in the development of Borneo, although
she ruled scarcely one-third of the area and population.

In 1946 Sarawak was ceded to Great Britain by Rajah Brooke

[1] Mt. Kinabalu was climbed for the first time in 1844. Enriquez (144).

and became a Crown Colony.   In the same year North Borneo, in-cluding Labuan, was given a similar status.   Brunei remains a Protected State under its Sultan.   North Borneo, Sarawak, and Brunei, together with the Federation of Malaya and Singapore, now form the Malayan Union under the supervision of the Commissioner-General for the United Kingdom in Southeast Asia.

The mineral products of Borneo are more or less equal to its agricultural resources, but do not fulfil the long-cherished hopes which the island's long-standing reputation seemed to justify.   At the end of the 18th century a large number of Chinese immigrants were attracted especially to the area known as 'the Chinese districts' in the valleys of the rivers Sambas and Landak.   About 30,000 Chinese not only worked the placer gold, but also attacked the lodes. They formed themselves into societies, became the real masters of the country, and were subjugated by the Dutch only after a long and bloody war.   In consequence of this struggle, mining activity was greatly curtailed and remains weak.   The Chinese no longer played much of a part in the extraction of precious metals in the western districts, and they had to face the competition of little European enterprises and even more that of natives.   The latter work with primitive outfits and melt down the metal in earthenware moulds for the local manufacture of jewelry and false teeth.   The quantity produced is much inferior today to what is obtained in Sumatra and leaves but a small surplus for export.   Another gold-bearing district is Tana Laut to the east of Banjermasin.

Diamonds yielded a good profit in the time of the Dutch East India Company, the market being in Batavia.   The efforts of the Dutch Colonial Government to re-start operations during the 19th century were without result.   Some gem cutting is done at Marta-pura near Banjermasin, but nowadays the exports are insignificant.

European interest in coal-mining is of recent date, the first to be associated with the work being Simonar, a French engineer (1880). But coal had previously been mined by Chinese and natives.   The coal is of moderate quality.   It comes from Tertiary measures which are very scattered, but lie on the surface or at little depth, and are nearly all on the east coast to north and south of the Kutai.   Since the Government mines in Pulu Laut (an island off the south-east coast of Borneo) were closed in 1932, the coal has been worked wholly by private firms, some of which operate down to a depth of 650 feet.   Javanese miners are engaged on contract, and improved equipment is used.   The most productive field in 1937 was at Rantanpadyang to the north of the Sankulirang peninsula.   But the total production did not amount to 500,000 tons.   The coal was mainly used by shipping and rubber-mills; but the supply did not

meet the demand in Borneo, and some had to come from Ombilin
in Sumatra.

Even if the English and Indonesian production were added

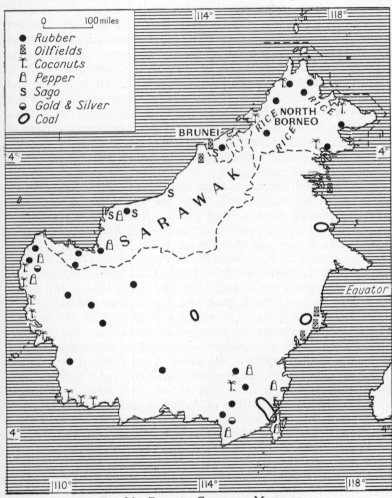

FIG. 26.—BORNEO: CROPS AND MINERALS

together, Borneo would be seen to have produced less mineral oil
than Sumatra before the recent war.[1] The main oil-field in British
territory is situated in the Baram district to the south-west of

[1] Since 1946 production in British territory has rapidly increased in the Seria
field. In 1952 more than 5 million tons of crude oil were extracted.

M.I.B.P.—15

Brunei within the borders of Sarawak. The chief oil-field in Indonesian territory lies in the Kutai basin, but there is another important one on Tarakan Island. They both belong to the Batavian Petroleum Company, which was the original company out of which grew the Royal Dutch Shell Company. The drill-rigs, which were originally at Balik Papan, were later removed into the forest, from whose midst rise the derricks and silver-painted tanks in which the oil is stored in the first instance. Oil and gas are taken by pipe-line and tanker to Balik Papan, which is about 90 miles from the most distant wells. Here the oil is refined and shipped. Yet Balik Papan is the most pleasant town in Borneo, with its pretty residential quarters built on hills whose slopes come right down to the shore. About 1000 Europeans in the pre-war population of 30,000 formed the largest White community in Borneo. In 1941 it was seriously damaged by bombing, but has now been reconstructed and modernised.

Pontianak and Banjermasin are bigger and older towns, but are less pleasant for Europeans. They are the outlets of the most densely populated districts in the island. North of Pontianak there are 50 persons to the square mile and in the Banjermasin district between the Barito and the Meratu Hills there are 130. Steam launches ascend the Kapuas as far as Putus Sibau 140 miles from the sea, and the Barito as far as Puruk Chau about 220 miles up. A few motor roads run inland. The two towns have grown up on the muddy banks of the Kapuas and Barito, where buildings have to be erected on piles. Chinese still form a third of the total population in Pontianak, the former chief gold town. Banjermasin, formerly one of the great pepper marts, had the advantage of being the administrative capital of the whole of the Dutch portion of the island as well as a position opposite Surabaya, and it was favoured by the spread of native rubber cultivation. The latter development was due mainly to the activity of Banjerese traders and reminds one of the rise of Jambi in Sumatra. The east coast also exports rubber and, in addition, fairly large quantities of pepper.

In the Indonesian portion of the island European plantations were far fewer and less extensive than in Sumatra. Nor do those in British territory seem to furnish proportionately more of the exports from those colonies, where rubber is today more important than copra, sago, and even tobacco, which was formerly the chief product of North Borneo.[1]

[1] There are very few rubber estates in the British portions of Borneo. The typical producer is a smallholder who, according to the state of the market, passes easily from the cultivation of the hevea to the production of copra, pepper, sago, catechu (derived from a leguminous plant, *Acacia catechu*), or *jelutong*, which is got from certain plants growing wild in the marshes and is used to make chewing gum, as is the *chicle* of Central America.

CHAPTER 11

CELEBES

(SULAWESI)

Celebes takes us into eastern Indonesia. It is no longer a matter of emerged portions of a fairly shallow submarine platform. To the east of Borneo the Sunda shelf sinks abruptly into Macassar Strait. Nor is this deep a unique feature, for farther east the submarine relief evinces an extraordinary complexity of narrow sills and deep basins. The land breaks up more and more, and the pieces become smaller and smaller till the heavy masses of Australia and New Guinea point to the existence of another barely submerged platform. In this part of the archipelago Asia crumbles and in fact comes to an end.

Peculiar Character of Celebes. Celebes is in striking contrast with its neighbour Borneo and also with Java. In area it comes between these two very different islands, but it is distinguished from them by its extraordinarily irregular shape and outline which, owing to the four long peninsulas converging on a central knot round Lake Poso, makes it look like some strange insect. The actual form of these peninsulas is due to the conflict of folds running in different directions. It has been supposed that the build of Celebes was not fundamentally different from that of Borneo, but represented a condition previous to that reached by the larger island, in which former arms of the sea have been filled up by river silt.

In truth the structure of Celebes, which is no less strange than its shape, reveals by comparison with the islands of western Indonesia a new development in which vertical movements often of very great amplitude have played a leading part. Pre-Tertiary history remains very obscure here. Ancient rocks, in particular schists and gray-wackës, outcrop at many places and are relatively more important than in Borneo, Sumatra, or Java. Perhaps they are remnants of the old continent which Abendanon names Æquinoctia and which disappeared completely under the waters of Tethys as early as the end of the Primary period. Some great orogenic movements which caused extensive emersion have been placed by Abendanon at the beginning of the Tertiary. The deposits accumulated in the geosyncline were uplifted in folds whose axis ran NW.–SE.; and granite intrusions mark out and consolidate these folds.

The Oligocene was a time of erosion and levelling, and Celebes, like all western Indonesia, developed into a peneplain. From the Miocene epoch onwards great vertical movements gave it its peculiar

shape.   The platform consisting of rigid materials did not resist the
strong forces of uplift which have been repeated, with spells of
activity separated by intervals of rest, until the present time.   The
end of the Pliocene and the Pleistocene were times of maximum
intensity.   The uplifted crust broke and sank in large slabs.   Hence,
the relief is one of extraordinary contrasts.

Submarine relief, which was accurately plotted from the soundings
of the *Snellius*, is quite different from that around Borneo.   Except
on the east, Borneo slopes very gradually down under the sea.   In
Celebes, on the contrary, great depths are found near the coast and
the inlets are veritable trenches deeply cut out as if with a gouge.
They give a sounding of nearly 1400 fathoms at the entrance to the
Gulf of Boni and close on 1650 at the mouth of the Gulf of Tomini.
If the sea level fell by 60 fathoms, Borneo, Sumatra, and Java would
be joined to Indo-China, whilst Celebes, on the other hand, would
have its shape but little modified.   A negative movement of even
500 fathoms would not make it unrecognisable.   The peninsulas
would grow longer, the one in the south-east sending out a point
towards the Sula Islands and the one in the south-west (Macassar)
branching out to touch the eastern ends of Java and Flores.   But,
though in a shrunken form, the gulfs would continue to lie between
the peninsulas.   The broken coastline of Celebes bears some likeness to that of the Peloponnese and Chalcidice; but here the gulfs
are far deeper.

Subsidence has not only given Celebes its whimsical outline: it
has also determined the relief of the interior.   Fractures cause a
strange compartmentation.   Many rift valleys occur in the island,
the largest of which is certainly the *Fossa sarasina* running nearly
N.–S. from Palu Bay to the Gulf of Boni and occupied by several
streams.   These rifts still contain lakes, like the big Lake Poso in
the centre, 1600 feet above the sea, and Lakes Matana and Towuti
at an altitude of about 1000 feet in the Verbeek Hills.

The uplifted portions which escaped subsidence stand in many
places between the depressions as very slightly tilted surfaces and are
to be regarded as remnants of the Oligocene peneplain which rises
to an altitude of 6600 feet in the centre of the island and is dissected
by erosion into long, narrow strips.   According to Abendanon, this
peneplain recurs in the north and even in Mindanao, and is crowned
here and there by humps usually carved out of granite.   The area
above the 6600-foot contour is relatively greater than in Borneo.
Many peaks to the west of Lake Poso rise above 8000 feet and in the
Latimojong Hills at the base of the Macassar peninsula to nearly
10,000 feet.

The uplift has naturally started a furious erosion which emphasises the diversity of the rocks.   To the north of Macassar it has attacked a fairly shallow Tertiary limestone stratum and given rise at some distance from the sea to a typical karst whose cliffs, as, for instance,

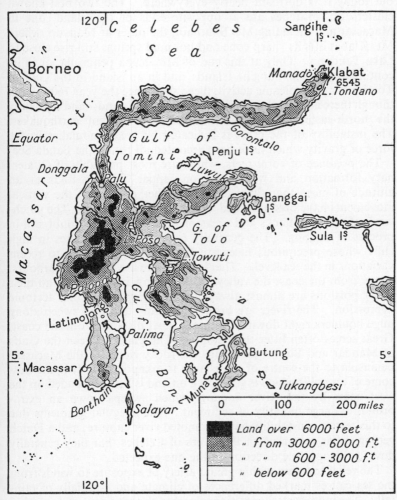

FIG. 27.—CELEBES

those at Maros, rise abruptly from the plain and are precipitous, cut into fantastic shapes, and honeycombed with caves. In other places, as, for example, in the Quarles Hills to the north of the Latimojong range, volcanic tuffs are fiercely slashed into narrow ridges.

Vulcanism was very intense in the Miocene period and again at the end of the Pliocene and Pleistocene, that is, during the convulsions of uplifting, when it laid down vast sheets of lava and tuff; but today it is dormant nearly everywhere. The two best-known clusters of volcanoes are at opposite ends of the island, one in Macassar and including Mt. Bonthain, the other at Manado, where Mt. Klabat lifts its sharp cone and hot mud springs still rise close to Lake Tondano. Only at this end of Minahassa peninsula, or in its continuation in the Sangihe Islands, and in an island in the Gulf of Tomini has any volcanic activity been seen since the year 1600. But though there is no further fear of eruptions, the island—and especially the north-eastern district—is afflicted with violent earthquakes. The instability of the crust is indicated by great anomalies in the force of gravity which have been recorded all round the Banda Sea.

The presence of coral reefs, which are most probably of Quaternary formation and which rest on Upper Tertiary folds at an altitude of more than 3000 feet, is another proof that the vertical movements have been repeated until a very recent date. The patchwork of uplifted blocks and areas of subsidence is no doubt still in process of making. The generally rocky coast often rises in high cliffs whose precipitous faces are broken by ledges due to recent variations in the sea level. That is why there are few good harbours. Away from the coast the valleys often narrow into gorges, and their wider portions are almost always due to the presence of a tectonic depression. The rivers are broken by many falls and sweep along huge boulders right down to within a short distance from the coast. Great screes often litter their slopes. The plain between the Gulfs of Mandar and Boni, which joins the rocky ridges of the Macassar peninsula to the centre of the island, is exceptional. It is the outcome of an uplift which is still going on and is being extended on the west coast by the River Sadang, which sweeps down an extraordinarily large quantity of sediment. The irregular gradients due to this tectonic instability have promoted river capture; and a Dutch geologist has remarked of the rivers of Celebes that they generally flow in the opposite direction to the one expected.

The relief together with a great variety of exposure to winds from the sea causes marked differences of climate and especially of rainfall. The more easterly position, closer to the continent of Australia, causes the mean precipitation to be less than that of Borneo. The total decreases to 48 inches distributed among only 104 days at Gorontalo on the south shore of Minahassa peninsula; to 42 inches in 102 days at Luwuk near the end of the peninsula that separates the Gulfs of Tomini and Tolo; and to a mere 21 inches in 81 days— the lowest figure in the whole of the East Indies—at Palu at the inner end of a bay on the west coast not quite 1° south of the Equator. But most stations get between 80 and 120 inches a year. Rantepao at an altitude of 2300 feet, at the inner end of the Gulf of Boni, actually has nearly 133 inches.

But the rainfall system varies greatly. We must limit ourselves here to saying that in the north of the island where the Equator crosses, rain falls all through the year, and dense forest covers the greater part of the area above the 1000-foot contour. In spite of the fairly long-established practice of clearing by fire, the variety and beauty of the ferns, the vigorous growth of rattans, the abundance of other palms, and the profusion of orchids crowding on the trees and of the Araceæ and mosses in the undergrowth, give a peculiarly luxuriant appearance to the mountain forests around Manado, which get the benefit of deep volcanic soil. On the driest lowlands, for instance near Gorontalo, around the Gulf of Tolo, and at the inner end of Palu Bay, a xerophilous vegetation of Casuarinaceæ, Dracenas, Cycads, and even Euphorbias and Opuntias makes its appearance.

Although the rainfall in southern Celebes does not on the whole seem less, it occurs more irregularly during the course of the year. The dry season is particularly marked on the west coasts of the peninsulas on which during the southern winter the south-east trades assume the character of a foehn on crossing the mountain ridges. Thus, 78 per cent. of the 112 inches of mean annual rainfall at Macassar occurs during the four months from December to March when the north-west monsoon is blowing. January has the high total of 27 inches, whilst August gets only 0·43 inch, which is far less than the 1·5 inch that falls during the driest month at arid Palu. So the dense evergreen forest appears only at high altitudes. Less vigorous than in the north, it gives way farther down to savana with teak and to sparse scrub which leaves the limestone rock bare or splashed with patches of lichen; and it has almost disappeared before the advance of cultivation in the Macassar peninsula. On the lowlands around the town of Macassar there is a great contrast between the rainy season with flooded ricefields and the southern winter when the streams dry up and the scorched ricefields bristle with dusty stubble after the grain has been harvested.

Since Wallace's time Celebes has been famous for its peculiar fauna, which is another outcome of isolation and compartmentation. The latest researches have somewhat modified the conclusions of the bold and brilliant naturalist. Wallace laid great stress on the poverty of the island in animal species and the local character of the species that did occur, which were mostly quite different from those found in the neighbouring islands and showed closer affinities with

Madagascar and the African mainland. He emphasised not only their specific individuality, but also their morphological peculiarities. For instance, the shape of the wings of the butterflies, which are often very beautiful, seemed to him to confirm both the ancient geological character of the island as a remnant of a very old, foundered continent and the universality of natural selection and the struggle for life which had been so forcefully expounded by Darwin. The progress of knowledge since Wallace's time requires some modification of the exact terms of his theory and leads to the view that Celebes was less isolated than he thought, that most of the species merely mark the transition between western and eastern Indonesia, and that the Cynopithecus, the anoa or dwarf buffalo, and the babirusa (which resembles the stag and is also like the boar with its curved upper tusks) are merely exceptions. The fact remains, however, that few countries show such strange local peculiarities and that compartmentation itself gives rise to a great variety of living associations in the interior of the island. This variety is seen also in man.

Diversity of the Population.[1] In spite of its far smaller area, Celebes has a larger population than Borneo. In 1930 the island contained 4,232,000 persons, which is 57 to the square mile. This superiority may be regarded as due to the length of coastline, a more fertile soil, and an equatorial environment of a kind less overwhelming to man. All the same, Celebes lags behind Java, though the two islands have much the same area. Celebes lacks Java's large proportion of soil whose fertility is renewed by active volcanoes and her facilities for internal communication. The island is closer to the formerly wild and almost empty Australian mainland and is more remote from the main sources of Eurasian civilisation.

As in western Indonesia the population is very unevenly distributed in the island. The most favoured districts are the two farthest from the centre. On the one hand, there is the Macassar peninsula, in which the mean density rises to 194 to the square mile and even reaches more than 325 to the square mile near the capital; and on the other hand, there is the long northern arm, where the Manado district has about 130 persons to the square mile. The total area of both these regions is quite small, and outside them the mean density falls to 13 to the square mile.

This curious distribution of population is due partly to soil and climate and partly to external influence. The most densely peopled districts are those in which volcanoes are either still active or were so till lately and which are inhabited by civilised communities. These are Macassar and Bugi in the south and Minahassa in the

1 Sarasin (157).

north, human settlement becoming sparser among the 'wild' tribes who are represented especially in the centre by the Torajas. In fact, an extraordinary, cellular arrangement of races ensues from the compartmentation of the relief. Whilst, if the coastal Malays are ignored, Borneo is inhabited by a single linguistic type, the Dyaks, scholars distinguish in Celebes eight groups of dialects, each at least as different from the others as are those in the little islands of eastern Indonesia. The fact is, communication between the divergent peninsulas of this tentacled island is far more difficult by land than by sea.

Macassar was destined to receive the first contributions from Asia and the West. In the 14th century it was certainly influenced by the Indo-Javanese Kingdom of Majapahit and shortly afterwards by Islam. Like the Javanese, whom they resemble physically, the Macassarese and Bugis became Muslims, though they remained faithful to a number of animistic practices. The mode of life of these two peoples differs little. They are both cultivators and sailors. Their skill as navigators certainly struck the Europeans on their arrival in the archipelago at the beginning of the 16th century. But since giving up piracy, the Bugis have engaged in coastwise traffic and oversea trade more than any others. Their ships are met with all over the East Indies. The broad bows, high poops, and general build point to a conjunction of various kinds of influence—Arab, Chinese, and even European. The Buginese community, which numbers about 1,500,000 souls, is the largest in Celebes and swarms all over the archipelago. Buginese colonies which keep in permanent touch with their homeland are found along the coast of Celebes as well as in southern Borneo, in Bali, Lombok, and many islands in the *Groote Oost*. Buginese mercenaries were even employed in Siam at the end of the 17th century.[1]

In southern Celebes the Macassarese and Bugis both use pile-dwellings grouped in villages of twenty to forty families. Owing to the persevering efforts of the Dutch administration, the villages have improved in cleanliness and health. Popular gatherings are enlivened by the bright colours of the red, blue, or green sarongs. The chief crop is swamp rice. It is grown only once a year owing to the drought in the cool season and is less carefully tended than in Java or Bali. Maize has gained ground of late in the interior.

At the other end of the island, more than 600 miles away as the crow flies, the Minahassans have developed rather differently and in a still more curious way. Facing north on the whole and showing signs in their language, physical appearance, and complexion of former connexion with the Philippines and even with Polynesia,

[1] Dampier (3), III, p. 119.

they remained in greater isolation than the southern peoples up to the 19th century, although out of hatred for the Spaniards the first treaty of alliance with the Netherlands was concluded in 1697. As was the case in the interior of the island, there was continual war between groups of villages. Dress often consisted of a mere girdle of bark. But coffee and missionaries entered Minahassa from 1820 onwards. The exotic shrub was cultivated by a system of forced labour under the eyes of Dutch overseers with the support of native chiefs, who quickly grew rich. The subtle flair of the Chinese brought them to this very distant island, but they did not increase as they did in Sumatra and Borneo; and in 1930 there were barely 40,000 of them in the whole island.[1] Protestant missionaries preached the Gospel and opened schools. In 1859 Wallace was already vaunting the effects of this 'paternal despotism' and thought the country altogether changed. To him the population seemed the happiest, most peaceful, the best equipped materially, and the best educated too in the archipelago. Nearly all the Minahassans are Christians today, though their Protestantism is naturally still full of pagan beliefs and customs. Nowhere else in Indonesia does school attendance reach such a high percentage, except perhaps in the Minangkabau district, where the people are Muslims.

Certainly, no other group of people in the archipelago feels itself to be so 'European' as the Minahassans. They readily take to the Western dress. Besides, many Dutch settlers and officials had married native women.[2] Many young men went to Java to earn a living as officials or as clerks or accountants in private firms. Minahassa lost no opportunity of displaying its loyalty to the Netherlands and proclaimed itself the twelfth province of the Union.[3] Manado, the capital, with its strongly built, airy, spacious wooden houses, which stand on piles amid flower gardens surrounded by quickset hedges, is situated on one of the most beautiful bays in the archipelago and is backed by an impressive volcanic setting.

The Gorontalese and Mandarese, who are situated between the Minahassans and the Macassar-Bugis, are the most important other groups settled on the coast of Celebes. The name Toraja is given to the inland peoples, and especially those in the centre of the island. They number about 550,000 and, in fact, form a collection of numerous tribes which at the beginning of the 20th century were still waging continuous war on each other. On the other hand, as they suffered from slave raids by the coast natives, they used the difficult relief as a protection and kept their customs, especially the

---

1 As against 134,000 in Borneo and 448,000 in Sumatra.
2 Cabaton (14), p. 330.
3 Bousquet (250), p. 130.

current practice of head-hunting. Their villages were usually
perched on hill-tops or ridges and were made into veritable fortresses

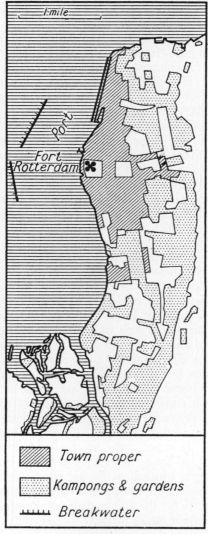

FIG. 28.—MACASSAR

with the huts close together between earthen embankments planted
with bamboos. They live by hunting, fishing, and collecting, and
by cultivating rice and maize in temporary clearings made by fire.

Dutch official organisation and missionaries have begun to change the Torajas completely, and intestine wars have nearly ceased. Part of the people now live in permanent villages built along the new roads, and *sawah* cultivation is spreading. Garments of beaten bark have quickly given way to imported textiles.

Diversity of Production. Forest products consisting of rattan, resin and various gums (especially copal), feathers and the pelts of wild animals still furnish part of the island's exports, though they do not include the chief product, viz. copra. The coconut tree is cultivated as a cash crop to some extent everywhere on the coast, not only on the Macassar peninsula and around Manado, but also at Gorontalo, Donggala, and on the Talaud and Sangihe Islands. Maize, which with rice is the basis of local diet, is grown mainly in the backland of Macassar and Palima, where it provides a surplus for export. Coffee, reputed to be the best in Indonesia, has suffered as in the other islands from American competition. Large estates, both European and native, are still found behind Manado, Macassar, and Palopo, at the inner end of the Gulf of Boni. Nutmeg and kapok occupy but a small place in the exports.

Trade passes through a large number of ports, but Macassar[1] (see Fig. 28) is the only one provided with modern equipment and is by far the busiest. In 1930 it had a population of 85,000.[2] Scarcely anything remains in the town of the old capital of the little native kingdom of Gowa, which was forced in 1667 to recognise the sovereignty of the powerful Dutch East India Company. The harbour has not been laboriously dug out of mud, as have those of Jakarta, Surabaya, Belawan Deli, and Palembang, for it has the advantage of a terrace of coral rock which allows ships to come right up to the fronts of the houses and, besides, it is sheltered from storms by reefs lying farther out. Since 1896 these advantages have been strengthened and extended by much construction. Macassar has spread out comfortably along the dry terrace planted with tamarinds and canariums, the commercial city being separated from the European quarter by Fort Rotterdam. It is not only the chief port in the island with almost a monopoly of the coast-wise *prahu* traffic, but also a port of call and an entrepôt touched at by big steamship lines, and it is connected with Java by an air service. It is especially well situated as a collecting centre for the commodities of eastern Indonesia, and it is the world's largest rattan market.

[1] Lehmann (96), p. 128.   [2] 335,000 in 1955.

CHAPTER 12

EASTERN INDONESIA

To the east of Celebes and Java the fragmentation of the East Indies continues right up to the mainlands of Australia and New Guinea. In an area measuring some 1300 miles from Bali to the Aru Islands and more than 900 from north of Halmahera to Timor the islands

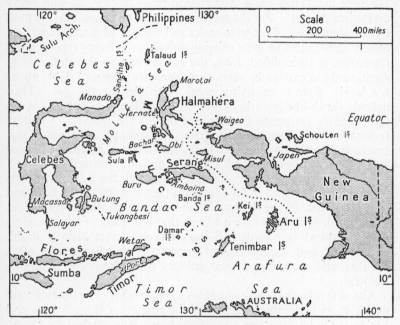

FIG. 29.—EASTERN INDONESIA

themselves represent only about 60,000 square miles. Timor, the largest, measures barely 11,500 square miles.

A certain structural scheme which was pointed out at the beginning of this work is evident in the fragmentation. To the south of the Banda Sea the Lesser Sunda Islands clearly prolong the Andaman–Sumatra–Java arc which has been bent into a hook by contact with the continental shelf of Australia. North of the Banda Sea the scheme is far less clear. The east–west grain noticeable in Buru and Serang and in Sula, Obi, and Misul runs through the Banda arc, but at the same time seems to be continued

237

in the still imperfectly known mountains of New Guinea. Farther north the outline of Halmahera resembles the Minahassa end of Celebes in suggesting a still unproven connexion with the north-south ridges in the Philippines.

Though, as we have seen, the present forms of the islands are the outcome of very recent tectonic movements during the Upper Tertiary and Quaternary periods, these movements have however affected more ancient material. Lower Tertiary and Secondary beds occupy a large part of Timor. The variety of the rocks greatly helps to differentiate the islands in this archipelago. Triassic or Neogene limestones raise their rugged relief in contrast with heavy crystalline masses. But the recent nature of the formation is proved by the abundance of eruptive rocks and coral, and many islands are merely very recent or even existing volcanoes. Every type of coral formation is exemplified, from the barrier reef to the atoll, not to mention those carried by vertical movements to great heights above sea level. Forests of living coral often delight the eye. Their delicate shrub-like growths, visible at a depth of five fathoms in the astonishingly transparent water, are one of the marvels of eastern Indonesia with their accompaniment of sponges, enormous sea-anemones slowly waving their hundreds of arms, brightly coloured fish with strange shapes, and huge orange and pink medusæ.

The fragmentation of the archipelago and the complex events which gave it its present form explain the diversity of the flora and especially that of the fauna. Endemic species which abound in eastern Indonesia have won it a fame that is already of long standing among naturalists. Birds and insects show an astonishing wealth of specific and morphological types. Their shapes are often peculiar, and their magnificent colours differ from one island to the next.

Above this basic diversity appears a remarkably clear development which is, in brief, the outcome of the transition from Asiatic and Malay lands to Australia and Melanesia. It is marked by an impoverishment of the animal world, at least in the higher forms; and mammals fall off eastwards till they number only a few species, including bats. Human life diminishes too both in quantity and quality. Population decreases in density, and there is a drop in the level of civilisation, measured by the usual standards. Lastly, we should have to add that there is a falling off in the vegetation, were the falling off not restricted to the southern region where the Sunda arc in Timor approaches to within about 300 miles of the Australian desert.

Distance from Eurasia retarded colonisation, but the natural fragmentation and the absence of any at all strong human group favoured foreign domination. It seems likely that over the greater portion of the region an originally Papuan population was partly driven eastwards and partly assimilated by immigrants from the west. The development was carried out at first by Malay traders from Java and particularly from Celebes and later by Chinese, Arabs, and Europeans from their respective homelands. These new-comers, and in particular the last named, restricted their efforts for a long time to a few tiny islands—Ternate and Tidore in the Moluccas and Amboina in the Banda group—whose monopoly of the production of valuable spices earned world-wide fame for them in days gone by. Today that monopoly is no more. The beginning of this century witnessed the gradual penetration of the Dutch into islands scarcely known before and the rise of fresh resources in these. Regular services of the Royal Packet Navigation Co. (K.P.M.) began to connect most of the islands with western Indonesia by way of Macassar. As a result of Dutch organisation Amboina has become a great centre of air services. The hopes roused by agricultural settlement and above all by prospecting for minerals in New Guinea were bound to benefit eastern Indonesia too.

The geographical classification of these scattered islands which can be made in the light of the foregoing general considerations coincides fairly well with the definition of the chief administrative areas. Eastern Indonesia is divided into two distinct parts by the 5th degree of latitude S. To the north of it are what, by extending the original meaning of the name, may be called the Moluccas; to the south are the Lesser Sunda Islands, in the west of which, however, are Bali and Lombok forming a sub-group which deserves special treatment. The eastern limit is formed by Misul and the Kei and the Aru Islands.

Bali and Lombok. Bali and Lombok are two sea-girt beads in this string of volcanoes which has already been described as clearly marked in eastern Java. Miocene limestones reappear with their karstic features in the south of Bali, in the islet of Nusa Penida, and more extensively in the south of Lombok, where they are cut off from the volcanic rocks by a depression larger and more open than in Bali. But the hills and soil of the two islands are mainly of an eruptive character, and the volcanic hill-masses still present very recent, though rather complex, forms. Below the summits lakes sleep in the calderas. Mt. Agung in Bali and Mt. Rinyani in Lombok tower up respectively to 10,300 and 12,400 feet above the sea and are landmarks seen from afar. Batur in the north-east of Bali is the most active volcano today. In the depression which corresponds to the *atrio* on Vesuvius and has its eastern portion occupied by a lake, little adventitious cones already clad in vegetation are surrounded by blackish, scoriaceous lava. The last flow destroyed a village in 1926. In former times its eruptions were far more powerful and ejected enormous quantities of matter chiefly towards the south. Tuff and breccia, which occur in masses gashed by narrow gullies and eroded by a violent surf, give rise to very fertile soil.

Drought occurs at certain times however. On the north coast of Bali at Singaraja, near the chief port of Buleleng, the rainfall is only 47 inches. The mean annual total increases slightly at Ampenan (54 inches) on the west coast of Lombok at the end of the central depression. As in eastern Java, the drought is greatest in the north of the island where there is shelter from the south-east trades. During the southern winter Singaraja has only 1·5 inches during the

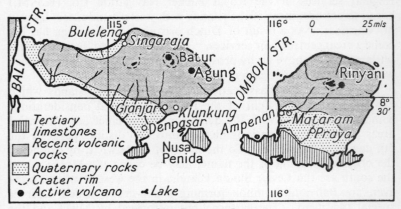

FIG. 30.—BALI AND LOMBOK

four months from July to October. In this season many streams dry up or are very small in volume.

The fragmentation of the relief and the irregularity of the rainfall have exercised the ingenuity of a swarming population. In some remote districts there persist little communities which are at times termed aborigines. For instance, in the mountains of Bali there are the Bali Agas, who have a fairly dark complexion, a relatively angular body, and remain almost exclusively attached to the old animistic cult; and similar characteristics are still seen in Nusa Penida and the nearby islets as well as in the some 3000 Bodhas in Lombok. But they have been overwhelmed by the influx of immigrants which began in the distant past. Communication is immemorial between Bali and Java, which are separated by a very narrow strait, and Hindu influence spread rapidly from one island to the other. Large migrations from Java to Bali took place in the

9th century and even more at the beginning of the 16th. When the Indo-Javanese state of Majapahit succumbed to the blows of Islam, communities which rebelled against the new faith and remained loyal to their traditional chiefs crossed the strait. Thus, Bali remains the archipelago's repository of Indian religions evicted from western Indonesia. Neither Islam nor Christianity has taken hold. Frankly, no evidence of pure classical dogma, Brahministic or Buddhist, can be found here. On the contrary, the beliefs and practices of the people reveal an astonishing and wonderful syncretism of immemorial traditions and foreign importations into a very beautiful island.

In this Balinese form of Hinduism the mixture is well compounded and no flaw is visible. Enriched with exotic elements, it has become deeply rooted in this fertile soil. The gods have multiplied and have gathered together in an astonishing brotherhood, influencing and cross-breeding freely with each other. The people of Bali 'worship what they meet in the morning on leaving their houses', a 17th-century traveller tells us.[1] The veneration of the great Indian divinities has been grafted on to a very vigorous amimism[2] whose multiplicity of rites is intended to influence and propitiate innumerable spirits—spirits of smoking volcanoes, rivers, and forests, spirits of the house and the ricefield, and, above all, spirits of the dead. The foreigner is struck by the crowd of shrines, or *puras*. These are large temples frequented by all. Their big gates of grey lava are decorated with many colours and give access to a series of courts surrounded by buildings. Of such a kind is the temple of Bezaki, which is on the slopes of Mt. Agung and almost inaccessible in the rainy season. Then there are the smaller temples in the market places (*pasar*) and in the villages and those belonging to peasant societies. Lastly, little household temples with tiny roofs of thatch, tiles, or galvanised sheets are grouped round the family dwellings. Altars and white memorial shrines are dotted about the fields. Every important act in this isle of the gods requires a religious ceremony which is often of touching grace or fiercely impressive. The traveller never forgets the processions of light-brown women and girls bearing on erect heads *slametan*, or offerings of fruit and flowers artistically arranged. They look like a sort of antique frieze adapted to the tropics. But the traveller also remembers the embarassment and the kind of horror felt at the sight of wholesale cremations, of vociferous bearers disputing over exhumed bodies and baffling the evil spirits by their circuitous and jerky gait, and at the acrid reek rising into the scorching air from the pyres of hundreds

[1] Olearius (9), II, p. 195.
[2] Stuttenheim (85).

of corpses on the ground or on catafalques marking the social standing of the castes.

Balinese Hinduism is isolated between Java and Lombok, for Islam has indeed almost wholly won over Lombok and has kept its hold, although the island came under the domination of Bali in 1740. About 30,000 persons in west Lombok speak Balinese, but Sasak converts to Islam form the great majority (658,000) of the population. Dutch penetration was late and bloody. Sitting in his coach the King of Bali received European envoys as early as the end of the 16th century, but it was only in 1894, after a military expedition which began with a defeat, that Lombok was occupied and placed under the direct rule of the Dutch. Part of Bali remained independent until 1908. The complete subjection of the island followed the famous *puputan*, in the course of which the last princes to hold out threw themselves with their dependants, wives, and children on the rifles and guns of the Dutch troops and, when not killed by this, stabbed themselves with their *krises*.

The European officials have made intelligent efforts to preserve Bali's extraordinary peculiarities. They have kept a strict eye on new-comers and restricted their activities, only a few thousand acres having been conceded to Europeans or Chinese.

In any case, European agricultural settlers would find little land available in Lombok or Bali. Population has increased in these island-refuges, and the density figures resemble those in Java. In 1930 the human burden on the land was 450 persons to the square mile, in spite of the high mean altitude above the sea. This teeming humanity is fed only by the exercise of skill that is wonderful considering the implements used. Certain it is that irrigation is organised as thoroughly and as well in no other part of Indonesia. Both relief and climate make it difficult, but the Balinese and Sasaks are past masters in the art of diverting and distributing water from the streams. Their embankments, the bamboo aqueducts they throw across ravines, and their underground canals, which are sometimes more than half a mile long and look like peepholes as they come out on to the valley-slopes, win the admiration of European engineers.

As in all Monsoon Asia, irrigation here is connected with rice cultivation. The broken relief has been admirably put to advantage for the arrangement of the *sawahs*. These spread over the plains and also climb very steep slopes. The terraces, which are often only one or two yards wide, follow and improve all the minor features of the slopes, go down to the walls of gorges, and venture right to the edge of narrow spurs separating canyons cut in the tuff. They may be seen in the beautiful valley of Tampaksiring in Bali, which is famous for the tombs of the princes cut in its rock walls and for the sacred springs which gush out in its hollows. The landowners using the same irrigation system combine into agricultural societies, or *subaks*, each having its own temple and meeting periodically to arrange the work in the ricefields and organise the festivals connected with it, in particular those held at harvest time. Here again the density of population is proportionate to the area of *sawahs* and to the fertility of the soil. It is 1165 to the square mile in the district of Gianjar in south Bali, but only 260 on the northern slopes of the island, which are more arid.[1] The average area of *sawah* per head of the population is 0·22 acre in Bali, 0·32 acre in Lombok.[2]

But the rice from the *sawahs* is no longer sufficient for local needs. The cultivation of the upland variety also benefits from skilful care. The *tegals* are themselves very often terraced. The sight of them is particularly striking on the limestone plateaus, where the terraces along the contour lines extend as far as the eye can see and often surround the innumerable hemispherical hills in the tropical karst right up to the summits. This is seen in Nusa Penida, where the density of population amounts to 290 to the square mile. The permeable rock makes water so scarce that the inhabitants of the islet have to catch the rain in pots and hollows in the rocks. Besides, most of the villages have a common cistern lined with clay and covered with a lid. In the dry season livestock is watered at springs on the coast several hours' walk away. On the south coast some of the springs rise more than 650 feet above sea level and are reached only by means of ladders. The number of cisterns was recently increased by the Dutch Colonial Government. The cultivation of upland rice has become careful horticulture. Rock projections are broken away and pebbles are removed or used for building low walls. On the narrow terraces the hoe is the only implement used and is generally wielded in a squatting position. On the *tegals* the native grows certain varieties of rice as well as maize, which in the hills becomes the chief food. Beans, sweet potatoes, cassava, yams, and groundnuts are sometimes planted among the cereals. The coconut palm remains the noble and graceful ornament of the whole countryside up to the 2600-foot contour and far from the sea air. In Bali the chief export crop is coffee, which nowadays is mostly derived from the *Coffea robusta*.[3] In Lombok the chief crop is tobacco.

Stockrearing is another source of income. The Balinese ox, which was carefully tended by the Dutch veterinary service, is famous throughout the archipelago. It is a small beast with a red coat

[1] Mohr (98), p. 487.   [2] 0·198 acre in Java.
[3] *Coffea arabica*, which is often left to itself and grows to a height of 30 feet forms real woods between 3000 and 5000 feet above the sea.

splashed with white and is shipped as far as Singapore to be used as a draught animal or for slaughter. Owing to the failure of Islam in Bali, pig-keeping is prosperous and leads to a fairly large trade. Minor rural industries continue to be active.

In these densely populated islands man's influence on the landscape has already gone very far. Bits of natural scenery just hold their own in west Bali, where the Dyembrana jungles are still almost un-inhabited and harbour stags, wild boars, and tigers. In the same island fine woods crown the upper slopes of the volcanic hill-mass, but nevertheless timber has to be imported for building. The area under cultivation covers about 64 per cent. of the total, which is greater than in Java. In Lombok it is far more restricted and covers only 37 per cent. because of the smaller area of volcanic soil and the difficulties of irrigating the wide Praya plain in the south-west of the island. Xerophilous vegetation with its dull, leathery, or succulent leaves is far more extensive in Lombok and includes little mimosas, opuntias, and euphorbias, which even in Java clothe the most arid parts in the east. In the line of Sunda Islands Lombok is the first in which the approach to Australia becomes evident to the naturalist owing to the presence of a large number of animal species related to those of that continent. Tigers and other wild beasts are wholly absent, but there is a large number of birds: pigeons, kingfishers, and, above all, parrakeets like the little white cockatoo which en-livens the countryside with its shrill cries and pretty yellow crests.

In both islands most of the population lives in large villages. The typical Balinese village is arranged on a regular plan and is crossed by a wide avenue bordered in some cases with fine trees and cut at right angles by narrower streets. These mark out the rectangular blocks occupied by one or more family dwellings. Each house is surrounded by a clay or dry stone wall higher than a man and sheltered from the tropical rain by little roofs of reeds, rice-straw, or tiles. A well-to-do peasant's house contains two or even three distinct courtyards. In the first stand the cowsheds, the rice barn (perched high on tall piles and covered with a steep-pitched roof), and in some cases the buildings meant for housing guests. Then around the central court are grouped the dwellings of the proprietor and his relatives. These are built on a brick foundation, have narrow doors, and are usually without windows. Lastly, there is the site of the temple, or *sanggah*, dedicated to the ancestors and household gods and surrounded by shrines belonging to individual members of the family. The village itself has its temple, or *pura dessa*, nearly always placed in the village centre on the spot where the periodical market, or *pasar*, is held. On the other hand, the cemetery and the esplanade reserved for cremations are outside the village at the end of the main central street, which is wide enough for ritual processions.

The Lesser Sunda Islands. Human settlement becomes far less dense eastward of Lombok. Though the area is six times as great as that of Bali and Lombok, the population is barely larger, being 2,000,000 instead of 1,800,000, or about 70 to the square mile. Nor is the decrease eastwards regular. The density varies from 190 to the square mile in the volcanic district of Maumere in east Flores to less than 26 to the square mile on the limestone soil in east Sumba.[1]

In truth, the effects of low rainfall are more or less aggravated or corrected by the type of soil. As a rule, drought is less marked on the north coasts, but is severe nearly everywhere for six months at least when the trade wind from the east prevails. Waingapu in Sumba, being situated at the inner end of a bay opening north-eastwards, gets 30 inches of rain a year, whilst Kupang at the south-western end of Timor and fully exposed to the monsoon from Asia gets nearly twice as much. But at neither of these stations does the rainfall from May to October inclusive amount to 2·8 inches. The year's rain is shared by 79 days in the capital of Dutch Timor, but by only 56 in the chief town of Sumba. In the dry season most of the streams dry up before reaching the sea. The evergreen forest, which still covers nearly a third of the surface in west Sumbawa, exists only in patches in Flores and Sumba; and beyond them it dies away not to reappear before the Tenimbar, or Timorlaut, Islands. Apart from the *Borassus flabelliformis* (or *lontar*), whose sap crystal-lises into sugar and whose leaves are natural water containers and are used for roofing, and the *Casuarina equisetifolia* (or *filao*), which is dotted about on the lower slopes and stony valley bottoms in eastern Timor,[2] the typical species are trees with dull, greyish leaves that fall in the dry season. Examples are: the eucalyptus, which grows spontaneously in Flores, Timor, and islands farther east; the *Butea frondosa*, whose meagre foliage belies its name; the *Melaleuca cajeputi*; and acacias. There are many species of Apocyneæ, Euphorbiaceæ, and thorny bamboo. *Santalum album*,[3] which was mentioned in Camoens' poem, is a semi-parasitic tree or shrub which abounds in Timor on rough soil and abandoned *ladangs*, but never forms pure stands. The impoverished, monotonous scenery already foreshadows Australian scrub. Trees seldom reach great height, but have twisted trunks and zigzag branches. They are often scattered about on savanas of leathery grass whose metallic reflec-tions glitter in the brilliant sunshine. In some valleys thorn bushes, creepers, or climbing plants form impenetrable thickets. The soil

---

[1] Mohr (98), p. 488.   [2] Wittouck (163), p. 343.
[3] Van Steenis (56), p. 393.

is sometimes even bare. Limestone islands like Roti and Savu look from the sea like rocky scorched deserts.

But the soil varies in permeability as much as in fertility. In fact, the most up-to-date researches confirm the complexity of structure in this line of islands which at first sight might be thought to be alike. Volcanoes are no longer present everywhere. To the east of Sumbawa the series of islands splits into two, and in the bulge towards Australia made by Sumba and Timor round the south of the Savu Sea volcanic activity ceased before the end of the Tertiary. The most recent signs of activity are found in lava flows in north Timor. Except in a few outcrops of granite and Secondary rocks, Sumba is wholly formed of Tertiary sedimentaries, mainly limestone, which rise no higher than 4000 feet. The greater part of Timor is of Primary, Secondary, and Tertiary rocks of very varied appearance and gathered into a complex structure. Brouwer, who, following Molengraaff, carried out a fruitful geological survey of the Lesser Sunda Islands in 1937, terms it Alpine. But he stresses the fact that it is the outcome of a long series of orogenic movements in which horizontal displacement was often greater than vertical. Metamorphic schists outcrop here and there, as a rule forming heavy masses which rise to 7760 feet in Mt. Mutis in the Dutch part and to 9800 feet south-west of Dilli in Portuguese territory. In some places the common rocks are sandstones, marls, and limestone of various ages and appearance; for instance, Neogene limestone resting on very folded Eogene, as in Sumba. But there are also Triassic limestones, and these sometimes form typical karstic plateaus, as in east Timor, where they rise near Builo to a height of more than 4000 feet. In other places, however, they are broken into small steep-sided *mesas* standing separately on the lower rock and called *fatus* by the people of Timor. These *mesas* often look like remnants of overthrusts; others have certainly been moved by landslide at a more or less distant period. The relief shows that Timor underwent a long period of erosion at the end of the Tertiary and was widely submerged before the last very recent and uneven movements of uplift indicated by the existence of Quaternary coral formations at altitudes that vary, but decrease fairly regularly from the centre of the island to its two ends.[1]

On the other hand, in the islands which immediately prolong the Sumatra–Java–Bali–Lombok arc the effects of vulcanism remain everywhere evident. The mantle of eruptive rocks is almost continuous, except in Sumbawa, and it hides all the rocks older than the end of the Tertiary. However, two series of existing volcanoes are distinguished. One includes the volcanoes in Flores, Lomblen, and

[1] In central Timor a system of faults parallel to the main axis of the island explains the existence of a rift (*graben*) filled with pliocene deposits.

south Pantar together with Mt. Tamboro, which is situated in the north of Sumbawa and rivals Krakatoa in violence. The other is situated on the east of Wetar and is strewn over the little islands that form a hook round the Banda Sea. Alor and Wetar, which are between the two lines of still active cones whose summits are often crowned with steam from solfataras, have not erupted since the end of the Tertiary. Volcanic morphology has been obliterated here as in northern Timor. It all looks, says Brouwer, as if volcanic activity was more and more sustained with distance from the continental shelf of Australia and as if this huge buffer had first stirred up eruptions by its resistance and then had stifled them under a pile of rock-waste or a line of new folds. The structure is simpler than in the secondary Sumba–Timor arc. The Upper Tertiary is still folded, but neither imbrication nor transported matter is visible. Very recent vertical movements have greatly influenced the evolution of the relief. Conformably with the profile seen in the southern

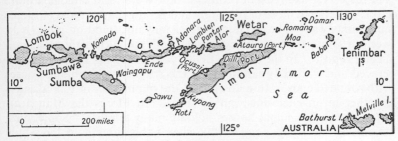

FIG. 31.—LESSER SUNDA ISLANDS

arc, uplifted Quaternary coral formations drop gradually down towards sea level westwards and eastwards from Alor and Wetar. In the north as in the south longitudinal, transverse, or oblique fracture often seems responsible for the coastline as well as for depressions inland, like the one seen in the Timor axis to the south of the highest range.

If native traditions are to be believed, the widening of the straits between Solor and Adonara and between Pantar and Lomblen must be attributed to very recent subsidence following on earthquakes. The inhabitants of the areas submerged must have taken refuge on other islands. Vatter places the last movements in the 17th century.

In all the Lesser Sunda Islands the lowlands are small and narrow. The southern islands are the most massive and least attractive. In Timor the mountains rise steeply from the north coast. The least difficult gap is that of the River Comoro to the west of Dilli, the capital of the Portuguese colony. Farther south the mountains change to low hills, but the width of the coast plain, in which the rivers end in marshes, barely exceeds three miles.

Mt. Tamboro in Sumbawa and several volcanoes in Flores exceed a height of 6600 feet. But as in Java relatively easy passages exist between these recent cones. The coastline often seems to have been determined by recent eruptions, as in Ende Bay in the south of Flores, and the deep indentations of this island are in contrast with the smooth lines of Sumba and Timor as well as with Alor and Wetar. The east–west road built by the Dutch in Flores crosses some three times from one side of the island to the other.

Among the human groups living east of Lombok the Papuan type, which was not wholly absent from western Indonesia, becomes very common, e.g. in the Atonis in Timor. Stature is taller, complexion darker, and facial features more marked. The prominent nose with its pronounced bridge is sometimes aquiline. Local peculiarities are also strengthened by the diversity of dialects, costumes, and dwellings. The dialects spoken east of Flores in Alor, Wetar, and Timor are more closely related to those of Amboina and Serang than to those of Flores and Sumbawa . The dwelling may or may not stand on piles.[1] In western Timor the huts are cylindrical with a conical roof resting on a central post. In the east the Belus, whose mode of life is more advanced and who are wealthier than the Atonis, build oblong houses with rounded ends. In many places the population of this island is together in an enclosing wall of stone. In Flores the Mangarais often live in communal houses holding many families. Sometimes, as among the Dyaks, one or two such habitations hold the whole village and are often perched on a ridge.

The basis of the diet is maize. Here and there sago is important, particularly in Wetar. The cultivation of rice on irrigated terraces seems generally due to a more or less ancient immigration of Javanese or Malay settlers who, for instance at the east end of Timor, settled on the coast. Ground under permanent cultivation, whether *sawah*, *tegal*, garden, or plantation, occupies but a small part of the whole area. For instance, only 4·5 per cent. of the sultanate of Sumbawa comprising the eastern portion of the island is cultivated permanently. Here continuous forest still covers 32 per cent., whilst the rest is used for collecting, for pasturage, and for *ladang*.[2]

Asiatic influence dies away gradually along the Sunda arc, and savage customs still persist in many places. The last ripples of Indo-Javanese culture seem to have reached Timor about 1200 and to have gone as far as the west coast of New Guinea about 1350. Islam

[1] Nguyen van Huyen (99), pp. 114 ff.
[2] Kuperus (162). In Timor the Atonis are continually destroying the forest and the soil by overstocking and abuse of the *ladang* system. Cp. an interesting monograph by Ormeling (161b).

itself, which is still so vigorous in Lombok, disappears farther east, and the work of Christian missionaries has met with success in Flores, Sumba, and Timor. The demand for forest products and spices has for a very long time maintained some trickles of trade between western Indonesia and these distant islands.

The prime movers in this trade were Malays, Arabs, and Chinese, little colonies of whom were found by the Europeans on their arrival. The former supremacy of the Portuguese at this end of the then known world is recalled by the division of Timor. After difficult negotiations in the middle of last century, Portugal secured Dutch recognition of her rule in the eastern half of the island as well as in the little enclave of Ocussi on the north-west coast. In spite of his admiration for Iberian colonisation, Wallace was struck on landing at Dilli with the contrast between the wretched mud and wattle huts and the swarm of officials in glittering uniforms.[1] Some attempts have been made to grow crops for export; in particular, coffee in the southern mountains and tobacco. But little of this activity remains.

Before the beginning of the 20th century the Dutch had scarcely secured a footing here, except in the little island of Damar between Wetar and Banda (1664) and on Kupang Bay in Timor (in the 19th century). Since 1907 they have focused their attention on these islands of the *Groote Oost*. Before the war the K.L.M. ran weekly, fortnightly, or monthly services connecting most of them with Macassar, Surabaya, and Jakarta. Plantations of coffee, tobacco, and sugarcane have been developed mainly by natives around little ports like Kupang. However, the *Arabica* has been falling off in Sumbawa since 1932, and official propaganda in favour of *Robusta* has met with little success. The Dutch veterinary service has worked effectively to protect and improve native domestic breeds, and buffaloes and little horses are shipped from Sumba and Sumbawa mainly to Java. Other products are usually passed through Macassar and consist of sandalwood, resin, hides, staghorn, and wax obtained from the huge combs which are hung on the upper branches of trees by the *Apis dorsata*. Sumbawa, Timor, and Flores already have a modest layout for tourists, with some rest houses, or *pasang-grahan*. The beautiful crater lakes in Flores, which are coloured by salts, afford the most famous sight in these islands.

The Moluccas. Properly speaking, the Moluccas are the little islands lying off the west coast of Halmahera from Ternate to Bachan. But since the 16th century it has been the custom to extend the name to include all the Indonesian islands situated between Celebes (or rather the outlying Sula Group) on the west and New Guinea on the

[1] Wallace (63), p. 145.

east, and between the eastern part of the Sunda arc on the south and the Philippines on the north (see Fig. 29).

The Group is distinguished from the preceding by its moister climate. On coming from the south, where Wetar and the neighbouring islands had presented scenery as bare and desolate as that of Aden, Wallace was pleasantly surprised two days later to see the luxuriant vegetation which adorns the little Banda Islands a short distance south of the Equator. The rainfall everywhere exceeds 40 inches and amounts to 50 inches at Ternate, 104 in Banda, and 138 inches at Amboina, the number of days on which rain falls at these three places being respectively 151, 181, and 201. Rain is caused by the north-west as well as the south-east winds, the relative importance of each depending on local conditions and above all on differences of aspect enhanced by a generally well marked relief of surface. The driest season in Ternate as in Banda lasts from July to October, that is, during the southern summer; whilst in Amboina Bay, up which it is easier for the north-west monsoon to pass, it lasts from October to March. But no month at any of these places gets less than 4 inches. We find here on the far side of Celebes very typical examples of the equatorial climate, as we did in Sumatra and Borneo.

The original vegetation type, which persists in most places either intact or slightly modified, is the evergreen forest. Of course, xerophilous associations still appear in places. For instance, near the east end of Serang there is a savana of rough grass dotted with *Melaleuca cajeputi*. Here and there in valleys in the interior of Halmahera the forest is broken by *glagla*[1] glades. In some of the little islands like Tidore, Ternate, and the Banda group, which were early inhabited, crops of maize, coconuts, bananas, and spices occupy nearly all the favourable area up to a height of 1600 feet above the sea. Higher than this there is mainly scrub. But in the other islands man's ravages have been checked by the sparseness of the population. The flora and fauna of Amboina were made famous as early as the 17th century by the scientific works of Rumphius. Countless natural history collections have been made in this island, and many specific names point to an origin in it. The big, smooth, buttressed trunks of the trees and the many species of *Ficus* which shower down aerial roots have caused the forests in the Moluccas to be reckoned among the finest in Indonesia. Arborescent Liliaceæ are especially abundant on the sandy coast strips, as are the Pandanaceæ whose thick, glossy leaves are everywhere used, as in New Guinea, for making mats, or *cocoyas*, ornamented with coloured patterns. In the mountains away from the coast the

[1] *Saccharum spontaneum.*

Agathis is often the dominant species, and *dammar* (copal) gathering is an appreciable source of wealth for many natives. But the sago palm is undeniably the most useful tree.[1] Usually shorter than the coconut, but heavier and bulkier, this palm grows in coastal marshes, in fresh water, or even on the damp level spaces that break the rocky slopes. The ribs of its big leaves are used for building houses and for making chests and boxes. When about ten or fifteen years old, it puts out enormous blossoms and then dies. Just before it blossoms, the stem is cut through near the ground and, except its very thin bark, is almost entirely turned into sago paste or flour, which is the principal food in the Moluccas, except perhaps in Obi, where rice prevails.

The plentiful rainfall allows dense forest to flourish even on porous soil. Such soil, though of different origins, does indeed cover most of the land area. As in the Sunda arc, the most obvious contrast is between the volcanic islands and those built mainly of sedimentary rocks. In the south the groups comprising Serang, Buru, Misul, Obi, and their continuation in the Sula Islands, show no sign of volcanic activity. Schist and granite are ringed with Secondary beds and crowned with Tertiary remnants. The last mentioned are nearly horizontal in Misul and Obi, in which the land does not rise above the contours for 3250 and 5300 feet respectively, but on the other hand they are vigorously folded in Serang and Buru. They form part of the little ranges lying along the main axis of these islands and reach a height of 10,000 feet in the middle of Serang and 8000 feet in the north-west of Buru. The complexity of the recent movements is proved by the very unequal uplifting of the Pliocene and Quaternary coral formations.[2] In the interior of the islands the rugged skeletons of old coral formations show through the mantle of luxuriant forest and are pitted with deep holes filled with red or black earth, as in Amboina and the Kei Islands. Living coral is still plentiful and forms wonderful 'sea gardens'.

In the Banda Sea many little islands, mostly uninhabited, are wholly of coral. All the same, the little group called the Banda Islands is volcanic in structure. The active portion is Mount Api, which still smokes; whilst the other islands are but fragments of the 'somma' and the remains of a huge cone smashed to bits by eruptions. North of the Moluccas Halmahera forcibly recalls Celebes by its digitate shape and its deep inlets separating four peninsulas which are so unevenly wide that the isthmus of Pasir is barely 2½ miles across. This isthmus, which is opposite Ternate, was once the scene of bloody struggles. As in the case of Celebes, the outline is no doubt due to subsidence, but the geological history of Halmahera

[1] Wallace (63), p. 289.   [2] Blondel (23), p. 417.

is still imperfectly known. Old eruptive rocks and Secondary sedimentaries have been seen in the centre and east. But on the northern peninsula several active volcanoes form a line, the 'Ternate line', which is continued in the little islands on the west coast. Indeed, whilst the highest cone, the almost perfectly symmetrical volcano in Tidore (5700 feet), is extinct, the one in Ternate remains the most active of the set and is always plumed with steam (5650 feet). It has erupted some fifty times in the last four hundred years, the eruption in 1763 being the most severe.

On the coast of these true Molucca islands beaches of black sand of volcanic origin and cliffs of lava fringed with rugged rocks alternate with beaches of dazzling white sand derived from coral reefs.

Earthquakes are especially frequent in the Moluccas and are often of great violence. In 1840 an earthquake destroyed the town of Ternate. The shocks spread southwards to the island of Bachan. In Banda shocks are noticeable every day. The earthquakes gradually destroy the old residences, many of which were built of beautiful stone imported from Europe at great expense and have been partly abandoned by their owners in a half-ruined state.

The land fauna contributes to the splendour of the Moluccas.[1] Adjacent to both Indonesia and Melanesia, the Moluccas have for more than a hundred years been one of the most famous zoological regions in the world. Mammals are extremely rare. Apart from bats, there are only about ten species. These include a monkey, *Cynopithecus nigrescens*, found only in Bachan and no doubt brought by man from Celebes; a civet cat, the only carnivore and also probably imported; a stag, the only ruminant; the strange babirusa, which is not found out of Buru; and four or five marsupials, in particular three opossums of the Cuscus genus with long prehensile tails, big eyes, thick woolly fur, and feeding on leaves of the trees on which they live.

The insects and even more the birds, together with the fauna in the 'sea gardens', form a living and glorious ornament of the Moluccas. Local types are numerous, and in most classes or orders every island contains one or two species of peculiar form. A little island like Morotai has several peculiar species of birds, although it is separated from Halmahera by a strait only some 30 miles wide. Wallace spent three years in travelling round the Moluccas, and his enthusiastic description of them should be read. No other island yields such a fine collection in so short a time as Amboina; and its insects are the most beautiful in Indonesia. Wallace joyfully sought for hours in the bark and among the branches of fallen trees in the

---

[1] Wallace (63), pp. 219 ff.

blazing sunshine for Curculionides, Longicorns, and Buprestes of vast size and brilliant colours, many of the species being at that time very rare or not included in European collections. Among the beetles he distinguished above all others the extraordinary *Enchirus longimanus* which, when its legs are stretched out, measures nearly 8 inches long. Few parts of the world have butterflies of such splendid colours and size, such as the Ulysses, which is bright blue and is very common in Amboina; or else the huge Croesus with its velvety wings of black and bright orange, on catching one of which on Bachan for the first time Wallace nearly fainted with pleasure.

This wealth of species is even more evident in the birds. Wallace counted 195 land species in the Moluccas as against 257 in the whole of Europe. Nearly one-third of them fall within the three groups, pigeons, kingfishers, and parrakeets; a proportion that suggests likeness with New Guinea, but is very different from India, where the thrushes, warblers, and finches are far better represented. The Moluccas are especially rich in parrakeets and contain 22 species belonging to 10 genera. Wallace saw enormous flights of crimson parrakeets alight on trees in Amboina to feed on the nectar. These birds are almost exclusively restricted to the Moluccas and New Guinea. From the same islands also comes the big red-crested parrakeet often sold in Europe. Wallace counted 21 species of pigeon, some of which fed on nutmeg, and 16 species of wonderfully coloured kingfishers. Birds of paradise make their appearance first in Bachan and Halmahera, and they become more common in the islands off New Guinea: Misul, Waigeo, and Aru. In 1598 Linschoten wrote that no one had as yet seen them alive; but their bodies when dried and cured caused wonder among the first Europeans to land in the Moluccas in search of cloves and nutmegs.[1]

These two products were indeed the cause of the extraordinary attraction and fame of the Spice Islands. The clove tree (*Eugenia aromatica*), of which the clove is a bud, and the nutmeg tree (*Myristica fragrans*), on which blossoms and fruit appear together and whose fruit bursts open when ripe, to show the dark brown nut enveloped in the scarlet network of the mace, are probably trees of native origin and at any rate were acclimatised in the Moluccas before the arrival of the Europeans.[2] The group seems long to

[1] Wallace (63), pp. 419–40. These birds were called *manuk dewata* (= God's birds) and by the Portuguese *passaros do sol*. Linnæus, who was the first to describe them, gave an account of two species in 1760.

[2] This is the opinion of van Steenis (56), p. 57. Wallace (63), p. 237, writes that many nutmegs came from trees of spontaneous growth in New Guinea. Cp. also Olearius (9), II., p. 415, who attributes the excellence of spices from the Moluccas to the 'dry, spongy earth . . . the ever saturated atmosphere'.

have been Europe's chief source of supply through various intermediaries before the voyage of Abreu, a lieutenant of Albuquerque,
opened direct trade in 1512. The enormous profits from this trade
brought on a bitter rivalry between the maritime powers of the West.
Sebastian del Cano, Magellan's companion, then Drake and others
brought back profitable cargoes to European ports. Drake
described the Sultan of Ternate in 1579 as loaded with gold and
precious stones.

In 1598 the Dutch arrived with Jacob Cornelis van Necq of
Amsterdam. He was welcomed at Amboina by the natives, who
cheered him from their flag-dressed caravels. Soon some Dutch
(*perkeniers*) settled in Banda to cultivate nutmegs. This was the
beginning of a monopoly which for decades was to bring in enormous
profits to the Dutch East India Company. In fact, to render the
monopoly effective, the Company improved on the system already
practised by the native rulers of restricting the production of the
precious commodities to definite areas—the little Spice Islands—
where supervision was easy and under the protection of strong,
well-armed forts.

Banda became the chief grower of nutmegs, whilst Ternate,
Tidore, and Amboina were the great producers of cloves and
supplied other spices too, such as ginger and cinnamon, the market
for which was less wide and the trade less strictly regulated. These
plants do not seem to have been regularly cultivated. Even in the
middle of the 19th century Wallace observed that the nutmeg tree,
which grows to 25 or 40 feet high, is graceful in shape, and bears
little yellow flowers and fruit of the colour and size of a peach,
needs little attention and no manure and has the advantage of soil
and especially of a climate which are exceptionally favourable.
Yet many plantations were established by Dutch effort. When the
soil was cleared, the tree grew under shelter of tall canariums.
The picking—done several times a year—and preparation for
market of this fruit and also of cloves required a fairly plentiful
supply of labour. Since the native population was neither large
nor hard-working, the Dutch instituted a system of forced labour
which quite often degenerated into cruel oppression. When the
markets were glutted through over-production and prices fell,
large-scale uprooting was carried out under the supervision of
'eradication officers'. Other Europeans were even murdered when
they tried to enter the islands to steal the secrets of the cultivation
and to get hold of seed which would germinate.

Real secrets do not seem to have existed, and it was difficult to
prevent the export of seed for a long time. The spice-producing
plants from the Far East were acclimatised in other islands and in

other tropical lands like India and Ceylon, the Mascarenhas Islands, and Zanzibar. As early as the 17th century the monopoly of the Moluccas seemed broken, except in nutmegs. Banda remains the chief producer of this spice in Indonesia, which supplies three-fourths of world consumption. But Indonesia produces only 2 per cent. of the cloves, the main centre today being Zanzibar, from which even Java must import in order to scent its cigarettes. At the same time as the political centre of gravity moved towards western Indonesia, the profits from the trade in spices fell off absolutely and relatively. In 1937 Indonesia produced 385 tons of nutmegs, 137 in Java and 248 in the Outer Provinces, which was an insignificant fraction of the total exports from these islands.

The islands are still renowned for wealth, but are some of the most sparsely populated parts of Indonesia. The Residency of the Moluccas, excluding Dutch New Guinea, but including the Kei, Aru, and other islands off its west coast, contained only 580,000 persons in 1930, which was about 18 to the square mile. This average, moreover, is raised by dense populations in Amboina and Saparua (212 per square mile), Banda (180), and Ternate (83).[1] These little islands still preserve in their ruined forts and in the effaced inscriptions on stone or brick tombs the memory of their former glory and the fierce rivalries which they caused. The other islands were not really occupied until the beginning of the 20th century. The people, who are a strange mixture of very various elements, afford a living testimony of a history that has been full of incident. The natives are generally all termed Alfurs, but are far from being an anthropological or linguistic unit. Yet no clear distinction can be drawn between the Malay, Papuan, and Melanesian types. The dialects spoken in Amboina are fairly similar to those in Flores and Timor, but less like those in Halmahera. And the northernmost part of Halmahera lies outside the Malayo-Polynesian speech-area and represents as it were the rearguard of the group of Papuan dialects which are found in New Guinea. Almost throughout the Moluccas the basis of the diet is sago, the abundance of which obtained from wild trees is said by many European observers to be the cause of the indolence of the natives. The number of coconut palms is increasing in many islands, and small areas of irrigated ricefields are met with here and there especially on the coast near settlements of people from over the sea.

The population of the Moluccas seems to have undergone fairly radical changes in the last few hundred years. Apparently the Papuans had begun to be driven eastwards long before the arrival of the Europeans. But the Dutch carried out large transfers in the

[1] Mohr (98), p. 491.

17th century in order to have a supply of docile labour. Thus, the people of Banda were driven towards the Aru Islands. The mixture is greatest and most difficult to analyse in the little Spice Islands especially. The Malay elements, which began to be introduced long before the coming of the Europeans, seem to have originated mainly in Celebes, but cross-breeding with native women was very common. The influence of Arab or Chinese blood is also noticeable in some individuals. The European contribution is not negligible, the Portuguese being far greater than the Dutch. The Christian, and usually half-caste, descendants of the Portuguese are called *Orang Sirani*, or Nazarenes, by the Malays. In Banda, Ternate, Bachan, and especially at Amboina, the extraordinary persistence of Portuguese permeation is recognised by certain physical features, by a number of words introduced into the Malay dialects, by the dress (especially for festive occasions: bell-shaped skirts with stiff pleats in the former Creole fashion), and by the religious ceremonies which even after conversion to Protestantism retain many Roman Catholic touches in their processions and music and recall the fact that the Moluccas were one of the chief fields of activity of St. Francis Xavier. The mixture of these Western features with native customs and rites helps to make the dances and songs of these communities strange, but pleasant sights. Many Christians from Amboina are keenly intelligent. Some used to serve in the Dutch army, whilst others were scattered all over the archipelago, working as clerks, schoolmasters, and hospital attendants.

The Moluccas have by their situation long fulfilled the duty of half-way house between the ports of western Indonesia and Melanesia. Trade with the coast of New Guinea was in Wallace's time the speciality of a few groups of Buginese or Macassarese sailors from Celebes or men from Serang. It was formerly a dangerous calling owing to the boldness of the pirates and also to the savage character of the Papuans in New Guinea. But from these distant islands, for long the *Ultima Thule* of the Far East, came valuable merchandise in the shape of spices, resins, barks, and other forest products, pelts, and feathers of the birds of paradise, trepang (or sea-slug), tortoiseshell, pearl oysters, and swallows' nests. The tiny island of Kilwaru in the Gorong group east of Serang, which was overcrowded with pile-dwellings and looked like a floating town, was then the chief market in the *Groote Oost* for the Bugis who brought from Singapore goods originating in China, India, Lancashire, and Massachusetts. Another very busy mart was the port of Dobo, which is still a busy place on the north-west coast of the Aru Islands.[1]

[1] Wallace (63), p. 368.

The competition of European shipping companies has revolutionised trade conditions. However, the use of *prahus* has not yet disappeared from eastern Indonesia. Bugis go to Jakarta or Singapore at the end of the eastern monsoon, buy cotton cloth, tools, and pottery and return by the western monsoon to the *Groote Oost*, from which, when the east winds begin again, they take back to Macassar the goods they have bought or bartered. Macassar has become the main collecting and distributing centre, compared with which Banda and Amboina do but little trade. The latter town, which stands on a deep bay, is still the administrative capital and chief town of the Moluccas and in 1930 had a population of 17,300, of whom 1878 were counted as Europeans. The Netherlands Indies Government had decided to take advantage of its central position between the Philippines and Melanesia to make it a main focus of airways. Another new development was the production of oil by the Royal Batavian Petroleum Co. around Bula Bay in east Serang. In 1937 production had risen to 72,000 tons.

CHAPTER 13

THE PHILIPPINES

That the Philippines form part of the East Indies cannot be disputed. Admittedly, the mountains of Formosa can be seen in clear weather from the top of Iraya, a mountain on the island of Batan off the north coast of Luzón. But the connexion with the islands to the south is stronger and, owing to the bifurcation of the group, has more than one link. The sills that separate deep basins and break the surface to form the Talaud and Sangihe Islands join the Philippines to Celebes; and two submerged ridges, still broader and shallower, from which emerge the Sulu Islands and Palawan connect the group with Borneo. The lowering of the sea level by 100 fathoms would leave only two very narrow straits between the Philippines and the north-eastern end of Borneo and would more or less restore the outline that existed in the ice ages.

The forms of life also point to the inclusion of the Philippines in the East Indies. The flora and fauna have been found to include species that occur in Formosa, but they are only survivals and are restricted to the mountains. Northwards the isolation of the group seems to have occurred as early as the Oligocene, and it had definitely come about in the Pliocene, for Dipterocarps, which are not found in Formosa, appear in the limestone rocks of that period at Sagada in northern Luzón, and they are still common in the Philippines. The freshwater fish are related to those in Borneo, not to those in Formosa.

The majority (62 per cent.) of the animal and vegetable species in the western East Indies also flourish in the Philippines, whilst only 26 per cent. are found in eastern Indonesia and Australia. This is proof that the connexions with Celebes and the Moluccas were shorter in time and more precarious than those with Borneo.[1] But distribution is far from uniform. Besides, local types are frequent and remarkable, and botanists and zoologists can distinguish as many subdivisions as there are islands or groups of islands. But on the whole the Philippines are certainly part of the East Indies, the northern part, and they continue without a break the study of the western and eastern East Indies.

[1] In the early Neolithic age, however, the Philippines seem, from tools found in excavations, to have formed as it were a bridge between China, Japan, and Formosa on the one hand and eastern Indonesia and Melanesia on the other. (Kolb (175), p. 142.)

Distance from the Equator and nearness to the mainland of Asia give the Philippines a monsoon climate, at least in their western districts, and on the other hand a prevalence, especially in the north, of typhoons, which are unknown elsewhere in the East Indies.

The peculiarity of the Philippines also appears in their population. They are obviously similar to the rest of the East Indies in the super-position and juxtaposition of ethnic groups and modes of life and in the succession and mingling of waves of cultural influence. Nearly all the streams of migration which have helped to form the existing population seem to have come from south-eastern Asia and mainly by way of Borneo. Most of the cultivated plants and domestic animals have been got from the same region. At the time when Sri Vijaya and its successor, Majapahit, flourished, Indian influence reached as far as Manila Bay. Islam followed in the path of the Indian and Arab traders and achieved its first conquests in the 15th century. By the time Legaspi arrived, Islam had become master of the Sulu Islands and the coast of Mindanao and counted many followers in Luzón. The relative proximity of the coast of Kwangtung, which was early occupied by a dense, hardworking population, brought about, if not the political overlordship of the great continental empire, at least an early and constantly maintained stream of immigrants and cultural elements into the islands from the Chinese world. The contribution of manpower, skill, and ideas became greater still from the 16th century onwards. Chinese immigrants since that time have been estimated to form 10 per cent. of the mixed population of the islands.[1]

The European share amounts to about 3 per cent., a high figure for a tropical country. It might be put even higher if not only blood, but also beliefs, spiritual atmosphere, and the ascendency of the Roman Catholic religion were taken into account. Europe's wonderful diversity is reflected in the East Indies. As colonies, the Philippines were the Iberian portion of the archipelago and are still distinguished by more than one feature from the British and Dutch parts.

Structure. As in all the East Indies, the existing outlines of the Philippines have been due to very recent phenomena. But the existence of a group of islands in these waters certainly dates back to ancient times. Stratified Secondary rocks, mainly shales, outcrop here and there, particularly in the north of Luzón, Mindoro, and Panay. Granite and other plutonic rocks (diorites, gabbro, and peridotites) are more widely represented, but they do not seem to be older than the Secondary era. Many are certainly of Tertiary origin, as is the case in the southern East Indies, their intrusion

[1] Beyer (167).

probably being contemporary with the great tectonic movements which began in the Miocene after a period of vigorous sedimentation.

A great part of the group is, in fact, built up of Oligo-Miocene sediments of much diversity of character and including sandstones, limestones, and shales. This 'Vigo series', which is especially clearly marked in the south of Luzón, is several thousand feet thick and runs in a broad belt from north to south in the group, but particularly through the eastern part. In the middle Tertiary an island, which was perhaps continuous, must have stretched from Luzón to Celebes through Samar, Leyte, and eastern Mindanao. The strata now appear dislocated and are often violently folded and penetrated by intrusive masses.

An unconformity marking an erosional phase separates the Oligo-Miocene beds from the Pliocene. The latter, which are termed the 'Malumbang series', have also been studied in southern Luzón. This series is far less thick than the Vigo—between 300 and 1000 feet —but their variable thickness and composition prove that deposition was irregular. Vertical movement has continued in fact very irregularly in time and space up to the present day. Its range in both directions is measured on the one hand by the depth of the ocean basins, which go down to more than 3000 fathoms in the Sulu Sea and 6000 fathoms in the trench off the east coast of the group; and on the other hand by the uplift of Pliocene coral formations which occur at a height of 6400 feet on Mt. St. Thomas in the central mountains in northern Luzón. The most recent movements are best shown by raised beaches as high as 1300 feet above sea level. The post-glacial positive movement has certainly greatly complicated the layout of the group. The greater frequency of cliffs on the west coast and of drowned valleys on the east coast may be due to a tilting movement still in progress round a north–south axis.

The separation into islands and the rapid erosion maintained by the instability of the crust and a heavy rainfall help to explain the often disorderly and chaotic appearance of the relief. The orientation of the islands and peninsulas and of the many ridges and valleys shows certain definitely prevailing directions, the oldest being apparently north-west–south-east and others south-west–north-east or north–south. These lines are so arranged as to give the group a double curve like that of the coast of Indo-China. The discordance in the grain of the relief makes analysis of the structure and landforms generally very difficult, and in fact it has scarcely been attempted in most of the islands.

The lowlands, which are the most densely peopled parts, form only a small area. Along the coasts they are discontinuous and seldom reach a width of 10 miles. Inland plains are either valleys

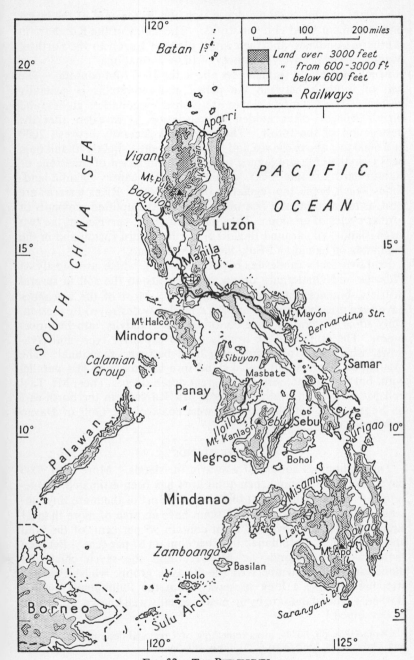

FIG. 32.—THE PHILIPPINES

which are possibly tectonic depressions or, in the case of the larger ones, sediment-filled gulfs or straits. The valley of the Kotabató in southern Mindanao and the central plain of Luzón to the north of Manila are respectively instances of these formations. Much of the land surface rises above the 1600-foot contour. The belt of foothills between the plains and mountains is generally narrow. The mountain-slopes are gashed by countless gullies, and their steepness, often hidden by vegetation, is revealed after the destruction of the forest. The ridges are generally between 2000 and 6000 feet above the sea and usually present a slightly undulating, heavy skyline, but are jagged in districts composed of limestone or certain hard volcanic rocks. Rain very often causes gigantic landslides which break the regularity of the slopes. River terraces are rare, as are also tabular features formed of the uplifted remnants of former cycles of erosion. They have, however, survived in the two large islands, viz. around Baguio in north-western Luzón and in the highlands of Lanao and Bukidnon in Mindanao.

Eruptive rocks (andesite, basalt, and tuff), which are mostly of Pliocene and Quaternary origin, add fertility to the soil in several districts, but are not present everywhere. Most of the volcanoes have been greatly damaged or even completely destroyed by erosion. Only some ten craters have continued their activity into historical times. The eruptions are usually of the explosive type, and lava-flows, which were once frequent, have become exceptional. The mountains that are still active stand in a line more or less parallel with, but well to the west of, the great ocean deep. Thus, Mt. Taal and Mt. Mayón in southern Luzón, Mt. Kanlaón in the north-east of Negros, and Mt. Apo on the west coast of the Gulf of Davao in Mindanao.

CHIEF ISLANDS

The Philippines consist of a swarm of islands. More than 7000 have been counted, and their total area has been estimated at one-fourth as large again as that of Britain. Most of them are tiny, uninhabited, and nameless; 466 of them have an area of more than 2¼ square miles; and eleven of them contain 95 per cent. of the land area. Luzón and Mindanao together contain 67 per cent. Between these two large islands lie Mindoro and the seven chief and moderately large members of the Visayas group, whilst Palawan stretches out like a long causeway from the Philippines towards Borneo. The islands are by no means equally well known, inhabited, or developed.[1]

[1] Kolb (175), pp. 60–84, gives something of a regional description. For the mid-19th century, see Mallat (177), I, pp. 161–346.

Luzón. Luzón, the largest in the group, presents great contrasts in relief over an area which only just exceeds 38,000 square miles. Its northern and more massive part has its more or less north–south

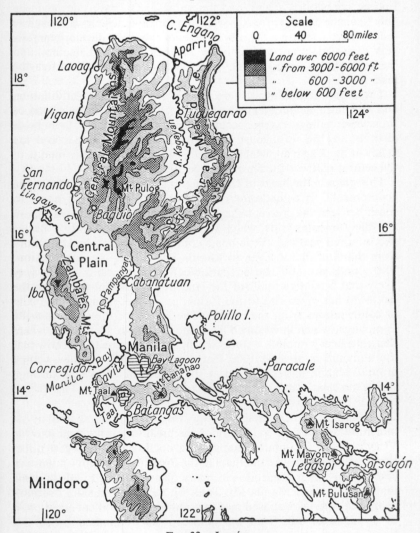

FIG. 33.—LUZÓN

orientation confirmed by the direction of its ridges and chief rivers; thus, the Kagayán and the principal mountains in the group which run to the west of this river. There are three parallel ranges with several peaks rising above the 6600 foot contour, the highest being Mt. Pulog (9600 feet) in the eastern range. Granite often outcrops in the central range among other igneous rocks and Secondary or Eocene sandstones, shales, and limestones. On both sides andesite and Neogene deposits are survivals of a top layer which was formerly much more extensive. Lofty erosional surfaces develop on this very varied material, especially around Mt. Dato and Baguio. To the east of the Kagayán the Sierra Madre nowhere rises to 6600 feet.

These mountains in northern Luzón are still imperfectly known and give little encouragement to settlers. Entry is difficult because transverse valleys rarely occur. The only relatively favourable districts are the west coast strip inhabited by the Ilocos and the valley of the Kagayán, which has been connected by motor road with the central plain of Luzón only since 1924.

This plain is the heart of the group and the seat of the Philippine government. It extends for over nearly 125 miles from north to south between the crescent-shaped continuation of the Sierra Madre and the Zambales Hills, which were isolated until recently. Barely two hundred years ago little boats could pass without breaking bulk from the Gulf of Lingayen to Manila Bay during the rainy season. Vast floods are still caused periodically by the rains. It is very likely that a relative uplift of the land (a negative movement of the sea level) has given rise to the formation of the plain with the help of contributions from the rivers. The largest of the streams is the Pampanga, which flows down from the Caraballo Mountains, where there is a heavy rainfall. Bores reaching down to bedrock show that the alluvium is at least 1000 feet deep. Away from the swampy ground Manila has grown up at the mouth of the Pasig, through which the clear water of the big Bay Lagoon runs off. The surface level of this lake is only 6½ feet above the sea.

Southern Luzón differs from the rest of the island and by its indentations and deep gulfs heralds the break-up of the land into the Visayas. The mountains change to a north-west–south-east direction, and the rivers, like the Bicol in the Province of South Camarines, conform to this. The soil is in many places enriched with volcanic matter. South of Manila Mt. Taal, whose dissected sides overlook a large caldera lake, caused many casualties by its violent eruption in 1911. East of Mt. Taal the landscape is dominated by several large extinct volcanoes, like Mt. Banahao (7000 feet) and Mt. Maquiling. Another group of volcanoes appears right in the south-east of the island and includes the huge peaks of Isarog, Balusan, and Mayón (8000 feet). The first two are extinct, but the last is still active and rises from the plain as a majestic and almost perfectly symmetrical cone about 80 miles in circumference. Its last eruption took place in 1938.

The Visayas. Separated from Luzón by a strait only some 9 or 10 miles wide and lying between that island and the Visayas proper is the still half-wild Mindoro. The north-west is a district of recent volcanic activity, but the pre-Tertiary base with its granite, diorite, and other eruptive rocks forms the greater part of the island and rises to an altitude of 8500 feet in Mt. Halcón.

All the variety of geological material and relief in the Philippines is exemplified in the little islands sprinkled over the Mediterranean lying between Mindoro and southern Luzón. Mt. Sibuyan in the centre of them rises to more than 6600 feet above sea level.

The large Visayas consist of seven islands differing in shape and structure and lying around the sea of the same name. Whilst Samar is separated from Leyte only by the narrow, regular San Juanico Strait, which looks like a drowned river valley, and whilst the wider Guimara Passage between Panay and Negros is only about 18 fathoms deep, the lead goes down to 320 fathoms between Negros and Sebu. The struggle between the two structural orientations (north-west–south-east and north-east–south-west) determines the shape of Masbate; but it is no easier here than in the interior of Luzón to follow from island to island the now broken continuity of the fold mountains. The ancient basement rocks with their Secondary beds and granite cores seem best represented in west Panay and central Sebu and Masbate. But on the whole a far greater area is covered by Tertiary beds tilted at a steep angle in west Panay, Sebu, and other places, and by Quaternary rocks, both sedimentary and eruptive. Mt. Kanlaón, an active volcano in the north of Negros, is the highest peak in the group and rises to 12,700 feet. The peaks also exceed 6600 feet in the western range in Panay and almost reach that altitude in the south-east of Negros. The longitudinal ridges in Leyte are mostly ragged remnants of extinct volcanoes and rise to about 4250 feet. The other islands do not reach the 3000-foot contour, but are also very varied in form. In Sebu erosional surfaces uplifted to different levels have carapaces of coral, which seems to point to an irregular and—what is fairly rare in the group—slow relative uplift of the crust. In Bohol countless limestone hills rising from a plateau display an advanced stage of karstic evolution. The relief of Samar, the biggest of the Visayas, is of deeply trenched Tertiary and volcanic rocks, but is without any apparent grain.

The mountains and hills come right down to the sea in many places, but the coasts are rocky and without many good harbours. The coast plains are generally narrow, but widen out at certain points. There is one in north-west Negros, for instance, which has been slightly uplifted by recent movements and, reaching inland for some 20 miles, is a choice district for sugarcane; and there are others especially in the south, but also in the north, of Panay; whilst others like the plain of Sibalom on the west coast of Panay have the advantage of the silt laid down in deltas. Facilities for irrigation are here added to the quality of the soil, which is often mixed with volcanic and coral material, and so foster a dense population.

Mindanao. Nearly as large as Luzón, but with a far smaller population and imperfectly known, this island also presents great differences of relief, though without the recurrence of that arrangement of parallel ranges which is typical of most of the northern island. Its shape has been simplified by the recent silting up of two great depressions: the valley of the Agusán in the north-east and that of the Kotobató in the south-west. Like the Kagayán valley in Luzón, the former seems to be, at any rate in part, a tectonic trench borrowed by a river which rises quite near to the Gulf of Davao and, like the Kagayán, follows a northward course for about 190 miles. The middle section of the valley measures 40 miles by 20 and is littered with lakes, swamps, and creeks, and is unhealthy and almost untouched by man. Before reaching the sea it narrows and is only 12½ miles wide at Butuan.

The Kotobató plain is due to the silting up of an arm of the sea, or at least an inlet which deepened towards the south-east up to within a short distance of Sarangani Bay. Ninety miles from its mouth the Kotobató is already only 100 feet above sea level, and the stream widens out until it reaches the mangroves on the coast. Its main feeder, the Pulangui, flows in a direction opposite to that of the Agusán, bringing in the contribution of the northern portion of the island.

The two plains lie within a structurally complex hill-mass. The Agusán valley is separated from the east coast by the Diuata range which rises to a height of 8500 feet, but breaks up in the south. To the west of the valley runs another north–south range dotted with volcanoes. Among them is Mt. Apo (10,000 feet), which overlooks the Gulf of Davao and is the second highest point in the Philippines.

Between the Kotobató and the range containing Apo the best-known district is the north-centre of the island, behind Misamis, including the uplands of Bukidnon and Lanao. Between the contours for 1600 and 2600 feet these uplands develop nearly flat surfaces whose slight undulations cut down into Secondary and Tertiary beds, large areas of which are covered with volcanic material. The big Lake Lanao was formed by a lava dam at an altitude of 2200 feet. Mt. Katanglad and Mt. Kalatungan, two worn volcanoes, raise their deeply gullied masses above the plateaus, which are dotted with little cones built up by the last eruptions and swollen in places by 'lahar' slides.

On the west Mindanao is joined by a 7-mile-wide isthmus to the Zamboanga peninsula, in which ridges (many with flat tops) are thought to have been carved out of diorite and metamorphic sandstone mantled with andesite. These features seldom rise to 3000 feet above the sea level and are, moreover, surmounted by worn volcanoes, the highest of which is Malindang (8000 feet).

Lastly, the Sulu Islands spread out in a swarm of coral and volcanic islets between Mindanao and Borneo. Palawan, on the other hand, runs unbroken for 250 miles. Its mountains, which rise to nearly 6600 feet above the sea, appear to consist largely of crystalline and metamorphic rocks in the south and Tertiary limestone in the north. The coast is fringed with coral all round.

CLIMATIC AND VEGETATION REGIONS

In spite of being broken up into islands, the Philippines stretch out over 17° of latitude in an almost continuous mountain barrier. This is the main factor in the great differences of climate, for the barrier stands right across the path of the chief winds, trades and monsoons. These grow stronger or give way to each other as the seasons pass and vary greatly in extent and in force and humidity according to time and place.

Distance from the Equator is certainly noticeable in the increase of temperature means and ranges. But in this island group washed by warm seas the increase is far less than on the mainland of Asia. Aparri on the north coast of Luzón in lat. 18° N. has an annual mean of 78° F. and Holo in the Sulu Islands in lat. 6° N. one of only 80° F. The difference in temperature between the means of the two extreme months certainly reaches 11° F. at Basco between Luzón and Formosa as against a mere 1·1° F. at Zamboanga in the south-west of Mindanao and more than 950 miles from Basco. But Hanoï in the same latitude as Basco has an annual range of 22·3° F. owing to its being swept by the northerly monsoon from off the continent of Asia and thus to its far cooler winters, whilst its summers are at least as hot. In Manila the mean diurnal minimum does not fall in any month below the February figure of 68° F.; and the mean maximum never exceeds 94° F. This extreme figure is reached in May before the beginning of the south-west monsoon. The temperature régime is like that in India and betrays the influence of the rainfall.

The total annual rainfall is less than 60 inches in a few sheltered valleys only, and especially in that of the Kagayán. At Baguio in

Luzón, 5000 feet above the sea, the annual mean is 180 inches and even at Iba on the west coast of the island it is 147 inches. Nearly everywhere it amounts to more than 80 inches and it exceeds 120 inches over considerable areas.

The heavy rainfall is explained partly by the almost universally abrupt changes of relief and partly by the frequent typhoons due to geographical position. Most of the group lies in the usual path of these cyclonic storms, here known as *baguios*, which form in the belt of greatest heat on the line of contact between contrasting air streams and as it were on their battle front. Most of them indeed take their rise near the Carolines and Mariannes and head west-north-west until they reach the mainland of Asia. A certain number turn aside towards the north and north-east before having reached the continent. A smaller number form immediately to the east of the Philippines. Masses of saturated air, being carried off in an upward swirling motion, give an enormous quantity of rain, and condensation itself, by setting free latent heat, maintains the swirl of air for hundreds of miles. Cyclones cross the north of the Philippines at every season, the greatest frequency and violence occurring between July and November. The mean path moves southwards during this period when the high pressure is also spreading south (see Fig. 4).

Between 1903 and 1934, 130 of these storms were recorded in the Philippines. In the centre of 110 of them the barometer fell below 29·3 inches and in 21 it read less than 28·3 inches. In such cases the damage is catastrophic owing to the violence of the wind and even more to the floods caused by huge waves breaking on the land and by enormous downpours of rain. At Baguio the rain gauge recorded 46 inches in 24 hours on July 14 and 15, 1911.[1] The greatest damage, however, is done on the lowlands. Typhoons become less frequent with distance from the main high pressure centres in Siberia and the north Pacific. They generally spare the southern Visayas and trouble Mindanao even less.

Yet in the Philippines climatic differences are due mainly to the rainfall and are more marked from west to east than from north to south. In the east the wettest months as a rule are November, December, and January, during which north-east winds strike coasts which are everywhere steep. But the fact most pregnant of consequences is the absence of a dry season. Whilst the above-mentioned months often get 15 to 20 inches of rain, there is, with rare exceptions, no month that has to be content with less than 4 inches.

On the other hand, in the west from the peninsula of Zamboanga

[1] And 88 inches from July 14–17. Kolb (175), p. 44.

to northern Luzón there is well marked drought during from four
to six months (see Fig. 6).   Nearly all the rain falls between May and
October, when the saturated air in the south-west monsoon, sucked
in by the low pressure disturbances which often pass across at that
time, yields particularly great quantities of moisture.   Then follows
the turn of the north-east wind, which, having got rid of its moisture
over the eastern districts, reaches the west coast in a dry state.   The
drought is especially marked in January, February, and March before
the thunderstorms which precede the oncoming of the monsoon and
coincide with the most oppressive heat.   In Manila the mean annual
number of days on which rain falls is 196, but only 45 of them occur
from October to May inclusive.   For several weeks the sky remains
cloudless, in the valleys cracks open in the fields, and vehicles raise an
unpleasant dust which covers the vegetation with a greyish coat.
The exploitation of the salt marshes around the Bay is possible for
about 150 days in the year.   In December, January, and February
the sky is often obscured by dense clouds of locusts which in a few
moments devour the young rice shoots.[1]   Drought is also serious
in the north, where the district of Vigan has known periods of five
months without a drop of rain.   The rainfall régime here is like that
in the Lesser Sunda Islands at the other end of the East Indies; but
in Luzón the summer rainfall is much heavier.

In the middle zone of the group the rainfall distribution is transitional between these two extreme east and west types.   The annual
total averages about 80 inches nearly everywhere.   The dry season
is shorter than in the west and occurs in February, March, and April,
except in the south, where it occurs in August and September (see
Fig. 5).

The rainfall system, together with latitude, determines the temperature system.   Means are slightly higher and ranges greater in the
west than in the east of the group.   The central lowlands and the
valley of the Kagayán show clear traces of the continental type.
Only there does the mean absolute maximum exceed 100° F. and
the mean absolute minimum 60° F.   The greatest range in the whole
of the East Indies within the space of 24 hours is certainly achieved
in April in the sheltered lowlands of Luzón.   As against a mere 12°
or 14° F. at places with the most typical equatorial climate, the
diurnal range in that month is about 24° or 25° F. at San Isidro in
the central lowlands as well as at Tuguegarao in the Kagayán valley.
These places also experience the greatest variations in rainfall from
one year to the next, a fact which has a good deal of influence on
agriculture and human life.   At Manila, for instance, May, like
April, is sometimes abnormally dry owing to the lateness of the

[1] Mallat (177), I, p. 160; MacGregor (51), p. 365.

monsoon; or the monsoon may end before its time in September. A break in the rains during the growing period of the crops quite often jeopardises the harvest, especially that of rice and sugarcane. Between 1865 and 1933 at Manila the ratio between the highest and lowest annual rainfall was about 4 to 1. To be precise, in 1885 the amount was 35·7 inches and in 1919, owing to the large number of typhoons, it was 154·3 inches.

In spite of signs of drought in many places, there is primary forest nearly everywhere in the Philippines. With all man's ravages it still covers more than half the total area. But its appearance varies greatly, and degeneration from the probable original type is already very marked in many places (see Fig. 7).

The coastal fringe of mangrove and *nipa* palms is discontinuous and varies in breadth. On the inland side of this fringe apart from the areas permanently under cultivation, the vegetation on the lowlands near the sea presents two chief features which are clearly exemplified in the western and central districts and in places where the rock is permeable and consists of sand, tuff, or limestone. Adaptation to drought is marked in such places by a seasonal fall of leaves in a large number of species.

The first of these xerophilous formations, which may, where mangrove is absent, reach right down to the sea, consists of a number of species of very different height, without bamboos or lianas and with but few palms. The most typical trees are the Pandanaceæ and often too the *filao* (*Casuarina equisetifolia*), which looks like a cypress. At the end of the Zamboanga peninsula and on the southwestern coast of Mindanao Australian affinities are indicated by the presence of clumps of eucalyptus trees (*Eucalyptus deglupta*).

Behind these on the hills and especially on old coral reefs below the 650-foot contour, where the soil is very thin and the surface pitted with holes, there is often a luxuriant forest association characterised by a wild vine (*Vitex parviflora Jussieu*) which is often called *molave* in the native tongue. Amid a confusion of low-growing species and dense bamboo thickets taller trees here and there send up gnarled trunks and twisted branches which seasonally drop their leaves.

Dipterocarp forests form about three-fourths of the wooded area and grow in very various soils. These trees often attain a height of 130 or 175 feet with a diameter of from 3 to 5 feet. But the botanical associations vary greatly according to edaphic and climatic conditions. In districts with a well marked dry season the annual fall of leaves never affects the forest as a whole, but is clearly seen by an increase of light and by yellowish tints. In the east, on the other hand, the forest is composed of different species, among which the gigantic evergreen Shorea often predominates; and there are plenty of palms and epiphytes. These do not make passage difficult, however, except along the banks of rivers or on spots recently cleared and overgrown with secondary vegetation.

The Dipterocarp forests in districts without a dry season are by far the richest in timber and are the most valuable in the Philippines, which are considered to be one of the best supplied areas in the tropics. Experts compare their timber value with that of the coniferous forests in high latitudes. They grow right up to about the 3000-foot contour. In districts with a dry season Dipterocarps begin to be scarcer from the 1500-foot contour upwards and are replaced by species of the genus *Quercus*. The latter are the dominant species in very mixed associations that often cover the very steep slopes on which the soil is thin.

In the central range in Luzón and in small areas in the mountains of Zambales and the south-west of Mindoro the *Quercus* association often changes into a pine forest that is especially characteristic between 3000 and 5000 feet. *Pinus insularis* and *Merkusii*, which are the only species of the genus represented in the Philippines and western Indonesia, never grow in dense clumps, but always singly or scattered at fairly long intervals on flat or sloping ground on which the only other plant is grass. The conifers become fewer and fewer and more and more degenerate up to the 9000-foot contour.

As elsewhere, the appearance of the forest changes as the force of the wind and the amount of the rainfall increase with height above the sea. The trees become stunted and their twisted trunks and branches become covered with mosses, lichens, ferns, and other epiphytes. Lianas, Pandaneæ, little palms, and tree ferns help to thicken the vegetation-type, which assumes its most characteristic appearance and greatest density at various heights from the 2600-foot contour upwards. According to Whitford, moss-forest is estimated to cover 8 per cent. of the area of the Philippines. The forest of dwarf trees—*Dacrydium*, *Podocarpus*, etc.—grows up to the highest summits, except however on Mt. Pulog, which is crowned with grassy slopes above the 8500-foot contour.

These various plant associations have certainly seen great modification in their distribution brought about by man in the course of centuries. It is not only that permanent cultivation has supplanted them in places and that, for instance, in low plains and valley bottoms the forest dominated by *Dipterocarpus affinis*, which likes swampy ground, has yielded to the advancing ricefields; or again that on long strips of sandy shore-belt coconut groves have been substituted for Pandanus forest. Even where the forest has not been destroyed, it has often changed in appearance owing to felling and even more to patch-clearing by fire and to bush fires. As always, the transformation has been most rapid and irremediable in districts of marked drought. Forest in which the prevailing species is *Vitex parviflora* often seems to be a very degenerate type. Pine forest continues to spread, helped by fire, at the expense of the stands of deciduous trees among which *Quercus* is predominant. Secondary forest covers at least two-thirds of the wooded area. It is the *parang* of the natives and is far denser than primary growths.

Secondary forest finds great difficulty in recovering if fires occur too frequently. Grass associations in which *Imperata* and *Saccharum*—the *cogonales* of the natives—prevail, are found even in the wettest districts; but they reach their greatest development in the centre and west, where they cover about 19 per cent. of the total area in the most densely populated belts in the Philippines.

FROM PRIMITIVE LIFE TO CIVILISATION

More than any other part of the East Indies the Philippines present an astonishing ethnical stratification. Anthropological research is far from complete; and, in spite of the fine work of American scholars like H. Otley Beyer,[1] the series of migrations and civilising streams have not been established with complete certainty.

The existing population contains the physical types already mentioned above. They are the Negrito, Vedda, and Papuan (who is most frequent on the east side); the Proto-Malay or Indonesian, who is either of a refined type with a relatively light complexion and often well marked features, or a coarser type with a darker complexion and a flatter face of Mongoloid cast; and, lastly, the Malay. These classes and types are defined only by average and betray every degree of mixture and transition. It is particularly difficult to distinguish Proto-Malays from Malays, the distinction being reduced for a number of scholars to the difference between the interior and coast peoples. Within historical times the gradual modification of the population has continued through the introduction of Indian, Arab, European, and, above all, Chinese elements.

Anthropological differentiations correspond only approximately to differences in civilisation and mode of life.[2] Nor does the latter consist of distinct and separate types, for the types merge into each other either through intermarriage or mere infiltration of culture. Intermixture, which is encouraged by Western settlement, has, however, been slower here than in other parts of the Malay world. The Spaniards came hither from across the Pacific. Their homeland was far away and separated from the Philippines by the breadth of

---

[1] Cp. the work of Beyer (167), and Kolb (175), p. 93.
[2] Cp. Kolb (175), pp. 106 ff. and the tables based on Beyer.

1.
Jakarta's main street. The clothes washing is an everyday occurrence. Note the bamboo rafts used for transport on the canals.

22.
A *batik* worker in Jogyakarta, Java. She is applying the design by means of wax in a small container not unlike those used in icing cakes.

23. The Borobudur, or temple to 'the enlightened' in Java

24. *The Cortège of the Sacred Elephant*, one of the reliefs on the Borobudur

two oceans and the New World. It was from New Spain that the islands had regular, though very infrequent, communication. Then again Iberian colonisation aimed at least as much at spreading the Gospel and cleansing the soul as at exploiting material resources. The work of the priests was wiser than that of unreliable and often corrupt officials and spared the natives those sudden social changes which are caused by the brutal clash of very dissimilar economic systems. In more ways than one the effect certainly retarded development, but up to the beginning of the century it secured for the Philippines a relatively slow and harmonious evolution.

The Negritoes and the Caingin. The people called Negritoes by the first Spaniards to arrive are more numerous in the Philippines than elsewhere in the Malay world. They are of low stature, averaging less than 4 feet 11 inches and have a dark brown skin. The Tagal word Aëtas is now used to designate them. Today they exist only in tiny groups in the interior of Mindanao, the western Visayas, and Luzón. In the east a few hundred Apayaos live in the *nipa* swamps along the north coast. In all they cannot amount to more than about 40,000, and only 10 or 12 per cent. of these could be considered pure-blooded. They are heading for early extinction because of their low birth-rate, considerable infant mortality, and interbreeding. With them will end the primitive mode of life in which agriculture, weaving, pottery-making, and metalworking are all unknown even in an elementary form and the shelter is a frail screen constantly moved from place to place. Even in 1916 Beyer counted no more than a bare 25,000 persons, not all pure Negritoes, who were still leading a wandering life based entirely on hunting and collecting. A certain number of these 'savages' are hired every year for heavy labour in their neighbours' ricefields or even go to work in the mines.[1]

Many Negritoes or half-Negritoes have already taken to shifting patch-cultivation which is also practised by most of the Indonesian communities. It rarely excludes the more advanced forms of agriculture. According to Beyer, it was in 1916 the essential basis of the food supply of about 380,000 natives, though it had already greatly modified the original vegetation. The Philippine *caingin* presents the ordinary appearance of cultivation on land cleared by burning. Among the less advanced clans hunting, fishing, and collecting are important means of securing food. Rice is less often sown in soil fertilised by ashes than are maize, sweet potatoes, and tobacco. A preference for rice generally goes with progress in

[1] On the condition and number of the 'savages' about 1840, see Mallat (177), p. 89 and *passim*. Note that in Spanish literature the 'savage' is often confused with the unconverted heathen.

FIG. 34.—LUZÓN: TRIBAL AREAS AND PROVINCES
KEY TO PROVINCIAL NUMBERING

1. Ilocos N.	9. Pangasinan.	17. Bataan.
2. Mountain.	10. Nueva Écija.	18. Cavitë.
3. Kagayán.	11. Tarlac.	19. Laguna.
4. Abra.	12. Zambales.	20. Batangas.
5. Isabela.	13. Pampanga.	21. Camarines N.
6. Ilocos S.	14. Bulacán.	22. Camarines S.
7. La Unión.	15. Tabayas.	23. Albay.
8. Nueva Vizcaya.	16. Rizal.	24. Sorsogón.

industrial skill, such as the making of dugouts by the Apayaos and weaving and pottery-making among the Gaddangs of northern Luzón. Most of the semi-nomadic cultivators, at least those in the interior of the Visayas and Mindanao (Subanus and Bukidnons), also work in metals. The regular shifting of a *caingin* rarely involves incessant moving of the dwelling-place. The latter becomes more stable as the period of fallow between the burnings is shortened. Whilst the Monteses in Panay change their dwelling every year together with the fields they till, the Subanus of Mindanao sometimes occupy the same spot for ten years or so.

Mountain Cultivation. Life becomes wholly sedentary when improvements in agriculture bring fields under permanent cultivation, and this is achieved by two very different sets of people and methods, some restricted to the mountains in northern Luzón and others spread more or less everywhere in the lowlands. Some of the mountain folk of northern Luzón have from time immemorial practised the most interesting and scientific form of agriculture in the Philippines. They are mainly the Ifugaos and Bontocs, but farther west there are also some smaller communities of Kalingas and Tinggian as well as Lepantos,[1] Kankenais, and Ibalois, who are all three reckoned as Igorots. In all they were about 300,000 persons in 1916.

This type of permanent cultivation greatly modifies the scenery. The slopes are carved into terraces rising one above the other in extraordinary tiers often several hundred yards long and even about 1000 yards at and near Banana in the Ifugao district, where the scene is particularly striking. Covering very steep slopes, the terracing goes right down to the valley bottoms on the narrow, tapering spurs separating the gullies and climbs up in places to more than 5000 feet, to the limit imposed by climate on the growth of rice. On these—frequently narrow—terraces soil and water conservation has required considerable never-ending toil in mountains where the rainfall is high, but the showers irregular and heavy. The almost vertical banks that separate the terraces are 50 feet high in some places, whilst the terraces may be only 10 feet wide. The banks are strengthened with large stones some of which jut out to afford foothold for climbing up. At the top there is a little embankment designed to retain water. Irrigation is especially necessary because the growing period of rice coincides here with the sunniest, hottest, and driest part of the year. Seed is sown in November and December, and the harvest is reaped in June and July. Water is led from springs and brooks to the terraces in bamboo conduits or ditches dug in the ground and carefully

1 Keesing (171).

maintained. Some of these which branch off from large streams flow along the slopes for two or three miles, crossing gullies by means of wooden aqueducts, so that every drop of water is used to the best advantage before reaching the valley below.

The whole work of making the terraces and cultivating them is carried out with very simple tools, mainly with a long wooden spade of a type found nowhere else in the archipelago. The water-raising devices used in Indo-China are unknown, and, where it has been impossible to take a ditch to a terrace, water is sometimes carried to the latter in pots.

Now and then various kinds of manure, like pigs' dung, ashes, grass, and dead leaves, are buried in the soil. After the rice has been harvested, taro and other vegetables and mushrooms are planted in the well manured upper parts of the ricefield.

The scientific cultivation of rice in terraces was perhaps introduced into Luzón at the same time as the use of iron; but its restriction in the Philippines and Luzón itself to this little area is not clearly understood. It goes along with a peculiar social and economic organisation which formerly included constant warfare between villages and head-hunting and the practice of many domestic industries. The village is still largely self-governing. Smallholdings are the rule, though many men are forced today to eke out a living by working on other people's land. The little community is traditionally administered by hereditary chiefs, who are as it were feudal lords with duties balancing privileges. They used to get dues and free labour for their fields, but protected and advised their people and in time of dearth fed them from the stocks in their own barns. They presided at the religious rites and ceremonies considered indispensable to the regular growth of the crops and good yields from agriculture and communal hunting.

The system is becoming outworn today. The former chiefs are tending to become merely large landowners holding big herds of oxen and buffaloes, monopolising an increasingly great share of the land, and controlling a train of humble families who are in debt and reduced to having only their huts and some patches of unirrigated land. As a result of over-population, of the opening up of the districts by modern roads, and the spread of the use of money, the Mountain Province of Luzón has 114 persons to the square mile and Abra Province 150. The hill-folk work in the mines at Benguet and even in the fields belonging to the Ilocans in the western lowlands. On the other hand, the Ilocans continually penetrate farther and farther into the back country. In contact with these hard-working, astute, and enterprising new-comers the agriculture of the hill-folk is quickly modified, especially in the west, where the

Tinggians soon assimilate the new-comers. The practice of growing a second rice crop in December on irrigated terraces is spreading. Though this cereal continues to be the favourite food, the supply of it is increasingly insufficient. Maize and, above all, sweet potatoes are always more cultivated on the dry lower slopes which nowadays are often ploughed and thus have a very short period of fallow. For instance, at Banana sweet potatoes may be grown in the same soil for five or more years running.

The cultivation of irrigated terraces by the Ifugaos, Bontocs, and neighbouring peoples, who were still head hunters up to not long ago, certainly takes us very far from primitive agriculture. It may even be considered to be the most scientific and most advanced form in the Philippines and one that approaches nearest to the horticulture of the Chinese and has been best able to adapt itself to natural conditions, The use of ploughs is impossible owing to the narrowness of the terraces.

Lowland Cultivation. On the other hand the plough comes into general use in the lowlands, where it has been known since time immemorial and nowadays is used by the great majority of native cultivators. It is the most important implement in rice cultivation. Rice is grown almost everywhere in the Philippines and is an extensive crop wherever the soil and climate can be taken advantage of by the dense population. Such is the case on the coastal plains in the Ilocan district in north-eastern Luzón and on the central plain of the same island, where the area covered is very great and is the largest in the Philippines. Nearly one-third of the ricefields in the group are concentrated there and yield about 40 per cent. of the total crop produced. Next in order of acreage of ricefields comes the eastern portion of Panay.

Methods of cultivation are as various as in the highlands and are visible in the appearance of the fields, whether or not these are surrounded by little embankments. Swamp cultivation in 1931 extended to about three-fourths of the ricefields and yielded more than four-fifths of the total crop. In many respects methods are, in spite of the plough, inferior to those practised by the hill-folk on their astonishing terraces in the central ranges of Luzón. Most of the fields depend exclusively on rain-water, which is retained by the little embankments until nearly harvest time. Though the irrigation works were begun by the Spanish Church at the end of last century and have been developed even more by the Americans, they still affect only 500,000 acres in the Luzón lowlands and eastern Panay. So, it is rare for two crops to be reaped in one year, as is done at the foot of the Zambales Range. Most of the lowlands are subject to the unfailing rhythm of the monsoon and are flooded from May to

November while the rice grows; and then after the harvest they are dried and browned by the north-east wind. Even now rice is often the sole crop, and the soil in which it is grown remains fallow until the next lot of seedlings are planted out in it. At times it is cultivated alternately with maize, sweet potatoes, or tobacco. In the eastern part of the group, where the rains are constant, the dates of the harvest are far more variable.

The plough with an iron share has also become the implement of rice cultivation in many parts of the dry plains and low hills where other varieties of rice are sown directly on to patches of land not enclosed by embankments. There the chief work is weeding, and this must be done again and again to prevent the smothering invasion of *alang*. The yield is generally much lower than that of swamp rice. The dry fields are, moreover, often reserved for two other crops that have greatly caught on since the arrival of the Europeans. These are the sweet potato, or *camote*, and more especially maize. In acreage maize takes second place in the group, coming just after rice. On the limestone soils which often occur on ledges of coral rock in the central Visayas it takes first place; and in eastern Negros, Bohol, and above all Sebu it covers 80 per cent. of the land under cultivation.

The densest and most advanced sections of the population of the Philippines live mainly by tilling the lowlands in this way with the plough. They are distinguished by their dialect rather than by their physical appearance and mode of life. Luzón contains five of the six most important groups representing 85 per cent. of the population of the Philippines. The Pangasinans and Pampangas in the centre of the island are retreating before the Tagals, who are the most civilised of the Filipinos, and even before the Ilocans, who are hemmed in on the north-west coast. The Tagals also live on the east coast of Mindoro and are spreading to south-eastern Luzón at the expense of the Bicols, who, on their part, have settled in northern Masbate.

Whilst racial differences remain very marked even in the lowlands of Luzón, the many Visayas are on the other hand the home of a relatively numerous people, the Bisayas, who are numerically the largest group in the Philippines. It has been calculated that about four-fifths used to live within $2\frac{1}{2}$ miles of the seashore The Bisayas have been gradually settling on the north coast of Mindanao and have begun to penetrate into the interior, introducing plough cultivation among the *caingineros*, or 'forest burners' The Moros, who are also spreading over Mindanao are relatively skilful cultivators, growing swamp rice in the Kotobató valley and on the shores of Lake Lanao. Besides this they succeed, by using a crop rotation with a short period of fallow, in producing a great variety of crops even on the *alang*-invaded deforested land, including upland rice, maize, sweet potatoes, beans, and groundnuts. Many farms are scattered about on the savana, whilst the villages are hidden amid groves of coconut and areca palms and bamboos.

In all these human groups smallholdings worked by the owner are the rule. They often consist of between 6 and 12 acres, but in over-populated districts like the Ilocan country they may be less than 2½ acres, an area which is not enough to support a family owing to the poor and irregular yield. Very large properties of more than 2500 acres are exceptional, and few even 250 acres. But the number of moderate-sized properties between 60 and 250 acres has increased. As early as the 17th century the Roman Catholic Church had acquired huge landed property all over the islands. On the other hand, the system of money-lending at high interest has often resulted in the practical dispossession of the debtor smallholders to the advantage of a class of *caciques* or *ilustrados*, many of whom have Spanish blood in their veins. Their estates are cultivated by tenants, or *taos*, who, for example on the land recently brought under cultivation in Nueva Ecija on the north-west of the great plain, live a fairly precarious life. In these conditions the old system of *aparcería* prevails in the ricefields, dividing the harvest in various ways between the owner and the tenant.[1] The latter is as a rule fairly fixed and settled. He may have domestic animals and even a parcel of land in addition to his dwelling, which is often less spacious and comfortable than that of the hill-folk.

Export Crops. Specialisation in the production of rice on some of the lowlands has certainly been encouraged by the needs of other crops which have been developed under European influence and are meant chiefly for export. Yet it is noteworthy that these export crops almost always remain the produce of native small-holders and that less than half the soil is devoted to the plantation system.

Tobacco, the only crop introduced by Europeans, occupies the smallest area. This American plant, which was widely disseminated by the Spaniards as early as the 17th century, did not become an important export commodity until right at the end of the 18th century.[2] At that date José Basco, the Governor, wishing to make the Philippines financially independent of Mexico, turned tobacco production into a State monopoly. Cultivation was concentrated in a few small districts and strictly forbidden elsewhere. New varieties and expert planters were brought over from Cuba. The

---

[1] According to the 1939 census 52·4 per cent. of the plantations were of less than 5 acres, and only 49·2 per cent. of the cultivators owned the soil they tilled. According to Spencer (183a, p. 39) 40 per cent. of the millions of people in the island group in 1948 were tenants.

[2] Jagor (169), pp. 324 ff.

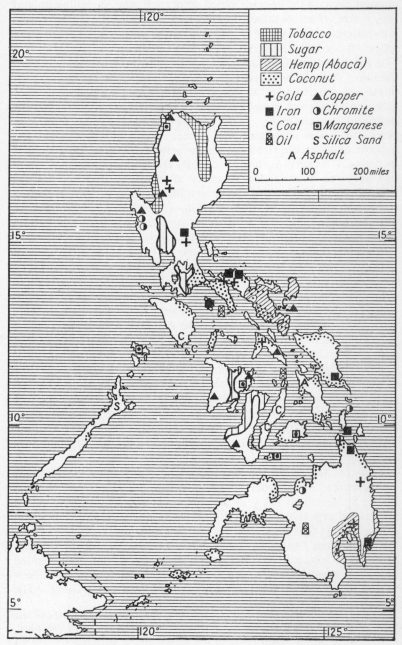

FIG. 35.—THE PHILIPPINES: CROPS AND MINERALS

supervised forced labour of the peasants brought in large profits to Spain, which was, however, soon to lose its American colonies. The monopoly was gradually relaxed, but was not abolished until 1882.[1]

Tobacco production, which occupied barely more than 1 per cent. of the area under cultivation, remains very concentrated. More than a third (37 per cent.) of the area under the crop is situated in the Kagayán valley, where the dry season is short and the alluvial soil periodically flooded by the river and its feeders. Another tobacco district is situated in the north-west of the same island and runs round the shores of Lingayen Bay in the Provinces of La Unión and Pangasinan. Here the plant grows in countless little valleys running down to the sea. In the Visayas the crop became important after 1840, but only in Sebu and Negros.

Though tobacco was no longer the great investment that it had formerly been and though about 1938–40 it represented only 3 or 4 per cent. of the total value of exports, it kept a by no means negligible place in the economic system of these districts. About 100,000 small cultivators lived mainly on the crop, the average area of their patches being one acre. Most of them owned their land, the rest being merely tenants like those working in the Kagayán valley on the estates owned by La Tabacalera, the chief company in the Philippines, which controls three-fourths of the production. Tobacco occupies the soil for only a part of the year, from September to May, but then it requires almost constant care. The planting itself and the preliminary ploughing, which must be carried out quickly, are often done by the co-operation of several families. After the harvest only the little drying sheds scattered over the countryside indicate the distribution of the plant.

Sugar was the earliest commodity to be exported from the Philippines. The cultivation of the cane, which was introduced from India either directly or by way of China, began to spread in the neighbourhood of Manila after the arrival of the Spaniards. But by 1835 exports had not yet reached 12,000 tons. After the cutting of the Suez Canal and until the end of the century production rapidly increased. Then a period of stagnation and even of decline followed, but the opening of the American market brought new vigour, and production reached its 'record' in 1934 with 1,578,000 tons. Its progress was irregular, and due more to increase in yield than to enlarging the area cultivated. That area represented about five times as much as was devoted to tobacco, but approximately one-third lay fallow every year or else was sown with rice or maize.

Sugarcane seldom grows above the 1600-foot contour. The

[1] See below, p. 316.

main productive districts, as everywhere else in the world, are non-swampy plains with a marked dry season and a large population. Negros heads the list with the highest yield, thanks to its volcanic soil in the south-west, which is, however, less fertile than that in the eastern bays, since these are rich in lime and potash. In the west of the island, which was still undeveloped in 1845,[1] 90 per cent. of the population live by cultivating this crop. Then come the central lowlands of Luzón and particularly the eastern portion in the Provinces of Pampanga and Tarlac. Here among the ricefields canes occupy only the least damp areas, and these are made conspicuous by the presence of big sugar-mills. Production in the other Visayas (Panay, Sebu, Leyte, and Mindoro) lags far behind that in Negros and Luzón.

Cane cultivation here is without the methodical organisation and scientific character that it had in Java. There are few plantations; and most of the crop comes from little family patches of between 5 and 10 acres cultivated chiefly on the *métayer* system. The yield is far smaller than in Hawaii or Java before the last war.

Under the name of 'Manila hemp' *abacá* fibre headed the list of exports from the Philippines from 1887 to 1922, but, owing to the strong competition of sugar, it has supplied only about 10 per cent. of the exports since 1930. The plant is not related to the one to which it owes its commercial name, but is the *Musa textilis*, closely connected with the banana, though without eatable fruit. It usually grows to a height of between 13 and 20 feet. The Philippines seem to have been its original habitat, and the natives have from time immemorial used the strong, supple fibres from the long leaf-covers for making ropes and even cloth. Its export began about 1830, and certain districts specialised in its cultivation. *Abacá* is far more exacting than the banana and requires rain throughout the year and rich, moist, but not marshy soil. These conditions are realised only in the eastern part of the Philippines. *Abacá* has become the chief crop in south-eastern Luzón and especially in the Bicol district. Other areas of fairly large production are Leyte, Samar to a less extent, and the east coast of Mindanao. But the most rapid expansion since the beginning of the century took place in the south-east of this last island around Davao. Here the area devoted to *Musa textilis* rose from 6200 acres in 1903 to 270,000 acres in 1937, that is, about one-third of the total area devoted to the crop in the Philippines. The plant benefits from the fertile soil resulting from the recent eruptions of Mt. Apo and from the regular rainfall brought by the east winds over a low section of the Diuata Mountains. But the development of *abacá* cultivation at Davao was mainly due

[1] Mallat (177), I, p. 317.

to Japanese labour and organisation. Behind the coastal coconut groves the *abacá* has pushed back the forest farther and farther up the slopes of Mt. Apo, for the plant flourishes up to an altitude of more than 3300 feet above the sea.

In this crop too native smallholdings of between 5 and 10 acres are responsible for most of the cultivation. The work is done without much care and leads to a very irregular production. The heaviest toil is the stripping of the fibre, a task that must be performed quickly and is carried out as a rule by hand with the use of a scraper. Large-scale production, however, holds a more considerable place than in other export crops and until 1945 was mainly in the hands of Japanese.

As in most of the East Indies, the coconut palm has from time immemorial been the chief food-producing tree and the main source of the supply of fats. As in Indonesia, and even more so perhaps, its cultivation has increased to meet the demands of temperate lands in Europe and, later, America and has extended its acreage at the expense of the coastal forests wherever the constitution of the soil permits it to reach fresh-water at no great depth underground. It has also spread over an area fairly far from the coast up to a height of 1600 feet above the sea. This expansion began about 1870, later than the other main export crops; but from that time it made steady and regular progress without marked interference by the Colonial Government in the business of cultivation. About nine-tenths of the produce were exported. Though less concentrated than that of sugarcane, tobacco, and *abacá*, the cultivation of the coconut has, however, become the prevailing, and in some places the almost exclusive, form of investment, especially in the waist of Luzón which runs south-west of Manila from Bay Lagoon to the Tayabas coast. The volcanic soil, short dry season, and facilities for transport by rail and water have contributed to the prosperity of the palm in this district, which contains more than one-third of the trees in the Philippines. Yet Luzón's relative share has been decreasing since the beginning of the century, for competition has been coming from the Visayas as well as Mindanao. In the latter the coconut palm has spread rapidly along the north coast and even more round the Gulf of Davao and in the south-west round Zamboanga.

Big plantations of more than 1000 acres occur less seldom in Mindanao. In the Philippines as a whole they form only 1 per cent. of the area under coconuts. The marked predominance of the native smallholder is less surprising than in other export crops because the coconut has been cultivated for such a long time, the work of tending the trees and collecting the nuts goes on all through the year, and the processes of preparing the produce for market are simple. Drying the nut in the sun still gives the best quality copra. The peasant is resourceful enough to plant under the thin shade of the young palms secondary crops, including rice, maize, cassava, and bananas, at least until the time when nuts are first picked. This begins, according to the variety of palm, when the tree is between the ages of three and eight. But the districts that export copra must, on the other hand, often import large quantities of rice and other foodstuffs. There the coconut palm is the dominant factor in the economic system as well as the characteristic feature of the landscape, spreading over large areas in pleasant, sun-bathed groves. The dwellings that shelter under its graceful fronds and among its curving trunks are more scattered than those in the ricefields, and in them life seems to slip by more calmly and quietly.

These chief crops, mainly intended for export, feed all the principal industries in the Philippines, except mining. Much of the produce does not leave the country until after having undergone more or less elaborate processes either in the districts where the crops are grown or in the ports.

MINING AND MODERN INDUSTRY

Among modern industries sugar employs the greatest amount of labour. Indian mills, intended to produce raw sugar (muscovado) and worked by buffaloes, mostly aim at supplying local needs, but are far from satisfying them. The first modern sugar factory was established in Mindoro in 1911 to deal with canes from a big plantation. With the second, which was at San Carlos in eastern Negros, began the system, which is very common today, of thirty-year contracts with independent planters. In 1935 there were in the Philippines forty-six sugar factories and four mechanically equipped refineries, employing about 50,000 hands.

Most of the tobacco is exported in leaf form, the rest being used for making cigars and cigarettes chiefly in Manila. Cigars are exported in greater quantities from the Philippines than from any other country. They are often made by hand still; but the more recent manufacture of cigarettes employs up-to-date machinery imported from the United States.

To these industries which work up the produce of the soil must be added those which since the war of 1914–18 have been making an ever increasing quantity of oil from copra for export. The majority of them are in Manila, where most of the big rice-mills, which are usually owned by Chinese, are also situated, though several operate in Cabanatuan in Nueva Ecija. On the other hand, the factories which since 1922 have been manufacturing desiccated products like coconut flakes and powder remain near the plantations, for they use, not copra, but fresh fruit.   In 1937 they processed about 6 per cent. of the nuts picked.   The big workshops in which *abacá* fibre is removed are also near the plantations.   However, they face the competition of primitive native workers and more especially those using the far more adaptable water-mill or petrol engine.

The number of workers employed in these modern industries dependent on the chief crops as well as those employed in sawmills was estimated in 1935 at roughly 120,000.   Progress had been rapid since 1914.   Production from little domestic industry for the purpose of comparison with the factories cannot be estimated.   It certainly occupies a far larger number of persons, but many of these work during only a part of the year, that is, the agricultural off-seasons.   As in other countries industry is declining owing to the competition of imported goods, and this is especially true of textiles.

On the other hand, some native manufactures have profited from modern facilities for exporting to distant markets, though they have had to be modified to suit the control of middlemen.   Thus, the manufacture of hats made from the fibre of certain palms has become mainly a town industry; whilst the embroidery trade now depends almost wholly on American dealers in Manila.   Of the new industries, the manufacture of boots and shoes greatly expanded, particularly in Manila, during the 1914–18 war.

Industrial progress is handicapped by the lack of fuel.   Coal produced in the little field in Sebu amounts to scarcely a tenth of the quantity imported; and there are no oil wells in the Philippines.

Lack of coal has hitherto prevented the development of metallurgy. But the reserves of iron ore seem fairly large, though they do not exist so much in the beds of phosphoric hæmatite which have been worked by Chinese and natives in the Provinces of Bulacán (north-east of Manila) and Camarines Norte (south-east of Luzón) as in the lateritic concentrations round Surigao Bay in northern Mindanao. In 1938 the Japanese succeeded in fact in importing from the Philippines more than 900,000 tons of iron ore.

Of the other useful minerals chromium seems to be most plentiful, the chief deposit being in the Zambales Mountains.   Next come manganese and copper.   Gold, however, was one of the principal mineral products, and the increasing quantity extracted raised minerals to second place in importance after sugar among exports from the Philippines.   When the Spaniards first came, the natives and Chinese were in many places already panning out the precious metal in wash-troughs and at times working the lodes in andesite and diorite deposits, but restricting themselves as a rule to placer mining. Mallat[1] stated in about 1840 that the natives in the Surigao district

[1] Mallat (177), I, p. 323.

used gold dust and nuggets as money both in making daily purchases and in their betting at cock-fights. In general the productive districts had continued to be so. Before the war of 1914–18 the busiest were at Mambulao Paracale in Camarines Norte. Since then the lead had been taken by those near Baguio. The small quantity extracted by natives was far exceeded by the amount extracted by mining companies. After the gold-rush in 1933–36 some fifteen companies continued to exist, many of them using modern equipment. Large dredgers lifted the alluvium, and the lodes were followed into the rock through long wood-propped galleries. In 1937 more than 40,000 workers were employed, and about 25 tons of gold were produced.

At the outbreak of war in 1939 mining products made up about a fourth of the total exports from the Philippines.

POPULATION

Distribution. Though we read that the population of the Philippines has increased threefold in fifty years, inequalities in development remain striking in different districts. They are of long standing, but became more marked during the last quarter of the 19th century and have been increasingly conspicuous since the American occupation. In many cases the districts which were already most densely populated have attracted settlers and encouraged their activities, in particular favouring cultivation for export. Of course, virgin soil has been cleared, and other land, which had already been cleared by burning in order to establish *caingin*, has been tilled in a less primitive manner with the use of the plough. If the official statistics are reliable, the annual rate of increase in the population during the years just before the war was greater in Masbate and Mindanao than anywhere else in the Malay world.[1] The development of a new district attracts people who are at first mere sojourners, but later gradually settle down. The movement is rather slow, however, and the transfer of population is caused less by the arrival of swarms of people from distant lands than by natural increase and by additions round the edges of districts already densely peopled.

The mean density of 140 persons to the square mile (1939) in the Philippines as a whole is calculated from figures that differ greatly from each other, and the density differs as much from district to district if it is worked out not on the total area, as it was above, but on the area of cultivable land. Thus calculated, the mean reaches 223 persons to the square mile; but, if the area under cultivation is

[1] Broek (1), p. 181.

taken, the mean becomes 984 persons to the square mile (see Fig. 10).[1]
Even in Luzón the provinces are very unevenly peopled. The
densest concentrations occur around Manila Bay. The Provinces
of Cavitë (510 to the square mile, and 578 to the square mile of
arable) and Rizal (492; 629) head the list and are closely followed by
Pampanga, which indeed has the greatest density per square mile of
arable (466; 696). These figures should be compared with the
relief map (Fig. 32) and with other maps showing the distribution of
crops together with their nature, yield, and method of cultivation.
More than the growth of urban centres like San Fernando, Cavitë,
and, above all, Manila, they mark the spread of cultivation and
especially of ricefields over the greater part (59 per cent.) of the
central plain. Another densely populated district is the north-west
coast, which is occupied by the Ilocans. Here the Province of La
Unión has 474 persons to the square mile, with 578 on the arable.
Several other provinces also far exceed the mean density in the
island, which is 186 (360). Among these are Batangas in the south-
west (352; 380) and Sorsogón at the south-eastern end (352; 414),
both of which have the least land still available for development.
The most sparsely peopled area in the mountainous north and in
particular the basin of the Kagayán. In Kagayán Province the
density falls to 88 (140), in Isabela to 52 (93), and in Nueva Vizcaya
to 28 (70).

The Visayas with a mean of 168 (274) offer very variable figures
of density. Sebu leads the Philippines with 572 (644), followed by
Bohol (320; 380), Leyte (287; 375), and Panay (285; 401). There is
thus a sharp contrast between neighbouring islands; as for instance
between Leyte and Samar, which supports only 52 (165) persons to
the square mile, and between Panay and Mindoro which has only
33 (59). Situated between the two densely peopled areas of south-
western Luzón and Panay, Mindoro seems to be particularly poorly
endowed. It has the lowest density in the Philippines, not counting
remote Palawan (15; 28). Regional studies are still too rare for
these surprising contrasts to be explained, and certainly physical
conditions are not a sufficient cause.

The large island of Mindanao, which is not without lowlands and
volcanic soil and is scarcely less indented than Luzón, has, however,
only 54 (88) persons to the square mile. But here too there are great
differences in density between one province and the next. Over
long stretches of the north coast opposite the Visayas the density
does indeed exceed 130 persons to the square mile, especially in the
two Misamis, the western one having as high a figure as 310 (551).

[1] Cp. Kolb's table (175), pp. 456-7. In 1955 the mean density exceeded 190
persons to the square mile.

In Lanao the density is still up to 90 (160), but falls to 31 (59) in the big Province of Kotabató, to 23 (49) in Agusán, and even to 18 (25) in Bukidnon.

In the Philippines as a whole a decrease in density of population is noticeable from north to south and also from west to east. The side facing Asia is more densely peopled and busier than the side facing the Pacific. The difference is like the one often noticed in Indonesia between the north and south coasts of the Sunda arc.[1]

Communication and Internal Movement. Demographic contrasts are reflected in the state of the internal communications. These have been greatly improved by the Americans, who have paid the greatest care to the road system, the inadequacy of which had much hindered them during the conquest. More than half the all-weather motor roads are in Luzón. The network is particularly close-meshed in the central plain between Lingayen and Manila Bays; but it also connects Manila with the north coast by way of the Ilocan coast and through the valley of the Kagayán as far as Aparri. Road connexions are rather less certain south-eastwards. On the other hand, the railway runs uninterruptedly from San Fernando in La Unión Province to Legaspi and also sends out several branch lines in the central plain. Out of 866 miles of track, only 132 are not in Luzón, and they are in Panay and Sebu. These islands, together with Negros, Leyte, and Bohol, are the only Visayas that have coherent road systems. Only some sections of the highways in Mindanao are all-weather motor roads, and they amount to only one-tenth of the mileage of roads of that class in the Philippines; but the tracks on which motor vehicles may run have as a rule increased in number.

These modern roads share most of the traffic today. A busy river traffic still exists on the lower and middle Kagayán for carrying tobacco to the coast and also on the lower Kotobató in Mindanao. But in Luzón the railway is the main carrier of rice, sugar, and copra for Manila, the greater part of those commodities—about two-thirds—being transported between December and March.

Here as in other countries the motor vehicle is competing fiercely with the railway. Carts drawn by oxen and buffaloes, though still seen in the streets of Manila, are falling more and more into disuse through the increase of roads equipped with bridges or ferries and passable by lorries at all seasons. Passenger traffic especially is deserting the railway more and more owing to the great increase in road transport companies. It is still a common sight to see a

---

[1] But exceptions are numerous. Mindoro and Palawan in the west are relatively poor. On the other hand, the south-west coast of Sumatra has long had a larger population than the north-east coast.

25. A group of actors in Jogyakarta

26. A seller of Wayang puppets at Sukabumi, Java

27. The main street in Macassar, Celebes

28. Fishing boats at Menado, Celebes

patched-up motorbus with a tired, back-firing, clattering engine and overcrowded with natives and parcels. Naturally, American makes, mainly Fords and Chevrolets, are most in evidence.

Nearly all the roads and railways still lead to the ports. The political and economic unity of the Philippines could only be achieved by a close network of maritime communications. Like the land communications, these have become busier, quicker, and more regular since 1906. The boats carrying on coastwise and interinsular trade still include in addition to steamers a large number of native sailing craft. The chief port in the Philippines both by shipping tonnage and the quantity of goods handled is Manila, which collects and distributes a large proportion of the rice, *abacá*, copra, and tobacco brought in by interinsular traffic. About four-fifths of the vessels plying on regular services among the islands belong to firms whose headquarters are in Manila. The two busiest ports in the Visayas are Sebu and Iloilo. Favoured by its central position, the former is a port of call for many ships belonging to important lines. It collects the produce of the Visayas and northern Mindanao, especially copra, *abacá*, and sugar. A larger number of ships, mostly of moderate or small tonnage, enter and leave Sebu than Manila. The same is true of Iloilo, which is not only the port of Panay, but also deals with the sugar from Negros. Besides these three well equipped ports, the most important are Aparri and Legaspi in Luzón and Zamboanga and Davao in Mindanao. The others generally have only open anchorages without port equipment.

The progress made in the ways and means of transport facilitates the temporary or permanent transfer of people. But seasonal displacements involve fewer passengers than might be believed considering the expansion of export crops and the specialisation which goes on in many districts. The fact is that family exploitation is still the rule nearly everywhere, and large-scale enterprise in agriculture—the plantation properly so-called—is the exception. In Luzón about 2000 natives used to go at the beginning of the year to the tobacco fields in Kagayán and some fewer to those in La Unión and Pangasinan. The rice harvest, which lasts several weeks, and the planting and reaping of the canes attracted on the average more than 5000 workers a year to the central plain, especially in its northern and north-western parts, where large holdings are not rare. Others take work in the coconut groves in the south of the island. The gold-mines also attract crowds of workers. But in Luzón most of the displacements are over short distances. In the Visayas sugar calls for outside labour. The canefields in Mindoro appeal to the Province of Batangas in southern Luzón, and from November onwards tens of thousands of natives from Sebu, Bohol, and Panay flock to the canefields in western Negros. The expansion of *abacá* cultivation in Mindanao and particularly in the Davao district used to cause a flow of migrants who generally contracted for a period of several years.

These temporary transfers often lead to permanent removals through the purchase of land or the renting of a farm. They promote racial fusion by spreading the more populous and advanced groups, such as the Ilocans, Tagals (rather fewer), and Bisayas (especially from Sebu). They also move about elements belonging to smaller groups, as, for instance, the Igorots in northern Luzón, and thus hasten their assimilation.

Differences in population and use of land still continue, as we have seen, and are no doubt more marked than formerly. Natural increase due to an excess of births seems quickly to make up for losses by emigration. So the American Government had organised official transfers, as the Dutch have done in Sumatra; and since 1913[1] its efforts have been directed mainly at Mindanao. The first settlements were in the Kotobató valley and proved a failure. Another attempt made after 1917 succeeded in establishing 15,000 persons (2500 families), comprising Bisayas from Sebu and Ilocans from La Unión and Pangasinan, in the valley of the Coronadal which flows into Sarangani Bay in the south of the island. Similar settlements were made one after the other in different districts in Mindanao, Mindoro, and the Kagayán valley. Those are in fact the positions of the greatest reserves of cultivable land; but no Philippine province is quite without available space. In 1935 the cultivable area was estimated at more than 44,000,000 acres, of which 12,000,000 or 14,000,000 were in Mindanao alone; whilst the area actually under cultivation amounted to only 9,000,000 acres.

It used to be calculated that the Philippines could feed a population of 50,000,000. But to some people the estimate seems exaggerated. A careful survey would certainly reduce the proportion of uncultivated land that is said to be cultivable. Account must be taken not only of the relief, which is often too chaotic for farming to pay, but also of malaria and other tropical diseases, difficulties of transport, and at times a feeling of insecurity. Thus, in Mindanao Christian Filipinos still fear the Moros. In 1939 a thousand Filipinos landed every month on the island at the ports of Davao and Kotobató and cleared the lots granted them by the Government along new roads before even the roads were finished. Such a rate of redistribution may well be thought to be fast enough. Naturally, the work was interrupted by the war in 1941.

Towns and their Foreign Elements. Whilst European settlement

[1] Ralston Hayden (180); Pendleton (179); J. Pelzer (197a).

seems of late years to have caused some rural dispersal by splitting up overcrowded villages, it has also fostered town growth. Little market towns are distinguished from big villages by the presence of a rectangular central *plaza* shaded by a few trees and periodically occupied by a crowd of sellers and buyers who are in some cases sheltered by a roof against the sun and rain. Around the *plaza* stand timber or stone buildings including the church, presbytery, shops with wide, open fronts, and residences with stone foundations, whose architecture and decoration display a mixture of Spanish influence and local styles.

Except in Vigan, which is situated a mile or two from the sea in the Ilocan country, a really urban appearance is only to be seen in the ports, and these are both administrative and economic centres. There are, for instance, in the Sulu Islands Holo, the chief Muslim centre in the Philippines and formerly visited by Chinese traders; in Mindanao the two recent cities of Davao, until 1945 a centre of Japanese settlement, and Zamboanga,[1] which officially acquired the rank of town only in 1937; and in Luzón Legaspi and Aparri.

Iloilo and Sebu are in a higher category owing to their economic importance and the number of their inhabitants. Situated on a coastal flat in southern Panay Iloilo (pop. 90,000) boasts commercial buildings and huge warehouses piled high with sugar from Negros. Sebu has a more eventful history and more varied business. Magellan called there and met his death on the marshy islet of Mactan. Legaspi founded the first Spanish fort there in 1565. Traces of this past still exist in Fort San Pedro and the Calle Colón (Columbus Street) in which galleries supported by heavy wooden posts overhang the pavements. The town has grown up on a narrow coastal plain at the foot of limestone hills long since cleared of their trees and is not only the economic focus for the central and eastern Visayas, but also a cultural and religious centre which has recently become the see of an archbishop. The business quarters are a medley of Chinese shops, edifices in the Spanish Colonial style, and one-storied houses reminiscent of little American cities, and all around under coconut trees stand native quarters, which are often sordid and veritable tropical slums. In 1888 the population was only 9600, but in 1940 it had risen to 147,000.

Manila remains the undisputed queen of the Philippines. In 1576 Martín de Goiti, Legaspi's lieutenant, reached the interior of

---

[1] Zamboanga was for long the only Spanish establishment on Mindanao. At the end of the 18th century Sonnerat saw in it a citadel built of stone and brick. Besides, the settlers were housed inside a stockade and 'cultivated their fields only under shelter of cannon, a few pieces being trained over the fields they try to till'. (10), p. 386.

the bay, behind which sheltered two native towns girt with wooden
stockades. In them resided Muslim chieftains. Tondo lay to the
north and Maynilad to the south. On the site of the latter in the
angle formed by the mouth of the Pasig and the sea the capital of
the Spanish possessions was built and hastily fortified against attack

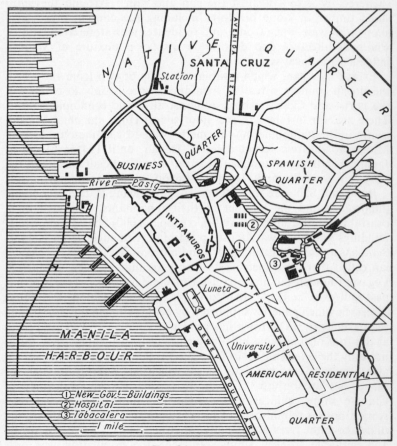

FIG. 36.—MANILA

by Chinese pirates, Japanese, and European rivals.[1] The old city
about two-fifths of a square mile in area, survived till 1944 in the
quarter known as Intramuros. Its quiet chequer-work of streets

[1] There are many descriptions of Manila. For the mid-19th century, see
Mallat (177), I, pp. 168 and *passim*; Jagor (169), p. 23 and *passim*. For 1939,
see Kolb (175), pp. 379 ff. A considerable number of buildings were destroyed
in Manila by the recent war, but reconstruction has made good headway since
1945.

lined with old houses whose first floors overhung the pavements had already appeared on a plan in 1610. From the walls the view sweeps over a block of houses dominated by the towers of many Roman Catholic churches among which the massive Cathedral of St. Paul is the only one to survive the typhoons and earthquakes which have occurred since the beginning of the 17th century. In 1944 Intramuros still sheltered a part of the Government Offices housed in more or less dilapidated ancient edifices. But as early as 1863 the Spanish Governor had taken up his residence in Malacanan Palace a few miles distant. The Congressional Building, modelled on the one in Washington, was built beyond the walls behind lawns spreading over the old moats which are now filled up. On the south side have been built the new administrative quarter and the American residential town with its clubs, the State university, and Luneta Gardens, which are continued to the shores of the Bay by Dewey Boulevard, a broad highway lined with palms.

The commercial city has grown up to the north of the river round Binondo Island, which lies between arms of the Pasig. The business centre tends to shift eastwards, gradually leaving the narrow Escolta Road for Rizal Avenue. On this side of the river stores and a swarm of Chinese shops are crowded along noisy streets, and there too are printed most of the American, Tagal, or Chinese newspapers. Farther north stretch the native quarters, where industrial workers and dockers live huddled together often in insanitary conditions. Most of the industrial buildings stand on the river banks which for long have been used only for loading and unloading cargoes. Since the turn of the century the Americans have built a modern harbour with five breakwaters and vast docks on the west side of Intramuros.

Manila has the advantage of a very favourable position at a point where the spurs of the Cordillera Central approach the sea and contact is made between fertile areas suitable for different purposes. On the north is a large plain on which rice and sugarcane are cultivated; on the south are the provinces with coconut groves. The natural capital of Luzón, it has been made by the Europeans into the chief town of the Philippines and one of the largest cities in the Malay world, with a population which probably numbered more than a million in 1950.

Most of the non-Filipinos live in the towns. They form some 20 per cent. of the population of Manila and include Asiatics, Europeans, and Americans, who live off the soil of the Philippines and have been the prime movers in its transformation. They consist, however, of communities differing greatly in their respective situations, number, and the parts they have played; and they help to make the spectacle of Philippine life one of the strangest in the Malay world.

The Chinese are by far the most numerous.[1] Of the 117,500 'Chinese citizens', only 35,000 were in Manila in 1939. The immigration of unskilled coolies continued secretly in spite of the extension to the Philippines in 1902 of the American Chinese Exclusion Law. Besides, the entry of merchants and business men was still allowed, so that between 1925 and 1934 the registered number of arrivals exceeded that of the departures by 20,000. Big Chinese merchant firms established chiefly in Manila largely control trade throughout the Philippines by means of agents and the systematic practice of advancing money on the crops. They direct the trade in rice and maize and own most of the warehouses and mills where the paddy is treated. They also own most of the saw-mills, many of the salt-works, and a large number of factories, both medium and small, for processing food-products, leather, tobacco, etc.

Besides this floating Chinese colony which is recognised in the censuses and consists to a very large extent of men, the population of the Philippines comprises many Sino-Filipino *mestizos*, most of whom are the issue of the union of Chinese immigrants with Tagal women. According to a recent estimate, there are at least 700,000 persons with Chinese blood in them. Many of them enter the universities and go in for commerce or the liberal professions. From their ranks have sprung several famous men, including Osmena, Arenata, and Emilio Aguinaldo, the national hero. Being settled in the country, they no longer have the same interests as the more recent or temporary Chinese immigrants. They might, however, before the war have united with them to oppose the pretensions of the Japanese and Europeans.

The 25,000 or so Japanese counted in the Philippines in 1939 had almost all arrived since the American occupation. They formed a more settled community than the Chinese new-comers. Japanese women were relatively numerous and half-castes far rarer. A high proportion of them were not middlemen, but real producers attached to the soil. This was the case in the Davao district, where they had greatly extended and improved the cultivation of *abacá*. Another, less numerous, Japanese colony lived mainly by market gardening around the town of Baguio. The Japanese share in commerce and industry, though still far smaller than that of the Chinese, had, however, been growing for some years.

·From the spiritual point of view and in the face of Asiatic influence, no other part of the Malay world seems to have been more affected by Europeans than the Philippines. This was due to the Spanish colonisation, which was mainly a missionary effort and founded in

[1] See above, p. 74.

the islands the most numerous and compact Christian community in the Far East. Though fewer in number than the Americans in 1939 and with half of them living in Manila, the Spaniards none the less continue to play an important part in the intellectual and economic life. Their activity is stimulated by new arrivals; whilst the long character of the Spanish occupation is marked by the existence of a class of Hispano-Filipino, and in particular Hispano-Tagal, half-castes numbering about 200,000 persons and often forming an *élite* owing to their intelligence and wealth. In the development of Philippine resources Spanish capitalists hold third place after the Americans and Chinese. In the tobacco industry the Spaniards lead with the big Tabacalera Company, and they own about a fourth of the sugar industry.

In 1939 the most numerous European groups after the Spaniards (4527) were the Germans (1149), English (1053), Belgians (170), and French (165).[1]

Owing to the remoteness of the islands and even more to the uncertain political situation, the number of United States citizens remains small, there being 8709 in 1939, not counting the troops. Few have settled down, apart from some representatives of the heroic age. They are mainly old soldiers and are found living here and there in out-of-the-way places with native wives. Officials and business men do not stay permanently. Though American capitalists are richer than those of any other nation and though for fifty years they have been hastening on the economic evolution of the Philippines, they seem to have been sparing here, considering the financial power of their homeland and the sums invested in other tropical regions like the West Indies.

Philippine Emigration. There were more Filipinos in Hawaii and the United States than Americans in the Philippines. Together with those in South Africa, they formed the largest groups of Malays outside the Malay lands. In 1907 when the 'Gentlemen's Agreement' stopped Japanese immigration, the planters in Hawaii appealed to the Filipinos, and in 1930 these formed 69 per cent. of the labour in the cane-fields in those islands. They consisted mainly of Ilocans and of Bisayas from Sebu aud Bohol and in 1949 they totalled about

[1] The French were fairly active in the Philippines during the first half of the 19th century before the conquest of Cochin China. *Emigrés* driven abroad by the Revolution had become civil or military officials in the islands, and French music masters had taught military music and introduced comic opera and country dances. A certain number had been murdered in 1820 with other foreigners. About 1840 there were still Frenchmen in Luzón, like Dr. Mallat, Oudon de Virli, the mining engineer, and La Gironnière who found a 'habitation' on the shores of Bay Lagoon and was the first European really to engage in agriculture there. Mallat (177), *passim.*

53,000. By far the great majority used to return home with their savings.

Besides these, about 45,000 Filipinos were counted in the United States census in 1946, 30,000 of them being in California. They were sailors and students as well as agricultural labourers, hotel and restaurant employees, and domestic servants, many of whom had passed through Hawaii and landed at Seattle or Los Angeles. A few hundreds were in the motor industry at Detroit. But the total of them all had been decreasing for some years, since immigration had been restricted by the American Government.

PART III

COLONIAL EXPANSION AND ITS EFFECT ON THE ECONOMIC SYSTEM

CHAPTER 14

POPULATION AND EXPORTS

Europeans have found in the Malay world one of the most favourable tropical regions for putting their colonising urge into practice. We should like to paint the picture of their work in the pages that follow, but it is a difficult business to pass fair judgment on it and estimate objectively the balance of its merits and defects. To claim dependence on one's own personal observations would not without reason be taxed as overweening conceit. The opinions of the apparently best informed and most sincere authors differ more than a little. For some no other region brings out as strongly what has been emphasised so often as to become a platitude, namely, the contrast between the material success of colonisation and its spiritual and moral failure. Few ever call in question this material success. But those who are loudest in praise stress the difficulties arising from the economic evolution, over-population, and the contact and fusion of many races. As may be imagined, there is never-ending controversy over the effects of European tutelage on the structure and equilibrium of native communities and on the happiness of the people. But then the criteria are necessarily coloured subjectively.

Although statistical data do not constitute adequate evidence, a few figures would seem necessary to begin with. They certainly furnish the scrupulous critic with a too narrow, but relatively safe basis. Whilst they call for comment, they dispense with much unnecessary talk.

The first fact to emphasise is the growth of population. It has not been the same everywhere. But in few lands has a drop in vital statistics seemed to betray the deep-seated anæmia which has occurred here and there among the native peoples of Australia and Oceania. A decrease has been observed on the little island of Enggano to the west of Sumatra, in Buru, in western Serang,[1] among some of the Torajas in Celebes,[2] not to mention New Guinea. But

[1] Van Eerde in Rutten (19), p. 355.

[2] Kruyt (in Schrieke (20), p. 5), a missionary, states that the Torajas of the Lake Poso district lost their zest in life when forced by the Dutch Colonial Government to leave their homes and go to dwell alongside some new roads, and that the death-rate among them rose steeply. This effect of European colonisation has often been pointed out in Oceania.

it seems to have been checked, thanks to the steps taken by the Colonial Governments and Christian missions, and in any case it affects but a few thousand natives. In this respect the Malay world as a whole behaves like other former colonial territories in Monsoon Asia, viz. India and Indo-China. This is not the place to discuss the absolute or relative value of the various censuses which have been taken in time and place. Official year-books tell us that the native population of Java and Madura rose from 12,514,000 in 1860 to 40,891,000 in 1930, that of the Outer Provinces from 7,370,000 to 18,247,000 between 1905 and 1930, and that of Indonesia as a whole from 37,348,000 to 59,138,000 in the same period, which represents an increase of 158 per cent. in 25 years. In the Philippines, if we disregard the older estimates in Buzeta's Dictionary, the figures 5,985,000 and 15,984,000 given in the official censuses for 1887 and 1939 respectively show an increase of 267 per cent. in 52 years. Lastly, in Malaya the increase from 2,673,000 in 1911 to 4,385,000 in 1931 is 164 per cent. in only 20 years.

These figures are certainly approximate and have been collected in different ways. The oldest censuses considered above, especially the one in the Philippines, may be regarded as not very accurate, and the immigration of foreign Asiatics—greater in Malaya than elsewhere—must not be underestimated. Nevertheless, it is certain that the native population has increased. Nor is this increase surprising when compared with that of other peoples in Europe and elsewhere. It arises from well-known causes: on the one hand, the fall in the death-rate due to medical attention and especially to wholesale vaccination and, on the other hand, the development of the land and the increased supplies of food available for the mass of people.

This leads to the consideration of another balance-sheet, viz. that of overseas trade, which taken separately from production is very difficult to estimate. The Malay world, which covers about 5·4 per cent. of the area of the lands within the tropics and contains about 12 per cent. of their population, had nearly a fourth (23 per cent.) of their total trade. This was far more than the share of tropical Africa, a region three and a half times as big and one and a quarter times as populous. These figures remain significant even though it is granted that the *entrepôt* and transit business at Singapore, the largest port, is necessarily included in the total.

It is in fact from this corner of our planet that since the beginning of the century one of the most plentiful streams of tropical produce has been flowing towards the industrial nations. Owing to the domestication of the *Hevea brasiliensis*, the Malay lands supplied 78 per cent. of the world's rubber exports in 1938. Their position

was certainly not so predominant in any other commodity, except
two of small volume, viz. pepper (79 per cent.) and that pharmaceu-
tical specific of first importance, Peruvian bark, and the products
derived from it (90 per cent.).   But yet their share in copra was 73
per cent., in palm oil 56 per cent., in sugar 14 per cent., in tobacco
3·7 per cent., in coffee 4·7 per cent., and in tea 16·4 per cent.   They
supplied 25 per cent. of the exports of sisal, nearly all that of Manila
hemp, and 70 per cent. of that of kapok.   Lastly, the Malay
countries shared in world export of tin to the extent of 44 per cent.
and at least 3 per cent. in that of petroleum.   This all fed a very big
overseas trade, the greater part of which still passed through the
Suez Canal in 1939.

CHAPTER 15

THE REGION OPENED TO WORLD TRADE

The Europeans did not force their way into a hermetically sealed Malay world. Relations had been established between the island-groups and the nearby continent long before their arrival, not to mention the mystery-wrapped migrations which had taken parties of people from the Malay world as far as Madagascar and the Pacific Islands. The export of spices and certain marine and forest products certainly has a long past. Trade became livelier with the Hindu settlements which open the history of the Malay lands, with Chinese emigration across the South China Sea, with the advance of the Muslims from the Hadhramaut and Sind, and, lastly, with the appearance of the Japanese.

The earliest historical records of Japanese voyages into East Indian waters go back, however, only to the 16th century. According to Albuquerque's commentaries, they sailed to Malacca with the northerly monsoon in January and returned in August or September to Nagasaki in the Satsuma district in south-western Kyushu or to the Ryukyu Islands. From 1540 onwards, at the time of the landing in Japan of the first Europeans with Méndez Pinto and St. Francis Xavier, they were met with in Luzón, especially on the north coast of that island. There they traded cotton goods, silk, weapons, salt fish, and gold for porcelain and, a little later, for Mexican silver. The shipowners engaged in this traffic were *daimios* and other persons of high rank, specialised merchants, as well as foreigners (Chinese and even Europeans). The Japanese seem also to have had trading establishments in Java and on the coast of Annam and Cambodia. Up to the beginning of the 17th century they also engaged in piracy. Some of them took service as mercenaries with Europeans or even with the Siamese. In 1570 there were 20 Japanese families in Manila, where in 1621 Archbishop Serrano estimated the number of this people to be more than 3000. Hideyoshi had thought of conquering the Philippines, and fear of a Japanese landing persisted for quite a long time.

This Japanese movement southwards was opposed by the Europeans, but stopped suddenly about 1636 when the Japanese Islands were closed to foreign influence, emigration forbidden under pain of death, and the construction of ocean-going ships prohibited.

But a new and decisive period begins with European colonisation; for with it direct communications—thenceforth to be constantly open—were begun between the Malay lands on the one hand and Western Europe and the coasts of America on the other.

Commercial Relations. In the four hundred years following Albuquerque's conquest and Magellan's voyage the progress of trade was to be greater than during the six preceding centuries. Yet it seems to have been relatively slow until about the middle of the 19th century, since it was handicapped by monopolies and by difficulties of ocean navigation. From the beginning European ships were far superior to native craft in construction and efficiency. The huge Portuguese carracks, like the one captured off Malacca by the Dutch, could accommodate at least six hundred men; and Dutch ships were even better than the Portuguese owing to their stability, improved rigging, the quality of the crews, their more powerful armament, and the greater effectiveness of their tactics.

Navigation was not only hampered by storms and calms, however, but also suffered from frequent attack by Asiatic corsairs or European rivals. Between piracy and trade there was no clear distinction, and most of the ships were armed for defence and indeed for attack, if opportunity arose. The risks run by passengers and cargo were thus very great. The voyage from Western Europe to the East Indies or *vice versa* seldom lasted less than a year and often took far longer. It was generally full of hardship.

The slowness of expansion and the difficulties confronting trade are on the whole to be explained by the very limited possibilities of freight. That is why it was preferable to increase the rate of profit rather than the volume of trade. Efforts were made to monopolise goods of high value, whose production could easily be controlled and whose transport was easy.

These monopolies were used at first mainly for the benefit of certain European ports. In the Iberian peninsula there were Lisbon, Seville, and, above all, Cadiz; in the Netherlands the chief was Amsterdam, but there were also Flushing and a few others. The trade routes to the Philippines and East Indies remained as different as were those originally used by the conquerors. Ships of the Dutch East India Company sailed round the Cape of Good Hope, whilst communications between Spain and the Philippines were maintained *via* New Spain across the Pacific. For close on two hundred years the Philippines seemed to be a dependency of New Spain rather than of Madrid and were thus as it were already an American colony.

Trade was far more strictly regulated on the Spanish route than on the other.[1] A fleet of 'licensed vessels' sailed every three or four years from Cadiz to Vera Cruz. As for the Philippines, from the

[1] Humboldt (195), IV, pp. 101 ff.

end of the 16th century they communicated with New Spain only by
the famous galleons, and then only at wide intervals. The galleons
were built of choice timber from the arsenal at Cavitë and were of
1200 or 1500 tons burden. At first twice and later once a year one
made the five or six months' crossing from Manila to Acapulco.
Sailing in mid-July or the beginning of August when the south-west
monsoon was at its height, the galleon carried muslins, coarse
cotton cloths, silks, gold and silver work, and spices which for the
most part came not from the Philippines, but China. Hence, the
galleon was usually nicknamed the *Nao de China*. The wind bore it
without a single stop to the coast of California, whence it sailed
along southwards. The cargo was taken to Mexico City and from
there was distributed throughout New Spain, only a part of it being
re-exported to Spain. At the same time silver bars and piastres,
together with a few Mexican or Spanish commodities including
cochineal, cocoa, wine, oil, and Spanish wool, were sent to Acapulco
to form the return cargo. The vessel sailed in February or March
with a few passengers, particularly parties of monks, set her course
almost due west with the help of the trade wind, and, after touching
at Guam, reached Manila in fifty or sixty days. The galleon was
often attacked. Thus, in 1740 after a heroic resistance it was forced
to strike its flag to Commodore Anson.

Trade between Western Europe and the Dutch 'factories' was far
greater. After Johan de Riebeeck had been sent out in 1651 by the
Dutch East India Company and had formed a settlement at the Cape,
this point acted as a good port of call and took the place of St.
Helena. Through it passed ships carrying precious spices from the
Moluccas together with many other commodities, a great many of
which came from China, Indo-China, India, and even Japan.

But trading between the Indies on the one hand and Mexico and
Western Europe on the other was far from constituting the whole
of the activities of the Europeans exiled in Malay lands. The
traders in Manila and on the Dutch stations trafficked with each
other and with ports in the neighbouring countries. This was the
trade of 'the Indies with the Indies' which had been first practised
by the Portuguese. Not only did it bring in fat profits to the share-
holders of the Companies in Europe, but, as it was more difficult to
check than the trade with Europe, it was even more profitable to the
Companies' employees, many of whom were guilty of peculation.
It also caused a very keen and often bloody rivalry between the
representatives of various European nations. For instance, it was
mainly to monopolise the silk trade between China and Japan at the
expense of the Spaniards that the Dutch East India Company
founded the trading post of Zelandia on the north-west coast of

Formosa to assist in destroying rival trading ships in the China seas.[1]

In the second half of the 18th century, however, the pressure of regulations imposed by mercantilism was relaxed. Spices, which had been the most profitable monopoly of the Dutch Company, no longer held first place in exports from the East Indies, having given way to coffee, which had been introduced into Java in 1696. The production of sugar, indigo, and probably cotton increased, and the trade grew. To ship these bulkier goods more vessels came from Europe. Many of them were not Dutch, nor did they land their cargoes at Amsterdam. At the same period direct, though still not regular, communications were opened with Spain, to which tobacco, sugar, indigo, and cotton were shipped from the islands. The last 'licensed' fleet reached Vera Cruz under the command of Ulloa in 1778.[2] From 1786 onwards the merchants in Manila, who had before been supplied from Mexico, were able to make direct purchases of European goods in Vera Cruz. The last galleon left Manila for New Spain in 1811; but another twenty years elapsed before the port was opened to foreign ships and traders, and then the latter were saddled with such high charges that in fact none of them established themselves there until 1834. But then trade suddenly came to life in Manila. About 1840 the port dealt not only with local trade in the Philippines, but was also in direct communication with the Moluccas, Batavia, Macao, Cadiz and Santander in Spain, Singapore, and Australia, to which last sugar began to be shipped in 1837.[3]

The relaxation of monopolies went with the expansion of English shipping, which had been achieved through the occupation of Dutch territories at the beginning of the 19th century. After these had been handed back in 1815, the predominance which had been acquired still persisted as a lasting reversal of Dutch domination in these seas in the 17th century. Great Britain now had the greatest share in the foreign trade of the Indies, and her ships were more numerous than any others in the ports of the archipelago. The foundation of Singapore in 1819 gave her a powerful trump card. The Netherlands found resistance difficult, though they instituted the Nederlandsche Handel-maatschappij in 1825. Singapore became the chief port in the East Indies, except for Dutch trade, which

---

[1] The Company also had interests in Indo-China; for example, it imported Japanese silver into Tongking and exported silk from Tongking to Japan. It even sent a mission to Laos under the leadership of van Wuijsthoff, who reached Vientiane in 1641. See Buch (188), 1936, p. 111; 1937, p. 212 and *passim*. See also A. Cabaton: *Les Hollandais au Cambodge au 17e siècle* in *R. de l'Histoire des Colonies françaises*, 2e trimestre, 1914.

[2] Humboldt (195), IV, p. 127.

[3] Mallat (177), II, p. 329.

continued to use Sunda Strait; and about 1840 Mallat stated that Singapore was already pouring goods into Batavia.

The cutting of the Suez Canal gave Singapore a further advantage by making the Straits of Malacca take the place of the routes through Sunda and Macassar Straits as the main gateway to the Far East. It greatly shortened the distance between Indonesia and the industrial nations of Europe, who were all short of raw materials and tropical foodstuffs. To this gain in time was added the advantage resulting from the progress in tonnage and speed of steamships. Furthermore, the seas had become safer. In 1848 three steamships were delivered to the Philippine Government from British shipyards for use in hunting down pirates.[1] These freebooters manned boats armed with little guns, having but a small draught and capable of being propelled by oars during calms. They therefore easily escaped deep into the inlets at the approach of the betraying smoke of a steamer; and they continued right up to the end of last century to capture native craft and raid coastal villages. The last to be reduced were the Moros of the Sulu Islands and Mindanao. The remains of forts and watch-towers along the coasts still call to mind the fear pirates used to inspire. Steamship navigation was slow in ousting sail. To the slow, spacious sailers were added fast clippers which continued to make the voyage to Europe until about 1900, though they became progressively fewer.[2] Many of the sailers loaded coal in England and discharged it in East Indian ports—Singapore mainly, but also Penang, Batavia, Semarang, Surabaya, and Macassar—for refuelling their rivals, the steamers. They then took cargoes of coffee, tobacco, pepper, and above all sugar and completed their loads in rice ports, like Rangoon, Saigon, and Bangkok. Manila, Sebu, and Iloilo were touched at by sailers, most of which had called at Hongkong and were carrying hemp and sugar to the north-eastern ports of the United States round the Cape of Good Hope. According to the season, passages were made through the Straits of Malacca or Sunda Strait or, when south China or the Philippines were involved, even channels farther east, like those of Bali, Lombok, and Alas, all leading to Macassar Strait. In order to avoid the north-east monsoon as far as could be done, it was possible to pass round the west of Buru and sail between Halmahera and New Guinea. The voyage from the Lizard to Singapore lasted one hundred and fifteen days on the average. The return journey took one hundred and thirty days. Conrad has celebrated in his stories the last days of sailing ships in the East Indies.

1 Kolb (175), p. 354.
2 Schott (201). Full and exact details concerning sailing vessels at the end of the last century (1883–1892) will be found in this article.

Under the pressure of the Cultuurstelsel and later owing to the growth of large private firms the quantity of goods exported from the Indies greatly increased. The increase was not only in volume, but also in variety, especially after 1870. At that date the exports of coffee and sugar were valued at 76,000,000 florins, which was nearly three-fourths of the total value of the exports; but in 1900, although the value of the export of those commodities was 108,000,000 florins, their share in the total was no more than about 40 per cent.[1]

The first quarter of the 20th century saw the 'epic' story and wonderful success of rubber in Malaya and Indonesia. More recently the success of another new-comer to the Far East, the African oil palm, has been consolidated in Malaya as well as in Sumatra. Mining—and, above all, tin from Malaya, Banka, and Belitong, and petroleum from Sumatra, Borneo, and Java—has still further increased the volume and value of the exports. This expansion went on until about 1930, though it was interrupted by the more or less lengthy and serious slump resulting from economic crises.

In spite of Spanish reserve and the obstacles put in the way of foreign enterprise, the Philippines were brought, though more slowly and at a later date, into the stream of international trade. British, German, and American firms and French planters also contributed to the development of the great export crops from 1850 onwards. Of these the chief were Manila hemp and sugar, Great Britain and the United States being the greatest buyers, whilst the tobacco exported continued to go mainly to Spain.

In the 20th century the great size of the American market caused a rapid expansion in Philippine sugarcane and coconut cultivation, the quantity exported far exceeding that of hemp and tobacco in 1940.

Up to the war of 1939–45 Europe remained the chief customer and main source of imports into the East Indies and Malaya; and most of the trade passed through the Suez Canal. The share of other countries was increasing, however, and steamship lines were being established to connect the Malay lands directly with the nations which were building up industrial systems on the shores of the Pacific. London and Amsterdam were finding it difficult to keep their *entrepôt* trade and their position as world markets.

The progress made by the United States at the expense of Europe was evident. Though the greatest producers of rubber were separated by the vast expanse of the Pacific from the world's chief consumer, the United States had become Malaya's principal

[1] Furnivall (15), p. 201.

customer, taking 44 per cent. of its exports in 1937 as compared with 11 per cent. taken by the United Kingdom and 16 per cent. by the whole of Europe; and American demands for rubber and palm-oil continued to increase. Apart from their share in crude oil extraction, which anyhow is difficult to estimate, most of their capital was invested in rubber and oil palm plantations in these islands and especially in Sumatra. Nearly half of the exports from Belawan Deli in the Oostkust of Sumatra went to the United States. Of the total exports from Indonesia the States took 11·7 per cent. in 1931, 18·7 per cent. in 1937, and 33·3 per cent. in 1940. This included 61 per cent. of the rubber exported, 57 per cent. of the palm oil, 64 per cent. of the tea, 60 per cent. of the tapioca, and 64 per cent. of the tin.[1] Between 1929 and 1940 Europe's share in imports into Indonesia fell from 47 to 31·2 per cent., and her share in exports from 36·6 to 15 per cent; whilst imports from the United States rose from 12·4 to 23·1 per cent., and the exports to that country rose from 11·4 to 33·3 per cent. The greater part of the produce purchased by the United States was bought directly from Indonesia, whilst in 1913 purchases had been made mainly through Dutch middlemen.

Thus, the United States imported more from Indonesia and Malaya than they exported to those countries. Consequently, the United States had a very unfavourable balance of trade with these countries; but this was set off by means of the favourable balance of trade which the United States had with Europe.[2]

Except in the Philippines, however, Europe continued to control the foreign trade of the Malay countries through her invested capital, her technicians, and the support of her Colonial Governments. But in the Philippines the United States quickly took first place after the privileges left to Spain had been abolished in 1909. In 1934 the vast market afforded by the States absorbed 80 per cent. of the exports from the Philippines, since they entered duty free. Once again, then, the busiest trade went across the Pacific, where it was encouraged by the opening of the Panama Canal. But it was no longer an occasional galleon scudding along to Acapulco, for in 1938 the Philippines did 72 per cent. of their overseas trade with the United States.[3]

[1] Boeck (187), p. 131.

[2] For the balance of trade between the United States and the Malay countries, see *European Trade* (League of Nations publication, 1941, p. 37) and *Economic Survey of Asia and the Far East* (United Nations, Bangkok, 1956).

[3] Average exports from the Philippines to the U.S.A.

33 per cent.	from		1899–1908
78	,,	,,	1936–1940
68	,,	,,	1948–1951
63	,,	,,	1953–1955

Imports from the U.S.A. to the Philippines

14 per cent.	in		1899–1908
67	,,	,,	1936–1940
77	,,	,,	1948–1951
69	,,	,,	1953–1955

Japanese penetration was also revealed by the overseas trade of the Malay countries, especially by the imports. Its progress corresponded to that of Japanese industry subsequent to 1913; and it was most marked in the trade with Indonesia, no doubt because there Japan did not meet such strong competition from the Colonial Power as that of the United Kingdom in Malaya or the United States in the Philippines, and because its protective tariffs were lower. In 1937 Japan supplied 6 per cent. of the imports into Malaya, 9·6 per cent. of those into the Philippines, but 25 per cent. of those into Indonesia.[1] The goods supplied were mainly manufactured: cottons and silks, metal fittings, bicycles, glass and pottery, rubber articles, paper, and chemicals, as well as foodstuffs like canned fish and vegetables, and, lastly, a certain amount of coal.[2]

Japan's share in exports from Malaya amounted to 7 per cent., from the Philippines 6·5 per cent., and from Indonesia 4·4 per cent. The goods included agricultural produce (rubber, sugar, copra, coffee, Manila hemp and maguey, and tobacco), timber, and minerals (iron ore, copper, and oil). Taking imports and exports together, Japan's trade with Malay countries was less than that of the United States, but the balance was very unfavourable to the latter and, on the contrary, favourable to Japan. This discrepancy seemed to justify the protectionist measures of the local Governments.

Nor did those Governments take a kindly view of the increase in Japanese shipping in their ports, since the shipping lines were aided by heavy State subsidies. In 1938 the Japanese flag took third place in Malaya and Indonesia just after those of Great Britain and the Netherlands in the total of overseas and coastwise shipping. In the Philippines it came after those of Great Britain and the United States in the value of goods carried, but led the United States in the tonnage of cargoes.

The Malay world had also expanded its trade with Australia, which country in 1939 supplied 3·3 per cent. of the imports into Indonesia and took 5·6 per cent. of its exports. It had become the best outlet for Indonesian tea and one of the greatest buyers of oil from the same islands. In return Australia sold Indonesia foodstuffs (flour, butter, milk, etc.) and an increasing quantity of manufactured goods.

The continued increase in trade with distant lands was faithfully reflected in the growth of the ports. These include the largest cities in the Malay world. Singapore was the undisputed chief of them owing to its being a port of call and a centre of collection and distribution, in addition to its local functions in an extraordinarily

[1] As compared with only 2 per cent. in 1913.
[2] For Japanese trade with Indonesia, see Broek (187), pp. 112 ff.

progressive colony. Vessels of more than 75 tons which entered and cleared in 1937 amounted to 32,791,000 tons. This placed Singapore among the world's fifteen largest ports and in the Far East ranked it after Kobe, Osaka, Hongkong, and Shanghai. After Singapore the principal were Penang and Port Swettenham in Malaya, Batavia, Surabaya, Semarang, and Cheribon in Java, Belawan Deli, Palembang, and Sabang in Sumatra, Balik Papan in Borneo, Macassar in Celebes, and Manila, Sebu, and Iloilo in the Philippines. The business of warehousing and re-export still helped to a fairly high degree in the activities of some of these, like Penang, Macassar, and Manila. Sabang, a recent foundation on the north point of Sumatra, was a port of call, but without the additional functions which had made Singapore important. The others were mainly local centres which reflected in their trade the more or less varied resources of their backlands and especially of the plantations. Batavia, Surabaya, and Manila, whose exports were very varied, were in contrast with Belawan Deli and Port Swettenham, which exported large quantities of rubber and palm-oil, Sebu, whose main trade was in copra, and still more so with centres that were more narrowly specialised, like Iloilo, whose only export was sugar, and Palembang and above all Balik Papan, which shipped crude oil.

Imports are usually more concentrated than exports. Thus, in 1937 Batavia and Surabaya together received 46 per cent. of the value of the imports into Indonesia, but contributed only 19·4 per cent of the exports. The discrepancy was still greater in Manila, where in 1938 more than 80 per cent. of the goods despatched to the Philippines were landed, whilst only 28 per cent. of the exports were shipped thence. The fact is that the exports being mainly raw materials and foodstuffs, were far bulkier than the imports.[1] Hence, they were embarked as near as possible to the point of production in many local ports which were visited at certain times at least by the cargo boats of regular lines or by tramps. These vessels found little accommodation there and had to anchor in open roadsteads.

Internal Transport. In this world of islands the ports are intended not only for trade with the distant lands which started them on their career of progress, but are also centres of a very busy internal commerce. A large number of small native craft still engage in this trade and contribute greatly to the picturesqueness of the ports as they glide between the smoke-plumed funnels of cargo boats and huge liners. They are of various forms.[2] The smallest are hollowed

---

[1] For instance, in 1937 Indonesia imported 1,996,000 tons of merchandise and exported 11,437,000 tons. Compare this with post-war figures given on p. 434.

[2] For the various boats in the Philippines about the middle of the 19th century, see Mallat (177), I, p. 250.

out of a single tree trunk and are sometimes fitted with two big bamboos at the sides to prevent them from capsizing. The *prahu* is a large boat with geometrical figures painted in bright colours on its sides and with its high, recurving stem adorned with a protecting eye. It is made of admirably joined planks without a bit of metal and carries sails, but can also be propelled with oars or a quant. Some Malay peoples, like the Bugis and Macassarese in Celebes, still make their living partly as coastal and interinsular carriers, a function they formerly combined with piracy. A certain number of Chinese also engage in this coastwise trade, taking advantage of the alternative monsoon winds to fill the big matting sails of their solidly built junks. Nowadays these boats are often fitted with auxiliary motors.

But most of the regular communication between the islands is carried out by cargo boats of moderate size which generally belong to companies and have a political as well as an economic purpose. The largest of these companies was the Koninklijke Paketvaart Maatschappij, whose white-funnelled boats used to appear in large numbers even in the harbours of Singapore and Penang. In 1937 the K.P.M. owned 130 steam or motor cargo-boats, and it carried between the Indonesian islands 600,000 passengers and nearly 2,400,000 tons of merchandise. Under Government contract it ran about 60 regular services and called at 400 ports. It played a considerable part in the progressive unification of Indonesia and in the development of native export crops. Other smaller and often Chinese-owned shipping companies carry passengers and cargo between Singapore, Penang, and Indonesian ports like Belawan Deli, Jambi, Palembang, and Pontianak. Before the war the Indo-Dutch Java–China–Japan Line served Manila in its regular runs from Java to Japanese and Chinese ports. But communication between Indonesia and the Philippines remained slight.

In the Philippines there was no regular boat service at the end of the Spanish rule, except between Manila, Sebu, and Iloilo. Trade between the islands was organised only at the beginning of the century by the American administration and was entrusted to subsidised companies owned by Spanish creoles, *mestizos*, or Americans and mostly having their headquarters in Manila. The tonnage was still inadequate and many of the boats obsolescent. The chief ports in the islands were connected by a network of regular lines which was fairly close-meshed in the Philippine mediterranean. But the east coasts were less well served.

From the seaports, or at least from some of them, trade penetrates inland along the rivers. Inland navigation is important only in the large islands and especially on the rivers in the eastern plains of Sumatra and Borneo, some of which can be ascended by boats of shallow draught for more than 60 miles.   In Luzón the Kagayán is used for carrying tobacco to Aparri; and in Mindanao the Kotobató valley sends its excess rice down the river.

Railway and road systems betray the unevenness of the economic development and distribution of population.   Java has the greatest railway mileage in proportion to area, whilst Malaya has the greatest mileage in proportion to total population.   Two lines of railway from Siam run into British territory as far as Gemas, where they join.   Thanks to the railway, Singapore and, even more so, Penang have become transit ports for fast traffic between Bangkok and the countries served by big liners which cannot afford the time to enter the Gulf of Siam.   Next to those the island best provided is Luzón, then far behind comes Sumatra.   Outside these there are only about 120 miles of track in North Borneo and in Panay and Sebu.

For the most part the railways are run by the Governments. They have a metre gauge in Malaya and 1·067m. elsewhere.   Some of the expresses on the long runs north–south through Malaya and east–west in Java have dining-cars and comfortable sleepers.   But the vast majority of passenger receipts come from natives travelling third or fourth class on short journeys.   Besides, the transport of goods has long been a greater source of profit than the carrying of passengers.   And the relative share of goods transport is being increased by the development of motor road services.   To the competition of the latter has been due the very slight extension of railways since 1920.

In truth, the modern road system had greatly expanded and improved since that year.   Roads often duplicate the railways in districts where the population is densest and trade busiest.   They open up new country where in wide plains they often supplement the use of navigable rivers and in mountain districts they give Europeans access to well-known beauty spots and hill stations.   Consequently, several run up above the 5000-foot contour.   A trunk road skirts the west side of the Malay Peninsula for 660 miles from Singapore to the Siamese frontier.   It sends many branches to the ports on the Straits, but only two across to the east coast, one of which reaches Kuantan in Pahang and the other Mersing in Johore. Many of the roads were originally cart tracks straightened and widened for motor traffic.[1]   Every year saw old wooden bridges and ferries replaced by strong steel or reinforced concrete constructions.

[1] For road traffic in Java at the beginning of the 20th century, see Gonnaud (192), p. 504; and for the middle of the 19th century, see Money (196), I, p. 15. All main roads had two tracks, one for cattle and the other for horses and horse-drawn vehicles.   The official posting service with its relays used to work even at night by torchlight.

In Java there were 14,300 miles of tarmac or metalled road over which motor vehicles regularly passed at all seasons. Just before the war progress had been faster still in the Outer Provinces, where the mileage was in 1940 about 18,000. One of the best-known roads crosses the Equator in Sumatra as it runs from Padang through Fort de Kock and past Lake Toba to Medan. There are some good motor roads in north and south Celebes also.

In the Philippines the roads have been greatly improved by American engineers. Half the all-weather motor roads are in Luzón, 16 per cent. being in the central plain alone. This district was not connected with the Kagayán valley and the port of Aparri by Balete Pass until 1924. Since then it has been possible to reach the capital from Isabela Province in a single day, a journey which previously took a week by the route along the coast and up the Kagayán. In Mindanao, which is far less well equipped, but has good prospects under the new Republic, two roads have recently been built across the island from Misamis to Kotobató and Davao.[1]

The bicycle is very common, especially in the towns. In Indonesia it is often pawned during the wet season. But since the beginning of the present century the motor vehicle has been quickly winning its way into many parts of the Malay world. The first car, a Benz, was landed at Singapore in 1896. The first Malay driver was trained by an Englishwoman. In 1937 there were 46,000 motor vehicles of all classes in Malaya, 70,000 in Indonesia (44,000 of which were in Java), and 48,000 in the Philippines. Motorbuses, mostly run by private enterprise and competing with each other, carry to market astonishingly large heaps of villagers with their parcels, poultry, and sometimes even pigs securely tied up. Lorries serve the ports and railway stations by collecting goods for export and by going deeper and deeper into the backlands to supply retailers, taking advantage of the dry season to use unmetalled tracks. The number of slow, creaking ox-carts was increased by the rise of large-scale cultivation, especially of sugar in Luzón and Java; but they are disappearing before the motor vehicle, though they have not yet all gone and they still venture even into the streets of towns. Cars pass lines of pedlars jinking along the footpaths beside the roads, bent under bamboo yokes with a load at each end. Locally-made goods and articles manufactured in far-off lands reach the most distant villages on men's backs or shoulders or, on rare occasions, on packhorses.

[1] Pendleton (179), p. 181.

CHAPTER 16

ECONOMIC SYSTEMS

The early arrival of Europeans and the gradual extension of their occupation of the Malay world would make an admirable topic in the history of colonisation. Indonesia in particular has provided a series of carefully studied experiments with more than a mere historic interest, for they have left their mark on the economic system of the present day. The practical nature of the Dutch has often been emphasised, but it did not prevent them from forming one theory of policy after another, though it restrained them from making a clean sweep and building all over again. Remains of ancient systems survived under recent additions, as they do in a geological section. In fact, one observer has stated, with some exaggeration, that it takes a geologist to understand the political and economic edifice which the Dutch built up in Indonesia.[1]

The Chartered Companies. The Dutch East India Company's system is well known. The Company founded in Indonesia the basis of considerable power which lasted about two hundred years. To ensure its monopoly of the famous spices, it soon had to intervene by force and diplomacy in the affairs of native princes and occupy the spice-producing territories or at any rate their outlets to the sea. In principle its revenues should have been derived from trade, but in fact they became nothing less than tribute when a native sovereign was forced to deliver commodities at fixed prices.[2] Before the end of the 17th century the Sultan of Bantam had to hand over all the pepper in his kingdom, and the chiefs of Preanger in western Java were bound to deliver fixed quantities of pepper, indigo, and sewing cotton. At the same time production was regulated without regard for the natives. In 1652 a treaty was concluded with the Sultan of Ternate by which in return for an annuity of 12,000 rix dollars he was to uproot all the clove-trees in his kingdom, since the Company wished to restrict the cultivation of the tree to Amboina and the Uliaser Islands near by, so as to facilitate its control and safeguard the monopoly. The people of Amboina were forced to plant 120,000 trees in 1656 and another 60,000 in 1658, and then in 1667 all further additions were forbidden. The Company even organised military expeditions to destroy trees. They were called *Hongi tochten* and were accompanied by atrocities and massacres. In

[1] Emerson (251), pp. 410 ff.
[2] See van der Kolff in Schrieke (20), pp. 102 ff; and Raynal (198), I, pp. 390 ff.

312

Banda a large number of the native population were driven away, and the land distributed among European or half-caste planters who were supplied with tenant cultivators from other islands. The prices paid for the produce varied, but were generally low. They were paid with imported goods assessed at too high a value, for the middlemen took their profits, and the poorly paid employees of the Company looked after themselves. Attempts at suppressing contraband led to violent struggles with native rulers and indeed to the occupation of Macassar and the neighbouring district in 1667–9. Rightly or wrongly, the foreigners were suspected of fraud and were in consequence themselves victims of swindles which were often cruel, like those recounted by Tavernier at the end of the 17th century.[1]

Restrictive measures were not finally abolished in the Moluccas until 1824, long before which time the Dutch had lost the monopoly of the production of spices. But in the 18th century a similar system had been applied to other products, like coffee, which had become the chief export from Java. Sugarcane cultivation was less strictly controlled in that island, because it had the advantage of its produce being consumed in quite large quantities locally and since it was mainly in the hands of Chinese who employed forced native labour on land alienated by the rulers. But its export was forbidden for a time so as to lower prices locally. Pepper cultivation was imposed on eastern Java, although the people there had no skill in it and though the climate was unfavourable. In the same district the people had to hand over teak and for that purpose to neglect their food crops and wear out their buffaloes. A tribute of tin was imposed on Banka. The Company also arrogated to itself the monopoly of selling commodities like opium and Indian and Persian manufactured goods, and from the time of van Imhoff's governorship (1743–50) it assumed real territorial sovereignty in many places. Outside Java, however, this rule did not extend beyond isolated 'factories' and their girdle of plantations and fortifications, as for example at Palembang and Banjermasin.

Though this commercial policy found a magnificent field of application here, it was not peculiar to either the Netherlands or Indonesia and coincided with the ideas held at the time. Chartered companies of the old fashion were the normal method of colonial development, particularly as formulated by the English Government in the Navigation Act of 1651 and the Covenant Act of 1660. Abuses arising out of the system itself and still more from the exactions of the employees were certainly more in evidence at the end of the 18th century. But the Amsterdam Company's downfall was

[1] Tavernier (11), II, p. 529.

mainly due to bankruptcy. The time of fabulous dividends had long gone by. Foreign competition, breaches of trust by the clerks, and the expenses of the headquarters office in the Netherlands had greatly decreased the profits. Above all, continuous armed intervention in the native states had entailed enormous expense, for the Company maintained an army of 46,000 men, including 20,000 Europeans. Lastly, war with England had brought on an economic slump which forced the Dutch Government to take over the Company. Though the other great East India Company, the English, survived for fifty years longer, it does not seem to have owed its survival to greater skill on the part of its directors or to the less conspicuous corruption of its agents, but to the fact that the great precocity of the industrial revolution in Great Britain had caused a fairly large number of Englishmen to be interested in the prosperity of India.

Besides, at least since the Regulating Act of 1773, the English East India Company had had its sovereignty much curtailed by the encroachment of the State. Its acts were subject to control by Parliament, and vehement protests were often raised in that body against the corruption and pride of the Company's agents. That was why Sir Stamford Raffles, a former employee of the English Company's, introduced a new spirit into the administration of Java, which after the conquest of the island was entrusted to him from 1811 to 1815. The Dutch themselves considered his period of office as a decisive stage in the history of Indonesia. As energetic as his immediate predecessor Daendels, the former Jacobin chosen in 1807 by King Louis of Holland, he had more tact, culture, and imagination, was very interested in the various types of local civilisation, and full of sympathy with the natives. Hence, he studied the history and language of the country and frowned on all feudal oppression, whether on the part of the native rulers or the Colonial Government. His programme, moreover, reflected the economic tendencies which were being developed in England by the industrial revolution and which ended in the triumph of liberal ideas. English cotton cloth was to be sold in Indonesia as well as in India; so let the natives grow rich. Free trade was encouraged as well as the use of metallic money. Raffles created a system of land-taxes which was applied slowly and was often modified, but nevertheless remained the key to the financial structure of Java.

State Controlled Cultivation. After the return of the East Indies to the Netherlands there was a period of transition lasting from 1815 to 1830. Great Britain, to whom Singapore had been handed by Raffles in 1819, kept and even strengthened her commercial superiority in the islands. Governors like Du Bus, a convert to liberal ideas, tried to encourage the production of coffee, sugar, indigo, and tea by means of free settlements of Europeans; but many considered it difficult to compete profitably with the slave-holding colonies in America. Du Bus's programme was still far from realisation in 1820 when van den Bosch reached the East Indies and set up the far different system which bears his name— Cultuurstelsel, or the system of forced cultivation.

Van den Bosch has often been regarded as the incarnation of the darkest oppression and ruthless colonial exploitation.[1] The truth is quite different. His many apologists here pictured him as a philanthropist who believed in the advantages of a strictly regulated economic system. Raffles's term of office had no doubt strengthened State authority at the expense of interests vested in powerful native or foreign oligarchies. But Raffles wanted no more monopolies or privileges. So long as liberals saw in Raffles one of their glorious forerunners, van den Bosch was decried by them. He introduced nothing new, but merely improved and organised. The system of forced cultivation to which he has given his name had been practised by the Company and by the harsh Daendels. Even Raffles had not abolished its operation in coffee production in Prianger. The new feature in Indonesia was that the State took the place of the Company. But crops had been monopolised by the State in other places, as was the case particularly with tobacco in Luzón at the end of the preceding century.

Until then the Philippines had had a commercial system rather different from that in Indonesia. Foreigners were far more strictly excluded. But in spite of their efforts, the trading companies in Spain (in Cadiz in particular) had only a small share in the trade. Most of the profits went to Spaniards living in Luzón, nearly all of whom were in Manila and were either merchants or ecclesiastical bodies, which lent funds on terms of bottomry, or a share in the venture, usually amounting to 50 per cent. Other people could also have a share in the galleon's cargo, and the badly and irregularly paid officials found compensation in this. *Alcaldes*, or provincial governors, could, if they gave up a portion of their emoluments, keep a certain percentage of the tribute they collected, whether in cash or kind, and use it for trading. This was a source of annoyance to the natives. Goods carried by the *nao* to New Spain were after keen competition sold to Mexican merchants at a profit which went as high as 200 per cent.[2] The goods consisted far more of merchandise bought in China than of Philippine produce. In 1782, however, the great Spanish Governor José Basco took steps to impose strict

[1] There is an interesting discussion of this by E. Chassigneux (190 *bis*).
[2] Mallat (177), II, p. 148.

control on the production as well as on the industrial preparation and sale of tobacco. Cultivation was restricted to the Kagayán valley and the north-west coast, and there every peasant was to grow 4000 plants and to sell his crop to State buying-centres. The administration of the monopoly was entrusted to a special minister, who every year fixed the dates of ploughing, planting out, and other work. Low grade produce was destroyed, and punitive expeditions were sent against refractory communities.

This arrangement was due not only to an effort to improve the economic system, but also to a political programme. Formerly, the Philippine budget, which had always showed a deficit, had been balanced only by means of subsidies termed *situados*, that were regularly paid by New Spain, which country took advantage of the payment to squeeze the Philippine Government. The islands now aimed at becoming independent of Mexico, whose approaching breach with Spain was foreseen. In the end this aim was achieved. The tobacco monopoly made the reputation of the Philippine product which was worth so much to the Colonial Government that it not only covered the cost of administering the government of the islands, but also enabled Spain to derive considerable profits. In 1866–7 when the expenditure of the islands was 4,500,000 Mexican dollars, the monopoly brought in 8,400,000 dollars.[1]

The Spanish system was carefully studied by the Dutch officials. But in the traditional and recent institutions in Java certain practices might be regarded as foreshadowing the new system. The power of the Javanese feudal lords was based on payments in kind levied on the peasants by virtue of the *adat*, or custom. The new Colonial Government had only to assume those feudal rights and duties. In some districts the peasants were already handing over part of their farm produce to private enterprises which paid their taxes for them. In the Preanger districts the taxes were actually paid in kind, mainly coffee, directly to Government agents. In short, it was merely a question of applying the procedure generally. The champions of the system and van den Bosch himself claimed that it would help both the Netherlands and the natives. The Netherlands, indeed, needed money, because their expenditure had greatly increased since the secession of Belgium in 1830–31. Java would, in fact, be merely paying her dues, whilst on the other hand the shipping, commerce, and industry of the Netherlands would be benefiting.

So it was decreed that the Javanese should hand over for export a fixed quantity of agricultural produce roughly equal to the yield from sixty-six days' work in the year. In return for this they had

---

[1] Details are given in Kolb (175), p. 280. For the tobacco monopoly about 1840, see Mallat (177), I, pp. 139 ff; II, p. 22.

their taxes remitted and in addition received a small payment. In principle one-fifth of the fields of every *dessa* was to be reserved for this forced cultivation; but in fact that area was often, especially in the case of sugarcane, alienated to European or Chinese contractors who undertook to feed those liable to forced labour. The Dutch administration turned itself into a gigantic agricultural undertaking. In 1856 there were only six hundred Europeans in Java who were not officials. The main task of the officials was to supervise the carrying out of the detailed regulations governing cultivation and see that the crop was prepared and stored in Government warehouses. They depended directly on the yields for their emoluments and rate of promotion.[1] As a reward for zeal native officials were guaranteed the inheritance of their land. The Government got rid of its stocks through the Nederlandsche Handelmaatschappij.

In several ways the system fulfilled expectations. After working expenses had been covered, there remained a clear sum, or *batig slot*, which was at first considerable and went into the Netherlands treasury. This quickly relieved the Dutch budget 'as if by a magician's wand'.[2] The home country was able to improve its canal system and to hasten the construction of its railways and of the fortifications on the Belgian frontier. In the years 1861–66 the contributions from Indonesia reached their peak. The Dutch merchant marine benefited even more than the British from the increase in exports, thanks to a preferential tariff. Amsterdam regained its colonial trade, great sales took place twice a year, and for about fifty years the town became the chief market in Europe for coffee and sugar. A cotton industry developed in the district of Twente in Gelderland. At first these results together with the commission granted to officials and the profits of those engaged in private enterprise hid the drawbacks of the system from the eyes of most Europeans both in the Netherlands and Indonesia.

There really were drawbacks.[3] The system was certainly praised in its day by well-informed, far-seeing observers like F. Junghuhn and A. R. Wallace. But slavery also found its eulogists on the plantations in America. The fact is, the system soon led to abuses, and all the basic principles laid down by van den Bosch in the famous No. 22 issue of the Official Journal for 1834 were violated. The area under export crops was extended beyond the expected limits under official pressure. At times not merely a fifth, but as much as one-third or one-half of the land, in places the whole of the irrigated soil, came to be put at the disposal of the sugar-mills. Instead of sixty-six days of work, as much as two hundred and forty

[1] Gonnaud (192), p. 494.   [2] Furnivall (15), p. 127.
[3] Van der Kolff in Schrieke (20), pp. 107 ff.

days and more were exacted per annum without counting unpaid forced labour on the construction of roads, ports, and buildings needed by the system. The meagre payments made for the crops varied with the prices of the produce and might fall to nothing. In spite of promises, the land-tax continued to be levied and was even doubled inside fifteen years. The chief crops demanded of forced labour were coffee, tobacco, sugar, indigo, tea, and pepper. They were often unsuited to the soil. Lacking space and time, the peasant neglected his food crops and adopted varieties of rice that grew quickly, but gave a smaller yield. Rice was even exported from this populous island. The alarm was sounded by the famine which laid waste the Cheribon district in 1843, when thousands of families moved away, leaving exhausted members behind by the roadside. Later on, famine hit the districts of Demak and Grobogan to the east of Semarang.

Yet in Java as a whole the material life of the native does not seem to have been worsened during the course of van den Bosch's system, in spite of the increase in population.[1] The famous saying: 'Men are born, married, and die on the indigo plantations' has certainly been repeated too often. It must be remembered that Western Europe has not been free from harvest failures and dearth. A potato famine laid Ireland waste in 1847 and the Netherlands themselves in 1845–6. In eastern Java where the area devoted to food crops was not unfairly reduced, sugarcane has brought new means of earning a living, for many natives live by moving the crop to the mill in their carts. The cultivation of soya and maize in rotation has spread, and rice has begun to benefit from the improvements which European skill and knowledge have made in the irrigation system. The first scientific institutes dealing with agriculture were established at this time. The native was taught new processes and methods of production. He was certainly not anxious to learn, but he gained something from the teaching. The van den Bosch system helps to explain the admirable variety of exports from Indonesia. It has been praised by many foreign observers, notably Money,[2] an Englishman, who wished to see it applied in India.

However, since it was discredited by its abuses and because it encouraged exactions by native chiefs, van den Bosch's system was violently attacked by people with liberal ideas, who reproached it, not without reason, for reviving slavery and stifling in the natives all feeling of personal dignity and all initiative. Hence, it seems to have been condemned by 1850, but it broke up gradually and took a long time to die. Legislative power over Indonesia had been transferred

1 Furnivall (115), pp. 130 ff.   2 Money (196).

in 1848 from the King to the States General, so that from then on colonial policy was no longer decided in secret council. The payment of commission to officials was abolished, and about 1860 State cultivation of tea, cinnamon, pepper, tobacco, and indigo came to an end in Java. Indigo had been the only success, whilst cotton, silk, and cochineal had failed. Coffee, sugar, and Peruvian bark went on longer in Java, as did pepper in the backland of Benkulen in Sumatra. Until 1877 coffee furnished at least 80 per cent. of the profits drawn by the Netherlands from Indonesia: the reduction of the area under the crop cultivated by the Colonial Government did not begin till 1892, nor was it completed before about 1916. The abolition of the system in sugar cultivation was gradual from 1879 onwards, one-twelfth of the area being given up every year. Indonesia's contributions to the Netherland's budget did not stop till 1878, but as early as 1870 less of the goods exported was produced by State cultivation than by private enterprise.

At the same period the official monopoly in tobacco had also been severely attacked in the Philippines. It was suppressed at the end of 1882 after a series of risings among producers, who were not paid in cash, but in treasury notes. The profits from State control had in fact been transferred to Spain, whose finances were heavily encumbered. The cigar and cigarette factories in Manila and its neighbourhood were closed and the stocks sold. As in the Dutch possessions, the system of State control had not had only ill effects, since the Philippines entered the world economic organisation under its influence.

Progressive Ideas and Capital. The triumph of progressive ideas was in short not complete in Indonesia until after the opening of the Suez Canal and the great improvement of navigation due to the introduction of steam. It was, moreover, something like the consolidation of British supremacy on the seas, for the merchant navy of the United Kingdom kept its long lead in the Indian and Pacific Oceans. After fifty years of British rule, owing to its position at the gateway to the Malay world and the Far East, Singapore clearly benefited by the cutting of the Egyptian isthmus. In 1867 the Straits Settlements had escaped from the clutches of the Government of India and had become a Crown Colony under the Colonial Office. The Treaty of Pangkor signed in 1874 opened the way to the establishment of a British Protectorate over the Malay States on the Peninsula and to the control of the tin market. The struggle to suppress piracy was intensified and became more effective. In 1873 war was declared on Achin by the Netherlands. Dutch occupation of Sumatra advanced slowly, painfully, and at great expense. Only after 1880 did the Netherlands Government recognise that the extension of its territorial sovereignty would perhaps not be ruinous,[1] and it was only at the beginning of the 20th century that the policy of intervention was widely applied in the Outer Provinces.

Security on the seas and penetration into new countries were twin designs dictated to the Western nations by their hunger for raw materials to feed their industries and supply the demands of their swarms of workers. The fulfilment of these aims increased the great attraction the Malay world had for Europe, owing to its fertile soil and good climate and above all to its profusion of people with a low standard of living close to the resources to be worked.

After this the investment of capital increased rapidly. But the flow was irregular, since it was interrupted by economic crises. In Malaya most of it went into tin-mining until the end of the century. The share that fell to agriculture was much greater in Java, an island with long experience, in which private firms had succeeded directly to the ownership of the State plantations, particularly those producing coffee, tobacco, and, above all, sugar. On the east coast of Sumatra tobacco cultivation spread round Medan. Of the foreign firms established in Indonesia the greatest profits went to the British. In the Philippines Spanish and English capital invested in the sugar business and, after the abolition of the monopoly, in tobacco went less into cultivation than into the industries preparing commodities for the market.

Commerce and transport also called for action. The construction of railways in Java and Sumatra was shared by the Colonial administration and private companies, and the great shipping firm, the K.P.M., was founded in 1888 to trade with the East Indies.

The years 1884–90 were a time of crisis owing to diseases in the coffee plants and sugarcane, to the competition of beet sugar with the latter, and to the MacKinley tariffs which shut out certain commodities from the United States, notably Philippine tobacco. In Indonesia the outcome of this was a concentration of capital, a trend which was to be completed in the 20th century. Small and middle-sized firms became absorbed or dominated by powerful companies like the Deli Maatschappij, which dealt with tobacco in Sumatra. Big banks with head offices in the Netherlands played an outstandingly important part in this concentration, themselves controlling many firms.[2] In Java, as in Cuba, the banks took over a large part of the sugar industry, for the mills received loans during

---

[1] Cp. the significant statements of the Colonial Minister in 1861, reported by Middendorp in Schrieke (20), p. 42, thus: 'I consider every extension of our authority to be another step towards ruin'; and in 1872: 'The expansion of our territorial possessions is neither our desire nor our aim'.

[2] For the work of the banks, see Furnivall (15), pp. 197, 335, and *passim*.

the crisis and were unable to pay their debts. Amsterdam fixed prices, allowing the Surabaya Syndicate, which acted as a clearing house, in its turn to fix the prices paid to the mills. These prices could be modified from month to month.

Scientific methods of cultivation and close attention to the world market made agricultural production more and more varied. Sugar and coffee no longer headed the list of exports from Indonesia, and Java tea won a place in Anglo-Saxon markets. The development of the motor vehicle involved an expansion of rubber production, first in Malay and later in Java. The overcrowded island no longer offered adequate horizons to the visions of business men, who therefore strongly urged the effective occupation of the Outer Provinces. The subjection of the archipelago was almost complete in 1909. Export crops, both European and native, spread quickly in Borneo, Celebes, and, above all, Sumatra, where the prosperity of tobacco and rubber was followed by success with palm-oil, tea, and sisal.

In 1939 Malaya was firmly anchored to its two chief resources, rubber and tin. It had, however, added palm-oil and pine-apples. In Indonesia the development of mining (tin, which had long been worked, and petroleum) had gone hand in hand with that of agriculture. In the Philippines the United States guardianship had, since the beginning of the present century, given unequal encouragement to the traditional products. In spite of the establishment of plantations in Mindanao, especially by Americans and Japanese, *abacá* lost its lead to coconut products and, by a long way, to sugar, which since 1909 had had the advantage of tariff protection in the United States. Thanks mainly to gold, mineral exports advanced to second place in the list of exports from the islands.

It is certainly not a mistake to see in the economic system of the Malay world one of the great triumphs of European capital and liberal ideas within the tropics. Yet such a view is too simplified and must be modified by a few comments. It would apply least inaccurately to Malaya, considering the freedom of ports like Penang and Singapore, which have been wide open to international trade and to the immigration of Chinese and Indian labour, and considering the racial upheaval caused by this immigration in the Peninsula. The Colonial Government seemed to be there only to preside over the development of a prosperity which the power of Great Britain and the position of the Peninsula seemed to make inevitable without further control. Liberal ideas in keeping with both her ideals and her commercial advantage appealed most to Great Britain who had command of the sea and a long start in industry. Of course, certain intellectuals like J. S. Mill, Cobden, and Bright carried doctrines to an extreme and advocated the relinquishment of colonies so as to abolish all economic privileges. As may be imagined, these notions were not put into practice.

It is strange that liberal ideas in economics should have been adopted by the Dutch also, since their position was very different from that of the English. There were several reasons for their adoption. First, the Netherlands were too small to develop Indonesia. They therefore welcomed foreign capitalists, technicians, scientists, and even officials along with their own. Their tariff policy was much like the open door principle and was in strong contrast with Spanish methods in the Philippines even after 1850.

It must be noted, however, that Dutch liberalism was much less consistent than the English. In Indonesia different economic policies followed each other, stepping on each other's heels, and even falling over one another. These were all praised by some and criticised by others and had their share of honour or blame in the situation as it finally was in 1939. After a first trial by Du Bus, a period of liberalism followed on the system of forced labour in about 1870. But as early as the beginning of the 20th century there was a growing tendency to return to a policy of increased State control. The new system was very different, however, from the one that bears van den Bosch's name. The well-being, if not the happiness, of the native was promoted to first place among the duties of the Colonial Government. Welfare surveys were set up to review his material circumstances. But these brought no obvious improvement; in fact, there is evidence that the native was worse off than before.[1] This raised the question, therefore, whether wealth was increasing at a slower rate than population.

The raising of the standard of living of the native was not only the main feature in the programme of idealistic philanthropists, young administrators fired by the protests of *Multatuli*,[2] and engineers fresh from Delft and imbued with scientific socialism;[3] it also seemed at the same time to chime in with definite interests. Nationalism was developing in Indonesia under the fostering wing of the Colonial Government. The Malay language, which was used in Government schools, spread everywhere; and the increased speed

[1] For the conclusions from this evidence and for the subjective appreciation subjoined, see Furnivall (15), pp. 393 ff. The most complete survey was, however, van Deventer's, published in 1904.

[2] *Multatuli* was the pen-name of E. Douwes Dekker, a former official in Java, whose book 'Max Havelaar' (pub. 1850) aroused much anger in the Netherlands and contributed to the abolition of the van den Bosch system. See Furnivall: *Netherlands India*, C.U.P., 1944, p. 161 and *passim*.

[3] Furnivall (15) p. 226.

and ease of communications between the islands and the extension of Dutch ascendency awakened in a few select persons the feeling of belonging to a common fatherland, a feeling which sometimes led to a dislike of Europeans. In the Netherlands, and in the district of Twente in particular, industrialists demanded outlets for their manufactures and called for an increase in purchasing power among the natives. Their employees agreed with them on this point, since they were afraid of the competition of cheap labour in the Far East.

From these various sources came the influence which led to the establishment of the 'ethical policy' whose principles were set forth by Brooshoft in 1921. Some Dutchmen like van Deventer went as far as to claim the return to Indonesia of all the sums paid to the Netherlands, the *batig slot* formerly derived from the produce of forced labour, and constituting in their eyes a debt of honour. Many economists insisted on the need to keep in Indonesia a greater part of the profits made out of their soil by the labour of their people. They stated that the despatch to Europe of interest on invested capital deprived the islands of goods which ought to have been kept for their own enrichment.

Private Capital and State Investment. The capital invested has been considerable, though its accurate calculation is difficult.[1] The data for Indonesia are the least unreliable.[2] On the eve of the recent war the total amount of foreign and Dutch capital invested in the islands was 4,800,000,000 florins, of which 3,500,000,000 had gone into private enterprises and 1,300,000,000 into central and local government loans. In 1900 the total invested was estimated at about 750,000 florins and in 1915 at 1,500,000,000. Dutch statistics have accurately determined the sources and destinations of this great stream of loans. The share invested by others than Dutchmen is significant, as is also the preponderance of agricultural undertakings.

In contrast with the Dutch, who were heavily handicapped by the privileges granted to the Nederlandsche Handel-maatschappij English firms to some extent kept their business going under the system of forced labour. By the time this system was abolished the English were firmly established and had profited largely from the opportunities afforded to private firms. English banks opened branches in Indonesia, where English investors were particularly interested in tea and rubber. About 1912 fifty out of one hundred and one rubber plantations in Java were British.

[1] See Callis (190). This is the latest information and is based on English documents.
[2] See Furnivall (15), particularly pp. 309–12; Broek (187), pp. 31–3.

Foreign capital, however, was invested mainly in the newly developing areas in the Outer Provinces. During the war of 1914–18 the Dutch were able to gain on their rivals. Their investments were far larger than any others in Java, where in 1929 the non-Dutch share of capital was estimated at 16·1 per cent., sugar production being almost exclusively in Dutch hands. The percentage was 36·8 in south Sumatra and 44·1 in Oostkust, where the only commodity to be almost a Dutch monopoly was tobacco. In 1939, of the capital invested in private firms in Indonesia as a whole 66 per cent. was estimated to be Dutch, 10 per cent. British,[1] 6·8 per cent. American, and 3·4 per cent. Franco-Belgian, the remainder being mainly Japanese, German, and Swiss.[2] It must be noted, however, that the Dutch figures include investments made by Eurasians, which are small, and also by Chinese, which appear to be barely less than those of the English.

Foreign capital was a great help not only in developing the plantations in the Outer Provinces, but also in working the oilfields and in establishing the industries preparing commodities for the market.[3] Between 1929 and 1939 European capital invested in oil amounted to about 61 per cent. of the total.[4] About four-fifths of the interest from the Indo-Dutch public debt went to Dutch investors, the remainder to British or American stock-holders.

Information about capital investment in the Malay Peninsula is less complete. [Capital was first attracted to tin-mining; but the demands of the rubber, oil palm, coconut, and pine-apple plantations have in the end become greater than those of the mines. About 1937 it was estimated that more than £120,000,000 had been invested in the rubber business. The British definitely held the lion's share in both mines and agriculture. After them came the Chinese. Yet the way was not barred to others like the French.

In the Philippines State capital as well as foreign investments, American and others, was put not so much into agriculture itself as into industries preparing the produce for market, and in particular into sugar-refining, drying and grating coconut, the preparation of

[1] The British percentage was estimated at 30 in rubber and 20 in tea and coffee.

[2] Non-Dutch capital was especially large in rubber (English, American, Franco-Belgian), palm oil (American and Franco-Belgian), and tea (English) plantations. About 1928, between the wars, American capital exceeded the Franco-Belgian.

[3] See Furnivall (15), p. 435. But the capital invested in textile and metallurgical industries in Indonesia since 1930 was mainly Dutch.

[4] See details in Furnivall (15), p. 311, and Broek (187), p. 32. These investments were mainly American and English. Of the capital of the company formed to undertake a very exhaustive and scientific search for oil in Dutch New Guinea 60 per cent. was American. (See Ter Braake (237), p. 68.) Scarcely anything is known about investments in other mining enterprises.

copra, tobacco, *abacá*, and into rice-mills, sawmills, etc.[1] United
States investments in State loans and in private enterprises were
valued in about 1944 at only 250,000,000 dollars. This represents
60 per cent. of the total foreign investments in the Philippines,
30 per cent. of the American investments in the Far East, and
1 per cent. of all American investments abroad.

The Dutch Government, it is true, had never quite handed over
the exploitation of Indonesia to private intitiative. Enterprises
under State control included not only monopolies like those in
opium and salt, some of the railways. the docks and harbours, the
supply of electricity, and posts and telegraphs, but also the mines.
Under the East India Company the Dutch. contrary to Spanish
practice in America, were content to buy mineral products from the
native chiefs. But in 1812 the Sultan of Palembang ceded his rights
in Banka and Belitong to the English Crown, whose representative
made a contract with Chinese miners to work the tin deposits in
Banka. The ownership of these mines was transferred in 1816 to
the Dutch Government, which reserved to itself the exclusive rights
to mineral workings in Indonesia until 1850. After this date
private initiative was encouraged, as it was in the business of agriculture. But the regulations of 1910 amended the mining ordinance
of 1899 and gave the Colonial Government greater scope for
engaging in mining. The regulations of 1918 went even further.
The object was not only to support the Treasury, but also to prevent
excessive removal of wealth from the colony. By the amendment
of 1918 the Colonial Government could reserve to itself the prospecting for and working of all combustible minerals, whether solid,
liquid, or gaseous. In 1940 three mines were being worked by the
Government, two coal-mines at Bukit Asem and Ombilin in Sumatra
and the tin deposits in Banka. Besides this, the Government held part
of the shares in other enterprises like the tin-mines in Belitong and
the oilfield at Jambi.[2] In the list of profits from industry presented
in recent colonial budgets Banka tin took first place. The parcelling
out and exploitation of teak forests began about the middle of the
last century under private initiative; but a regulation of 1897 foreshadowed the gradual disappearance of free enterprise and the
extension of official control, which is now complete. On the other
hand, State plantations had been gradually reduced and in 1937

[1] See the table in Kolb (175), p. 344.

[2] In good years the profits earned by the State from the tin-mines amounted
to between 40,000,000 and 50,000,000 florins, i.e. one-tenth of the budget for
ordinary expenditure. (Broek (187), p. 48.) The Colonial Government also
participated in the recent working of bauxite and nickel-mines. After 1939 the
threat of war had induced the Government to give direct help to many industries
which prepared commodities for the market. (Id., p. 79.)

comprised no more than about 50,000 acres, which represented barely more than experimental stations.

Recent Government Control. Though the agricultural enterprises privately owned by Europeans no longer seemed to be threatened by Government monopolies, they did not regard the growing competition of the natives without anxiety, for the latter's share in the value of the exports was fast increasing. The Governments were bound to take a different view, since they had to consider the betterment of native life and the happiness and well-being of free peasants to be the chief aim of Colonial administration and the White Man's burden. Since the petty cultivator, or *tani*, had little means, was lacking in forethought, and had no experience of the world market, he had to be aided by the Colonial Governments, even though the old liberal principles were violated and the big planters inconvenienced.

The peasant's lot was not the only thing that required the constant attention of the Governments. The world depression reached the Malay lands in 1929 and led the Colonial Governments to interfere more and more in the realm of economics. Great was the sorrow of those who held liberal views, and both English and Dutch set out unwillingly along the path of intervention. But they could not refuse to do so in the face of a 20 per cent. fall in the volume of exports between 1929 and 1931 in Indonesia as well as Malaya and of a catastrophic drop in prices. In 1934 copra was worth no more than one-fifth of its value in 1929, and rubber suffered even more. Customs duties were therefore revised so as to tighten the bonds with Great Britain and the Netherlands. Production itself was regulated in an effort to ensure a permanent balance between export and food crops, to lessen the amount of imports from abroad, and to introduce an economic system restricted to the Empire, whilst giving the colonies the opportunity of themselves satisfying their essential needs. Restrictions were also placed on the entry of foreigners. It was characteristic of the Dutch, however, that they hesitated to share in plans for international control, like the Stevenson plan for rubber and the Chadbourne plan for sugar.[1]

In many ways the evolution of the Philippines remained as peculiar after the American conquest as it had been under the Spaniards. The free trade instituted in 1909 had entailed a closer and closer dependence of the colony on the United States. At the same time under the combined pressure of private interests and lofty ideals a keen opposition appeared in the States to the free entry of Philippine produce and more especially of the chief one, namely, sugar. At the very moment when the islands could no longer do without the

[1] Cecile Rhote (199).

American market a programme of modified political self-government was painfully elaborated in such a way as to end in the almost complete independence of the Philippines. These plans were assisted by the fact that relatively to Malaya and Indonesia large plantations played a very much smaller part here than did native production.

CHAPTER 17

PLANTATIONS AND SCIENTIFIC AGRICULTURE

The word 'plantation' is used here to mean an agricultural concern which exploits a fairly large area and is not under native management. Natives are connected with it only as wage-earners. It operates mainly for export, usually with an agricultural technique which differs greatly from that of the natives and with methods that may be termed scientific. Plantations, as thus defined, have nowhere else had such great success as in the Malay world.

There are several causes of this. Among them must certainly be included the climate, which owing to differences in relief and aspect offers a considerable range, from equatorial uniformity to a tropical type with clearly marked wet and dry seasons. Owing to volcanic action the soil itself is more fertile than in the average tropical country. But the decisive factor seems to be the abundance, docility, and relative skill of the labour available. Even today, in spite of the careful organisation of recruitment, it sometimes happens that a plantation which is poor in soil, but easily able to get the necessary labour, will give a better yield than another which has the advantage of fertile soil, but is far distant from an adequate source of labour. The wealth of man-power in certain parts of the Malay lands, particularly Java, Luzón, some of the Visayas, and a few little Molucca islands (in which the population was replaced by forced immigration of labour from other islands), was the chief cause of the restriction of European attention to them alone for so long.

PLANTATIONS

Jan Pieterszoon Coen, the first Governor General to reside in Batavia (1619–1629),[1] planned to increase the number of European smallholders in Java and to establish a kind of peasantry of European stock.[2] But the Dutch East India Company soon found it more expedient for the increase of its trade to use natives as labour either by putting pressure on the chiefs, who were obliged to pay tribute in kind, or else by buying up estates whose dispossessed inhabitants became mere serfs. The Company freely granted to individuals the rights which it claimed for itself over land and labour. Thus, a

[1] Previously the Governor had had no fixed residence, but was often in the Moluccas.

[2] The idea of having recourse to Germans was mooted more than once. (Raynal (198), VI, p. 391.)

328

number of Europeans, mostly 'creoles ... or disappointed souls who had retired from the Company's service',[1] took to cultivating nutmegs in Banda and others to planting sugarcane in the plains of Java. The latter activity, however, seems to have been largely handed over in the 18th century to the management of Chinese who kept the mills working with canes delivered by the tenants.[2]

The Spaniards took to the Philippines the *encomienda* system which they had used in their American possessions. A large part of the land, and the best at that, was thus handed over with its natives to the ownership of the Roman Catholic Church or to Spanish or half-caste families, who were termed *Caciques*. The natives who cultivated the *encomiendas* were not hired labourers, but tenants of smallholdings, or *inquilinos*.[3] Certain plants which were introduced at this time into the Philippines from the New World were after a time to spread all over the East Indies. But the export of agricultural produce remained insignificant until the creation of a State monopoly in tobacco began to encourage the cultivation of the plant, which, however, was left in the hands of smallholders up to the end of the 18th century. Spanish inertia at this time caused Raynal to express regret and bitter criticism.[4]

⌠In short, it is scarcely possible to speak of real plantations in the Malay world before the 19th century.⌡ But they existed in the West Indies, tropical America, and the Mascarenhas Islands, which were nearer to Western Europe and had a supply of imported negro labour. The establishment of the independence of the American colonies, followed by the abolition of slavery, brought on a very serious crisis on plantations in the New World and attracted the attention of European investors to the immense possibilities of Indonesia. Just before its final downfall the Dutch East India Company had had to alienate a great deal of its plantations to Dutchmen or Chinese, and after the Company had been wound up the Government made further grants of its land. Between 1820 and 1830 the official tendency was to encourage privately-owned European plantations for the production of export crops; but the realisation of this aim was hindered by the organisation of State plantations meant to give quick relief to the financial difficulties of the Netherlands. Private enterprises which survived between 1830 and 1850 were exposed to vexatious interference by officials of the Cultuur system, who secretly forbade labourers to work for the private owners and requisitioned the labour at times, especially seed-time and harvest, when there was great pressure of work. The planters suffered from tiresome formalities and even malicious spoliation.

1 Raynal (198), I, p. 313.   2 Van Hall (215).
3 Mallat (177), II, p. 255.   4 Raynal (198), III, p. 111.

The protests of the injured parties contributed to the failure of van den Bosch's system between 1850 and 1870. This was the period during which the great industrial countries felt their appetite rapidly increasing for tropical raw materials and in which the cutting of the Suez Canal and improvements in navigation brought the Far East nearer to Europe. Plantations benefited by all these favourable factors and went on to develop their own special characteristics.

The efforts of progressively minded persons, one of the most eminent of whom was Fransen van de Putte, a Minister of State, led to the Agrarian Law of 1870, which became the basic charter of colonial policy in Indonesia. Land sold to individuals by the Company or the Government had almost all been bought back before the outbreak of war in 1941. In 1938 only 1,235,500 acres remained in private hands, and, besides, this area was partly given up to the food crops of the more than a million natives living on it. It was mainly all in the Residencies of Jakarta and Buitenzorg (Bogor), which were the oldest districts of European settlement in Java.

The Law did not trust the native's forethought and so forbade him to sell his land to a settler (whether Dutchman or not). Since its enactment the settler has been able to acquire only his garden and the ground on which stand his house and the buildings required for his work. The rest has had to be rented on terms approved by the Colonial Government. Unoccupied Crown lands were let on long leases, generally of seventy-five years' duration, a period judged sufficient for amortisation and the realisation of reasonable profit. The area needed for the increasingly extensive native crops was to be carefully reserved. Anxiety to safeguard the future of the natives and to save them from their own thoughtlessness was evident in this legislation. But it was bitterly criticised by the settlers, who accused it of being an obstacle to the development of small- and average-sized European plantations and of hindering the growth of a settled White population.

In Malaya, where the native population is not nearly so large as it is in Java, the grant of agricultural concessions was not so strictly regulated. Reserves had been arranged; but, outside these, the Crown lands might be bought outright on condition that a land-tax was paid and the land developed.

On the other hand, American legislation in the Philippines was still more hostile than the Dutch in Indonesia to the alienation of culti-vable land to settlers. The laws have often been modified since the beginning of the present century; but in principle the area granted to an individual or a company may not exceed 2500 acres.

In no part of the Malay world was the settlement of European smallholders systematically encouraged by the Colonial Governments. Hence, such people played but a tiny part in production as a whole. Of the thousand 'European' smallholders in Indonesia the majority were half-castes, 'Indos', and nearly all lived in Java.[1] They eked out a living on properties averaging some 25 acres, growing food crops and in addition one or two export crops including coffee or less often coconuts, teak, kapok, cinchona, rubber, or tobacco. Some of them kept livestock and tilled market gardens in the mountains around Bandung, Malang, and elsewhere, so as to supply the towns with milk, fresh meat, and vegetables. They rarely tilled the soil with their own hands, but employed a few natives to do the work. Under the Dutch régime they insistently advocated a change in the Agrarian Law to permit them to become owners of the property that had been granted to them or which they had rented. The Indo-Europeesch Verbond, which includes not only half-castes, but also Europeans born in the East Indies or having children born there and wishing to stay there, had with the Government's support striven to form associations of smallholders. Success had been achieved in the Residencies of Besuki and the Lampongs between 1600 and 2300 feet above the sea on soil congenial to the coffee bush.[2] The White smallholders were still less numerous in Malaya and the Philippines, where they were as a rule petty officials or retired soldiers.

Most of the plantation area consisted of properties exceeding 120 acres in extent. Properties of up to 750 acres might be worked by individuals or a few partners, but beyond that plantations were nearly always owned by joint stock companies. The capital sunk in these concerns was considerable.[2]

The distribution of plantations had changed since the beginning. Up to about 1870 there were scarcely any outside the Moluccas (Banda and Amboina), Java, and a few places in western Sumatra. At that time they were certainly most extensive in Java. After 1870 they continued to increase in this fortunate island, but they also grew in number on both sides of the Straits of Malacca; and in 1938 the largest concentrations were situated in the Oostkust of Sumatra and the western side of the Malay Peninsula.

Java. In Java 7 per cent. of the land under cultivation[3] was occupied by plantations,[4] and the variety of produce and of methods of exploitation remained greatest in this, the chief island, with its long experience as a colony. Two facts not unconnected with each

[1] Cp. Fuchs (212); van Hall (215). [2] See above, p. 324.
[3] 1,452,155 acres in 1937. [4] Robequain (200), pp. 37–57.

other stand out in the process of evolution. First, during the 19th century the cultivation of tea, cinchona, and rubber was added to the long-established crops of sugar, coffee, and tobacco; secondly, the plantations on the hills and mountains (*Bergkulturen*) have ended by becoming more important than those on the lowlands. Rubber covered the largest area (557,000 acres), after which came tea (259,000 acres), coffee (223,000 acres), sugarcane (206,000 acres), tobacco (73,000 acres), kapok (57,000 acres), cinchona (38,000 acres), coconut (18,000 acres), cacao (15,000 acres), pepper (6,000 acres), nutmegs (4000 acres), elastic from *ficus elastica*, gutta-percha, coca, palm oil, gambier, and plants yielding essential oils.

Relations with the wage-earning labour differed with the district and crop, but depended mainly on local density of population. Sugarcane was still the chief crop in the lowlands of Mid and East Java. The value of the sugar exported from the island was only slightly less in 1937 than that of rubber. All the right conditions were combined here to favour the chief and oldest crop grown on tropical plantations: viz. rich soil, plenty of rain interrupted by a dry season, and, above all, a superabundant population. The last factor was particularly appreciated after the abolition of slavery, but had already been widely used under van den Bosch's system. After the coming into force of the reforms introduced by the Agrarian Law of 1870 a remarkable compromise was set up under strict official control between the native economic system and the capitalist concerns. By it canes were grown alternately with food crops on the most fertile and best irrigated soil, but occupied only a small part of the area cultivated, never as much as 5 per cent. of a whole residency or as much as 10 per cent. of the area of a canton. It was planted in the same field only once in three years, thus giving an opportunity in the interval for the cultivation of one or two crops of rice or unirrigated plants like maize or soya. During the twenty years, which is the usual period of lease, the soil was used for sugarcane in only six seasons each lasting from 15 to 18 months.[1]

The labour required for this intensive cultivation was recruited in neighbouring villages, to which the workers generally returned every evening. The needs of the plantation were irregular, being especially great between May and the end of October, when the cutting of the canes and the planting of the new crop took place simultaneously. But the system entailed no unemployment, since in the interval the

[1] Cp. however, the corrections made by van der Kolff (in Schrieke (20), p. 122) and Pelger (197a), p. 172. The influence of sugarcane plantations was much more widespread than is suggested by the area covered in any year. Owing to the rotation, they dominated some 20 to 25 per cent. of the *sawahs*, and the best of them at that.

peasant went back to his traditional crops. His wages and cash received from the rent of land to the sugar companies supplied an addition to his means. Nor was he cut off from the family circle.

Tobacco plantations were worked on a similar system, the crop being only a few months in the ground. The system was seen in the Jember district in East Java and in the Klaten district at the foot of Mt. Merapi, the most fertile parts of the island, where tobacco and cane cultivation went hand in hand.

In Java shrub plantations which will tolerate or prefer high ground used sometimes to be able to find the necessary labour near by. But requirements become harder to supply when the plantations climbed to more than 3250 feet, often occupying the former site of dense and uninhabited forest, or a place which had only been used for primitive collecting or for *ladang* cultivation by a sparse population. Some of the crops required a large additional supply of labour at certain seasons. For instance, the harvest might coincide with the busiest weeks in the calendar of the native cultivator. For all these reasons plantation managers had to recruit at least part of the workpeople in villages which were more or less remote from the plantations. In such cases the coolies were lodged in a kind of camp, an arrangement practised on rubber and coffee estates in East Java and on the rubber, tea, and cinchona plantations in the Prianger district. Most of the sugar exported from Java comes from districts in which the density of population exceeds 750 persons to the square mile. On the other hand, shrub plantations are often concentrated in places where the density falls below that figure. After the Bantam province, in which the soil is too poor for European enterprise, Buitenzorg in the west and Besuki in the extreme east are the two least densely-peopled provinces in Java with 492 and 501 persons to the square mile respectively. In 1938 these provinces also had the greatest percentage (20 and 18 respectively) under European crops out of the total area under cultivation.

The Oostkust. The population figures given above look still larger when they are compared with conditions which Dutch settlers found nearly all through the Outer Provinces. That is why settlement was so late in these islands. The greatest achievement and one which overshadows all others has occurred in the Oostkust. Medan, the capital of a little Malay sultanate in the north of the lowlands of Sumatra, was the centre of agricultural undertakings which were among the largest and most impressive of European successes in tropical lands.[1] In 1937 European plantations around the town covered about 900,000 acres. This was 73 per cent. of the total area

[1] See above, p. 165.

cultivated by Europeans in Sumatra and 65 per cent. of the European plantations in the whole of the Outer Provinces.[1] Between the belt of mangrove or coconuts along the shore and the slopes of the mountains of Batak, in low lying country where away from the river banks there used to be mostly dense forest and marsh, there spread today as far as the eye can see lines of rubber trees and oil palms divided into sections by the streams and roads. Other plants, including tea and sisal, had taken possession of the hills of Simelungen on the slopes going up towards Lake Toba. The oldest tobacco plantations in the Oostkust Province crowded round Medan. Cultivation of the crop is quite different here from in Java, since it needs a fallow lasting seven or eight years and is adapted to a different economic system and to a nearly uninhabited district.

In 1930 the density of population reached 45 to the square mile in the Oostkust. In about 1880 it must have been barely 5. In the intervening fifty years the number of Europeans, the general staff of this conquest, had risen from 522 to 11,079. These figures explain the transformation of the landscape and indicate the labour problems involved in the development of this practically virgin soil.

At first, the tobacco planters used Chinese labour recruited by agents in Penang and, later, Singapore. Then the Deli Planters' Union engaged them directly in Kwangtung and Fukien. Most of them were taken on board at Suchow by German boats until 1914, then by those of the Dutch K.P.M. In this way 305,000 Chinese landed at Belawan Deli between 1888 and 1931. Meanwhile, the tobacco planters had turned more and more to the reserves of manpower in Java, and others imitated them. Javanese emigration to the Outer Provinces was encouraged by the Colonial Government, which regarded it as an excellent remedy for overpopulation. Not so strong or hardworking as the Chinese, the Javanese fairly readily adapt themselves to the orderly work on a plantation, since they had already been trained in European undertakings in their native island. They could be entrusted with delicate tasks, quickly became skilful at tapping rubber trees, for instance, and could even be made into good *mandours*, or overseers. To start a plantation where dense forest must be cleared and burnt, the Batak was preferred to the Javanese, since he is unequalled in tree-felling and in carrying out the burning according to the wind. The sheds for drying tobacco were often made by Boyans, who came from the Bawean Islands between Borneo and Madura.

The recruitment of Javanese was at first left to special firms, and these used mostly to send vagabonds. But in 1916 the matter was

[1] The plantations of the whole of the *Buitengewesten* were scarcely equal to those in Java alone.

taken in hand by an organisation set up by a planters' association called the 'Adek' (= Algemeen Delisch Emigratie-Kantoor), which was subsidised by the Government. The arrangement was advertised in the villages, and especially those in Mid Java, by labourers who had already worked on the plantations. As emigration fluctuated with the demand for labour, it was very irregular. In times of crisis the returning labourers would now and then outnumber those emigrating, as happened in 1931. K.P.M. boats carried the emigrants from Surabaya, Jakarta, and Semarang. Under the indenture system instituted by the Coolie Ordinance of 1880 the labourer engaged to serve for three years and was guaranteed medical aid, food, wages, and a gratuity under Government supervision. But he was under the lash of special penal sanctions for breaches of the terms of his contract. However, after 1911 work termed 'free' took the place of the contract system more and more. The emigrant could choose the firm with which he was to work, leave it after giving notice, and discuss the terms of his contract. Official control of the treatment of labour continued, but it was becoming in fact unnecessary, for the conditions of labour on the plantations had greatly improved since the beginning of the century. In 1937 barely 10,000 indentured labourers remained in the Oostkust Province, and by 1950 there should have been none left. It was owing to the Oostkust Province of Sumatra that in 1937 the plantations in the Outer Provinces nearly equalled those in Java in area and slightly surpassed them in the value of their exports. Outside the Oostkust Achin had the greatest plantation area, 116,000 acres. No other province in the island had as much as 50,000 acres, nor did any other part of the Dutch East Indies, not even Borneo or Celebes, in which Minahassa had the lion's share. In the Lesser Sunda Islands there were slightly more than 5000 acres of plantation, and nearly 35,000 acres in the erstwhile famous Moluccas.

Malaya. Apart from tobacco, which had been introduced ages before, the rise of agriculture in the Oostkust accelerated chiefly after the beginning of the century with the boom in rubber. The province followed in the steps of Malaya with a slight lag. It was in the latter country that the Brazilian tree was persistently and patiently domesticated and achieved its most astonishing dissemination. When the first plants or seeds were imported at the end of last century, the agricultural exports from the Peninsula consisted only of sugar, spices, copra, and gambier. These products no longer count, so to speak, in Malayan trade, which on the other hand in 1938 supplied 41 per cent. of the world's consumption of rubber. Owing to the rise of other producers in Southeast Asia, including Indonesia and Indo-China, its relative share, which had been 50 per cent. in 1920 and 53 per cent. in 1929, had of course decreased; but it kept a leading place.

In 1937 rubber estates covered about 2,000,000 acres in Malaya. Most of them are situated in a belt some 30 miles wide and stretching out for about 500 miles from Singapore to the north of Wellesley Province opposite Penang. The western States from Johore to Kedah inclusive contain 91 per cent. of the area under rubber in the Peninsula.

For more than 20 years British and other European capital which has been in search of profitable investment in agriculture has been sunk in this industry. In Malaya there is none of that variety of plantation crops so noticeable in the Oostkust and even more in Java. However, since 1920 big firms have adopted the oil palm, as has been done in Sumatra, thus associating the produce of latex with the oil-bearing tree which seems most apt to profit from scientific cultivation and most favourable to the stability of European exploitation. At the end of 1937 the African oil palm covered only 70,000 acres in the Peninsula. Besides the foregoing, about one-third—perhaps some 20,000 acres—of the area under coconuts might be regarded as belonging to European or Chinese estates. Of the 74,000 acres under pine-apples by far the greater part was cultivated by Chinese. Coffee covered only 17,000 acres.

In Malaya the labour needed for the Peninsula's vast plantations could not be found on the spot, as they were in Java, or in a neighbouring island under the same government, as was done in the Oostkust, and the plantations were largely responsible for the immigration which has given its character to the population of Malaya. Chinese immigrants take various forms of employment, but a good many of them are employed on European plantations and formed about half the labour employed on estates in the former Straits Settlements and Johore. Elsewhere in the Peninsula Indian labourers were in the majority in 1937, where there were altogether 237,000 on the big Malayan plantations as against 77,000 Chinese, 23,000 peninsular Malays, and 13,000 Javanese. On every 100 acres under rubber there were 15 or 20 coolies, between 12 and 17 of whom were Indians, on the European concessions. The recruitment of Indians was one of the great troubles of plantation managers, who under the Kangani system often had all the responsibility, even in joint stock companies owning several estates and controlling several thousand acres.[1]

In Malaya middle-sized plantations were often controlled by agencies. These organisations by sending experts to the estates

[1] Since 1945 the percentage of Indians employed on the plantations has fallen off, to the advantage of the Chinese and Malays.

gave them the benefit of experiments and information which might otherwise have remained unknown to an isolated plantation. Each estate kept its financial independence, but the agency was itself often the owner of one or several plantations in the group it controlled.

So far as variously-based statistics allow of comparison, the position in 1941 in respect of European crops in Malaya, Sumatra, and Java was as follows. Malaya was definitely ahead of the two Dutch islands. Its plantations, counting the area under cultivation and not the whole of the concession, covered between 2,200,000 and 2,400,000 acres.[1] Java, whose plantations covered about 1,450,000 acres,[2] was closely followed by Sumatra with 1,250,000 acres. These figures showed a total of more than 5,000,000 acres under European plantation in this little corner of the Earth.

The Philippines. Plantations have not been equally successful elsewhere. The former Outer Provinces, without Sumatra, contained less than 150,000 acres. The Philippines, too, have not proved favourable to their development. This is due to historical as well as geographical causes. The Philippines are remote from the great route-foci of the Straits of Malacca and Sunda, around which the Colonial Powers have hitherto concentrated their efforts. The Spanish colonial system greatly aggravated the isolation of the islands. Other nations were jealously excluded by laymen and churchmen alike from Spain as well as by half-castes who wished to keep for themselves the advantages arising from the position of Manila as the go-between in the trade between China and the New World. The monks opposed the settlement of European colonists, since they were often unmanageable and argumentative (*gentes de razón*) and might therefore loosen their hold over the souls and social life of the natives.[3] Agricultural produce had a negligible place in the cargoes which the galleons carried to Acapulco. Though export crops increased in the islands after the end of the 18th century, they still consisted mainly of native produce. Tobacco, which was a State monopoly, benefited from the strict control exercised by officials over the peasant communities.

In the first half of the 19th century when, under the pressure of progressive ideas and the activities of English and American traders, the Philippines began slowly and, as it were, regretfully to be opened to foreign trade and ships, a certain number of Europeans, Chinese, and half-castes became interested in sugarcane. The jealousy of the authorities and the clergy helped in 1820 to foment a popular rising which ended in massacres. About 1840 a few individual

---

[1] Mostly in the western third of the Peninsula.
[2] Of these 43 per cent. were in the west, 18·4 in the centre, and 38·3 in the east.
[3] Humboldt (195), II, p. 281.

M.I.B.P.—22

Spaniards and some of the convents and chaplaincies owned moderately large properties in Luzón, but these were cut up into smallholdings worked on the métayer system and producing mainly sugar and indigo. The current opinion was that a European who took to farming would be ruined. In Negros in 1866 a score of Europeans, most of whom had steam mills, set up as sugar planters on land which they bought from half-castes and natives and cultivated with hired labour or, more usually, through tenants who were given part of the produce. At the end of the century when Spanish rule was brought to a close, the latter system prevailed in the production of the chief export crops.

Although under American protection the supporters of large plantations and those of the native system of tenure still opposed each other more vigorously than ever, the latter have been once more getting the better of it. The law restricts the area of land which may be acquired by White settlers, whether Americans or not, or by firms. The reasons are various. First, there is a desire to avoid the evils of monopoly and absenteeism and to encourage the building-up of a solid native peasantry. Secondly, the sugar-growers in Cuba and Puerto Rico, on the other hand, wish to restrict a dangerous competitor on the American market. Real plantations, on which settlers who own or lease the land superintend the production by hired labour of a crop for export, are seldom found in the Philippines. Large estates exist, but they are generally divided among native tenants whose oral or written contracts with the owner vary greatly as to terms. The only attempt at running a sugar plantation with hired labour was made by the Mindoro Sugar Estate. The enterprise came to grief, and the company had to cut up its concession into smallholdings. The Spanish Tabacalera Company, which buys three-fourths of the total crop in Luzón and even owns estates in the middle valley of the Kagayán, has had only one plantation cultivated with hired labour, and this is meant solely for experiments. The rest of the Company's property is let out to tenants. In the Philippines the big plantation is best represented in the islands which have been most recently occupied and are sparsely peopled. This is particularly true of Mindanao, where there are plantations of coconuts, pine-apples, rubber, and, above all, *abacá*. In the Davao district before the recent war the Japanese had set up joint stock companies and private firms with large capital for the purpose of cultivating *abacá*. In 1937 a block of plantations of about 60,000 acres was held by forty-six Japanese firms, which in addition controlled at least as great an area remaining in the hands of Japanese or Filipino smallholders.[1] In spite of the efforts of

[1] Kolb (175), p. 233.

certain American associations, this island has not become the great producer of rubber that the enormous consumption in the U.S.A. seemed to warrant. In 1939 the only scientifically run rubber plantation in Mindanao belonged to the Goodyear Rubber Co., its trees consisting wholly of *clones*[1] from Sumatra. In this large island rubber trees covered barely 12,000 acres, nearly all of which were situated on the Zamboanga peninsula. The expansion of rubber plantations was handicapped not only by the regulations which restrict the acquisition of land, but also those which prohibited the entry of Chinese coolies. The labour on the plantations in Mindanao consisted mostly of Ilocans and Bisayas. Their numbers were very small compared with those on plantations on the Malay Peninsula or the Oostkust Province of Sumatra.

SCIENTIFIC AGRICULTURE

⌐The success of the plantations was connected with the progress of scientific agriculture.⌐ The Dutch have won golden opinions by the improvements made by them in tropical agriculture, and the name of Buitenzorg enjoys special fame.[2] The celebrated Botanical Gardens were founded as early as 1817 at a spot which attracted botanists owing to its nearness to Jakarta, its heavy rainfall, and the survival of a forest vegetation almost intact in places. For more than a hundred years specimens of the plants of Malaya, Indonesia, and the Philippines as well as exotic tropical species from similar regions elsewhere have been brought together here and systematically classified, so that they can be studied in conditions as nearly like as possible to the state of nature. In fact, interest in Buitenzorg goes far beyond its reputation for luxuriance due to its magnificent avenues of canarium, its tiers of palms, its liana section, and its ponds of Victoria Regia. The Gardens sacrifice less to the picturesque than do those at Peradenya (Ceylon) and Singapore. From the beginning its purpose was declared to be scientific and practical. But it was made into a model institution by Melchior Treub, its director from 1883 onwards for nearly thirty years. He increased the number of laboratories and attracted many foreign research workers to them, and he created the wonderful subsidiary station at Chibodas on the slopes of Mt. Gede at the edge of a virgin forest which climbs up to an altitude of some 10,000 feet. He also made the *Annales du jardin* into one of the most valuable periodicals on tropical botany and succeeded in meeting the needs of pure scientific research as well as those of the plantations.

[1] See below, p. 344.
[2] Ch. J. Bernard (204); Dammermann (210). Under the Indonesian régime the name has been changed to Bogor.

Thus, the experimental Gardens at Buitenzorg preserve many specimens grown from exotic seeds and become venerable ancestors, whose descendants have multiplied in cultivated areas.   Tea bushes were introduced from China and Japan in 1826; coffee bushes from Africa replaced the Arabian variety which was too subject to *Hemileia vastatrix*; rubber trees were imported more than sixty years ago, the *hevea* alone being successful—and splendidly so; and the *elæis* oil palm, whose selection was to be followed up on the Oost-kust of Sumatra.

Indeed the practical work grew to such proportions that Treub had to urge private firms to organise special institutes at their own expense, and these also produced good results.   In Java there were several of them.   The oldest and most famous was the sugar institute at Pasuruan in East Java.   In 1928 it had in its biological, chemical, and technical sections forty-eight remarkably well qualified research workers and had at its disposal funds amounting to 1,800,000 florins.   In 1921 all the other experimental sugar institutes were amalgamated with it.   The two big planters' associations in the Oostkust of Sumatra each had its research centre at Medan.   They were the Deli Planters' Union for tobacco and the Avros (Algemeen Vereeniging van Rubber-planters Oostkust van Sumatra) which dealt with all the other crops, but especially with rubber and palm-oil. During the boom from 1920 to 1929 these private experimental stations tended to cut adrift from the Government, and Buitenzorg restricted itself more and more to theoretical researches.   But during the slump they had to curtail their activities, and the Government was forced in many instances to take the place of the planters' associations and, though itself embarrassed by the tightness of its budgets, to resort to export duties in order to keep up the laboratories and experimental gardens.   Malaya also has its agricultural institutes, the best known of which is the Rubber Research Institute at Kuala Lumpur.

At first the production of the most important commodities for export had been empirical, and it was in the research centres that production was gradually perfected and became scientific.   Pedological study has been carried so far in Java that the island possesses a soil map which many European countries might well envy.   The disastrous effects of clean weeding on the old plantations have been met by terracing the slopes and by the spread of leguminous cover crops which are also considered valuable as green manure.   Buitenzorg keeps a large series of specimens of these leguminous plants to demonstrate one of the chief developments in tropical agriculture. War has been waged methodically and perseveringly against parasites, which are so various and active in these winterless climes.

Some types have been counteracted by others introduced from abroad. Thus, the hymenoptera, which is the enemy of the coffee borer, was taken to Java from Uganda. Selection has enabled young plants to be grown and distributed in order constantly to renew the plantation stock. Artificial fertilisation, grafting, and the sorting of seed have been tried in turn. The methods of collection and the preparation of the commodity for market have also been steadily improved. Care has always been taken in practice not to carry experiments too far, but to get the best results with the least costs. By publishing results and by frequent meetings of experts improvements have quickly been made known and methods of production kept homogeneous. By these means yields have been increased, whilst costs have been reduced, and this has brought about a continually increasing export of plantation produce.

Sugarcane. Sugar is a particularly impressive case.[1] Canes had been cultivated in Java long before the coming of the Europeans and was usually consumed by chewing. On the average the crop gave barely 8 cwt. of sugar to the acre. This figure increased in the course of the 18th and 19th centuries, thanks to irrigation and improvements in industrial technique. But rapid progress began after the slump at the end of last century, which coincided with the appearance of the *serah*. This was a disease caused by a parasitic cryptogam, which devastated the plantations. From 1886 to 1941 the experimental stations, especially the one at Pasuruan, steadily increased the yield from both field and factory. In 1900 five per cent. of the sugar content was still left in the megass, but in 1930 the residue was hardly more than $3\frac{1}{2}$ per cent., and besides, the megass itself was used as fuel or fodder. Java and Mauritius were almost the only producers of cane sugar to export white sugar quite ready for use. Even greater was the progress due to improvement in methods of cultivation and to the selection of varieties. We saw above[2] how cane production in the overcrowded lowlands of Mid and East Java where there was an annual dry season had reached a stage of adjustment that was near perfection. The very restrictions which overcrowding forced on firms acted as a stimulus. Since the cane was not to occupy the rented land more than 18 months in three years, so as to give an opportunity for native food crops to be grown, the stump had to be uprooted after every crop had been cut and ratooning was never allowed, as it is in so many other countries. Since the quantity of water available was limited not only by the capacity of the canals, but also by the requirements of native crops, efforts had to be made to use it sparingly and to distribute it carefully in the growing period. A rotation of crops

1 Cayla (207).   2 See p. 332.

was systematically arranged. The different kinds of soil were catalogued. On every large plantation the result of the analysis of specimens was plotted acre by acre on large-scale maps, the chemists attached to the plantation working at the analyses between the times when the factories were busy. In this way the kind of manure suitable and the quantity required were determined. Sulphate of ammonia was often used. At intervals of a few weeks the manure was exactly measured out for each plant according to the number of trees and the total amount of manure to be applied per acre. Then water was poured into each hole to dissolve the salts. It was an instructive, and rather sad, sight to see the coolies at a blast of the *mandour's* whistle bending over the furrows in unison and pouring out the water.

A rise in yield has been due more to selection of the cane than to improvements in cultivation. When the station at Pasuruan was established in 1886, nearly the whole area was planted with *Zwarte Cheribon* which barely gave 52 cwt. to the acre. More productive varieties, P.O.J.100, B.247, B.I.52, and E.K.28, came into favour one after the other. In 1927 the last two raised the average yield to about 105 cwt. per acre. By 1928 P.O.J.2878 covered 65 per cent. of the cane area in Java and 90 per cent. in 1929. The average yield was then up to nearly 120 cwt. per acre. This cane not only gives a high yield and is immune from *serah* and other diseases, but is also far less sensitive than any other variety to variations in soil and climate, so that every day during the whole crop season it ensures the amount of canes needed for the full working of the mill.[1] This wonderful variety originally came from the crossing of a sugarless, but very hardy, wild cane with a highly bred cane that was rich in sugar, though subject to disease. In 1928 the number of canes studied at Pasuruan for the selection of P.O.J.2878 was reckoned by an expert at 200,000. This cane was one of the greatest technical triumphs of tropical agriculture. In 1929 at the beginning of the slump a new hybrid, 3250, was already being produced.

Rubber. The success of rubber cultivation has been still more striking.[2] The methods are sufficiently different from sugar production to deserve detailed description also. The tree is exotic and was introduced only at the end of last century. Its cultivation was actually a European invention, and the methods in use today are mainly the results of English and Dutch experiments, though the contribution recently made by French planters in Indo-China was

[1] P.O.J.2878 has also enabled seed-plots in the mountains to be given up. Only a few are kept for the practice of artificial fecundation, which is unsuccessful in the lowlands.

[2] Cramer (209 *bis*).

far from negligible. ⎰The plantations, covering nearly 3,750,000 acres in the Malay lands, have developed mainly at the expense of the forest. There was no need to make the cultivation fit into the native economic system, as was the case with sugarcane. This advantage was, however, counter-balanced by a complete ignorance of rubber cultivation and a scarcity of labour. ⎰

The story of the wonderful adventures of the *Hevea brasiliensis* has often been told. In 1877 the first rubber plants reached Singapore and Buitenzorg from the stock of seeds brought from the Amazon region by Sir Henry Wickham and successfully germinated in the warmth of the hothouses at Kew. Little plantations began in 1890. The oldest inhabitants can remember the despatch of the first seeds from the Botanical Gardens at Singapore in old dollar-boxes supplied by banks in the town. Owing to the start had by Ceylon and Malaya, most of the plantations in Indonesia began with seed from those countries. Rubber did not at once arouse great interest in business circles. At first, it was planted with coffee and was regarded merely as a shade-tree to be removed when it became a nuisance. In 1907 the Rubber Growers Association, which in 1935 controlled plantations in Malaya covering 1,700,000 acres, still existed on an income of £200 a year. In 1898 there were not 2500 acres of *hevea* plantation in Java. The *Ficus elastica*, which had been cultivated as early as 1864, was still preferred, and between 1900 and 1907 many plantations had both *Ficus elastica*, *Manihot Glaziovii*, and *Castilloa elastica*. Not until 1909 did the Forestry Service in Indonesia decide to adopt the *hevea*. But in 1910 the development of motor transport made the price of rubber shoot up, and *hevea* began its marvellously prosperous career.

Its progress has not been without risks and set-backs. The tree begins to produce only six or seven years after the seed has been planted, and a great deal of capital is needed to establish and maintain a plantation until tapping can begin. Clearing away forest is a heavy task. To begin with, inspection paths are laid out on compass bearings and opened up with cutlasses to enable the nature and quality of the land to be examined. The paths gradually become cart-tracks and facilitate transport while felling is in process, and then in the end they are made into macadamised roads on the plantation.

⎰The main improvements in husbandry[1] were, first, the progressive giving up of secondary crops like coffee, cassava, and pine-apples, whose yield allowed the planter to be less impatient in waiting for the first tapping, but which checked the growth of the *heveas*. Secondly, clean weeding was given up. It had been a crude transference to

[1] Cayla (208), Soliva (230).

the tropics of the practice originating in temperate climes of re-
moving all weeds.   When adopted in Ceylon, it resulted in a great
deterioration of the soil, which quickly lost its humus through the
direct action of the sun's rays and was swept away by the run-off of
rain-water, especially in hilly districts.   Between the wars the use of
cover-crops of leguminous creeping plants spread chiefly from the
Oostkust.   This procedure was replaced sometimes by a practice
apparently simpler, but in fact more subtle and laborious, namely,
the creation of a natural or semi-natural covering of the soil by
planting a forest association as like as possible to the original
habitat of the *hevea* after the elimination of species which were
aggressive or harmful to the trees.

But the most important development was the general use of
grafting.   As early as 1913 it was found after many experiments that
the *hevea* could be grafted.   This opened the prospect of an enormous increase in yield far more rapid than could be achieved by
selection through normal reproduction.   After choosing *heveas*
with a high yield, a great deal of knowledge had to be gathered so as
to apply the method to large areas and to create 'clones', or offspring of the chosen tree produced by non-sexual processes.   Before
being distributed, these clones had their quality tested at the experimental stations, the chief of which belonged to the Rubber Research
Institute at Kuala Lumpur, the Avros in Sumatra, and the Buitenzorg
establishment.   From these came the great number of grafted trees
which from 1930 onwards covered huge areas in Malaya and Indo-
China.   Some of this was new ground, but as a rule *heveas* from 20
to 25 years old were felled to make room for the new trees.   The
change proved to be a great success.   A plantation of *heveas* all
grown from seed gave in the twelfth year an average yield of 450 lb.
of dry rubber to the acre.   But this figure was already reached in the
sixth year, that is, at the first tapping, by grafted trees which in the
twelfth year could yield more than 2200 to 2650 lb., 2800 to 3000 lb.
with a well-known clone like Avros 49, and even more than 4400 lb.
with T.J.1, a selection from Chiomas near Buitenzorg.

The proper method of tapping the *hevea* was not known at first.
Of course, the gouge and knife had replaced the *machete* of the
Amazonian *seringueiros*, but a whole series of incisions whether
running spirally right round the tree or arranged in a fishbone
pattern leading to a vertical drain, exhausted the *hevea*.   At times
the coolie climbed a ladder to reach more of the tree-surface.   With
these methods the recuperation of the latex-bearing tissues was
difficult, the growth of the tree slow, and the yield poor and sometimes completely arrested.   Later on, prophylactic methods of
tapping were used which allowed the tree to rest and gave it a longer

life, at the same time achieving a saving of labour.   Experiments were made to discover the optimum density of trees to the acre, and the value of the different kinds of soil was carefully studied together with the effects of various manures.

In spite of this remarkable progress, rubber cultivation has been practised too short a time for the best methods to have been found, and it is still in the experimental stages.   The problem of cover crops remains unsolved, and the use of manure has not become general. The most economical method of tapping is still being sought, as is also the optimum density of trees to the acre.   Grafting itself seems to be an abnormal procedure and is sometimes accused of producing brittle trees with too thin a bark and slight resistance to disease. Some experts predict that in the future grafted trees will no longer be used, but only those grown from seed derived from clones of proved quality.

Machinery has enabled a reduction in man-power to be made in the factories.   The coagulating basin holding a few quarts has been replaced by an aluminium vat with a capacity of more than 300 gallons.   Train mills arranged in series allow as much as 4400 dry lb. to be treated per hour.   Quick, improved methods of smoking and drying produce a homogeneous article with the long-sought consistency in mechanical properties.   But the sheets are often still valued according to their appearance, and collaboration between planter and mill-owner has been slight.   A beginning has been made in exporting latex not in dry sheets, but in liquid form concentrated by centrifugal action, evaporation, or a kind of skimming process.

Palm-Oil.   The oil palm (*elæis guineensis*) affords another instance of the domestication of a tree far from its original home.   In this case the distant home was Guinea, and once again Malaya was the adopted country.   There it has been wonderfully successful; but it has done even better in the Oostkust of Sumatra.   Introduced into Buitenzorg from Réunion in 1848 at first as an ornamental tree, the oil palm was not really cultivated till 1910, when it was taken up by some enthusiasts, among whom was Adrien Hallet, a Belgian. Here it found a suitable climate, soil which was excellent in places, and, above all, an unrivalled technical and scientific organisation that had already made its reputation in the rubber boom.   In 1938 oil palms had been planted on 69,000 acres in Malaya and 207,000 acres in Indonesia, which makes a total of 276,000 acres, of which 235,000 were yielding fruit.   Those Far Eastern plantations which were not yet in production in 1920, were exporting 276,000 tons of palm-oil and 56,000 tons of nuts in 1938.

The difference in treatment of the tree in West Africa is singularly instructive. There the palm grows naturally or else gets only intermittent and slight attention; the trees stand at irregular intervals among other forest species; they are laden and wrapped about with epiphytes; and the varieties are very mixed and their bunches of unequal size. To make a plantation of 25,000 acres like the one at Johore Labis in Malaya[1] a dense forest area is first surveyed by air, then divided into blocks of 250 acres, and methodically cleared and burnt. In 1929 eighteen months after the first ring of an axe, 7400 acres of young palms have been planted and 5000 more put in in 1935. The seeds, taken from boxes, grow into plants from among which a strict selection is made by a process of artificial fertilisation. The female inflorescences are wrapped in oilcloth and at the right moment the pollen chosen is blown on to them with a little pair of bellows. A metal plate fixed to the stem is marked whenever a bunch is picked and thus shows the yield exactly. The tree is carefully cleaned and the barren leaves pruned off. Between the rows of palms there is a thick cover crop of leguminous plants or selected grasses. In undulating country terraces are made to check the loss of soil. A vigorous struggle is carried on by means of poison, virus, and trained dogs against rats, which are fond of the oily fruit; and against caterpillars arsenic dust is sprayed on the trees and special flies bred indoors are released in the plantations.

In Africa the native wastes much time in forcing a way through to the tree, in climbing up the bole whose height is increased by the effort to reach the light, and in carrying the nuts a long distance to his hut. In Malaya paths laid out as soon as the forest has been cleared away, and constantly improved, give easy access to the palms. Owing to a wise spacing out, the trees grow less quickly and develop their bunches at no great height above the ground. The coolies seldom carry the heavy bunches more than 100 yards[2] without coming to a motor road. On Johore Labis there are 110 miles of such roads, and they all lead to a narrow-gauge railway which takes the nuts to the mill in the centre of the plantation.

This very striking contrast in cultivation and transport is repeated in the process of preparation for market. Among the negroes extraction is done by the women with a primitive domestic implement. Not only is the oil content of the nut small, but also some 30 or 50 per cent. of the oil is lost, and what is left is impure and very acid. In the East with powerful plant in big mills the kernels, which start by being far richer, yield more than 95 per cent. of their oil and, as they are treated while still fresh, the percentage of acidity does not usually exceed 3, as compared with between 15 and 40 in West Africa.

[1] R. M. E. Michaux in *Semaine du palmier à huile* (219), pp. 23–58.
[2] 500 yards on some plantations.

The result is not surprising. Whilst a grove of palms in Africa would, even after some attention, give no more than half a ton per acre annually in the most favourable conditions, the yield in Eastern plantations amounts to one ton for six-year-old palms and increases from year to year until it attains three and a half tons from trees ten years old. Costs are lowered still more by the reduction in the labour required, the cutting out of the need for packing, and the efficiency of the machinery, the motive power for which is supplied by burning the nutshells. In fact, transport is very often in bulk by road, rail, or sea in tanker vehicles or ships. What a contrast there is between the 600-ton tanker from Port Swettenham or Belawan Deli, warmed by spiral pipes so as to keep the oil liquid[1] and the West African puncheon, 'Marseillais', or Liverpooler, rolled by a negro along the road to the wharf. It was admitted that tropical Africa, the home of the *elæis*, could not compete with the Malay lands except by importing selected seed and employing the methods tried out in the Far East during the previous thirty years.[2]

Cinchona and other Plantation Crops. Cinchona has certainly had its best-known success in Java,[3] though its place in the list of exports from the East Indies is far lower than those of rubber and palm-oil. The plant is a native of South America and was introduced about 1845, but the most delicate and profitable task was the acclimatisation in the mountains in the Priangan Residencies of a new variety brought from Bolivia by Ledger about 1870 and steadily improved. The seeds of the *Cinchona ledgeriana* are flat, winged, and very small. There are on the average 3500 of them in a gramme, and a gramme was worth 10 florins in about 1927. The bark is the valuable part of the tree. The seeds come from trees selected for the amount of sulphate of quinine in the bark, the thickness of the bark, and the circumference and dimensions of the trunk. They are picked out one by one in a dark room on illuminated ground glass and then distributed in accurately weighed quantities to be spread evenly over every square yard of the sifted compost forming the seed-beds under shelter of ferns and straw. The plants stay there and are carefully watched for between six and ten months before being set in the ground. *Cinchona ledgeriana* is often grafted on to *Cinchona succirubra*, which is far less rich in quinine, but hardier and will grow at a lower altitude. Plantations are made at the expense of

[1] King (106), p. 145; Schoofs (226). At Meulaboh on the west coast of Sumatra the oil runs from the river-tanker to the ocean-tanker by means of a pipe-line on the wharf. The steamer is loaded in a few hours. Belgian Congo has recently adopted these methods of bulk transport. Pointe-Noire in French Equatorial Africa is to have the advantage of it also.

[2] Since the end of the war rubber (*elæis*) plantations have made rapid progress in tropical Africa, though the total production of palm kernels and palm oil is still chiefly derived from wild trees. In 1953 Indonesia and Malaya together provided rather less than a quarter of world production.

[3] Frontou (211); Kerbosch (220); see also M. Musset in A. G., 1942, pp. 64–7.

forest which is cleared off, but not fired, on soil that is usually terraced and sometimes drained. The branches are lopped to begin with; and the trees themselves are destroyed at latest after thirty years. The yield seems to be best between the ages of 12 and 15 years.

From about 1885 the bark from the Priangan Residencies eliminated the competition of other countries, in particular Ceylon and India. It formed some 90 per cent. of world production, which means in fact that it had the advantage of a monopoly. Since then the efforts in other countries had by 1939 barely gone beyond the experimental stage, and tropical America itself, the home of cinchona, imported seed from Java.[1]

These examples should serve to illustrate the value of Dutch achievement in scientific agriculture, without, however, forgetting the part played by the British who were the actual pioneers of rubber and oil palm cultivation. Other evidence might be adduced, as, for instance, the perfection of tobacco and tea cultivation in Sumatra and Java and the extreme care required in the treatment of the leaves of both plants. In Sumatra the cost of sorting tobacco amounts to from 5 to 10 per cent. of the total expenditure of the plantations. The most recent success has been in sisal cultivation in the Oostkust, though its circumstances are still shrouded in some degree of mystery. The acclimatisation of the American agave (*Agava rigida*) was followed in 1920 by the first shipment of 718 tons. In 1937 this had risen to 53,000 tons. The plant is sometimes grown in rotation with cassava, for the two crops are complementary in some requirements; but they are both exhausting. The soil has to be heavily manured, and the waste water from the tapioca and fibre mills is distributed through the fields by a system of gutters.

Abacá cultivation had many improvements initiated by the Japanese growers in Davao. The 25,000 acres cultivated or controlled by them were ploughed, intensively manured, and had even begun to be irrigated. The damage caused by certain animals was effectively checked by the use of special traps; after the fibre had been removed the waste was returned to the soil, which, moreover, was protected by a leguminous cover-crop (*Centrosema*). The removal of the fibre was facilitated by the use of water mills or petrol engines or by the powerful machinery with which some of the factories were equipped.

---

[1] Whilst the tea and coffee plantations in Indonesia suffered greatly during the recent war, 35 per cent. of them being destroyed, cinchona plantations were well maintained by the Japanese, who needed them. But necessity led the Allies to develop cultivation in other tropical lands, and quinine production has increased rapidly especially in Guatemala, Belgian Congo, the Cameroons, and India. See below, p. 438.

CHAPTER 18

DEVELOPMENT OF PEASANT AGRICULTURE

It is not surprising that, profitable and varied as it is, European exploitation should occupy but a very small part of the land under cultivation and also of the cultivable area in Malay countries.[1] In Java, where the oldest plantations are to be found, they covered about 1,360,000 acres in 1940, which is less than one-fifteenth of the land under cultivation, though only 68 per cent. of the total area of the island was cultivated. In other islands it is impossible to estimate the area under cultivation because the temporary patches, or *ladangs*, are scattered about. Moreover, the statistics of countries not included in Indonesia make no clear distinction between European and native crops. Nevertheless, it is certain that the latter are by far the greater both in area and in volume and value of production, except, however, in western Malaya and the Medan district in the Oostkust.

Causes of Development. But it is of greater interest that native agriculture is not restricted to supplying local needs. In 1936 it was estimated that 30 or 35 per cent. of the agricultural produce in Indonesia was exported.[2] Native producers were sharing more and more in the exports, though they certainly shipped abroad a far smaller proportion of their produce than the European plantations.

This orientation of native cultivation is of recent date. In 1898 European agricultural enterprise was still responsible for 90 per cent. of the exports from the East Indies. In 1927 it had fallen to 69 per cent. and in 1937 it was only 53 per cent. Fraught with great consequences, the development cannot hide the fact that the Malay lands must first and foremost ensure the subsistence of their inhabitants. But this is not considered when the great foreign markets stand wide open, though it is called to mind from time to time by slumps.

It is not always easy to give details of the development of native crops in tropical colonies. There are few clear documents which

---

[1] In 1940 plantations in Malay occupied about 7 per cent. of the total area, in Java 4·4 per cent., in Sumatra 1 per cent., and in the rest of the Outer Provinces 0·04 per cent.

[2] For both agricultural and mineral production together the percentage was 35 or 40, as against 7 per cent. in the U.S.A., according to C. Rhote (235). This article gives the percentage of each leading product that is consumed locally. It varied from 1 per cent. for rubber to 97 per cent. for rice and soya.

can be turned to good account concerning Malaya and the Philippines. But in 1929 the International Colonial Institute, which had taken up the matter, published an excellent and very substantial report by Dr. B. Smits on the modes and factors by which this development took place in Indonesia up to 1926.[1]

The causes are legion. Progress was in part guided and in part submitted to by the colonists, whose views differed as to the good done by it. That the interests of planters and merchants might differ on the matter will easily be understood. European agricultural concerns could not look with a favourable, or even an indifferent, eye on the indefinite expansion of native export crops which were becoming serious competitors of their own, were curtailing the labour available, and were disturbing the hitherto carefully controlled markets. Merchants, on the other hand, were able to make good profits out of the expansion of these crops. As a rule the native cultivator could scarcely dispense with their help in disposing of his produce. Moreover, goods imported from distant countries were distributed by them among the natives, whose purchasing power was a direct function of the value of the exports.

That is why the part played by the Chinaman, who is a born middleman, had been great both in collaborating with European firms and in carrying on all kinds of business from bartering with the peasants to exporting produce abroad. However, in these matters he himself now suffers from the competition of natives, which has become more effective owing to Government support. Some Malays, too, like the Achinese, Minangkabaus, Banjarese, and Bugis, have encouraged the new crops owing to their fondness for trading.

Emphasis must next be laid on the considerable influence of the banks and great commercial firms, European, American, Japanese, and Chinese, with their many branches and agencies. The Dutch policy of the 'open door' and the liberal British system in Malaya have led to keen competition between them, and they have constantly tried to expand their business by accepting a very small rate of profit. The native producer has benefited by this and with these attractive conditions in view has expanded his cash crops.

Commercial activity has naturally been accompanied by improvement in ways and means of transport. Improvement began early in Java, but is more recent in other islands. The progress of sea communications between the islands and in particular the remarkable organisation of the K.P.M. with its many boats calling at an ever growing number of open roadsteads, greatly fostered copra production on the coasts of the Malay lands and, later, indirectly assisted

[1] B. Smits (227); Robequain (200), pp. 114–25.

other ventures of native agriculture which grew up thanks to the railways and roads now running into the backlands.

Nature and Distribution of Crops grown by Natives for Export. Native agriculture has, however, fared variously according to locality. It has used different methods and applied itself to different products. In overcrowded lowlands it has found some difficulty in turning to export crops, since the land there is almost wholly devoted to local subsistence and especially to rice cultivation.   We have seen that in Java the sugarcane had succeeded in worming its way into the rotation of crops only by the direct action of European firms which had rented land for intermittent use under strict terms of contract.   In this case the native is a mere wage-earner.   It was often the same with tobacco in the Principalities in the centre and east of the island. Apart from copra, the chief exports of native-grown produce from the lowlands of Java were derived from the so-called secondary crops which the peasant grows in the interval between the rice and sugarcane seasons.   These crops included maize, cassava, sweet potatoes, yams and other tubers, various leguminous plants among which soya and groundnuts took a leading place, and tobacco, which is grown on *sawahs* or *tegals* and sold mainly in packets (*krosok*) of dry leaves. However, perennials like pepper and kapok, whose produce is chiefly meant for sale, or like areca nut, which is partly consumed locally and partly exported, are welcomed in the gardens in the lowlands. Tea deserves special mention, not only because it formed the third largest native export from Java (after tapioca and copra), but also because in many places in the western mountains it has spread over areas that were once forest and had been cleared for patch cultivation.   The opportunities for this had been strictly limited in Java owing to the ban on *ladangs*, though on the other hand *ladangs* remained in current use in the former Outer Provinces.

Exports of native-grown commodities had not, however, had their progress checked by the flow of capital into the plantations in the Outer Provinces any more than they had had in Malaya.   In fact, they had made the most surprising advance there, for many of them are derived from exotic plants whose cultivation has been adopted by the peasants, even though these plants might appear to be in the special sphere of European plantations.

In sparsely peopled districts, indeed, it was possible for the natives to use large areas for the new crops without encroaching on the space needed for their own subsistence.   They had only to make use of *ladangs* and merely to till them more intensively either by prolonging the duration of use between the two periods of fallow or by making more or larger patches.   Nor did they fail to do so.   It has happened that, after the arrival of the Europeans and especially since the end of the 19th century, strong demands for export crops have been made to some of the under-populated territories. The districts whose inhabitants have profited most from the new crops are situated right in the western portion of the Malay world along the Strait most frequently used by ships passing between the Indian Ocean and the South China Sea on one of the world's greatest seaways. They are western Malaya, Sumatra (especially the east), and the south, west, and north-west of Borneo. These districts are grouped about Singapore, which, thanks to its position and even more to Great Britain's skilful commercial policy and the tireless activity of the Chinese, has been unrivalled as a centre of energy. This function is of recent date, however, for Raffles did not found the English settlement till 1819, and the Suez Canal was not opened until fifty years later.

Except for sugar and coffee from Java, the native cultivator in Malay lands up to the 19th century contributed to the exports little more than spices: cinnamon, nutmegs, and cloves from the Moluccas and pepper from Benkulen, Bantam, and the coasts of Borneo. Besides, these contributions which were complementary to the system of primitive collecting had for most of the time the character of tribute exacted by the Dutch East India Company. Van den Bosch's system in the first half of the 19th century was by and large merely an extension and improvement of this compulsory method under the close supervision and for the profit of the Netherlands Government. After the beginning of the 19th century, however, spices were no longer the chief exports, their production being exceeded by those of sugar and coffee.

Whilst in the East Indies outside the lowlands in East and Central Java canes are hardly cultivated for export, coffee has found excellent conditions in some of the other islands. *Coffea Arabica* was introduced into the East Indies in 1669. As a species, it is tolerant of altitude and even requires it in the tropics. So it became quite acclimatised in the mountains of Sumatra, in the backlands of Palembang, Benkulen, and Padang, and in Minahassa as well as in the Priangan Residencies in Java. When in consequence of the ravages of the *Hemileia vastatrix*, which had crossed from Ceylon to the East Indies about 1870–75, the *Arabica* was more and more replaced on plantations by African forest species—greatly improved by grafting, whilst keeping their resistance to disease—and the *Liberia*, imported in 1876, and the *Robusta*, in 1900, were also taken up by the natives in the Outer Provinces. Coffee proved very suitable for native cultivation. Planted on the *ladang* at the same time as the food crops, it begins to yield its fruit when the food crop has been harvested completely. The skinning and drying of the berry can be

29.
Moro *vintas* on the Sulu Sea.
Note the double outriggers.

30.
A typical scene in the Philippines. The cart and water-buffalo are everyday sights.

31.
Manila. The mouth of the River Pasig with Fort Santiago and the Walled City on the left.

32. Winnowing rice in Luzón, Philippines

33. Terraced rice-fields in Java

carried out without any expensive equipment. Already under the Cultuur system Government control over the coffee trade had become precarious owing to the great number of small producers. In Java the coffee monopoly had had to be joined to that of salt, the two products being exchanged for each other in official warehouses.[1] But smuggling was still active and was profitable to private traders. In 1937, whilst the coffee exported from Java came almost wholly from European plantations, on which it was often intermingled with rubber, it did not form one-third of the quantity shipped from the former Outer Provinces. In 1937 67 per cent. of the total amount of coffee exported from Indonesia and nearly all the 7000 tons of Arabica shipped abroad was grown by natives.

The history of the *hevea* is more famous and picturesque than that of coffee. Together with the *Ficus elastica* and others which yielded latex, the tree was growing in gardens and *ladangs* in Malaya, Sumatra, and Borneo as early as the beginning of this century when the period of high profits opened for European planters. The first *heveas* to be cultivated by natives are recorded as growing at Jambi about 1904, and the first cargo of latex from them was shipped in 1911. At the end of 1915 about 3,000,000 trees were counted in this Residency. *Heveas* cultivated by natives made their appearance in the Residency of Palembang as well as in Borneo before 1910. Pilgrims to Mecca played a large part in spreading the seed at an early date. They heard of the success of the American tree as they passed through Ceylon and Malaya, and a considerable trade in seed, brought mainly from Penang and Malacca, grew up through them in 1910. The Chinese helped to spread the new crop by growing it themselves and even more by undertaking the sale of native-grown latex. When the Chinese on the west coast of Borneo failed to make a profit out of gold-mining, they used at one time to try to make up for this by cultivating gambier; but after 1910 they turned to the *hevea*.

The tree suits the *ladang* system even better than coffee. It flourishes on very different kinds of ground, even on very steep slopes. Its cultivation is simple. After rice or cassava has been harvested, the *hevea* continues to grow unmanured among a spontaneous secondary forest growth, for the native does no more than check the overwhelming tendency of the vegetation by thinning it out now and then. The tree even does good. As it is generally planted more closely than on the plantations, it occupies and protects the soil and checks loss by erosion. Young stands are healthy, vigorous, and of fine appearance. Of course, the tapping and preparation of the latex are often carelessly done, the bark destroyed, and the rubber badly

[1] Money (196), I, p. 256.

smoked and dried. However, improvement is taking place. Though in general the peasants still refuse to graft, they accept clone seeds which are at times distributed free; and they are adopting less harmful methods of tapping than daily incisions round one-quarter of the circumference. The implements required cost little. The latex is often coagulated with alum in an empty paraffin tin and is rolled out on a board into a sheet, which is then hung up to dry. Though the commodity thus produced may contain certain impurities and is at times mixed with little bits of bark, it can be worked over in a remilling establishment. This kind of industry was at first confined mainly to the Chinese, and the mills used for it had increased in number in Singapore, Penang, Malacca, and other ports in Malaya. Preparation at the source of production has improved owing to the spread of the use of little hand rolling-mills and the construction of curing-sheds at trading centres. The interests of European agents and traders, who, like the Chinese middlemen, have different views from those of the large-scale planters, encouraged the increase of rubber cultivation by the natives. In fact, big firms tended to do without the help of these middlemen and to deal directly with consumers in Europe and the United States. Besides, the Colonial Governments supported the smallholders and commissioned native agents to teach them the best methods of production.

In short, though exact comparison is difficult, native production per acre was not known to be less than that of plantations on which there was no grafting; and sheets of rubber from the new curing-sheds were of a quality approaching that obtained from European mills.

The increase in rubber-growing by the natives was due to all these causes. But the controls that European producers had thought would be to their own advantage rather furthered the development. The failure of the Stevenson plan was typical. It owed its name to the president of the Commission which the British Government sent out in 1920 to save the rubber plantations, which were threatened with a serious crisis due to overproduction. At that time English capitalists controlled nearly three-quarters of world production. Expansion was restricted, and the desired result quickly seemed to be reached, for the average price of raw rubber, which from 8s. 10d. in 1910 had fallen to 2s. 5d. in 1919 and to 11d. in 1922, rose again to 4s. 4d. in December 1925. But the big producers had counted without the natives. As prices had risen, so rubber trees had multiplied in the *ladangs* in Sumatra and Borneo, more quickly than on European plantations, and that without the formation of companies or the issue of shares and advertisements. Between 1922 and 1928, owing mainly to the natives in the Outer Provinces, Indonesia's share in rubber production had risen from 25 to 38 per cent., whilst that of Malaya had fallen from 73 to 58 per cent. The Dutch, who had before this been themselves disagreeably surprised, had instituted a vast enquiry, which reported about 1925 that rubber trees in Jambi Residency alone numbered 10,000,000 or 15,000,000. As world demand did not increase fast enough and American consumers were holding off, the Stevenson plan had to be given up in 1928. Prices fell, and a very severe crisis shook the rubber market.

Thus, rubber raised in an extremely acute form one of the most serious problems connected with colonisation, namely competition between European and peasant producers, one armed with his capital, proud of his organisation and technique, and helped by his knowledge of the market; the other having the advantage of a low standard of living and securing unexpected profits from casual and slovenly cultivation. When prices rose, the peasant rubber grower in Jambi could be seen buying patent leather shoes, gramophones, bicycles and cars, and imported cigars and canned foods.[1] If the price of rubber fell, he would at first start exhaustive tapping of the trees to maintain his earnings by producing a greater quantity. Should the fall in price go on, he would leave the trees untouched and make other *ladangs* in which to cultivate the traditional food crops. He would not return to the rubber except when hard pressed for want of cash to pay his taxes or defray the expense of a family rite. When attracted once more by high prices, the peasant would resume the intensive exploitation of his rubber trees and would plant more seeds in the ashes of another forest clearing. In sparsely peopled districts such as occur frequently in Sumatra and Borneo, he would even call in foreign labour for tapping. This was done in Jambi, for instance, where the tappers were given half or two-thirds of the produce. The reactions of local growers are hard to foresee, and control is very difficult when the producers are countless in number and the plantations of rubber trees scattered through the forest in a country without a cadastral survey or even an accurate map.

The interests at stake were too important to be left to run their own course. The Dutch East Indian planters succeeded in having native rubber production regulated by an export duty which varied according to the state of the market and the restrictions laid down by the international agreement of 1934. This elastic and, in fact, unfair tax provoked serious discontent. A regular census of producers had to be made, which, when completed in Indonesia in 1936, made the natives liable to individual inspection, as European estates were. The count showed nearly 790,000 native rubber plantations, the

1 Le Fèvre (222), p. 114.

average size being about two acres. With a cultivated area some 250,000 acres larger than the European plantations native production in 1937 accounted for 49 per cent. of the total amount exported from the East Indies. This came almost wholly from the Outer Provinces, for out of 590,000,000 native-owned rubber trees, about half of which were producing, there were barely 8,000,000 in Java, and these nearly all in the west.[1]

In Malaya, too, native-owned rubber plantations are numerous. They are often mere gardens near the village with the trees growing close together and mingled with other useful plants. But with the Malay, or in some cases the Indian, smallholder rubber may become the important and almost the only crop, especially in the south of the Peninsula. In British Borneo, as in the Dutch portion, native smallholders produce far more than the large plantations. Sarawak in particular is a country of smallholdings. In 1938 it was reckoned that some 230,000 acres under rubber were divided into 93,000 holdings.

The distinction, varying with the district and the product, between shipments from plantations and those from native sources reveals the influence of both the conditions in which the different crops are grown and the policies of the Colonial Governments. At first sight it is surprising that of two palms like the coconut and oil palms the former should be almost exclusively cultivated by natives,[2] whilst the other is one of the most typical representatives of the plantation system. Closer attention soon clears up the matter. The coconut palm has been cultivated from time immemorial in the Malay world. At first coconut groves spread by the natural dissemination of the nuts along the seashore. The tree does not as a rule begin to bear fruit until it is about seven or eight years old, sometimes even as late as ten years. When the nut is broken, the kernel is easily separated from the shell by primitive, but well-tried, methods. After being dried in the sun or smoked over a wood fire, it becomes the commodity known as copra, which is easily stored and transported to overseas oil-refineries. On the other hand, the oil palm was greatly favoured by large-scale European exploitation. Like the American *hevea*, it was unknown to the natives. But it could only be adopted by them with far greater difficulty, for, in truth, few trees have benefited so much from plantation conditions. By selection and

[1] The greatest proportion attained by native rubber cultivation as compared with European was reached in 1938 in Borneo and in Sumatra in the Residencies of Palembang, Jambi, and Westkust. Owing to the decline in the plantations, native rubber production has greatly increased since the end of the war. See below, p. 429.

[2] More than 90 per cent. of the copra from Indonesia and the Philippines came from native sources, and this proportion must have increased still more after the war.

improvement in cultivation it has become the world's greatest producer of vegetable oil to the acre and it sometimes begins to bear at the age of three years. Unlike the coconut, its soft fruit requires timely picking and rapid treatment to give no more than the very faintly acid oil demanded by European industries. The natives could not compete with the large plantation, which has roads and narrow gauge railways running through it, plenty of closely supervised labour, large refineries right in the centre of the cultivated area, and adequate means of shipment.

The reason why the native share in exports has shown a much greater increase in coffee than in tea is that the latter commodity demands a far more complicated preparation in order to satisfy the taste of European consumers, a taste moreover that has been created and maintained by the skilful publicity of large English firms. It is not surprising either that the native had practically no hand in the cultivation of cinchona, since it is a scientific business and the product requires careful preparation, has a small output, and is therefore easily controlled.

In the case of other plants the influence of colonial policy prevails over technique. It is clearly evident that as sisal is a Mexican agave which was taken to Sumatra from Africa, it would not easily penetrate into the native economic system because of the difficulty of stripping the fibre. But on the other hand, *abacá*, which is a banana-tree native to the Philippines, appears to suit the European plantation system. It is a herb which, sending out shoots from its rhizome, occupies the ground for several years in succession and has usually spread at the expense of the forest. It is certainly very easy to cultivate, but it can be improved by scientific methods of selection, and the industry benefits from the use of machines for stripping the fibre. Hand-stripping as the natives do it, may give a high quality product, but it is a long, complicated, and even risky business. The Japanese started many improvements on their plantations in Davao. However, the cultivation remains chiefly in the hands of the native smallholder. The same is true of tobacco and sugar, which are among the chief exports from the Philippines. Clearly this is one of the consequences of Spanish colonial rule and later of American policy, for both these nations allowed Europeans to invest far less capital in agricultural schemes than was the case with plantations in Malaya and Indonesia.

The case of sugar in the Philippines is significant.[1] The principal development has been the replacement of little mills by large factories, called 'Centrals', which increased in number chiefly during the boom in 1916–22. In 1916 raw, or muscovado, sugar still

[1] Y. Henry (218); Kolb (175), pp. 248–70.

formed most of the quantity exported, whilst in 1926 white sugar led by a long way. The sugar refineries attract the Philippine, Spanish, and American investor. In 1935 Philippine investments, which were mainly of Government funds in the Philippine National Bank, amounted to 168,000,000 *pesos*. Most of the American capital comes from San Francisco and Honolulu. But the direct cultivation of the soil by the owner of the Central is exceptional in the Philippines, whilst in Java it is the rule. The refinery owner has a contract with the proprietor of the cane-fields, who is often a *mestizo* and who himself lets out his land to be worked by a tenant farmer (as is widely done in Negros) or else on the *métayer* system. In short, sugar cultivation in the Philippines is in the hands of more than 20,000 native tenants. Methods of cultivation are as out-of-date as the systems of tenure. Of course, the soil is on the average less fertile than in Java and the climate more uncertain. But the low yield of 24 cwt. to the acre as against an average of 104 cwt. in Java is due to the poverty of the tenants and their way of working by rule of thumb. Drainage and irrigation are not much practised; slips are not grown in seed-beds, but in fields before the canes are cut; or else the canes are allowed to ratoon three or four times. There is no rational system of rotation, manure is little used, and the soil is exhausted by continuous cultivation. As selection is not practised, many varieties persist. All the heavy work falls within the same period, the canes are often cut before they are ripe, and the mill is not regularly supplied.

Native Export Crops and the Plantations. The question of the respective values of the two types of cultivation, European and native, must now be faced. It is a difficult one, because the necessary data are either imponderable or, as often happens, do not exist, and because the answer depends on the point of view of the observer.

With many crops the advantages of the plantation are at once manifest. The chief are rapid development of the land, high and regular yields, and ease of control. Europeans can scarcely contain themselves for pride on seeing line upon line of rubber trees or oil palms growing where a few years before had been wild and almost uninhabited forest. The sight is certainly one of the most striking testimonies to the efficiency of colonial exploitation.

One must not, however, be complacent over this first impression or be content with statistics of production. One of the most professed—and the most commendable—aims of colonial governments is to raise the standard of living of the native. But there is no sure test to be applied in order to assess improvement. If we go by material gain, we certainly find great difficulty in making our estimates, for, whilst the profit made on exports is to be reckoned on the credit side, the loss due to the abandonment of or decrease in food crops must be placed on the debit side. Careful comparisons made in 1927 seem to show that the native did not benefit so much in districts in which the greater part of the exports were supplied by plantations, but that his advantage lay rather in native small-holdings.

On the other hand, though it is impossible to calculate all the elements of human happiness, it is certain that happiness is not proportionate to the net income from man's labour and that well-being and comfort owe a great deal to a regular and progressive development of social conditions. Plantations often uproot natives from their homes. This cannot be avoided, since plantations must as a rule be established on unoccupied land where population is sparse and must therefore employ labour drawn from a distance and force it for several months or even years to live an artificial life far from the native village and family circle. The sugar estates in Java must be regarded as exceptions, since they had the good fortune to start a profitable and scientifically cultivated crop in areas over-populated and so to find their workers close at hand.[1] But life was very different for the employees on tea plantations in the Priangan Residencies, most of whom came from the neighbouring plains and for the coolies on the Oostkust or in Malaya, who came over the sea from Java, India, or China and lived for several years as exiles in a foreign land. Foreign labour is also employed by natives for the cultivation of crops for export; e.g. rubber in Sumatra. But the terms of engagement are far looser than on the plantation, where labour consists mainly of wage-earners pure and simple.[2]

Planters vigorously assert the advantages of their system, which they claim to be an excellent palliative for over-population, since the savings brought home by emigrants cause districts overloaded with a swarm of wretchedly poor people to benefit by the earnings derived from the opening up of new country, and, if care is taken to recruit not individuals, but whole families, the very desirable transfer of people may become permanent. Those who hold the opposite view answer that in fact the sexes are generally very unequal in number on European concessions, family life is rare, and temporary immigrants are in the great majority everywhere; and that it is true that, though

[1] For sugar-cane itself, cp. van der Kolff's warning in Schrieke (20), pp. 122–24. Of course in prosperous years the plantations have distributed millions of florins to peasants in the form of wages and rent. But this kind of cultivation which requires constant rotation under European control has led the natives to lose interest in the fields, since these seem no longer to belong to them.

[2] Boeke (186), p. 136.

a certain number of married couples have been successfully settled, the number of effectives on plantations almost always varies according to season and type of work, so that a more or less high percentage of floating labour is needed.

It is argued, too, that the plantation is an excellent school for the native. Not only does it instil in him habits of hygiene and foresight, but it also teaches him the value of regular, methodical work; and it shows him the wonderful results of selection, manuring, and new methods of cultivation. In Tapanuli in western Sumatra, for instance, the little Javanese rubber cultivator quickly adopted selected varieties and the use of artificial manure. It is difficult, however, for the native to carry out on the few perches of his little plot of land all the various practices used on vast estates of hundreds or thousands of acres, on which work is strictly controlled and becomes mechanical.

In short, the two systems—plantation and native patch—had their justification in historical circumstances, geographical conditions, and technical requirements. Neither deserved to be eliminated by the other. Their relative positions differ greatly today from place to place. In spite of the pressure exerted on the Philippine Government by certain European and, later, American business interests, the plantation has made little progress in this group. Its greatest success occurred in Malaya and north-eastern Sumatra between 1900 and 1920. But on the whole in Indonesia there was a distinction —certainly unique in the world—between the two types of tropical agriculture.

Improvements in Native Agriculture. Since the beginning of the century there had been an increasing tendency in Colonial Governments to protect small-scale cultivators and the native peasantry. Slumps have demonstrated the weakness of even the best thought-out plantation system.   For its success to last, the continual lowering of costs through improvements in technique has not been enough, for its success postulates free trade throughout the world. The desire to achieve national self-sufficiency set bounds to the attempt. Monopolies and strict control of crops were countered by high tariffs, quotas, and the competition of substitutes. The ruin of the indigo plantations is significant. Between 1880 and 1885 this commodity was still fourth largest export from the East Indies, being surpassed only by sugar, coffee, and tobacco.[1] This history of sugar in Java affords another illustration. In spite of the extraordinary achievements of Dutch science and organisation, the commodity saw its

[1] Between 1898 and 1920 the number of indigo plantations in the Principalities —the chief productive district in Java for the crop—fell from 99 to 14 and the exports from 617 to 58 tons.

markets suddenly occupied by Western European beet and then by cane sugar from Cuba, India, and Formosa. The area under sugar-cane fell from 470,000 acres in 1928 to 67,000 acres in 1935; production fell from 2,900,000 to 500,000 tons; and 800,000 seasonal labourers were deprived of the addition to their income they had been wont to find in this paying crop.

In 1936 the total wages paid to the natives by plantations were hardly a tenth of those paid in 1928. Owing to the delay in signing the Chadbourne plan, the Dutch Colonial Government had to take drastic measures. Production was reduced to one sixth of the total capacity of the factories; many sugar-refineries were pulled down and their machinery and rails sold as scrap iron. Not a few individuals and companies were ruined. Between 1937 and 1942 production rose again, but the plan elaborated just before the war aimed at the final elimination of the least favourably placed plantations and the reduction of the equipment to only half of its former capacity.[1] The Oostkust Province of Sumatra with its varied plantations was itself hard hit, and of nearly 700,000 Javanese who worked there in prosperous times only 134,000 were still employed in 1936.

On the other hand, the irregular and often unexpected efforts of native cultivators to grow crops for export induced the Governments to intervene directly in the affairs of the peasantry. Nor was this a new thing. The need for it had long been proclaimed, and the peasant had already felt some benefit from it, including the introduction of new plants and acquaintance with better methods of cultivation due to the Church in the Philippines and by the system of forced labour in Indonesia. But later the measures were carried out more skilfully, more perseveringly, and more comprehensively. It was no longer intended merely to increase production, but also by controlling the development of native society to keep it balanced, to guide the humble cultivator, the *kleine man*, gently towards a better standard of living, to protect him against his own impulses and against the rude blows dealt by world crises on his traditional economy, and, lastly, to make him wish to profit from his own initiative and from work well done.

Peasant cultivation from its very nature shows greater flexibility than the plantation to external influence. When a commodity is selling badly, its production can be curtailed in the case of an annual; shrubs and trees can be left alone for some time without risk to their lives. This is not equally true of all, however. The rubber tree bears the cessation of tapping better than the tea bush tolerates not having its leaves picked. Overheads which fall so heavily on

---

[1] The war and the Japanese occupation once more helped to hasten the decline of the sugar industry in Java. See below, p. 426.

plantations, which usually depend on a single crop, are of little account to the peasant. In lean years when money becomes scarce in the villages, he will fall back on his own resources and will give up growing on his land the crop which formerly brought a profit, but can now no longer be sold. Paraffin will be replaced in his lamp by vegetable oil, and flint and tinder will take the place of matches. He will be satisfied with cheaper cloth and will earn by domestic industry or peddling the wherewithal to pay his taxes and to buy salt, brine, and other articles which he cannot do without.[1] In 1935 the economic depression was seen to have less serious effects on the people of the country than on the Europeans, 10,000 of whom were unemployed in Indonesia. Most of the sugar factories had to stop work, and the plantations suffered great losses, whilst their unemployed labourers simply went back to their native villages. The elasticity of native economy was admirable. Nevertheless, in overpopulated districts like Java crises reduced the resources of the peasantry to dangerously near the minimum. Not only were the people emaciated in body, but they were also troubled in mind, since they were unable to understand the sudden variations in prices and wages caused by a combination of circumstances throughout the world.

The stability of the autochthonous communities could not be assured merely by official regulation and engineering technique, but required an ever closer understanding of the psychology and social life of the people of Southeast Asia. The broadening of minds which were walled in by routine and the cure of ills that enfeeble or destroy the body call for a deep knowledge of mentality and a patient and expert observation by geographers, ethnologists, and sociologists of the relation between man and his physical environment.

The new ideas appeared in the help given to native agriculture to increase its yield and make it more regular, to establish a proper balance between food-crops and produce for export, and to ensure greater profit for the peasant's work. We have seen above[2] what extensive irrigation works had been carried out in Java since the end of the last century and how meticulous study not only of the relief, soil, and drainage, but also of the methods of cultivation and traditions of the countryfolk had led to constant improvement in the canal system and distribution of water in this over-populated island. In other parts this modern work had so far affected quite small areas, but it had helped to reduce the import of rice into districts in which export crops had spread rapidly since the beginning of the century,

[1] Van der Kolff (221).   [2] Page 199.

as, for instance, in Malaya,[1] the lowlands near Luzón, and, finally, Sumatra and south-western Celebes, where irrigation was mainly intended to help the little Javanese settlement.

Whatever treasures of experience were accumulated by successive generations of native cultivators of rice and other food-crops, yields are still poor, for the peasant does not plant selected seed, seldom uses manure, and has nothing but primitive implements. Groups of agricultural advisers were formed. In Indonesia they took the place, in fact, of the inspectors in van den Bosch's system; but, as they were not in the service of a monopoly, they had a more complex task, whose sole object was to improve native agriculture. They were intermediaries between the peasants and the purely research establishments. After local enquiry, they offered practical solutions to problems that had arisen and they circulated these solutions by means of a service recruited almost exclusively among the natives and designed to supply information and give training in agriculture.

The Effects of Usury. But it would be of little use for the small cultivator to increase his crop, unless he profited directly from so doing. The share taken by middlemen is often excessive. Here and there the Government had had to interfere; thus, in East Java the Dutch administration provided advice for Madurese smallholders, who were too easily tricked by European or Chinese buyers; and it even established public markets.[2] But the trader is a moneylender also. Like many other peasant communities in Monsoon Asia and elsewhere, the Indonesians are oppressed by a burdensome system of usury which, whilst it certainly is due to lack of forethought and poverty, helps extraordinarily to aggravate their unhappy condition. In times of scarcity or when a family occasion occurs, the peasant cheerfully gets a loan; nor does the debt disturb his sleep; but he has so much difficulty in paying it back that the interest accumulates, and he has to pledge his crops and property. The usurious rates of interest generally asked correspond to the risks run by the lender and the steps to be taken to recover or renew the loan and keep an eye on the real estate which forms his security. This usury is generally carried on with a trade in grain and other farm produce. It is sometimes practised by Europeans or Eurasians, natives, Indians, or Arabs, but the past masters of the business here as in Indo-China are the Chinese.[3]

---

[1] In Malaya a Drainage and Irrigation Department was set up in 1932. At the end of 1937 about 37,000 acres were being systematically irrigated, mostly in Perak and Selangor.

[2] Goubeaux (214), p. 20.

[3] The middlemen, mainly Chinese, are moneylenders, collectors, and carriers,

Usury cuts down the peasants' earnings in varying proportions which are difficult to assess accurately, but are certainly considerable. Many of the moneylenders are immigrants who send home a portion of their gains. The native thus works on a good many days in the year for the benefit of his creditors and loses the capital indispensable to the improvement of his land and his house, the purchase of implements, selected seed, cattle and manure, and to the storage of his crops.

These loans at high interest end in the creditors taking over the land. After pledging their crops the peasants have to mortgage the land itself and thus become tenants permanently in debt. This is the usual condition of the smallholder in the Philippines, and quarrels between *aparceros* and landlords, strikes and riots among the *métayers*, farmers, and agricultural labourers are far from being rare, and the problem of the distribution of land often comes under discussion. In 1925 out of every 100 heads of families in Java only 50 owned or seemed to own their land. Of these 50 only 3 were regarded as well off, 35 worked for others, mainly for other natives; and, besides these, 5 were employed on European estates.[1]

Hence, it was extremely desirable to set up a system of people's banks so as to supply the native with the capital required for his current needs at a very low rate of interest; and at the beginning of this century one was established in Indonesia in a form often copied later. Owing to the difficulties of the task, the advance of huge sums and the risk involved, such a system could only be undertaken by the Government. A central treasury controls the people's banks which are entrusted with the giving of loans, and at first the banks used money advanced by the central treasury. Their struggle with the moneylenders was fairly effective, but slow and difficult. The money often went in the first instance not to the little cultivator, but to the landowner, whose land formed security and who had himself become indebted to the banks and big moneylenders during a slump. But as he in turn advanced money to his tenants, the banks were actually fattening usury. The little cultivator must be reached

and they prepare native produce for export, viz. rice, maize, ground-nuts, kapok, rubber, tobacco, coffee, and coconut. The native competes vigorously with the Chinaman in only a few places, in particular in Minangkabau and Palembang Districts, southern Borneo, and southern Celebes. A moderate estimate of the share that falls to the producer places it at half the price paid by the consumer. But it is sometimes far less and may fall to one-eighth of the selling-price in the case of commodities of small value, like sweet potatoes. Boeke (186), p. 178.

[1] Meyer Ranneft in Schrieke (20), p. 81. Out of 10 other heads of families in the 100, 2 were officials and 8 employed in native commerce or industry. As the transfer of land for debt is not recorded in official registers, its detection is very difficult and consequently the progress of transfer is hard to estimate. (Boeke (186), p. 42.)

directly; but he is still passive and inert. The ultimate object is to base the people's banks on the free co-operation of the users and to supply the local banks with money not for third parties, but exclusively for the villagers. Such an aim assumes the development of native mentality, which is taking place slowly, and a desire for progress and improved comfort which is appearing by degrees in the rural masses. In 1938 there were 540 co-operative societies in Indonesia, 427 of which were savings and loans banks. Many others were for debt redemption, the associations undertaking to sell the crops; and a few were producers' or consumers' societies.

Co-operation between Plantation and Native Cultivators. In short, the time still seemed far off, if it ever came, when the co-existence of the plantation and the native smallholding would become impossible. At first, since they were unrelated to each other, they might look like rivals; but they have not merely hampered each other. The introduction of exotic plants and the research into improvements in agriculture, of which native cultivation later took advantage, were undertaken for the benefit of the plantations. It was in order to survive in face of the native smallholder's competition that the plantations have constantly had to improve their organisation and technique. The history of rubber cultivation is a good example of this rivalry, by which the consumers benefit.

At times a closer tie, a real co-operation, might be seen between the capitalist plantation and the smallholding peasants. It happened particularly when the produce from smallholdings was worked up by European industry before being exported. This had been the case with many Philippine commodities, especially since the arrival of American capitalists, who have invested in industries of transformation far more than in production itself. To the cigar and cigarette factories existing even in the days of Spanish rule had been added many sugar refineries, 'Centrals', which at times deal with canes from their own plantations, but also use those from native smallholdings in far greater quantities. The smallholdings have been organised on a co-operative basis recognised by the Government for the improvement of cultivation and the supervision of the faithful execution of contracts by the Centrals. Some co-operative societies have their own technical staff of scientific agriculturists, chemists, and accountants. Improvements do not seep down quickly to the tenants, but it would be even more difficult to reach each of them directly. On the other hand, the kernel of the coconut, instead of being exported in the form of copra, has its value raised more and more by the extraction of the oil, which is done in large factories.

In Indonesia this development was less advanced. But, especially in the Priangan Residencies, native-grown tea was often prepared for export by European factories, where it formed an addition, termed 'cottage leaf' to the usually more plentiful product of the plantation.

In north-eastern Java native-grown tobacco was bought by Europeans, who dried and fermented the leaf.[1]

Perhaps there will be many schemes enabling not a few of the advantages of the plantation to be fused in some form of compromise system with those of native smallholdings, since these smallholdings seem to be indispensable to social equilibrium.

1 About nine-tenths of the kapok exported from Indonesia (more than two-thirds of world production) was native-grown, mainly in Mid and East Java. But the ginneries mostly belonged to Chinese.

CHAPTER 19

THE PROBLEM OF INDUSTRIALISATION

In colonial territories there was the same contrast in industry as in agriculture between the traditional native crafts said to be out-of-date, and powerful organisations of the Western pattern. But as in agriculture, one realises that conditions are temporary. The main problem is to determine the manner and rhythm of an inevitable development and to forecast the prospective relations between the two kinds of industry, one surviving from the past and the other foreshadowing the future.

Mining. First of all comes mining, which produces raw materials, largely for export. Some of its products were not used before the coming of the Europeans, others were extracted only in small quantities by primitive methods. Of course, those methods had been improved, in the case of the Sumatran gold mines by the Hindus perhaps and certainly by the Chinese, who were to be found almost everywhere—here as elsewhere in the Far East—at the beginning of mining operations. It was in mining, however, that European technique was to win its earliest success. For the sinking of shafts, tunnelling of galleries, removal of masses of waste, and the washing and refining of useful minerals there is no comparison between the old methods and Western machine processes. The former, though still practised in spare moments here and there even by workers in modern establishments, produce only a tiny proportion of the gold and tin exported from the East Indies. There is a striking contrast between the tin wash-trough shaken by the native washer on the one hand and the pontoon dredgers in Perak or Belitong, which remove several million cubic yards in the course of a year.

As, on the other hand, certain mineral products have an assured market, sometimes locally in the country itself, but more often in the metropolitan or other countries overseas, it is not surprising that their extraction should be the object of large companies with huge capital and that the native should have been reduced here as on the plantations to the condition of a hireling. The Chinaman has not allowed himself to be easily got rid of. His resistance is particularly evident in Malaya, where it is encouraged by the scattered nature of the deposits of tin and by the later intervention of the European engineer. Some Chinese owners have been able, with European help, to adopt the new technique and introduce highly efficient machinery. However, even here the Chinese share in production as a whole has steadily declined since the beginning of the century.

The mineral products almost always have the advantage of being mined near the sea and they have accounted for 20 per cent. of the value of exports from Malaya and 25 per cent. of that from Indonesia and the Philippines.

Most of the ores worked in Malay lands come from ancient eruptive rocks (Permian, Jurassic, Triassic, and above all Cretaceous) which have intruded through the sedimentary beds. The metallic elements have often been separated from the other constituents of the rock and concentrated; and they have filled cracks in the beds nearby. The Permo-carboniferous system, though in most parts of the world the seat of coal formations, is here composed of deep-sea deposits without the mineral, which like oil is found most abundantly in Tertiary beds. The distribution of the principal fields is connected with the former prolongation of the mainland of Asia. When above water the low coast of the Sunda shelf was favourable to the accumulation of organic matter which could be changed into coal or mineral oil and in which were sandwiched sedimentary and volcanic rocks. The whole grew thicker on the subsidence of the geosynclines. The folding at the beginning of the Quaternary period formed anticlines into which the oil ran.[1]

Tin derived from granitic intrusions is much more plentiful than other metals.[2] Malaya and Banka, Belitong, and Singkep in Indonesia supply nearly half of world production, the greater part being refined in factories in Singapore or Penang.[3]

The extraction of ore is still carried on at different points in the Malay Peninsula. On the other hand, Banka and Belitong have two large concerns with power stations, huge charcoal ovens for refining the ore, timber yards, laboratories and hospitals, and food depôts, as in fact nearly all the food for the employees has to be imported. The Malay lands are less well endowed with other useful ores.[4]

---

[1] Rutten (33), pp. 200 ff. Ter Braake (237), pp. 7–20.

[2] Van den Broek (231). Today tin is far behind mineral oil in export value.

[3] From 1934 to 1940 a certain amount of tin ore from Indonesia was exported to the refineries at Arnhem and since the end of the war to those in Texas.

[4] Yet reserves of bauxite with a high content have been found in the Rhio group and especially on the island of Bintan. Working began in 1935, and production rose to 275,000 tons in 1940. At the time of the Japanese invasion the construction of an aluminium factory was being begun near the Wilhelmina Falls on the Asahan, the outlet of Lake Toba. (Ter Braake 237), p. 79.) Besides this, nickel deposits similar to those in New Caledonia began to be worked in 1937. In 1940 some 55,000 tons of ore were extracted, mainly from the mines at Tolitoli at the extreme end of the northern peninsula of Celebes, and were exported chiefly to Japan, this country having taken Germany's place as the principal buyer.

34.
Pickers of tea-leaves at work in the
Cameron Highlands, Malaya

35.
A plantation of oil-palms at Layang
Layang, Johore

36.
Tobacco growing in the Province
of Deli, Sumatra

37.
A rubber plantation near Singapore

38.
A peasant plantation of areca palms in
Achin, Sumatra

39.
A typical plantation of *abaca* (*Musa tex-tilis*—Manila hemp) in Davao, Philip-pines. The plants are three years old.

The iron ore extracted in Malaya and the Philippines forms but a minute percentage of world production, and the same is true of copper in the Philippines. On the other hand, the Philippines are beginning to be important for chromium and manganese, the value of which is nevertheless still far less than that of gold.

In Malay lands the Philippines have become the leading producer of this precious metal and in 1939 took seventh place in world production.[1] Indonesia no longer justifies the reputation for fabulous wealth in gold which was once associated with the name of Java. In fact, traces of former gold workings are more numerous in Sumatra and Borneo than in that island. The total production from Indonesia in 1939 was barely more than 2·2 tons of gold and 18 tons of silver, extracted by some ten companies, the largest of which operate in the backland of Benkulen.

The value of the exports of oil far exceeds that of any other mineral in the Malay world. It comes almost exclusively from Sumatra, Borneo, and Java. In Indonesia the value of the exports of oil was about five times that of tin in 1938 and nearly four times in 1954. Oil is also the chief mineral raised in British Borneo.[2] Except in Serang, where it was extracted from the Triassic beds, the oil is got from Tertiary sedimentaries which have been folded, but usually to a slight degree. The deposits that have been located are not all workable, either because the oil has not been able to concentrate in porous formations at the top of anticlines, or else because it has been able to escape through cracks or erosional channels. Petroleum is more widely distributed than tin, but is of more recent exploitation and is thus subject to an even more vigorous concentration of capital. This is favoured by the fact that in Indonesia the owner of the soil has no claim to minerals below the surface. Two big groups shared the production: the Royal Dutch Shell Oil Co., an Anglo-Dutch concern, and the Standard Oil Co., an American trust. In 1939 production did not reach 4 per cent. of the world total, but it was the highest in the Far East. Prospecting was active outside Indonesia in western New Guinea, where, moreover, the Government of the Netherlands Indies had reserved the working rights. Except on two fields in eastern Borneo, all the oil produced was refined on the spot, the largest refineries being those of the Royal Batavian Petroleum at Balik Papan. Methods of boring and extraction were much improved and were equal to the best in the United States. The depth of the wells varied between 650 and 4600 feet.[4]

The Malay lands are poor in coal, for this mineral is hardly worked except in the old Tertiary beds. There it is often much like the coal

1 In 1940 35 tons were extracted, but in 1950 only 10·3 tons.
2 For oil extracted in British Borneo, see pp. 433–4.

from the Hercynian deposits in Europe, whilst the water content greatly increases in the Upper Tertiary strata, and the coal passes into lignite or even peat. It sometimes happens, as in the mine at Bukit Assem near Palembang, where the coal has been changed into anthracite, that recent intrusions of volcanic rocks have matured the coal before its time. This poverty in coal[1] will certainly be an obstacle to the development of transforming industries and especially of metallurgy. Coking coal is rare, but there is hope that iron may be smelted with charcoal or by electricity.

Transforming Industries. Apart from mining there were in Malaya modern industrial concerns sometimes worked by Chinese, but more often by Europeans. Most of them were intended to prepare agricultural produce for export. They included sugar refineries, mills turning out sheet and crêpe rubber, presses for extracting oil from coco- and palm-nuts, factories for treating tea leaves, cassava rhizomes, sisal or *abacá* leaves, and pine-apple canneries, etc. They were very often placed centrally or in the immediate neighbourhood of plantations and worked mainly for export to distant countries. Together with mining these industries led to the introduction of machinery into the East Indies, but they were not connected with the problem of the industrialisation of colonies which had been so much discussed in recent years.

This problem was indeed serious, because it involved the prospect of a complete change in imperial economic systems. On the arrival of the Europeans in the East Indies industry was not unknown to the local populations, but it was only of the domestic kind, producing everything required to satisfy needs, whether material, such as food, clothes, and personal ornaments, furniture, and vehicles; or mental, such as artistic productions and objects connected with religion. It was very widespread, generally complementary to agriculture and therefore intermittent, and employed only very simple, hand-operated tools. The highly specialised craftsman kept no stock of either raw materials or manufactures, since the latter were sold in local markets as soon as made. This industry gave rise to but a small amount of exports, which was more or less balanced by the import of certain luxury goods, especially Chinese cloth and earthenware.

It was through the Arabs and even more through the Chinese that the produce of Western industry entered Malaya, even before the Europeans themselves. Imports increased after the establishment of European 'factories', the profits from them being reserved to the metropolitan country by a system of agreements. At the same time

---

[1] The total annual production was about 3,000,000 tons in the Malay world as a whole, and coal had to be imported, in spite of the surplus obtained in Indonesia. In 1939 the Netherlands Indies exported about 520,000 tons to the Philippines, Singapore, Hongkong, China, and Indo-China.

the 'factories' devoted themselves to trade 'between the Indies and
the Indies'. In the 19th century the development of machinery
enabled European industry to produce in such large quantities that
machines have rightly been considered to be one of the chief causes
of colonial expansion. It was then that the exchanges of raw
material for manufactured goods which were to reach their full extent
after 1880 were organised between the industrial metropolitan
country and its tropical territories.

Native industries could not but feel the effect of this development.
In spite of its cheapness, their produce could not well continue to
compete with Western commodities, whose prices were constantly
being lowered by the progress of technical knowledge and skill,
rationalisation, and mass production. However, the decline of
native industries has not been uniform, and they have not all died
out. A study of statistics, enquiry in the shops and especially in the
bazaars, and an investigation of movable property and modes of life
would give a tolerable picture of their various fates.

Manufactured goods formed a high percentage of the imports into
all parts of the Malay world. The percentage was, however, higher
in Indonesia and the Philippines than in Malaya, which was far from
self-sufficing in foodstuffs. Among the goods of European or
American manufacture textiles of all sorts reached the highest figure
in value. They included woollen, cotton, and rayon thread and
cloth, and ready-made clothes. Then came very various types of
metal goods from sheet and bar iron to household ware of iron and
aluminium; machines and fittings from locomotives and motor
vehicles to wireless sets, sewing machines, and electrical equipment.
The quantity of paper imported indicated the progress of local
publishing, and especially of the native press, as well as the amount
required for wrapping; whilst the imports of fertilisers showed the
needs of the plantations.

These manufactured goods were not all intended merely for the
Europeans and their businesses, but also to satisfy the wants and
new tastes of the native masses. The goods were plentiful in the
towns and, though scarcer in rural areas, they were everywhere to be
seen and penetrated right into the heart of the remotest mountain
districts. Yet they had not ruined the domestic industries. Bales
of imported cotton cloth unbleached, dyed, or printed with various
patterns according to the taste of the customers, struck the attention
of visitors to the markets. But native weaving still survived and
was increasingly supplied with machine-spun yarn. Materials for
building native houses, furniture, tools, and interior decoration still
usually came from the little handicrafts that exist in nearly all
villages or were the preserve of a few groups of specialised hereditary

craftsmen. Their products, including pottery, mats and basket-work, vessels of wood or bamboo, *sarongs* and hats, and articles connected with religion, crowd the bazaars in town and country. Some very strong native cloths still enjoyed a high reputation; and rice was thought to be more tasty when boiled in native pots than in aluminium or enamel vessels.

In Java alone the number of people trying to earn a living by their handicrafts was estimated in 1938 at a million and a half; and this figure should certainly be multiplied two or three times to include the peasants of both sexes who had found in handicraft an inter-mittent occupation and a complementary source of income indis-pensable to their lives. The proportion of craftsmen seemed parti-cularly high in densely populated districts, like Mid Java or the neighbourhood of Manila, where land was scarce.

So, up to 1939, though the crafts have suffered to some extent, they had held out in country districts against the invasion of foreign goods; but they would probably soon give way before the rise of modern industry when this was established in the region itself.

Let us see what the condition of this modern industry was in 1939 so far as accuracy is possible with statistics which are imperfect and difficult to compare. In numbers employed and value of production it remained fairly small. If the many factories attached to planta-tions are left out of account, most of the industries were concentrated in a few ports, where they found raw material, fuel, immigrant labour, whether local or from the mainland of Asia, consumers in plenty, and facilities for export. Thus, at Penang and even more at Singapore, these industries benefited from the *entrepôt* activities in the ports. Many smoke ovens in them treated low-grade rubber from the Peninsula, Indonesia, British Borneo, Siam, and Burma. The two great workshops belonging to the Straits Trading and the Eastern Smelting Companies smelted tin not only from the mines in Malaya and Indo-China, but also small quantities from Alaska, East and South Africa, China, and Australia. With rubber was associ-ated the manufacture of footwear, tyres, hoses, toys, and also aluminium coagulating vats for the plantations, whilst part of the equipment needed in the tin mines was made at Ipoh and Kampar in the district of Kinta. Other establishments with modern equipment consisted of machine repair shops or shipyards for building small vessels or else they produced foodstuffs (beer, ice, aerated drinks, alcohol, biscuits, tapioca, and coconut and groundnut oil), soap, building materials (cement and concrete blocks), printed matter, matches, and tobacco.

Apart from the shops working tin, there were no large concerns in Malaya, and most of the factories employed no more than 150 hands.

Hardly anything was exported beyond agricultural or mineral produce needing but a slight transformation, such as sheet rubber and tin ingots.

The Dutch and American territories presented a picture which differed only slightly from this. In Indonesia, apart from the 45,000 workers employed in mining, modern industries were well manned by 120,000 persons in 1936. In 1937 the value of their total production was estimated at much less than half that of the traditional industries: 78,000,000 as against 180,000,000 florins. They were most numerous and varied in Java, since this overcrowded island had a plentiful supply of labour. In 1937 omitting the mills on plantations, Java had 2276 establishments which came under the Factory Act, whilst the Outer Provinces had 1428. Most of the factories in Java employed no more than between 10 and 200 hands, only a few employing more than 1000. Many of them are situated in the three towns of Jakarta, Surabaya, and Semarang, but efforts have been made to escape from the attraction of these large ports and to set up factories in the heart of the overcrowded districts in the east and centre of the island; for instance, at Tegal, Bandung, Garut, and Probolinggo. Among the most remarkable establishments set up before the war may be mentioned factories for the production of soap, margarine, paint, glass, and toothpaste, two breweries with an annual output of about 1,760,000 gallons of beer, and big cigarette factories producing some 10,000,000,000 cigarettes, not only of the European type, but also of the native kind, or *kretok*, in which the tobacco is scented with Zanzibar cloves and rolled in a maize leaf. The Goodyear Tyre and Rubber Co. used to make tyres in Java. Repair shops had been turned into assembly works and even manufactured travelling bags for pilgrims to Mecca, bicycles and other machines, and a portion of the equipment needed in sugar-mills. General Motors assembled motor vehicles at Jakarta with parts imported from the United States. Lastly, several modern spinning and weaving mills were already working in Java in 1938, like the one at Garut which employed more than 1500 hands and the one at Tegal which specialised in white fabrics. Paper mills with very up-to-date equipment used raw or partly worked material and themselves made the necessary potash and chlorine.

In the Philippines, too, modern industry was still on a small scale, in spite of the progress made under American stimulus, especially since 1914. Apart from factories preparing the staple commodities for export, viz. sugar, coconut oil, and hemp, nearly all of which were scattered about in the districts producing the raw materials, most of the manufactured goods were made in Manila and its neighbourhood, others being produced in Sebu. Elsewhere there were only little workshops. The period between the wars had seen the development of the boot and shoe industry which in part used imported leather and almost met the needs of the group; and of the cigarette industry, which was often associated in a single concern with cigar-making, but employed far more machinery, especially for the favourite American cigarette which competed more and more with the Spanish article. A commodity peculiar to the Philippines was the wax candle, which was connected with the Roman Catholic religion. Manila's foundries and metallurgical shops had begun to produce nails, bolts, and spare parts for machinery. They employed about 1500 hands.

Advantages and Dangers of Industrialisation. Clearly, modern industries will increase in number in Malay lands. But one would like to know at what rate the increase will move and whether the development will closely follow the lines laid down in Western countries.

The advocates of industrialisation have had ample opportunity of proclaiming its economic, social, and political advantages.[1] The purchasing power of the population depends on a fairly small number of agricultural products exported in a raw or half-raw state. The prices of the products vary a great deal, whilst those of imported manufactures—whose cost is added to by the expense of carriage over a long distance—oscillate within far narrower limits. The rise of local industries would give more stability to the life of the people and would be a source of well-being. The concentration of population in certain districts creates very favourable conditions for this development owing to the plentiful supply of cheap labour. Though the output of the Malay worker is lower than that of the European workman, it can be raised by judicious training. Furthermore, industrial development will be one of the most effective remedies for the evils due to overpopulation, which are not adequately countered by improvements in agriculture or emigration.[2]

The political advantages would be no less evident. The budgets and social equilibrium of distant countries would be less affected by crises due to overproduction and a fall in world prices. Not only would the new industries meet local demands to a great extent, but they would also certainly enable profit to be made from exports to neighbouring countries. In case of war they would conspicuously improve the possibilities of defence. In times of peace their competition would not be as ruinous as it was at first thought to be for the Protecting Power's industries, which might themselves

[1] On this subject, see Hulshoff, van der Wærden, in (232). See also Broek (186), pp. 76–86; Rhote (235).
[2] Van der Wærden (232).

establish branches, branches that might act as bases for the conquest of markets in the Far East. The Protecting Power would supply these offspring not only with capital and technicians, but also with the equipment needed to set them going. Some of the consumer goods which it was wont to sell would find markets contracting, but others expanding, owing to the increase in purchasing power among the swarming local population.

Lastly, it was added that industrialisation is the destined end of national progress, and tropical lands should attain it, just as their Protecting Powers in the temperate belt have done. It would be a selfish and short-sighted act to try to prevent such a development, which is necessary not only for the material prosperity, but also for the moral and spiritual health of the Malay community. The investment of local or Chinese capital in industry would, furthermore, diminish usury and the terrible oppression that it exercises over the peasant. Reason may demand the control of industrialisation, but forbids it to be fettered.

These arguments were countered by the opponents of industrialisation. That they too should be influenced in their opinion by their interests is not surprising. They emphatically affirmed that, in spite of the optimistic assertions of its advocates, colonial industry would cut off many factories in the home country of the Protecting Power from their safest and most profitable markets; that the profits arising from imports was but a fair return for the efforts and sacrifices made by Europeans in these tropical lands; and that to favour the economic independence of the dependencies would thereby hasten their political autonomy and the ripening and fall of the fruit from the tree.

It is further urged that conditions in the Malay lands are not all favourable to industrialisation. Indonesia certainly has a big surplus of petroleum; but the Malay world cannot supply its own needs in coal, and its reserves are problematical. As for 'white coal', practical achievements have so far been small, and the potential should not be exaggerated. The small size of the river basins in the limited area of the islands increases the irregularity of the flow of the streams owing to the alternation of wet and dry monsoons. Borneo is the sole exception to this rule.

Not only would motive power often prove insufficient, but so also would raw material in many of the industries contemplated. Metallurgy would not only be without coking coal, but would also lack iron ore. There is not much sericulture, and cotton production is inadequate even for present needs.

The transforming industries would, moreover, require safe outlets in the Far Eastern markets, which are said to be wide open. In fact, though, industry has increased not only in Japan, but also in China, Indo-China, and India. There would still be the home market; but even there it would be necessary to struggle against the competition of certain foreign countries which are ready to dump goods and which have a further advantage in their cheap labour, their organisation, and the start they have already had. Protective tariffs would not suffice to guarantee the prosperity of the new industries, since they would raise the cost of manufactures which should remain within the reach of the very small purchasing power of the masses.

Lastly, there is no certainty that the rise of industry would provide an effective remedy for overpopulation. Big factories would kill the local crafts, which are already weakened by the competition of imported goods. One industrial worker would thenceforth suffice for production that would ensure the existence of a large number of persons. In many rural districts in Java and the plains of Luzón the evils of overpopulation would on the contrary be exaggerated.

The war of 1914–18 greatly diminished the trade between the East Indian colonies and their Protecting Powers, the world depression in 1930–35 brought to light the weakness of the economic system then existing, and the war of 1939–45 increased still further the isolation and embarrassment due to this weakness. Hence, there has been a vigorous recrudescence of discussion of the problem.

Under pressure from opposing interests, but also, it would seem, as the result of deliberate policy, the Colonial Governments adopted a compromise solution. Breaking away from the progressive policy, whose benefits and efficiency had long been proclaimed, they had, especially after 1931, to tighten the economic bonds between the colonies and the Protecting Power at the expense of foreign buyers and sellers by means of quotas, bounties, tariffs, and the granting of privileges to steamship companies. But at the same time they made plans for the introduction of a moderate amount of regulated local industry. Only such establishments were permitted or encouraged as could stand on their own feet without tariffs that were burdensome or prejudicial to the general interest. Several of the industries mentioned above were due to this policy. Local factories were set up in Java by Dutch and foreign companies, like the textile manufactures in Twente or the American Rubber Tyre Co., which exported to Indonesia. As early as 1882 the Government of Indonesia had given an impetus to the extraction of mineral oil by advancing funds free of interest to further boring operations. But the greatest direct Government assistance provided by the granting of capital for industrial development has been due to the National Development Co., in the Philippines. Yet, in spite of this provision of capital, throughout the colonies in the Malay world the industries needed for the defence of the countries had only just been started at the time of the Japanese attack.

One of the chief aims has been to safeguard the existence of minor native industries and, if possible, to inspire them with new life and to prevent the overcrowding of the workers in sordid slums like those in Bombay or even in certain Malay towns like Sebu. With this special object in view the Netherlands Government had advanced 25,000,000 florins to Indonesia in 1937. Travelling instructors working in harmony with the Education Department were entrusted with the duty of studying existing processes and recommending and afterwards popularising desirable improvements.

The native textile industry, which is the most important in Java, was to be the first to benefit from these measures. In 1937 the number of old-fashioned looms was estimated at more than 200,000; but improved hand-looms had increased from 500 in 1931 to about 20,000 and power-looms from 45 to 4,500. Efforts were also made to introduce new methods into the manufacture of white porcelain at Bajarnegara, and into the brick-making in the Brantas valley which serves the needs of Surabaya; and to improve agricultural equipment, which was, however, to remain very simple and cheap.

Efforts were further made to hold the balance between factory and domestic industry. In Java many workshops organised by natives or Chinese and employing a few dozen or even hundreds of work-people form the link between the domestic workshop and the big humming European factory with its large glass windows. It would be well if these businesses did not compete with each other, but gave mutual support. The industries of *batik*, shoe-making, native cigarette production, and basketry also seem to allow of the same diversity of organisation.

Local industries, which work for export, like the making of plaited hats in Java and embroidery in Luzón, have profited most from European assistance. The embroidery is a good example of an industry that has been improved and strengthened by the Euro-peans. It is very ancient, having been introduced by Spanish, French, and Belgian nuns with the object of decorating the churches and enlivening their ceremonies. But its prosperity dates from the war of 1914–18, when imports of French and Belgian embroidery into the United States ceased. American firms then set up in Manila central workshops in which imported cloth—mainly crêpe de Chine, georgette, and batiste—was cut out. It was then distributed with some sewing cotton to the workers in their homes. These workers were particularly numerous in the rice plains near Manila and also northwards right into the province of Tarlac and southwards into Batangas. The sorting of the embroidered tissues is done at selected places before the work is sent to Manila. The giving up of certain processes, especially the traditional ornamental patterns, is unfortunately too often the price to be paid for this development. Today the types are standardised according to the requirements of the importers.

In 1939 manufactured produce occupied a very small place in the exports from the Malay lands; but they were making appreciable progress. And the most industrialised islands, Java and Luzón, were already finding important customers in other islands of their respective groups. In 1936–7 Java greatly increased its sales of *sarongs*, cigarettes, tyres, soap, and beer.

As in agriculture, the smooth, healthy development of industry requires every class in the local community to play its part. It demands not only the hands of trained workers, but also the capital and initiative of the upper classes. Hitherto, the only way for a native to grow rich has been for him to lend money at high interest, a practice which has led to the monopolisation of land through the taking over of property for debt. On the large estates thus acquired the new owner generally made few improvements, and the traditional methods of agriculture were perpetuated under a system by which the land was let to farmers in a variety of ways either for rent or on *métayage*. However, an interest in new forms of business had been aroused and for some years had been slowly increasing among rich local people. Some had joined together to form transport firms; whilst others had started small-scale manufacture or contrived to organise craft industries. Though private capital does not play so large a part as the Government in establishing sugar-mills in the Philippines, yet it does give some assistance, as it does also to a lesser extent in the preparation of coconut and hemp products for the market and in setting up saw- and rice-mills.

The association of the ordinary people with industrial undertakings is encouraged by the Governments and is progressing mainly at the expense of the Chinese. Hence, it tends to check the leakage of capital to foreign countries. But it is desirable that the development should also lead to a progressive modification of the economic structure and that private gain in industry should be brought into harmony with an improvement in the lives of the peasants. Many observers who have a good knowledge of the native environment do not think it utopian to try to kindle new life in the villages by introducing a system of co-operation. When organised for buying as well as selling, a co-operative system would enable the craftsmen to avoid living from hand to mouth and to escape the ruthlessness of merchant-industrialists, whether Chinese or native. It looks as if co-operation should be the main factor in an agricultural revival, and it might play a similar part in maintaining and improving small and middle-sized industries in overcrowded districts. Its success calls for the loyal combination of a picked body of natives who would devote themselves to this good cause. At the same time it requires a complete change in the mentality of the peasants and a desire in each of them to escape routine. Economic evolution would perhaps itself lead to this result, but Government action should hasten developments.[1]

. [1] On quite recent industrial developments, see below, p. 442.

PART IV

COLONIAL ACHIEVEMENT

CHAPTER 20

SOCIAL AND CULTURAL ACHIEVEMENTS

Although the Malay lands form a geographical unit in the hot belt between the mainlands of Asia and Australia, they have not been uniformly influenced by European colonial systems. It is usual to contrast the material results of those systems with their social and cultural effects. From the latter point of view the difference between the Spanish *conquistadores* on the one hand and the English and Dutch on the other springs at once to the mind. The Spaniards took as their prime motive the winning over of pagans to the Cross and were stimulated in their task by the close competition of Islam. The English and Dutch pursued the business of enterprising traders and were anxious to make money. With them the mercantilism of chartered companies or State monopolies was succeeded by a progressive capitalism which introduced other methods, but was always prompted by the desire to make a profit.

At the end of the 19th century the two types of system clearly displayed their respective peculiarities. Nearly the whole of the Philippines had been converted to Roman Catholicism, but agriculture, which remained entirely in the hands of the natives, was scarcely improved in its methods and produced very little for export. In Malaya and the East Indies, on the contrary, plantations sprang up in large numbers in some places, causing a great displacement of labour, but producing large quantities of goods for export; yet in spite of recent evangelical missions, the majority of the people are not Christians. The annexation of the Philippines by the United States, that most purely capitalist country, caused a rapid advance and introduced new features into the economic system of the islands, but did not upset the social and cultural character which had been acquired during more than two hundred years under the influence of Spain and especially of the Spanish Church.

This is not the place to decide between these two types and to express an opinion of any value. The student who wishes to understand can, to begin with, only touch on the complexity of facts and

381

admire the varied picture resulting from a combination of very different geographical, historical, and ethnical factors.

On second thoughts, however, the contrast between the two types does not appear so sharp. It would be improper to describe it in the sweeping manner which some people allow themselves to use; to say, for instance, that Spain soared above the practical world and cared only for the salvation of souls, whilst the others restricted themselves to economic exploitation and neglected the task of educating and uplifting the local people. Both of these procedures have led to inhuman deeds, but also to beneficent institutions. The Spaniards massacred as conscientiously in the name of Christ the Saviour as did the servants of the Dutch East India Company in order to safeguard the monopoly of the spice trade. Today Christian missionaries, and the big plantations too, maintain schools and hospitals. If one wishes to take a common-sense view and judge according to human reason, one must admit that the end does not always justify the means and that the way in which things are done matters.

The test of a good colonial system, or at least the one adopted in this chapter, is not only conversion to a new faith, even if it be the faith which is so deeply impregnated in the Western World; nor is it purely and simply the imposition of a system of secular morality and agnostic idealism; and certainly it is not the increase of trade per unit of area or per head of population. But these facts are not to be ignored, for they are all relevant to the justification of colonial systems and to the demands which might be made on them in the future: that is, the interest taken in the native, who should be regarded as a human being and should be treated as such.

In truth, it would be easy to show that the motives activating Spanish colonial policy were not wholly disinterested; that they were not purely idealistic at bottom; and that it too rested on a mercantile system which was less strict, less efficient, and less skilful than the English and Dutch systems and which above all, as it changed very slowly, seemed terribly out-of-date at the end of the 19th century.

On the other hand, one need not be blinded by the material benefits derived by the English and Dutch from their Malay colonies or by the commercial boom in the Philippines under American tutelage, but should appreciate the generous intentions and achievements of these Western nations. In them the practical sense of the man of business is very often associated with moral scruples which cannot fairly be termed hypocritical and it would be an exaggeration to say of their anxiety for the lot of the native that in their inner conscience and in the face of public opinion it merely hides a lust for gain or simply reconciles itself with the clear-cut interests of the Europeans.[1]

It would be interesting to show by means of quotations how far consideration for the natives is reflected in the intentions and actions of the nations who invented the colonial systems. Evidence of it might be found as early as the 16th century in the missionaries, administrators, and traders. But the 19th century was the time when it developed fully and was advanced as the determining principle of colonial policy. In Sir Stamford Raffles it appears clearly. He wished to replace feudalism by a free economic system in Java not only to exalt his own country, but also to increase the welfare of the natives. He studied the history of the Malays with sympathy and enthusiasm and had the Borobudur surveyed; he founded Singapore with the foreknowledge of the great part it was to play in the imperial edifice; and he drew up a scheme for Malay education.[2] A little later van den Bosch expected from a strict application of his system that not only would his country gain in wealth, but also that the life of the East Indian peasant would be improved. It was also with this aim as well as on the score of human dignity that young and progressive Dutch thinkers violently attacked forced labour, which besides was prejudicial to private undertakings. From the end of last century a large number of documents and facts show that the peaceful evolution of native communities was placed in the forefront of attention. Many administrative measures were taken in favour of the humble native, the *kleine man* of Java and the 'little brown brother' of the Philippines. They were the effect of a general evolution of ideas in the metropolitan countries, of that 'humanitarianism' whose finest triumph had been the suppression of slavery. They also resulted from a more intelligent organisation of the Imperial economic systems, from the uneasiness of the European nations as to the future of their colonies, and from the constantly deepening knowledge of native social structure and civilisation. In this direction certain well-informed men like Raffles and Crawfurd, van Vollenhoven and Snouck Hurgronje, as well as the missionary movements, have had definite influence.

It would be useless to try to acquit colonial policy of all self-interest and it would be difficult to apportion exactly the share of the

[1] In an intelligent and humorous book about United States policy in the Philippines an American writer says that it is a hotch-potch of 'evangelical fervour, altruistic motives, hesitant nationalism, and ruinous grandmotherliness'. (Anderson (164), p. 318.)

[2] Cp. Raffles's words, quoted by Egerton in *Sir Stamford Raffles*, p. 233: 'If the time should come when the British Empire had passed away . . ., these monuments of her virtue will endure when her triumphs have become an empty name'.

different factors in the transformation of native society. But it is certain that economic developments have had considerable effect. The construction of roads and railways, the rapid expansion of crops for export, the birth of modern industry, the growth of urban centres, and other facts mentioned in the foregoing pages have had obvious repercussions. It will suffice here to dwell a little on what is often called social and cultural policy; that is, the care given directly to the bodies of the natives by medical attention or hygiene and to their minds and souls by means of education and the preaching of the Gospel.

CHAPTER 21

MEDICAL ATTENTION AND HYGIENE

There is no doubt that the expectation of life among the local peoples has been greatly increased by the European colonial systems. In 1939–40 security reigned throughout the Malay world, being maintained by police patrols even away from the coasts and towns. Piracy on the high seas had been finally suppressed; and in the interior of the islands head-hunting and raiding, which used to keep tribes like the Dyaks of Borneo and the Bataks of Sumatra in perpetual fear of attack, were things of the past.[1]

Even more than the establishment of peace, medical attention has been the cause of an increase in population and expectation of life. This fact is obviously largely responsible for the over-population which here and there imposes a difficult problem on the Colonial Governments. But it is not clear how they could have reached a solution without casting off one of the definite burdens of the White Man and without repudiating Kipling's injunction to 'bid the sickness cease'.[2]

Tropical medicine owes much to the research work of Europeans in the Malay world. Discoveries have been made and methods of prevention and cure perfected here and then passed on far and wide to other countries. Just as experimental stations did in agriculture, so medical research centres, including those set up by the Governments and those of the Pasteur Institute as well as others maintained by large companies like those owning estates in the Oostkust, have blazed the trail.[3] Vaccination against smallpox began in Java as early as 1804. Vaccine, now much improved and able to keep its virtue for a long time, can be used today in the remotest districts. In 1937 more than 5,000,000 people were vaccinated or re-vaccinated in Java and Madura and nearly 2,000,000 in the Outer Provinces, Epidemics have become far more rare and much less deadly. Thus, right up to 1910 the Karo-Bataks used to give their ages according to the number of epidemics of small-pox they had gone through, for such epidemics recurred almost regularly every eight years.[4]

[1] Nieuwenhuis, in Schrieke (20), p. 26.

[2] It should be noted that the death-rate, which fell a good deal in Java and other islands after the end of the last century, has been falling but slowly during recent years. It stood at about 19·5 per thousand as compared with 8·5 in the Netherlands. (Boeke (186), pp. 96 and 163.)

[3] Flu in Rutten (19), pp. 207–26.

[4] Middendorp in Schrieke (20), p. 43.

Inoculation has also greatly lessened the ravages of cholera, which indeed has been practically eliminated from Jakarta. The plague, which did not appear in Java till 1911, has been vigorously countered by the evacuation of huts swarming with infected rats and by the construction of new houses protected against those rodents. This method was almost completely successful in the east of the island, where the plague had only 44 victims in 1937 as against 14,435 in 1914. Leprosy has been more difficult to overcome, but an increasingly large number of patients have been collected into special villages in which attempts are made to ensure a normal life for them, whilst at the same time a study is made of the nature of this still mysterious disease and of the methods of curing it. The most famous of these establishments was founded by Dr. Heiser on the island of Culion in the Philippines.[1] Thither he took by boat patients collected by himself from all over the group, and a handful of devoted American doctors and French nuns showered attention on them. Another remarkable leper colony is that of the Rhenane Lutheran missions at Huta Salam in the Batak district.

Intestinal diseases due to various parasites, the most horrible of which is the hookworm, are very widespread. But they are disappearing before increasing popular knowledge of hygiene, improvements in house sanitation, and the supply of pure water to the natives in towns and even in villages. The water comes from springs or wells—some of which are artesian, as in the Philippines— or filtered from rivers. Among common diseases in the tropical and temperate belts tuberculosis of the lungs is one of the most fatal, especially in overcrowded and insanitary quarters in big towns. This disease and pneumonia cause respectively 81 and 97 deaths in every 1000 in the Straits Settlements.

In Malay lands as in the whole of the tropical belt the most harmful disease is malaria. Its attacks are not so fierce and its effects are usually slower than those of the plague or cholera. But though these epidemics are foreseen and kept strictly in check by means of vaccines and serums, there is no malady which levies so high a toll of human life. A person who harbours *Plasmodium* in his blood may be unaware of the fact or may seem to adapt himself to it. But many deaths are directly or indirectly attributable to it. To calculate the death-rate due to malaria most of the fevers of unspecified origin and of convulsions among children would have to be added to the ascertained cases of the disease. Not only does malaria greatly help to lower the mean expectation of life, but by its insidious action, its periodical attacks, and the frequent absenteeism which it entails it is also a powerful factor in degeneration.

[1] Roosevelt (181), p. 217.

A good deal of the technique used in the struggle against malaria was discovered and improved in Malaya and the East Indies. The development of large plantations and the construction of roads and railways, together with the seriousness of the attacks, stressed the urgency of the fight. The endemic disease was complex in appearance and mysterious in character. The turning up of the soil, the clearing of the forest, and the displacement of population entailed by road and railway construction and the establishment of new plantations brought on fresh outbreaks of malaria. The death-rate among labourers employed on the placer washings rose to frightful heights. In certain cases the whole labour force had to be renewed two or three times before the work was finished. European employers were themselves severely attacked by the disease.

The task of undertaking a methodical and scientific struggle was entrusted to permanent scientific organisations equipped with abundant means for the work. Observation showed that the essential cause of the many forms under which malaria appeared was the great variety of anopheles carriers.[1] They belong to different species which have neither the same habitat, nor the same habits, nor the same virulence. Thus, in Java malaria is generally rife in a mild form in the ricefields, except during the period immediately preceding the harvest when there is a proliferation of *Anopheles aconitus*, especially in the east of the island. But one of the worst forms of the disease appeared in the neighbourhood of Jakarta when ponds were dug on the coast for the purpose of breeding fish. At first the mangroves were blamed; but their destruction still further encouraged the propagation of the mosquito responsible, *Anopheles ludlowii*, which was got rid of only when the fish-ponds were cleaned out. This species, which also swarmed in Singapore, lays its eggs in the brackish, but light-drenched water of the lagoons in western Malaya. The radius covered by it may far exceed 1000 yards from the spot on which the eggs are laid. *Anopheles umbrosus* is also found in the lowlands of Malaya, but, unlike *ludlowii*, it loves shade in the dense forest and disappears with it.

Very far from being restricted to marshy lowlands, as is sometimes thought, malaria often has far more victims in hilly country up to 3000 feet or more. When the hills in western Malaya were cleared over large areas in order to plant rubber, malaria broke out in a terrible form due not to *Anopheles umbrosus*, but to *A. maculatus*, whose larvæ live only in clear water which flows gently and is warmed by the sun. After the conquest of the Philippines American soldiers who had moved up to the hills in search of a healthy camping ground suffered far more severely than those on the coast.

[1] Swellengrebel and Rodenwaldt (242).

The different varieties of anopheles certainly help to explain the uneven distribution of population in Malay lands. Nieuwenhuis[1] points out that whilst in Borneo, for example, the coast plains are often free from malaria, the low foothills are infested with it. Above 2000 feet it abates, thus permitting a denser settlement of more vigorous communities like the Kenya Dyaks, who live in villages of from 1500 to 2000 souls in the upper valley of the Kayan, a feeder of the Kapuas.

Hence, the struggle against malaria is based on entomology, a science which owes much to English and Dutch malaria specialists in the Far East, like Swellengrebel and Rodenwaldt. Of course the preventive use of quinine, the interruption of contact between man and anopheles by means of mosquito nets and finely meshed wire screens are always helpful measures. Night work on the placer washings is forbidden; the workers must be collected in camp or village between sunset and sunrise; and recruits are placed under observation so as to avoid infecting healthy workers. But the destruction of the insect-carrier demands special measures for every marshy area and every threatened town, if the 'malaria chain' is to be broken and the pathogenic complex of man-mosquito-hematozoa separated.[2] An improvement in the health of temporary placer workings requires at least that a film of oil should be placed on water-surfaces around the camp to a radius of half a mile, which is the longest distance the great majority of species can travel. In permanent settlements the drainage must be arranged so as to get rid of places where eggs are laid by doing away with all natural pools of water. This is achieved by constructing open canals, underground drains, and masonry conduits whose course and gradient are carefully studied. In 1930 there were 150 miles of drains for the protection of Kuala Lumpur. Gemas, a big railway junction in the interior of the State of Johore and a hotbed of very dangerous malaria, was made quite healthy by 1923. Many other cases might be quoted; for instance, the success at Sibolga on the west coast of Sumatra, where the district had become quite uninhabitable. Thanks mainly to the struggle against malaria the general death-rate on the plantations of the Senembah Company in Sumatra fell from 60·2 per mil. in 1897 to 9·1 per mil. in 1908. The work is entirely controlled by doctors.

Research has been costly,[3] but is a saving in the end. An enormous amount remains to be done to eliminate malaria from

---

[1] Nieuwenhuis in Schrieke (20), pp. 11–15.

[2] Home (238).

[3] In 1930 a sum of the order of 100,000 Straits dollars was spent on the struggle against malaria in Singapore, Penang, and Kuala Lumpur.

among the native population. But the results achieved in the Malay lands form one of the chief triumphs of the European colonial systems. Malaria is now known to be avoidable.

Since the end of the 19th century, attention has been directed to the physiology and diet of the natives. Eykman's researches in the Weltevreden laboratory between 1887 and 1895 are considered to be among the most successful. Then there were those of Grijns, Teding van Berkhout, and Radsma de Jansen. It is recognised that beriberi, which was particularly widespread among plantation coolies and workers in big towns is caused by eating polished rice, that is, rice from which the outer skin has been removed by milling. On European concerns the remedy was simple. On the plantations of the Senembah Company the death-rate from beriberi fell from 70·7 in 1897 to 31 in 1910 when rice was once more eaten unpolished. The discovery helped to emphasise the part played by vitamins in the diet—a part loudly proclaimed nowadays, but till then very slightly known—and led after careful research to an accurate recognition of the inadequacy of the food eaten by natives.

The essential aim, not yet achieved, is to determine the ideal proportions—different from those in the temperate belt—of proteins, fats, carbo-hydrates, vitamins, and salts of various kinds needed in a tropical diet;[1] to discover how far it differs from the existing proportions and to find a way of reducing the differences. Research into this matter is entrusted today to special institutes. Recent study has shown that an increase in household expenditure does not necessarily lead to an improvement in the diet. The profit derived by the native from export crops is not always sensibly used; and the increasing number of small rice-mills has encouraged the eating of polished rice and canned food even in rural districts. The development of rubber cultivation in Malaya and the western portion of Indonesia has often taken place at the expense of food crops and kitchen gardens. What most often upsets the balance of the native diet is the lack of nitrogenous foods like fish, meat, eggs, and fresh vegetables.[2]

[1] Jansen (239). [2] Pærels (209), pp. 211–20.

CHAPTER 22

CHRISTIAN MISSIONS

As has often happened in European colonies, the preaching of the Christian Gospel went hand in hand with the conquest and exploitation of the Malay lands.   But the method of spreading the Gospel and the consequences arising from it have differed greatly according to the system of the various conquering nations and the spiritual soil presented for the new seed.

Here, as in America and with rather similar methods, Christianity was first introduced by the Portuguese and Spaniards.   It is unfair to speak of a kind of organised, systematic collusion between priests and traders.   On the other hand, it is not difficult to find instances of secret or overt opposition between ecclesiastical and lay policies. But obviously, ideas are spread at the same time as goods and the same ship often brings the monk and the trader.   When one of them precedes the other, it is not usually by much, and they soon catch up each other.   They have the same origin, language, and civilisation to mark them out from the native inhabitants.   Their aims are not identical, but yet the glory of Christ must be asserted in this world and, whilst the soldier or trader in times past naturally tended to confuse that glory with the success of his arms or the profit from his trade, the priest was often obliged to use the secular arm in support of his proselytising or in defence of his threatened foundations. One of the *conquistadores* in the Philippines in the ardour of his propaganda swore by Christ that there was more gold in Luzón than iron in Viscaya.   The missionary is not merely a man who prays and preaches, but, even more than the priest in our own rural districts and suburbs, he depends on a very strong sense of the practical for the success of his cause in a heathen land.   To maintain and develop their spiritual work, the monks developed the land and even took part in local trade.[1]   Malacca and Macao were episcopal sees as well as great commercial cities in the time of Portuguese domination.

The difference between the spread of Christianity in the Philippines and the rest of the Malay world is a matter of great interest.   In the Philippines most of the population belong to the Roman Catholic Church (about 16 million, or 80 per cent. of the population in 1956); but elsewhere Christians form a small minority, numbering about $2\frac{1}{2}$ million in more than 90 million natives.

[1] On the subject of ecclesiastical trading in the Far East, see Chappoulie: *Une controverse entre missionnaires à Siam au 17e siècle*, Paris, 1943, introd.

The explanation sometimes advanced is that the temperaments of the colonising peoples were different and that the enthusiastic missionary spirit of the Iberians was in contrast with the tolerance or even indifference of the Dutch. The chief reason, however, seems to be the resistance to conversion made by the natives in the two areas. The boundary of the Christian region, which does not include all the Philippines, the Sulu Islands and even Mindanao being excluded, is convincing evidence that Christianity has found great difficulty in securing a footing among people already set fast in Islam. This religion arose in western Asia later than Christianity, but reached the East Indies earlier. At the beginning of the 16th century it had already established one of its citadels in the southern Philippines.

From their arrival, however, the Portuguese undertook the conversion of the natives. Like the Spaniards they declared that the spread of the *santa fe católica* was the whole object of colonisation. Their chain of outposts, which were quickly set up from the Indian Ocean to the shores of Southeast Asia, were relay stations for trade and at the same time missionary centres. The pioneers of the new Faith started mainly from Goa and Macao. The Moluccas attracted both monks and traders. Roman Catholic missionaries landed from the first Portuguese ships to reach Ternate and Amboina in 1511. St. Francis Xavier, formerly a Navarrese gentleman, arrived at Ternate in 1546. The new Faith spread very fast. At the end of the 16th century the Gospel was preached not only in the precious Spice Islands, but also on the shores of Sumatra, Borneo, Java, and Celebes. It is difficult to be exact about the number of converts and the depth of the spiritual change. The figure of 60,000 Christians in Ternate at the time of the expulsion of the Portuguese seems excessive and the conversion appears to have been superficial. The missionaries organised full dress ceremonies which delighted the natives, who, after a few concise explanations of dogma, were baptised *en masse*. It was only after this that the rudiments of the catechism were taught. Consequently, when the Portuguese empire in the East Indies declined, Islam quickly resumed its hold.

Things went differently in the Philippines, where Spain halted the advance of Islam, which on its other flank she had expelled from the Iberian peninsula.[1] However, the priests who landed after the conquest of the islands by Legaspi did not come directly from Spain, but from Mexico. The conversion of the Philippines was closely allied with the conversion of Mexico. It was part of that extraordinary achievement which bears witness to the expansive force of the Roman Catholic Church in Spain in the 16th century. When

[1] H. Bernard (245).

Mexico was to a great extent converted, the Philippines looked like a splendid advanced base for the conquest of the rest of the East Indies, Japan, China, and Indo-China. The Jesuit Alonso Sánchez declared that they 'seem to be as it were a seed of the Gospel in the midst of this new world . . . like a fortress and a garrison placed there by God for the good of all'. But Philip II did not agree to the plan for an expedition to China, which was laid before him by the priests not only as a profitable business, but also as a crusade. In Japan the Spaniards' task of spreading the Gospel was brought up short by the decree issued first by Hideyoshi in 1587 and renewed by Yeyasu in 1614 for the expulsion of Christian missionaries. Thus, the end of the 16th century marked the zenith of Iberian expansion. Spain, who had conquered Portugal and ruled most of America, was the dominant power in the Philippines, Moluccas, Formosa, Malacca, and India and was negotiating with the sovereigns of Cambodia, Japan, and China. The control of the Far Eastern territories was based on Manila, which became the residence of the Governor of the Philippines and was, with Macao, the chief centre of Roman Catholic missions in the Far East. As late as the 19th century the bishops of Cochin China used to be consecrated in Manila, which had been made the seat of an archbishop by Clement VIII in 1595.[1]

The political decline of Spain dimmed the religious splendour of the Philippines. Nevertheless, owing to the large number of converts in them, the islands were destined to remain the chief stronghold of Roman Catholicism in the Far East. As in Spanish America,[2] this astonishing missionary achievement was due to the mendicant orders—Franciscans, Augustinians, and Dominicans—far more than to the regular clergy. The friars were often the first to penetrate into the remotest districts, where they settled without thought of returning home and quite soon became the real rulers. A very great deal of conversion was accomplished during the forty years following Legaspi's arrival. As in Mexico, so in the Philippines two tendencies appeared among the missionaries. Some were inclined to build the new Faith on the fragment of truth contained in the pagan soul; others wished to make a clean sweep and break away entirely from the old superstitions. Yet it seems that at first they were not very exacting and, like the Portuguese, often performed collective baptisms by sprinkling a crowd. But here the continuity and progressive expansion of the Spanish occupation could not but help the Roman Catholic missions.

The missionaries skilfully made use of the native taste for drama and music. The priests taught them to sing in their own language

1 Mallat (177), I, p. 365.   2 Ricard (247).

the Ten Commandments, the Lord's Prayer, *Ave* and *Credo*, and, during Lent, the Passion.   They even gave a Christian character to their dances.   They instituted splendid ceremonies and processions which included *pasos*[1] and in which the crowd bearing candles and banners walked under floral arches to the sound of fanfares.   The churches were doubtless sometimes built on the sites of former sanctuaries.   The old beliefs themselves were not rooted out, but merely covered up skilfully with Christian doctrine; and they often show through still.   There is no doubt that this local form of Roman Catholicism is even now encumbered with superstition and that it has not put an end to the practice of sympathetic magic, sorcery, and the fear of phantoms and ghosts.[2]   It is still steeped in an atmosphere of animism, and offerings of fruit, rice, and meat are made to the spirits of the departed which are hidden in the foliage of tall lonetrees on the slopes of certain mountains.   The same might be said of many other countries which had been converted to Christianity far earlier, and it is not enough to warrant the statement that the work has been a failure.   Roman Catholicism has made a mark on the people of the Philippines which will certainly last for a very long time.

Various judgments have been passed on the social and political effects of this missionary work.   Here as elsewhere the Spanish Church tried to undertake the government not only of the soul, but also of the country itself and to organise a theocracy.   To achieve this, the Church wished to keep its members as much as possible free from external contact.   Hence, it was largely responsible for the long isolation of the Philippines, their late development, and the obsolete form of their economic system.

Yet the Roman Catholic Church has been an undoubted source of benefit.   The priest, or *padre*, founded villages round the churches and governed them, dispensing justice, building hospitals and schools, introducing many new crops, like maize, cocoa, and probably the sweet potato, and developing indigo and sugarcane, the latter having previously been used by the natives merely for seasoning food or providing juice which they drank warm when ill. The priest also taught the use of stone and lime and the method of making bricks, and he superintended the construction of dykes and irrigation works.   He has been accused of enriching himself at the expense of his parishioners and of keeping them strictly in apron strings.   But he also protected them from the oppression of the civil

[1] The *paso* was a dramatic sketch.   Cp. Mallat's description of festivals in the Philippines in the 19th century.   (177), I, p. 375.   For similar festivals in Mexico, see Humboldt (195), I, p. 378; Ricard (247), pp. 203, 213, 218.

[2] Mallat (177), II, p. 84.

power and the enterprise of unscrupulous adventurers and greedy speculators. More than one reliable observer in the 19th century right up to the end of Spanish rule agrees in recognising in the Filipinos an appearance of quiet happiness, well-being, and comfort which is not often found elsewhere in the East Indies or the tropical mainland of Asia. Many priests ruined their health by their long and in many cases permanent exile among the natives. About 1840 Mallat, the French doctor, noticed many cases of neurasthenia and madness among them.[1]

The bloody religious rivalries which occurred in Europe in the 16th and 17th centuries had their echo in the Far East on the arrival of the English and Dutch. When Drake was leading round the world England's budding maritime power and his hatred of popery, he touched at Ternate in 1577. The Dutch, who were carrying on a life-and-death struggle in the Netherlands against Spain and the Roman Catholic Church, made the Portuguese garrison at Amboina capitulate in 1604 and at once had the cross removed. They captured many Portuguese and Spanish ships, frequently held up the local oversea trade, and at the same time interfered with the voyages of Roman Catholic missionaries from western Europe to the East Indies. Hence the voyages, which were also delayed by bad weather, sometimes lasted two or three years. The capture of Malacca in 1641 cut the route between Goa and Macao, the two great citadels of the Portuguese Church in the East. Father Alexander of Rhodes, who was born in Avignon and became the most famous missionary to the Annamites, took three and a half years to travel from Macao to Rome. As he passed through Malacca in 1646, he complained of hearing the former Roman Catholic bells 'ringing for the detestable practices of the heretics' and preachers 'uttering a thousand blasphemies against the Virgin and Saints'.[2]

However, though the Dutch East India Company declared the safeguarding of the Christian Faith and the conversion of the heathen to be the main motives of its activities, it gave free scope to Islam and often used it for political ends. At the end of the 17th century Tavernier wrote[3] that the Company 'loved saving money better than saving souls . . . that it aimed only at increasing the talent of Mammon and not that of the Saviour'; and he was indignant at seeing the ladies in Batavia chewing betel even in church and always having their mouths full of liquid red, as if someone had smashed their teeth. Of course, Tavernier is under strong suspicion

[1] Mallat (177), I, p. 388.
[2] H. Chappoulie: *Rome et les missions d'Indochine au 17ᵉ siècle*, vol. 1, Paris, 1943, p. 64.
[3] Tavernier (11), III, pp. 261–63.

of prejudice against the Dutch; but certain it is that their attempts at spreading the Gospel were far from attaining the results reached by the Spaniards in the Philippines or even by the Portuguese whom they replaced in the southern East Indies. The Company's efforts at making the Church in the Indies subservient to its interests stifled missionary activity. Walæns Seminary, which was founded at Leiden in 1623 to train ministers, was suppressed ten years later. A fairly large number of parishes were created in the 17th and 18th centuries in Dutch territory. But at the downfall of the Company in 1795 there were no more than five ministers, and these were without curates to visit the sick.

The Dutch Missionary Society (*Nederlandsch Zenderling Genootschap*) was founded in 1797 under the influence of German Pietism and English Methodism and of the Moravian Brethren, a community of which had established itself at Zeist in the Netherlands. In 1820 a royal decree united all the Protestant Churches in the Dutch East Indies under a single authority, the commission called the Hague or Indies Commission.[1] From 1850 onwards a successful missionary effort accompanied, or even preceded, the occupation of the Outer Provinces. It was led mainly by Dutchmen, but also consisted of Germans, Swiss, Englishmen, and Americans. These were all Protestants. The first Roman Catholic missionaries landed in Batavia in 1808 during the governorship of Dændels. The first station occupied by them on Dutch territory outside Java was at Padang (1834). Monks began to arrive in 1855, Jesuits in 1859, and other Orders followed. Protestant converts are still the most numerous, their most compact communities being in the Batak country (where Rhenane missions have been most active since 1861), Minahassa, Amboina, and Timor. Members of the Roman Catholic Church form about one-fourth of the Christians in Indonesia. More than half of them are in the Lesser Sunda Islands, expecially Flores, where the Steijl Congregation of the Divine Word has its field of work. It is not surprising that Christian missions should have won most of their success among the non-Muslim population. A few converts have been won over from Islam; but these are exceptional and are nearly all progressive natives in Javanese towns.[2]

The total number of Christians was about two and a half million in 1956, or slightly more than 3 per cent. of the population of Indonesia. Until recently the control of the parishes everywhere remained with the Europeans, but yet Indonesian ministers were increasing in number. The various Protestant sects in Indonesia

---

[1] Besides this, a Missions' Consulate was established at Batavia in 1906 to represent Protestant missions with the Government of the Dutch East Indies.

[2] Bousquet (65), p. 164.

tended to unite to form a kind of religious federation and to strengthen their independence of the European religious bodies which had created them.

The champions of the propagation of the Gospel have reproached the Dutch Colonial Government with its mistrust, or at any rate indifference, towards missionary work. In truth, though the Government has usually recognised publicly the charitable work of the missions, it has carefully restricted and kept a watch on them for political reasons, and in particular to avoid Muslim reactions. All missionaries had by article 177 of the Constitutional Law of the Dutch East Indies to be provided with a special entry permit given by or in the name of the Governor-General, and each mission had a clearly defined field.[1]

In Malaya Government control is limited to giving advice (not necessarily taken) to missionary bodies if their activities would provoke resentment among the inhabitants of the Malay States, where Islam is recognised as the established religion and where the Christian Churches have attracted only a small number of Malays, Chinese, and Indians.[2]

In the Philippines the American occupation ('a piece of evangelical work', as a recent American critic ironically terms it) has considerably weakened the political power and wealth of the Roman Catholic Church, but not its hold on the people's hearts. The monks and friars have lost the considerable power which they had acquired. By agreement with the Holy See most of the Church lands were sold to the tenants. In 1898 there were more than 1000 Spanish monks in the islands, but at the end of 1903 there were no more than 246.[3] American Roman Catholic missions have often taken their place; but the Spanish touch in Filipino Roman Catholicism will be hard to remove in spite of the formation of an Independent National Church by Bishop Aglipay, the rival of Quezón at the first Commonwealth election. Converts to this national church have been secured chiefly among the Ilocan people. The American Government also sent as many Roman Catholic officials as possible to the islands. Protestant missionaries, most of whom belong to the Episcopal Church, work chiefly among the hill-folk of the interior.[4]

---

[1] Since 1942 this article has not been in force and there has been complete freedom of religion. President Sukarno never misses an opportunity to assert the equality of all religions in the eyes of the law and to recommend mutual tolerance.

[2] There are 85,000 Roman Catholics, of whom 40 per cent. are Chinese.

[3] At the time of the American conquest the lower clergy were recruited exclusively, or nearly so, from among half-castes or natives; and they generally backed Aguinaldo's revolt.

[4] In 1949 there were in the Philippines 350,000 Protestants belonging to 19 different denominations, most of which had joined the United Church. Roman Catholics formed 87 per cent. of the total population of the islands.

CHAPTER 23

EDUCATION

Up to the 19th century the Christian missionaries, whose calling made them anxious to form the mind, were the only Europeans to undertake the education of the native inhabitants. Lay teaching began in the Straits Settlements and Indonesia about the middle of the century, but in the Philippines not until the end of that period. Before 1941 State education had become the rule everywhere. However, besides the official schools there existed private institutions which were usually controlled and subsidised by the Colonial Governments, the control being stricter in Indonesia than in British or American territories. Most of the schools belonged to Protestant or Roman Catholic missions, whilst others were Muslim, Chinese,[1] or, in Malaya, Tamil schools which were almost wholly maintained by companies owning plantations.

Education of the local people raised very serious questions for the Colonial Governments.[2] To what standard should it be limited or raised? In what language should the teaching be carried on, the vernacular or the language of the occupying power? What should the youth of the country be taught, and what was to be the academic programme? These were the three questions most commonly discussed, questions that have been answered in different ways according to time and place. The education systems also reflected the temperaments of the different colonising nations. They exhibited the prudence and meticulous conscientiousness of the Dutch, the Englishman's tendency to leave things alone, trusting to economic developments to take care of them, and the enthusiastic and rather simple faith of the American in the value of his ideas and the efficacy of his methods in quickly making the Filipinos fit for self-government.

When Europeans first landed, the people in the Malay lands were not all illiterate. The infusion of Hindu culture had permitted the development here and there of a not valueless literature in prose and verse. The texts, written in Hindu script on palm or banana leaves, were kept at the courts, but were also read, recited, and sung in the villages during the periodical gatherings. In Java and Bali especially, the *guru* was an honoured member of society, being

[1] In Malaya more than half the Chinese schools were managed by Chinese committees without State subsidy.
[2] Wyndham (248).

both priest and teacher.   But he could hardly have given more than religious instruction.   Islam itself does not seem to have extended its programme beyond a recitation of the Koran in Arabic, until it was spurred on by the competition of European schools.

The education given by European missionaries was for a long time denominational also.   In its orders to the Governor-General in 1617 the Dutch East India Company instructed him to establish good schools everywhere 'in order to instil the Christian religion'.   The catechumens and converts were to be allowed to read some of the Scriptures, the Ten Commandments, and prayers, and to sing psalms and canticles.   To this they sometimes added the rudiments of arithmetic.[1]

This stage was left behind in Java and the Straits Settlements before the middle of the 19th century in the first State schools.   The Colonial Governments wanted at first to train junior clerks and book-keepers for their work and assistants to help European officials in a task that was growing more and more complex.   They also took care to train some of the chiefs for their new obligations and re-cruited from among them the high native functionaries, like the 'residents' and the *wedonos* in Java.   With the rise of liberal ideas, the education of the masses was proclaimed—especially in the metropolitan country—to be a moral obligation and an essential duty of a colonial power.[2]   The application of the principle was difficult; indeed, very onerous.   Though Dændels, that Napoleon of the East Indies, had recommended the establishment of schools in the residencies, there were only five of these in Java in 1851.   But in 1865 there were 58.   Their teachers were now paid from Colonial funds, and the schools formed part of an education system whose establishment had been decreed by the famous Statute General of 1854.   Yet the schools were still used merely for the purpose of preparing young Indonesians of the upper and middle classes for official duties; and it was only at the beginning of the 20th century that popular education made rapid progress and spread from Java to the Outer Provinces and from the Straits Settlements to the Federated and Unfederated States.

In the Philippines the standard of education in Spanish schools rose slightly during the second half of the 19th century.   The arrival of the Americans entailed a complete recasting of the aims and methods of education, for the new occupying power believed in a rapid diffusion of education among the masses.   In 1901 a thousand American teachers landed and were posted throughout the islands

[1] About 1840 Mallat wrote (177), II, p. 246, that nearly all the Tegals could read and write, for primary schools were maintained everywhere by the *pueblos*. The statement would seem exaggerated.   [2] Chailley-Bert (133), p. 272.

with administrative and medical duties added to their educational tasks. Popular instruction consisted of reading and writing in a local tongue (usually in Roman characters), the rudiments of arithmetic, and easy object lessons. The aim was to combat illiteracy, to give a little knowledge of hygienic habits and practices which would improve rural life, and to pick out the best pupils for some further education.

The statistics are incomplete and often difficult to compare, but nevertheless it is possible to find a few interesting figures on which to make relevant comments. First, the schools were still far from being able to take all the children. In Indonesia, where the population exceeded 60,000,000 in 1936–37, the primary schools were attended more or less regularly by about 2,000,000 children. Hence it may be concluded that only 40 per cent. of the children between the ages of 6 and 9 were registered pupils.[1] Besides, the percentage differed greatly according to district, being moderate in Java, relatively high in the Minangkabau country and the northern half of Celebes, and relatively low in the south of Celebes and in Borneo.[2] In Malaya the Malay Vernacular Schools (primary schools meant for Malay children) had in 1937 an average of 118,000 pupils out of a total Malay population of more than 2,000,000.

Thus, it is certain that on the eve of the war in 1941 a large number of children were still without even the rudiments of education. But the progress made should be recognised, for in Indonesia the primary schools had had only 100,000 pupils at the end of last century. Many obstacles delayed the improvement of popular education: a shortage of teachers, of text-books adapted to the region, and of suitable buildings; the multiplicity of local dialects and racial groups; and a lack of understanding in many parents, who preferred to keep their children at home for simple jobs like watching cattle or collecting wood or grass. Furthermore, the disproportion of the sexes was very great in school attendance and lessened but slowly. There were five boys to every girl in Indonesian schools and about eight boys to every girl in Malayan schools.[3]

[1] Djadjadiningrat (246), p. 65. This official percentage seems to be too high. And it is probably another exaggeration to state that the proportion of pupils was four times as great in the Philippines as in Indonesia. (Lauriston Sharp: *Far Eastern Survey*, Feb. 27, 1946.)   [2] Atlas (13), sheet 9.

[3] There were also financial difficulties. Of course, in Indonesia popular education was not wholly free. Yet the taxes paid by families or big landowners in the district or levied on market tolls sufficed only for the building and maintenance of schools as well as for the current requisites. Salaries were paid and furniture bought out of subsidies from the Colonial Government. The grant for education varied according to the economic situation. (Djadjadiningrat (246), p. 19.)

For all these reasons it cannot be surprising that the percentage of illiterates should still be high. The definition of the term 'illiterate', on which the statistics depend, is however not always the same. Thus, the census in Indonesia in 1930 showed that 6·5 per cent. of the native population could read and write. But the figure included only those who could read and write the officially recognised alphabet, which is almost always the Latin alphabet. Now, many natives are familiar with other alphabets; for example, in western Java and Madura the Arabic alphabet is used, since the religious texts are written in it. Among the illiterates women were far more numerous than men. For some years vigorous efforts had been made to lessen the number, and for this purpose the number of village libraries had been increased. The efficacy of the measures taken was proved by the increase in the number of readers, of letters sent through the post, and of newspapers printed.[1]

Above the primary education, secondary and even higher standards were reached by schools in Malay lands, but such institutions contained a relatively small proportion of the pupils. They were distinguished from primary schools not only by the age of the students and the level of attainment, as is the case in the metropolitan countries, but as a rule also by the language which served as a medium for instruction.

The problem of the language to be used as a medium is one of the most difficult that face Colonial education. It does not exist for the children of the Europeans, who are taught in their mother tongue and receive an education which is modelled on the curricula in the homeland and will prepare them for the same examinations. But what language should be used for the native inhabitants who form the great bulk of school children? Shall it be their mother tongue, a language commonly used in business matters, or the language of the metropolitan country? The native tongues are many, but they are often unsuitable for expressing abstract or scientific ideas and their use would greatly complicate education. In Java alone, where standardisation is relatively advanced, three distinct languages are spoken: Sundanese, Javanese, and Madurese. In the Philippines there are 87 languages, the most widespread being Sebuan and Tagálog. But neither of these is spoken by more than one-fifth of the native peoples of the group.[2]

There is, however, one language which is very widespread and in

[1] In 1938 the number of persons above the age of 10 who could read and write was estimated at 48 per cent. of the population of the Philippines.

[2] The most highly developed native languages, like Tagálog or Javanese, are often difficult for the European to learn on account of their pronunciation and also the shades of meaning they convey according to the social hierarchy.

common use, except in the Philippines, in commercial transactions between people of different race. This is Malay; not literary Malay, which is difficult to learn, but a simplified and popular form with an elementary syntax and impoverished vocabulary which nevertheless contains along with native words terms borrowed from outsiders who visit the coasts. The Europeans themselves learn it easily. But though it is adequate for the business of everyday life, it is ill adapted to the teaching of history, physical and natural sciences, ethics, or philosophy.

As for the language of the metropolitan country, its spread may seem to have been not only a convenience, but also a contribution to the glory of the imperial nation. Furthermore, it seemed to make association between the Europeans and the local races easier and to allow the latter to rise at once on to a higher plane of civilisation. But it was painfully acquired. Children in elementary schools—the very great majority of school children—retained it only as a distorted pidgin tongue and found it of no use when after two or three years at school they went back to their rural surroundings. Their brief efforts would have been better devoted, it seemed, to acquiring practical knowledge in a tongue which was familiar or easily learnt rather than to learning a few words in a foreign language.

This problem of language has not been uniformly and finally solved. It may be said that until recently the metropolitan countries had made scarcely any effort to spread their own languages. This restraint was not due to disinterested motives alone. Other reasons, not stated at all or else in veiled terms, were added to the arguments mentioned above. The monks in the Philippines not only saw no use in teaching the native inhabitants Spanish, but they also regarded ignorance of the language as the best guarantee of their power over the Filipinos, because the European officials, soldiers, and traders seldom knew the local dialects. In fact, at the end of the 19th century there were only a small, select number—mostly *mestizos*—of *ilustrados* in the islands who knew Spanish. A curious popular literature had grown up, which was a transplantation into local dialects of the poetic fashions of the Middle Ages in Spain and consisted of *corridos*, *novenas*, and, above all, poems on the Passion.

For a long time the Dutch had the same reluctance to spread their language. They said they did not wish to inflict needless trouble on the native, but they also wanted to keep him on a different plane from the European and to save him from hoping to secure appointments which could or should not be offered him.[1] It is significant that Portuguese should have continued to be spoken in Batavia up to the beginning of the 19th century. Dutch expansion spread the

[1] Chailley-Bert (133), pp. 182, 242; Bousquet (250), pp. 124 ff.

Malay language rather than that of the metropolitan country. Malay had had to be adopted quite early by Protestant ministers in the Moluccas so as to oust Portuguese Catholicism more quickly. For convenience' sake it had also become the official language.[1]

The Americans are the only ones who had made teaching general in the metropolitan tongue. Being a young nation inexperienced in colonial administration, they had perhaps been moved by a generous wish to stimulate the cultural advance of the natives, but they had also been influenced by the desire to eradicate Spanish. English had spread very quickly in the Philippines, for in about 1925 it was estimated that a million native inhabitants spoke this language. But most of them still spoke only an ill pronounced, corrupt form which has been termed 'bamboo English'.[2] Spanish kept its popularity with the average Filipino and was used as well as English in the law courts. But Tagálog has been proclaimed the national tongue; and even in the lobbies and halls of the University of Manila students converse in Tagálog as often as in English or Spanish.[3]

In 1930, after three hundred years of Dutch rule in Java there were barely 140,000 natives in the island who could write the Dutch language. In the rest of Indonesia the number did not amount to 200,000, fewer than 50,000 being women. In the primary schools the teaching was done almost wholly in Malay or, less often, the local dialect. Up to 1941 in the higher standards the use of Dutch increased progressively until in secondary and higher grades it was almost exclusively used. Speakers in the Volksraad might express themselves in either Dutch or Javanese, a variant of Malay. In the towns both natives and Chinese seemed to use 'pidgin English' nearly as often as Dutch when dealing with Europeans. Many educated natives, like the Reformists of the West Coast Province of Sumatra, spoke English also. Naturally this, the language of business, prevailed in the Malay peninsula, where its spread was encouraged by the great racial mixture and the modest part played by the Malays in the economic life of the country. Yet, in spite of some hesitation on the part of the Colonial Government, Malay had become the medium in native primary education.

The choice of language was clearly bound up with the educational programmes. The wider and more complex these became, the more the shortcomings of the native tongues were felt and the greater became the advantage of the Western language.

[1] Drewes in Schrieke (20), pp. 140 ff.   [2] Roosevelt (181), p. 193.

[3] On the situation of native languages in 1936 in the Philippines, see Bartlett's interesting article (244). Tagálog is a foreign tongue to more than 70 per cent. of the people of the Philippines. Experiments tried since 1948 seem to suggest the use of various vernaculars during the first two years and then a turn to English. This has the special advantage of forging and maintaining a link between the school, the family, and the community as a whole.

It often happened that at first these programmes were modelled on those in the metropolitan country. The aim, in fact, was to train native assistants quickly for administrative posts. The European teachers had no special training and but little knowledge of the new country, the physical world about them, or the pupils whom they were appointed to teach. As there were no books in common use, these were also imported from the metropolitan country. Between 1901 and 1910 children in the Philippine schools were issued with books used in New England and showing a farmhouse with its roof covered with snow.[1]

The need for adaptation was soon recognised, but the process of adaptation was slow and difficult. Yet by 1941, progress had gone fairly far nearly everywhere and bore witness to what had often been wonderful and too little known efforts, to much ingenuity, and a keen understanding of native needs. Special text-books had been prepared for the teaching of local geography and history; the object lessons related to the tropical environment; and the data of problems were taken from the life of the place and indeed from the minor transactions in the bazaar.

Not only were the curricula progressively better adapted to the country, but they also paid an increasingly judicious attention to the mode of life awaiting the various pupils. The great majority of these would not be at the primary schools for more than three or four years. Hence, it was useless to overload their memories with sentences learnt by heart and to be either forgotten or become material for a vain and distressing parrot-like repetition. So, popular education was being more and more identified with the rural surroundings. The aim was to make it one of the principal factors in the revival of the peasantry. Theoretical education was restricted to what would at once be useful to the child when it went back to its family at the age of nine or ten. The schools often had a garden or a field in which the child was instructed in the cultivation of new plants and in the use of more rational and fruitful methods. With the teacher's advice he reared hens, ducks, and pigs. The tiny profits derived from this work were left to the children, and prizes were given for the best returns. At the same time the school might be turned into a little producers' and consumers' co-operative, thus foreshadowing the ideal village community. The improvement of the little rural occupations and crafts was not forgotten.

However, in 1940–41 only a small minority[2] went beyond this

[1] Roosevelt (181), p. 186.
[2] So in 1925 in the Philippines 82 per cent. of the pupils did not stay more than four years at school, whilst in the United States 91 per cent. stayed more than six years. (Roosevelt (181), p. 190.) In 1936–37 in Indonesia barely 17,000 natives took advantage of the second stage of education.

popular education. At this stage there was a transition from the native to the Western system.[1] The curricula afforded common treatment, and native children might be seated on the same benches as the sons of Europeans. The fact is that the people who were to become officials had to be trained to support the Europeans, to be able to live constantly in contact with them, and to follow their methods of work. The ambition of every native family was to see its boys win certificates which would admit them to these posts. Hence, there was great eagerness everywhere for the Western type of education, and the Colonial Governments had to check it owing to the increasing number of unemployed certificated persons, 'white collar' natives who were proud of their new knowledge, but were out of a job, restless, and embittered. Efforts were made to divert as many of the pupils as possible from official employment, to turn their ambition in the direction of agriculture, commerce, or industry, and to instil into them initiative, a sense of duty in the social sphere, and a willingness to undertake risks in business matters. Occupational and technical schools were set up everywhere; but the results in 1941 did not yet correspond to the effort expended and the money spent. It is difficult to eradicate an age-old opinion which regards the legitimate or illicit income from public office or moneylending as a sure, convenient, and honourable way of attaining to wealth.

At the apex of the scholastic pyramid higher education was still poorly represented. In Indonesia it comprised three faculties, law and medicine at the universities of Jakarta and Jogyakarta and the polytechnic at Bandung, which last was founded by means of subscriptions from industrial and commercial firms. In 1936–37 the total number of students was 1038, of whom 240 were Europeans, 529 Indonesians, and 269 Chinese. Among the Javanese the number of girls from aristocratic or wealthy families was increasing. The degrees conferred were not yet strictly equivalent to those taken in the Netherlands, so most of the young Dutchmen and a few of the native people used to go to Holland to finish their education. In addition, the Colonial Government was planning to establish as soon as possible (the chief obstacle was financial) a fourth faculty, that of arts, which would admit to certain official careers and at the same time would train research workers who would study the country, its history, and civilisation.

The indifference of all but a very few Indonesians to the study of local matters was indeed astonishing. When one of them had a certain amount of education and had his mind improved by a secondary school course, he was more often attracted by the philo-

[1] These transitional schools (*Schakelscholen*) had increased in number in Indonesia not only for the natives, but also the Chinese.

sophy, literature, and art of the West than by those of his own country. Perhaps this was the outcome of the mental condition usually known as 'an inferiority complex' and the desire to escape from it. Or it may be that the Indonesian merely avoided studies which seldom led to sufficiently well-paid appointments. Things were changing before 1941, however, as was shown, for instance, by the number of Indonesians who visited the museums and by the establishment in Indonesia of 'wild' schools with nationalistic tendencies.[1]

The enlightenment of the Malay peoples as to their own history, origins, and spiritual and social evolution will undoubtedly be one of the glories and the best justification of Western colonial systems. The British were probably the first to show sympathetic and well-informed interest in the study of the ordinary life of the Malays as well as in the highest aspects of their personality. This was illustrated particularly in the works of Marsden, Raffles, and Crawfurd. The Dutch[2] entered the field later, but have accomplished great things in ethnology, linguistics, history, and archeology. The results of their researches have been used here and there in this book, though the aim has been to restrict the first two parts to geography. There is no question here of presenting an account of this scientific work or of mentioning the names of the scholars. But van Vollenhoven (1874–1933) and Snouck Hurgronje (1857–1936) should be remembered for the enormous influence of their works on Dutch colonial policy. The former brought to light genuine Indonesian customs, or *adats*, which were still surviving under a covering of borrowings from abroad; the latter keenly studied both the peculiarities of Islam among the Malays and the relation to Islam in general. These two men evolved principles which formed the basis of the administrative policy in Indonesia at the end of the Dutch colonial régime.

Among the researches which have thrown light on the origins and forms of civilisation in the East Indies epigraphy has been one of the most fruitful in discovering the history of Indian influence. It owes much to H. Kern, a Dutchman, and G. Coedès, a Frenchman. But the most significant achievements have been in archeology in Java. The Archeological Department was founded only in 1913 as a permanent institution which was to extend its activities to the whole of Indonesia. It has methodically catalogued ruins scattered through the islands, restored such buildings as are of great artistic

[1] Furnivall (15), p. 376.
[2] See the survey of Dutch science in 1930 in Rutten (19), especially the articles by N. J. Krom on archeology, pp. 305–28; C. van Vollenhoven on the progress of legislation in relation to religion and local customs, pp. 375–82.

interest—when restoration was possible without risk of error—and thus replaced a confusion of stones by the most precious remains of Javanese history.

When the past had thus been dug up by the Europeans, it became no longer a matter of indifference to those who were native to the country. Some of the minority who had absorbed Western culture would like a larger place in school curricula to be given to the study of Indo-Javanese antiquities and literature and even of those of India, the great spiritual foster-mother of Indonesia. The people still take a keen interest in the heroes of Indian and Muslim epics, and especially Arjuna and Amir Hamzah, both of whom have secured a place in Indonesian literature, and books recounting their deeds are still the most popular in cheap libraries. On the other hand, according to a well-informed Dutchman[1] in 1930, Indonesian literature had not adopted any typical personage from European literature, and translations and adaptations of Western writings, though numerous, still reached only a very limited circle. Charlie Chaplin and Tom Mix had alone really become popular.[2]

Yet, new tendencies have appeared in the younger generation. It is by no means proved that Western culture cannot be assimilated by Malay minds even in its more subtle forms. And it is doubtful whether such assimilation would necessitate a complete renunciation of the traditional sustenance.

[1] Drewes in Schrieke (20), p. 157.

[2] Young intellectuals in the Philippines, nevertheless, eagerly studied the works and speeches of great American statesmen like Lincoln.

CHAPTER 24

POLITICAL DEVELOPMENT

Naturally, educational systems and curricula were closely related to Government policy, for they corresponded to one of the most obvious duties of a metropolitan country, viz. the raising of the intellectual level of the natives. But the modifications they underwent and the discussions they brought about are indications of the solicitude imposed on the metropolitan countries by this task of developing the people of the country and enriching their minds. Many people thought not without at any rate apparent reason, that the emancipation of countries held in tutelage might be hastened by these measures.

Every metropolitan country officially proclaimed the ultimate aim of its colonial system to be the capacity it gives to the natives to govern themselves without falling under the domination of another foreign power. But there was no agreement as to the time required to fulfil the conditions needed for self-government, and the attainment of autonomy is readily postponed to a distant date or else promised to future generations. There was a tendency, it must be admitted, to consider it as an ideal; and an ideal, like perfection, is probably an unattainable goal.

That seemed to be the mental attitude of the Netherlands towards Indonesian affairs. On the other hand, the Americans appeared quite ready to recognise the independence of the Philippines. In Malaya the British hold an intermediate view, which was ill-defined owing to national opportunism and the demographic condition of the Peninsula, where the real natives are overwhelmed by recent immigration. For the study of political relations between a metropolitan country and its tropical 'colonies' and the development of those relations, the Malay countries afford the student a very interesting field, only a most inadequate idea of which can be given here.

In 1940 official denomination revealed the diversity of political status. In Malaya there were Crown Colonies, which consisted of the Straits Settlements [1] and the Federated and Unfederated Malay

---

[1] The Straits Settlements comprised the island of Singapore to which were attached Christmas Island and the Cocos group, Penang Island with Province Wellesley on the mainland opposite, and the Dindings, Malacca, and the island of Labuan off the north-west coast of Borneo. The Dindings were handed back to Perak in 1934.

States. The State of Brunei was on the same footing as the last. Indonesia comprised 'directly administered territories' and territories said to be 'self-administering' (*Zelbesturende landschappen*) and still often called 'Native States'. The Philippines then formed a 'Commonwealth'.

But what do these terms mean? The reality is far more complex than would seem from this juridical classification. Hence, *a fortiori* the current distinction between 'colony' and protectorate cannot adequately express the facts and often seems to be purely formal.

Indonesia. Up to 1941 in Indonesia there were no protectorates recognised as such in international law. The whole territory was an integral part of the domains of the Netherlands, and the inhabitants enjoyed a common citizenship as subjects of the Dutch Crown. The 'self-administering' States were those which kept their native rulers owing in many cases to historical circumstances connected with Dutch intervention and by virtue of a treaty. There were 269 in Indonesia as a whole, only four of which were in Java, where they formed the well-known central Principalities. These covered only a small portion of the island and contained barely 10 per cent. of its total population. All the rest of Java was under 'direct administration'. In the Outer Provinces, on the other hand, the Native States covered more than half the area and contained over 8,000,000 persons, or 47 per cent. of the total population. They varied greatly in importance, but none of them had a population greater than 350,000, many of them of less than 20,000, and some only a few hundred persons. There were in Sumatra alone 143 self-administering States, 102 of which were in Achin.

It would be a mistake to think that the natives were less controlled by the central government in the 'self-administering' States than in the others, that traditions still lingered there longer than elsewhere, or that the Europeans in them were merely remote and unobtrusive protectors. In fact, during the 19th century the Dutch Government tended to control the occupied territories more and more strictly and directly, and this tendency applied particularly to Java. The policies of Dændels and Raffles started it on these lines, the system of forced cultivation necessarily developed it, and the temperament of the people and circumstances kept it in operation after the spread of progressive ideas. What had been done out of self-interest in order to safeguard monopolies and fill the Treasury was later done for duty's sake, to prevent abuses and exactions by the chiefs, and to protect the humble peasant. As was rightly said by Chailley-Bert, a discerning observer of conditions in Java at the end of last century, the Dutch declared their preference for a protectorate, but they used the word in the full sense which it had lost. They protected the native peoples, but so closely and with such keen and attentive solicitude that they prevented them from being really independent. The individual was certainly better screened from injustice and arbitrary treatment, but the country had not become self-administering for all that. The native, it has been said, was treated like a child whose governess was the Dutch Government. The hereditary chiefs, who were often nominated by the Colonial Government, became in fact mere officials. The 'Regent' himself was given a fixed salary, but he was usually chosen from the same family. In theory he was above the Dutch 'Resident' in the hierarchy and sat in a higher seat in the council. But in truth the Resident was the real master in the 'Regency' and through his agents ensured the execution everywhere of the orders issued by the central administration.[1]

Of course, this centralisation whose abuses are obvious and were vigorously denounced was relaxed from 1904 onwards. The extension of effective Dutch sovereignty over the Outer Provinces into new areas which had remained almost untouched by the colonial administration permitted the application of formulas more pliable than those in Java, where traces of all the old systems survived. Decentralisation seemed favourable not only to good government and the political education of the people, but also to the continuance of the tutelage of the Netherlands, which was threatened by nationalistic tendencies often linked with Communism. Java itself gained from the new spirit. In this island, which was nearly all directly administered, the native Regent had indeed since the beginning of the century often been given wider powers than those he had had under *adat*. If he had an intelligent Resident and was himself loyal and energetic, he could achieve useful aims within the framework laid down by the Colonial Government. Some Regencies contained a population of more than 500,000 persons, others like Buitenzorg, Bandung, and Malang as many as a million.[2] In fact, the powers of the Dutch officials seemed less in Java than in the Outer Provinces.[3] Bali, another directly administered island, kept its rajah, but though Dutch supervision limited his traditional exactions, it also made sincere and effective efforts to safeguard the unique appearance of the island and to preserve its peculiar religion and social structure.

On the other hand, the Oostkust of Sumatra was divided into 34

[1] Chailley-Bert (133), pp. 148 ff. For the work of the '*contrôleurs*' at the end of the 19th century, see p. 228.
[2] In Java each of the 17 Residencies comprised some three, four, or five Regencies.
[3] Emerson (251), p. 441.

native States, whose princes formerly reigned despotically over the few Malay villages situated on the estuaries and at one time benefited by gifts presented by plantation owners. Since, as was said, the plantations boomed tremendously, the actions of these princes, overwhelmed by debt as they often were, seem ridiculous in the light of the upheaval caused in the country by exotic methods of cultivation and the influx of immigrants due to the concerted measures of the Colonial Government and the joint stock companies. The principalities of Solo (Surakarta) and Jogyakarta remained under their native rulers, termed *susuhunans* or sultans, as repositories of Indo-Javanese culture. But another result of indirect administration had been the protraction of the system of exactions by the local chiefs for a longer time here than anywhere else in the island and also of an arbitrary and oppressive system on the sugar plantations.[1]

In practice, if not in law, it was impossible to draw an accurate line of distinction between directly and indirectly administered districts so far as concerned the limits and effects of European action. In the lower grades the methods of administration were very varied, but all led up to the offices of the central Government. Yet from the time of van Vollenhoven the whole system was based on the desire to maintain and even restore native traditions wherever they did not conflict with the main principles of colonial government. The difference between directly and indirectly administered districts, it should be noted, was still further obscured by the almost general application of the principle of extra-territoriality. Outsiders—not only Europeans, but Asiatics too—escaped the local jurisdiction, a very important fact in a province like the Oostkust.[2] Dutch criminal law was in force almost everywhere. A recent observer drew the conclusion that there was in fact no protectorate anywhere, but merely colonial or European forms of administration which made more or less use of native agents. Dutch officials were proportionately far more numerous in Indonesia than British officials in India,[3] in spite of the abolition of many of the '*contrôleurs*' under the Residents. There were not only judges and tax-collectors, but also policemen, and in fact their powers covered the whole of social life, even beyond the text of the ordinances, for the execution of Government policy. The functions of these 'social engineers' continually intervened in native communities and usually included presiding at the frequent meetings (*vergaderingen*) of officials with

[1] On the bad administration of the Vorstenlanden about 1900, see Chailley-Bert (133), pp. 123 and 151
[2] Emerson (251), p. 404.
[3] Cp. the comparison with British India in Furnivall (15), p. 247.

leading Europeans and natives to discuss problems affecting a given district.[1]

The number of native officials had, however, increased more rapidly than the Dutch. There were 75,700 in 1937 as against 17,034 'Europeans'. Furthermore, recent years had seen the establishment in Indonesia of elected bodies to express native public opinion, and these bodies could not fail to lessen the powers of Dutch officials in the Netherlands and the Indies. They nearly always consisted partly of nominated members and partly of others elected by restricted suffrage, both types belonging to the three main groups in the population: Europeans, Indonesians, and Asiatics from outside the Malay lands. But the representation was not proportionate to the size of the groups. At the head of the elected bodies was the Volksraad, which was instituted in 1916 and reorganised in 1926. It was a mixed body consisting of 30 native members (11 of whom were elected) out of 60 and was intended to share the work of legislation with the States General in the Netherlands. Its real influence, especially that of the native members, was still very small at the outbreak of war in 1941.[2] The Regency Councils, whose members were either nominated by the Colonial Government or elected in two stages, seemed to be equally timid in opposing the wishes of the Regent or Resident. In the Outer Provinces,[3] Indonesian Councils presided over by the 'contrôleurs' dealt mainly with material matters like the construction of roads and markets and the institution of fire stations. The Indonesians were also represented on the municipal councils. Great efforts had been made especially to revive local government in the villages and to make it effective. Representatives were urged to collaborate actively in raising the peasants' standard of living, improving agriculture, bettering the sanitation of houses and streets, and assuring the success of institutions like the *Volkscrediet* (= Popular Credit). But minds are not easily stirred. The Dutch themselves recognised the inadequacy of the results; but was it right to hasten progress? The plan seemed good, and the tree promised to yield good fruit, but the Dutch official continued to be its watchful gardener.

In fine, it seems very unfair to say that the Netherlands were without a theory of colonial government and that their conception of administration was still wholly commercial.[4] In truth, the Dutch

[1] Furnivall (15), p. 260.

[2] For details about the Volksraad, see Schiller (253), pp. 5–10.

[3] For the administrative reforms in the *Buitengewesten*, see Middendorp in Schrieke (20), pp. 50–70, with instances taken mainly from the Karo-Batak district.

[4] Bousquet (250).

were continually watching and criticising their own actions. Dutch colonial officials, for instance, had written more than their British counterparts and were more inclined to theorise. To their scruples must be attributed the cautious and often apparently hesitant policy which was put into force long after the promulgation of new ordinances and left traces of previous systems for a considerable time. It must also be said that colonial policy was greatly handicapped by the absence of a fairly large native middle class of the kind that might have played in the development of the country the same part it played among European nations. Chinese, and Arabs or half-castes occupied the place and fulfilled the functions of this class. This supplanting of the natives was still more obvious in Malaya.

Malaya. Unlike Indonesia the whole of Malaya outside the Straits Settlements clearly fell within the definition of protectorate in international law. But here again political forms had little substance. The powers of the Governor of the Straits Settlements suffered little from his being termed High Commissioner elsewhere on the Peninsula. British policy has been mainly guided by the desire to develop a sparsely peopled land quickly and so by the need to import a substantial supply of labour. Compared with the newcomers, the Malays have played but a small part in the economic development, even as the least skilled of labour. The Colonial Government has had to bring about a rapid expansion of public services, like railways, roads, post offices, etc., without even consulting the rulers of the States. Of course, the companies which worked the tin mines or ran the rubber plantations exercised great influence, as they did in the Oostkust of Sumatra.[1]

Being ousted from the economic field, the Malay had gradually lost all control of his own country and had tended to become a 'rare ethnological specimen'. The administrative activities of the hereditary rulers no longer went beyond their Malay subjects and the business of the Muslim religion. In everything else they were scarcely more than figure-heads—figure-heads moreover surrounded, according to British practice, with greater state than their counterparts in Indonesia and able to indulge in outbursts like those of the Sultan of Johore, which were embarrassing to the central power. Although a Federal Council was instituted in 1909 and consisted of Malay, Chinese, and Indian members as well as British officials, the administration of the four Federated States was centralised more and more by the British authorities in Kuala Lumpur. Of the six Unfederated States, Johore, which had been transformed by immigration, was very different from Kedah and Perlis and even more

[1] Emerson (251), pp. 176 ff.

so from Kelantan and Trengganu, which have few mines or large plantations and maintained the traditions and atmosphere of the old Malay courts more fully than elsewhere. In them the British officials, who were there as elsewhere the real rulers and controlled the budgets, could apply themselves most easily to governing the people and carrying out to the advantage of their own country a decentralisation which the economic crisis of 1930 made more desirable. At the end of his comparative work Emerson, an American, stated that on the whole Malaya was further from self-government than Indonesia. It lagged behind Burma, Ceylon, and the Philippines.

The Philippines. Americans were more stand-offish than the Dutch in their attitude to the Filipinos, even the *ilustrados* being only very rarely admitted to the American clubs in Manila. In this attitude of reserve and in their dislike for mixed marriages, the Americans are like the British. But there were great differences between the colonial policies of Great Britain and the United States in their territories in Southeast Asia. From this point of view and compared with the United States, Great Britain was more like the Netherlands.

Indeed, the recent history of the Philippines affords a unique instance of a colonial power which not merely seemed to wish to hasten the independence of the conquered territory, but even showed this desire by its actions. Emancipation was not postponed to a distant and indefinite period, but has actually taken place. This would seem to indicate a feeling of generosity and progressive ideals unprecedented in the annals of imperialism. In reality, the factors of American policy, which have often been analysed, are very complex; and this explains the delays and vacillation of the Government in Washington.

The United States cannot forget that they themselves were originally colonies which revolted against the Mother Country. In the Dutch, who were freed earlier, this feeling exists, but is fleeting and less keen. Americans are not colonial-minded and ever since their rather unexpected conquest of the Philippines have justified their action by proclaiming that they had come not to conquer, but to educate a people who were still passive so far as liberty was concerned, to devote themselves disinterestedly to their guardianship, and to fulfil the duty of trusteeship to which their conscience and the Divine Providence called them. They have never set up a Colonial Office, and the Philippines remained in charge of an Office of Island Affairs under the Secretary for War.

That Mammon should appear beside the good angel, collaborating mischievously with him, is not altogether surprising, and in their policy there were other less pure motives forming that selfish factor which Americans themselves readily admitted.

In the first place, since the United States consist of a vast territory with enormous natural wealth and a huge domestic market, they have not until recently felt that keen need for oversea expansion so strongly felt by some other nations. Secondly, the Philippines brought in no profit; on the contrary, they were an expense to the United States, as many Americans have pointed out. The administration of these far-off islands and the education and medical aid given to the local population were all very costly. And the price was all the greater since from 1909 onwards Philippine produce had had customs preference in the United States, a fact which helped to raise the cost of living. Besides, many private interests had suffered, and producers of beet sugar, vegetable or animal oleaginous commodities, and especially those who had invested large sums in the Cuban sugar industry, sums amounting in 1930 to 800,000,000 dollars, grumbled at the competition of Philippine sugar and coconut oil.[1] Lastly, racial interests and the American Federation of Labour opposed Philippine immigration, which was also shown preference.

But the grant of independence to the islands was attacked by other arguments, and here again self-interests often mingled inextricably with duty or humanitarianism. On the side of interest were ranged groups of American exporters, the customs union having made the Philippines one of the best markets for United States cotton goods, cigarettes, and dairy produce. Then there were the industrialists who worked up coconut oil imported free of duty, and, lastly, American capitalists who had invested a few dozen millions of dollars in Philippine provincial and municipal loans, in industrial or commercial businesses, or in plantations.

On the whole, these private interests were weaker than the sections that favoured independence, but their arguments were backed by the civil and military officers in the Philippines. These 'Manila Americans', who belong to big exclusive clubs, like the Army and Navy Club, claimed to be the supporters of a legitimate imperialism and declared that the emancipation of the Philippines would fall in with the interests of the United States no more than it would befit the mission and reputation of their country. The development of the islands was far from complete, and its care should not be given up to other imperial nations. The natives would not be ready for independence for some time yet and, left to themselves, would quickly fall a prey to another less generous and harsher nation. The United States were morally obliged to continue their trusteeship for at least two or three generations. It was to Britain's American

[1] Labrouquère (252), p. 78.

cousins that Kipling addressed his famous amplification of the White Man's Burden in 1899.

Lastly, the Philippines were wonderfully well placed as outposts of the continent of Asia. Maritime expansion and above all the domination of the Pacific were indispensable to the greatness of the United States. The islands formed a stage, a wonderful relay station for spreading American commerce and civilisation in China, a marvellous base for the triumph of American trade and science too and the Yankee spirit.[1] It would be absurd and criminal to abandon the place to their Japanese or perhaps Slav competitors.

It must be added that the population of the Philippines is not homogeneous. The hill-folk in the Visayas and Luzón are hostile to the 'civilised' natives. They already had the advantage of special administration. So had the Moros. These Muslims in the south feared lest independence should hand them over to the mercy of the political *caciques* in Luzón. The Christian missions in the Philippines were divided between the fear of seeing American political and military backing disappear and a readiness to win the support of Filipino aristocracy against the Muslims.

After reading this summary of opinions and interests, the apparently inconsistent ways of American policy will be better understood. Neither of the two views could easily override the other. Governors who believed in 'the Philippines of the Filipinos'[2] were succeeded by others who tried to delay emancipation and gave freedom of action to everyone, White colonials as well as men of every racial group in the Philippines.[3] However, the cause of independence made headway, slowly at first from 1901 to 1913, rapidly from 1913 to 1920, and more moderately again from 1920 to the outbreak of war in 1941. As early as 1901 the military Governor was replaced by a civilian, and the Filipinos were admitted to a share in the municipal[4] and provincial government, some of them even rising to moderately high positions in the law and civil service.

The first general elections were held in 1907 on a system which was slightly modified in 1935, giving the vote to all male adults able to read and write in Spanish, English, or Tagal.[5] The organic law of

[1] Cp. the quotation from a speech by Senator A. J. Beveridge of Indiana (in Anderson (164), p. 41): 'The Philippines are ours for ever . . . and just beyond the Philippines are China's illimitable markets'.

[2] E.g. Taft, the first American Governor of the islands; and Harrison (1913–21) during Wilson's Presidency.

[3] E.g. Wright, Ide, and, as a successor to Harrison, General Wood.

[4] According to Mallat (177), I, p. 354, municipal government was fairly progressive about 1840 in the time of the Spaniards.

[5] In a plebiscite in 1937 women showed themselves in favour of being given the right to vote.

the Philippines, known as the Jones Act of 1916, set up a representative system with a Senate and a House of Representatives. The landed aristocracy and intellectual leaders who developed under Spanish rule found in a parliamentary constitution not only a platform from which to voice their claims, but also a new and convenient instrument by which to wield influence as well as to secure recurrent opportunities of satisfying their vanity and taste for eloquence, intrigue, and patronage.[1] They dominated the Congress and as early as 1921 reduced the proportion of American officials to 4·5 per cent. In 1935 there were only 116 Americans 'in government service'. The financial muddle due to State Socialism, which had been introduced in view of the growing industrial system, did not fail to cause uneasiness in the United States.[2] But the party in favour of independence, which arose in Spanish times, steadily kept its majority and by its propaganda in the United States caused a commission to be set up in 1918 under the chairmanship of Manuel Quezón. In 1934 the Tydings-McDuffie Law, passed by the Congress of the United States, accepted by both Philippine Houses, and ratified by a plebiscite, laid down that after a ten-year period of transition the islands should become an independent republic. Up to 1946 there would be a Commonwealth, and this was officially proclaimed on November 15, 1935, amid the pealing of church-bells and great popular enthusiasm. The first President was Quezón. The Governor-General was replaced by a High Commissioner whose duties were to ensure the control which the United States reserved to itself over the finance, customs, and military defence of the islands.

But the Tydings-McDuffie Law included economic and military clauses which were bound to cause much discussion and cast a shadow over the brilliant success of the *Independistas*. It was provided that Philippine sugar, which had been subject to a quota even in 1934, should become progressively liable to the ordinary customs duty on entering the United States. Hit in one of their essential crops, which had owed its boom to protection in the United States, the islands were threatened with a very serious crisis. The Law, as an American senator said, had a strong odour of saccharin.

---

[1] The Commission set up by Quezón in 1935 to study the agrarian problem reported that 'the hue and cry of the peasantry is for a radical change in the present scheme of their relations with the all-powerful moneyed and landowning classes. In all the provinces surveyed it has been found that the average tenant does not enjoy his constitutional and inalienable civil and political rights', and that the peasant is quite unable to resist 'without courting the displeasure of the landowner and running the risk of being deprived of the land he tills'. (Quoted from *Asia and the Americas*, Oct. 1945.)

[2] Labrouquère (252), pp. 28 ff.

Besides, American imperialists found in the international situation and particularly in Japanese policy powerful arguments against abandoning the islands. Shortly before the war the Joint Preparatory Committee on Philippine affairs had recommended that the transition period which was due to end in 1946 should be extended to 1961.

POSTSCRIPT

It would be extraordinary if the work of the Western peoples did not tend to make the local population want to lighten and throw off their tutelage and to give them the means of so doing; for that is the fate of all colonisation, so long as the natives are not exterminated or reduced to insignificant or helpless minorities. No one is surprised to find in most of the nationalistic thinkers and champions persons brought up on Western ideas.

In fact, however, the aspiration for independence was to be found before the war only in little groups of intellectuals and was far from being translated into a single coherent idea. It experienced some difficulty in detaching itself from wider movements which tended to absorb the Malay lands into some international association, whether Communist, pan-Asiatic, or pan-Islamic; and it had perhaps even greater difficulty in overcoming regional particularism.

The pan-Malay movement claimed to unite in a federation with a population soon to exceed 130 million souls, a people who display indisputable racial and cultural affinities and having in the Malay vernacular a language widely used for ordinary purposes. However, this is not enough to make a homogeneous unit. The Malay lands have indeed never in all their history achieved unity. Even in the periods of their greatest expansion the magnificence of Indo-Sumatran Sri Vijaya or Indo-Javanese Majapahit offered little more than a prelude to the still remote growth of national sentiment, and in fact they ended in failure. Islam might have been an effective cement, but it lost its chance of winning over the East Indies as a whole early in the sixteenth century, when the greater part of the Philippines was snatched from it by Spanish Christian missionaries. Lastly, there was the division of the Malay lands into British, Dutch, and Hispano-American spheres, which had less to do with each other than with Western Europe, the United States, and other parts of the world.

Differences in political status and economic system, as well as cultural policy, and attachment to theories of empire which were seldom in agreement have altered and, so to speak, divided pan-Malay claims into sections. Besides, the Western colonial systems have had the effect of favouring immigration. Many of the immigrants keep in close touch with their native lands, and their racial groups differ in occupation and mode of life from each other and

418

from the natives. This is especially true of the Chinese. In this way racial diversity is strengthened by a social and functional pluralism which checks all tendency to the unification of the Malay world. But unity may be realised on a cultural level. Thus, a group of intellectuals in Manila have formed a Pan-Malay Committee which publishes a journal, *The Pan-Malaysian Quarterly*. This does not prevent attempts to strengthen cultural relations with Japan, Indo-China, and even India.

The influence of external ideas. In reality the pan-Malay movement was easily absorbed by the more ambitious ideas of pan-Islamism, pan-Asianism, and Communism, which coming from abroad became part of or were diluted with it.

A certain amount of nationalistic idealism, for instance, was hidden in the Sarekat Islam movement. The name lays stress on its religious aims, but also masks a more realistic objective. It was started about 1910 by a soceity of Muslim traders who were hostile to the Chinese. In asserting their Muslim faith the East Indies are certainly expressing opposition to the Europeans and to the great majority of Chinese, but yet their faith is not free from foreign influence. Islam's centre is a long way off, but from it go out calls to orthodoxy and appeals for reform. The 75 million Muslims in the Malay lands form a community which is very remote from Mecca. In Javanese towns the sight of crowds of women all dressed in white prostrating themselves in the squares definitely used to impress one as an assertion of particularism and of reserve towards their foreign masters. Islam, however, remained supranational. It was not regarded with disapproval, but on the contrary it was favoured and almost petted by the Dutch, whose Colonial Government aided the transport of pilgrims to Jedda. It was also by flattering Islam that the Japanese tried to win over the Malays to their cause.

The Malay lands are even more easily induced to enter the pan-Asiatic movement which regards the regeneration of the world as dependent on the emancipation of Asia, that cradle of races and mother of great religions. The lightning rise of Japan caused her to be recognised by many intellectuals in the Far and even the Middle East as the champion of that sublime aspiration, and she was urged to undertake it by Sun Yat-sen and Rabindranath Tagore. The first pan-Asiatic Congress was held in Nagasaki in 1926 at the very time when British trade was being boycotted at Hongkong by the Chinese.

The defeat of Japan has allowed other Asian powers to claim the leadership in the thrilling work.[1] Great efforts have been made by

[1] See the anonymous *Cultural Relations between Asian Countries* in *Politique Etrangère*, Nov., 1955, pp. 587–600.

India to appeal to the Buddhist Faith, which is highly respected by Indian thinkers, but is far more widespread today in Southeast Asia. Without neglecting the influence of Islam on her civilisation, India has sent specialists in Buddhist civilisation and the Pali language (the ordinary tongue of this religion) to Indo-China and Indonesia and in addition she has despatched teachers of Arabic and Persian to Indonesia. The University of Jakarta has a chair of Indian studies, and the Indian Council for Cultural Relations issues a quarterly journal (*Thaquafat-al-Hind*) in Arabic. At the end of 1951 a Conference of Indian Culture was arranged in Burma, where Buddhism is stronger than in India, and in 1954–5 there was held the sixth Buddhist council, attended by 2,500 members from all Buddhist countries, with the object of fixing the canon of the sacred texts and to undertake the translation of them into the languages of Southeast Asia. An international Buddhist university has been founded in Rangoon, whilst a centre of Buddhist research (*Magadha* centre) is being founded in Bihar to organise international co-operation among Buddhists.

Japan herself is resuming her scheme of a Great East Asia on cultural lines. She can base her plans on the high intellectual value of Zen Buddhism as well as on her longstanding assimilation of Western science and technique in her universities and laboratories. In 1955 out of a total of 3768 foreign students in Japan no fewer than 3244 were Asiatics.

But the leadership of eastern Asia is aimed at by another power, namely, China, whose imposing past and recent astonishing transformation exercise a strong influence on the young nations of Southeast Asia. This acts not only through her extraordinary political revival, but also through the attention which she pays to Chinese communities settled in foreign countries and the efforts she makes, by the formation of special schools and other means, to maintain their loyalty to their original fatherland.

Today Mao Tse-tung's victory lays almost all China under a Communist Government allied with the Soviet Union. The consequences of this fact to the Malay lands and Indo-China are still unforeseeable, but they have considerable possibilities. Communist propaganda has not neglected the East Indies. At first it had some success in the towns. It was thought to be at the bottom of the riots in Manila in 1935 and other troubles. In Java between 1922 and 1927 the influence of the Russian Revolution was felt in a series of strikes and risings, which led the Dutch Government to adopt severe measures of repression and to deport 1300 persons to the Upper Digul territory in New Guinea. The Communist party in the Indies was thus deprived of its leaders, as were also some more purely nationalistic groups. After the deportees had been set free by the Japanese, the great variety of tendencies and the rivalry of doctrines and personalities were definitely manifested in the multi-plication of political groups as well as in the fierce struggles between the Indonesian 'republican' army and the troops of Communist leaders who for a time controlled the eastern portion of Java. Certain it is that today among the Malay peoples the feeling of admiration for China is mingled with certain fears concerning her powers of biological and ideological absorption. Communism does not refrain in fact from an expansion which we may still call colonial, though it denies the name; in the Malay countries large areas, which are still more or less unpeopled or underdeveloped lie very near to the swarming population of China.

Pan-Islamism, pan-Asianism, and Communism have each to some degree helped to hasten the downfall of the colonial systems built up by the West. It remains to be seen whether they will come to terms with the nationalistic sentiments that are growing up every-where today and which, far from making a coherent State of the Malay lands, are tending to disrupt and break up the larger units which the Colonial Governments had succeeded in forming.

Nationalism in the Philippines. In the Philippines national senti-ment was encouraged by the Spanish policy of maintaining an obsolete economic system and later by the rights granted to the natives by the United States. It has long shown itself in revolts, the most famous of which—led by Aguinaldo—took place at the end of the period of Spanish rule. It has also appeared in the slogan 'The Philippines for the Filipinos', which is still impatiently thrown at the Americans. Yet it should be noticed that the Moros and to a less extent the hill-folk in Luzón are hostile to a too strict application of a scheme which would place them at the mercy of 'Filipino' politicians.

In fulfilment of the promise contained in the Tydings-McDuffie Law, the United States granted independence to the Philippines in 1946. But it would be going too far to say that the islands have wholly escaped from American tutelage. The great assistance afforded by the United States in the economic reconstruction of the Philippines has of course been offset by certain economic and mili-tary obligations. The Bell Trade Act of 1946 was a bitter pill, but it was difficult for the Filipinos not to swallow it. Naval, air, and military bases remain at the disposal of American forces in the islands. About fifty are planned and a few are now occupied. Quotas—fairly large ones—have been fixed for sugar, copra, and other Philippine products which are especially favoured on the American market. But American imports into the islands are not subject to a quota and, moreover, enter either free of duty or on the terms of the most favoured nation clause. Americans are not to be regarded as foreigners in the islands, but will have equal rights with the Filipinos to exploit the natural resources. Moreover, a thousand may settle there per annum, but only a hundred Filipinos a year may be received into the United States. Philippine money will be tied to the dollar until 1974, so the *peso* rate will be too high for the establishment of national industries within the period appointed by the new Republic. The local press does not fail to attack this policy as colonial in all but name and as tending to reduce the 'little brown brother' to the level of a hewer of wood and drawer of water. It reproaches Uncle Sam with appropriating the whole edifice of the so-called Republic, leaving only the attic to the Filipino.

There are about four million electors, but it is doubtful how many of them freely exercise their votes. The political parties are not so much groups differing in their social and political programmes as they are cliques which fight each other for power or else agree to share it. Anti-Communism often seems to be associated with a desire to suppress the active competition of Chinese merchants and to maintain the privileges of the local aristocracy. In central Luzón the wretched, landless cultivators who were enlisted by the Americans in the war against the Japanese had formed armed bands which, under Communist leadership and the name of *hukbalahap* (people's anti-Japanese forces), had demanded a redistribution of the land and for long held out against the Government troops. The agrarian problem has not yet been solved. Under-employment is still rife in rural districts. This leads to a movement of population towards the towns, which raises further difficulties.

Developments in Malaya. There has not been in Malaya, any more than in the Philippines, any movement to bring about the unification of the country with other Malay lands. The Peninsula is quite near to the centres of culture that formerly existed in Sumatra and Java and it has always had close trade associations with these islands, whence come many members of its Malay population. But the Malays on the Peninsula comprise merely one-half of its total population and compared with the Chinese (who are almost equal in number, and who have always been more energetic in their pursuit of a livelihood) play a relatively small part in the economic life of the country.

At the outbreak of the last war, the whole of the Peninsula was British or British protected. There was the Crown Colony of the Straits Settlements, which included Singapore, Penang, and Malacca, and there were the nine protected Malay States. Of the nine States, four formed the Federated Malay States with a central Federal Council (though each of the four States also had a separate local legislature with circumscribed powers). The remaining five Malay States each had its own separate and distinct administration but with, of course, British guidance, protection, and direction.

In 1946, after the last war, one government was formed for the whole country (except Singapore), though it was not till February 1, 1948, that the Federation of Malaya was formally constituted. This comprised the nine sovereign States and the two British Settlements of Penang and Malacca. There was a central Federal Council and separate State and Settlement legislatures for matters reserved for local governments. A federal citizenship was created open to all persons of proved loyalty and attachment to the country.

Singapore, predominantly Chinese (about 90 per cent. of its population of over one million), remained a separate Crown Colony. Had Singapore been joined with the rest of the Peninsula the Malays would have been outnumbered in the country bearing their name. Provision was made in Singapore, as in the Federation, for early elections, and both Singapore and the Federation soon elected their own Ministers, led by a Chief Minister.

The main problem facing the Federation of Malaya was the 'Emergency', that is the attacks by Communist banditry. During the years of the Japanese occupation Chinese Communist bands took to the jungle and received British encouragement, having arms and equipment parachuted to them to enable them to conduct harassing guerrilla attacks upon the Japanese. They set up a network of jungle hide-outs whence they imposed a stranglehold of intimidation upon the people. When they found that the new Malaya was not ready to accept Communist leadership they returned to their hide-outs and began attacks on non-Communists. The task of rooting them out proved formidable. Not the least important of the measures taken was the creation of the 'New Villages'. Half-a-million people living at the foot of the jungle-covered hills, whence they were easy prey of food-swooping gangs, were lifted up and resettled, with homes and means of livelihood as well, in securer parts of the country. Such measures as this and the strengthening of the local armed forces very slowly but surely reduced the Communist powers of aggression.

On the other hand, important political developments assisted the progress towards self-government. The three main racial groups in the Federation (Malays, the Chinese, and Indians) formed a single political front known as 'The Alliance' (an appropriate description, for the parties remained separate and distinct) which won every seat except one in the elections. Their leader the Chief Minister, Tunku (='prince': his father was Sultan of Kedah) Abdul Rahman (president of UMNO, the 'United Malays National Organisation'), was able to conclude arrangements for self-government within the British Commonwealth, which was proclaimed on Merdeka (='Freedom') Day, August 31, 1957.

Singapore's progress towards self-government also suffered from Communist-inspired terrorism, such as violent labour disturbances and Chinese student riots. (The 1951 'Hertogh' riot was different in origin, being caused by religious fanaticism.) The vital strategic importance of Singapore as a military base on great trade routes created another problem. But once again nationalist aspirations brought the chief political parties together. Though the mission led by Mr. David Marshall (a Singapore-born Jew), the first Labour Front Chief Minister, was not successful, the efforts of his successor, Mr. Lin Yew Hock, brought within measurable distance a State of Singapore enjoying internal self-government within the British Commonwealth.

Brunei, the British-protected Malay State in the northwest of the island of Borneo, has of late years enjoyed unprecedented economic progress on account of the oil found there. So far, however, there has been no call from the people for any measure of self-government—the educational system, introduced since the last war, will no doubt, as it extends, provide a stimulus. The neighbouring State of Sarawak, which was formerly a dependency of Brunei for many years and formed a kingdom, of which the Brooke family were hereditary rulers, became in 1946 a Crown Colony with a governor and a Supreme Council (and Divisional Advisory Councils). The remaining British possession in Borneo, namely British North Borneo, which had been governed from 1882 to the time of the Japanese invasion by the Chartered Company (a trading company) of British North Borneo, also became a Crown Colony in 1946. Included in British Borneo is the island of Labuan, which before the last war was one of the four Straits Settlements.

A Commissioner-General for the United Kingdom, with his headquarters in Singapore, was appointed in 1948. Without separate appointments his duties covered those of the Governor-General of Malaya and British Borneo (a Colonial Office appointment) and those of the Special Commissioner (a diplomatic Foreign Office appointment) of the United Kingdom in Southeast Asia.

The Republic of Indonesia. In area and population Indonesia forms the main division of the Malay world. Its history and development seem to justify its claims to the leadership of the pan-

Malay Union.   So far as it fell in with their own programme, the
Japanese supported this claim.   Even before the war the tendency
to unify the islands appeared in propaganda in favour of a common
language.   Vulgar Malay, 'bazaar Malay', had been chosen by the
nationalists, since it was the most widely spoken, easiest to learn,
and most democratic, there being no variation in its vocabulary and
idioms to suit the grades of the social hierarchy, as is the case in
Javanese.[1]   Their efforts were greatly furthered by the Japanese
occupation, during which the use of Dutch was forbidden.   Since
1945 the intellectuals have set themselves enthusiastically to compile
grammars, text-books, and vocabularies.   In this way an 'Indonesian' language is being moulded, and systematic efforts are being
made to enrich it.   Words are borrowed either from richer local
tongues—Javanese in particular—or from foreign languages like
Dutch.   This tongue is still the medium of culture used by many of
the leading Indonesians today, who were educated at the Universities
of Leiden and Utrecht or, in the case of the less fortunate ones, in
Jakarta or Bandung.   Speeches in 'Indonesian' were allowed in
the Volksraad even before the war.   The documents of the recent
Round Table Conference were drawn up in Dutch and 'Indonesian'.
In case of dispute an English version is to be authoritative.   English
is now the compulsory second language in the secondary schools.

The most vigorous resistance to the re-establishment of the colonial
system came from Java and Sumatra, the two islands with the most
glorious past and the most affected by Dutch influence.   But the
handful of nationalist intellectuals freed by the Japanese invasion
clearly appreciated the danger of the political splintering of the
population of 75 millions to whom the Dutch had applied various
methods of administration, but withal made into a solid unit.   To
ward off this danger they proclaimed at Jogyakarta on August 17,
1945, the very day after the Japanese surrender, the establishment of
the Indonesian Republic, whose purpose was, first, to prevent the
restoration of the Dutch Colonial Government and, secondly, to
succeed to that Government's authority over all its former domin-
ions, forming a unit to be known thenceforth as Indonesia.   The
republicans realised the first part of this programme.   After a four-
year struggle between 'guerrillas' and Dutch troops, delegates from
the Netherlands and the provisional Government of Indonesia
assembled at a Round Table Conference at The Hague.   By virtue
of the decisions made on December 27, 1949, Queen Juliana solemnly,
unconditionally, and irrevocably transferred the sovereignty of

[1] The Dutch had themselves greatly helped to spread this form of Malay
by setting up the *Bulai Pustaka* ('Home of the Book'), whose numerous publications were distributed by travelling libraries.

the East Indies, which had been held by the House of Orange since 1814.

The transfer was made to a Federal Republic entitled 'The United States of Indonesia'. Collaboration between Indonesia and the former Colonial Power (to which are closely connected Surinam, Curacao, and the Dutch West Indies) was to be assured by the establishment of a Netherlands-Indonesian Union with Queen Juliana at its head. This Union never really came into being, however, for it was unceremoniously abrogated by the Indonesian Government in February, 1956. The Netherlands High Commissioner is merely an ambassador, and the relations between the two Governments will follow the usual diplomatic channels. Dutch capital invested in the islands will be treated like that of any other nation.

On the other hand, will the Republic of Indonesia succeed in preserving unity and in retaining the leadership of the United States of Indonesia? Its rulers played a predominant part in getting rid of the Dutch, but by the agreement made at The Hague it was, however, only one of the States of the Union. Of course, federalism was supported by the Netherlands Government, which hoped by so doing to maintain the essential points of its place in the archipelago by acting as referee between the States. But federalism also reflects in various ways the racial and religious diversity, the degree of cultural and economic development, and the resistance of feudal survivals. Eastern Indonesia (the former 'Great East'), with its capital at Macassar and its population of about 17 million, poses as the champion of federalism against the unitarianism of the Republic of Indonesia.

But the Republic of Indonesia has not hesitated to act vigorously against federal leanings. It deliberately incorporated within itself several 'autonomous' territories in western Indonesia, and in eastern Indonesia it has suppressed at Macassar and Amboina risings which had threatened to end in secession.

A variety of interests, including political claims, religious particularism, regional demands, remnants of traditional feudalism, and the rivalry of military cliques, has produced a swarm of parties. The two most important are the Nationalist (P.N.I.) and the Muslim (*Masjumi*). The extreme tendency of the latter is represented by Darul Islam, which aims at absolute religious orthodoxy and theocratic government. This party has remained for several years master of West Java to all intents and purposes, has its own army, police, and tax collectors, and controls the working of the oilfields. Communism is widespread among the railwaymen, dockers, miners, and plantation labourers and must be reckoned with by every

Government. The Indonesian Republic also meets characteristic opposition from advanced Christian communities like those in Minahasa and Amboina. Sumatra complains that too great a proportion of her taxes is swallowed up in the general budget of the Republic.

Thanks to President Sukarno, a skilful and popular leader, and to his moderate policy, the country is recovering, though slowly and painfully, from the anarchy into which it had been plunged by the departure of the Japanese. Bandits are still active, and trouble is frequent in certain parts of Sumatra and even more so in the Moluccas and Java.

The Chinese must also be mentioned, though unlike those in Malaya, they form only a small minority in Indonesia. Of course, they hold an important place in commerce and banking; but their hold on the economic life of the country is far less than in Malaya. They may even in some degree feel an inferiority complex in their relations with the Indonesian masses.

Elections for representative assemblies could not be held before October, 1956. But the prestige of the young Republic was enhanced by the Bandung Conference in 1955, which was attended by delegates from Asia and Africa claiming to represent a thousand million persons. Furthermore, the persistent claim to the so-called Irian (Dutch New Guinea), that bone of contention, has been skilfully used to kindle the flame of nationalism throughout the islands and to forge a spirit of patriotism in Indonesia.

Yet it remains a delicate task to mitigate the local particularism fostered by insularity, to satisfy the ambitions of politicians, and appease the appetites of their supporters. Unity seems indispensable, however, to the achievement of real independence. It is easy to see the dangers of too loose a federation in which no superior authority would be capable of harmonising the activities of the component States. Each State would probably try to be as self-sufficient as possible, and this would make control difficult and would encourage the subordination of local governments to powerful foreign firms. This brings us back to economic and social matters.

PRODUCTION AND COMMERCE[1]

Now that independence has been achieved and national coherence more or less assured, the new States are faced with the same problems as troubled the Colonial Governments. By far the greatest difficulty is caused by poverty. To the hungry masses independence is sheer

[1] The publications of the Economic Commission for Asia and the Far East (E.C.A.F.E.) certainly remain the best source of information concerning the economy of Southeast Asia.

mockery. What is needed is to raise the standard of living of the steadily increasing population.

The recent struggle dealt a severe blow to the Malay world. Considerable material damage was directly due to the war and particularly to bombing and, worst of all, to the four-year military occupation by the Japanese and the disorders following on their expulsion.

The Japanese had subordinated everything to the success of their campaign and the realisation of their political ambitions. Here as elsewhere there was total war. The invaders took over not only the government, but economic matters as well. White officials and the personnel of private companies were thrown into concentration camps and replaced by Japanese who surrounded themselves with picked natives. Japan's advance, rapid though it had been, was finally checked in Burma and New Guinea. But the Malay countries found themselves cut off from their chief customers and sources of supplies in Europe and America while the occupation lasted, and their dealings were perforce limited to 'Greater East Asia' and to what in arrogant anticipation the Japanese termed even more pompously 'the Greater East Asia Co-prosperity Sphere'.

The realisation of the Japanese plan was frustrated by difficulties of supply, their transport being disorganised by lack of maintenance and the wear and tear of material which could neither be repaired nor replaced. Their merchant navy was most inadequate and from 1943 onwards was under constant threat from Allied bombers. They unsuccessfully tried to cut up Southeast Asia into a certain number of parts, each of which was to endeavour to establish some degree of economic self-sufficiency; and at the same time they encouraged the destruction of the colonial systems set up by the Westerners.

Only slight use could be made by Japan of the large surpluses of raw materials which up to then had flowed towards distant markets, and so her commanders decided to curtail most of the economic crops. The plantations of rubber, *abacá*, coffee, tea, pepper, kapok, and nutmeg were partly uprooted or cut down and replaced by food crops or by cotton and other fibres intended for Japan's enormous textile industry, since she herself was cut off from her usual sources of supply in the United States and India. The area used for sugar-cane and tobacco was more easily reduced, as these plants occupy the soil for only a few months. Many of the mills equipped for preparing produce for export were demolished or robbed of their plant. Not a few other kinds of factories were the favourite targets of the air forces on both sides.

Even food crops fell off. To meet the needs of the war and their defensive preparations the Japanese transferred thousands of natives from one place to another. Then, again, requisitioning and a scarcity of imported goods took away from the cultivator all desire to produce more than his barest needs. Some of the irrigation canals in Java became useless through neglect. Many domestic animals died of hunger or fatigue and were not replaced. Confusion and poverty were aggravated by the inflation of the currency due to the issue of a mass of new notes—'occupation' notes (called 'banana' in Malaya) and, later in Indonesia, 'republican' notes. Part of the arable land fell into the hands of speculators, usurers, and black market dealers, whether Indonesians or Asians from the mainland, who took advantage of the poverty of the people. In many districts the population was seriously undernourished and clothed in rags when the troops of the Protecting Powers returned. Since the village communities were disorganised, tens of thousands of peasants had moved into the towns and there swelled the proletariat.

Reconstruction is going on more or less slowly according to the kind of product and the place. Generally speaking, the pre-war level of production has not yet been reached. In Indonesia, reconstruction is being most difficult in Java and Sumatra, owing to the seriousness and long duration of the troubles which followed the Japanese defeat and because European companies were the most important part of the economic system of the islands.

In Java the sugar industry, which had begun to recover from the serious crisis in 1928–35, once again suffered severely. Many mills were demolished or turned over to other uses. Of the seventy-five refineries which were working at the time of the Japanese invasion and in 1939 were producing 1,575,000 tons of sugar, thirteen only were still at work in 1948, and they were producing barely 43,000 tons. Since then others have been set to work again, but exporting was not resumed until 1952, when 12,000 tons were shipped abroad. In 1955 out of a total production of 857,000 tons, the quantity exported amounted to only 176,000 tons, a figure well below the 1,672,000 tons exported in 1938.

The production of hevea rubber decreased by a half between 1939 and 1948, but then increased rapidly until 1951, when it reached 818,000 tons. In 1955, however, it did not exceed 733,000 tons. This may indicate a lasting decline due to the ageing of the trees, to the ravages of erosion in hilly districts like southern Sumatra, and to the more and more marked preponderance of smallholdings over large estates. Since the last war rubber has become the chief economic resource of about 50 per cent. of the population of Sumatra.

In tea plantations the area cultivated is hardly more than a third of that used in 1935–9; but production exceeds a half owing to the purchase of leaf from smallholders. In Sumatra 75 per cent. of the pepper plantations have been destroyed. A comparison between the figures of coffee, cacao, tobacco, and sisal production in 1939 and 1955 shows a real collapse.

Export figures have relatively decreased even more than those of production owing to the increase in population.[1]

It has been necessary to increase the area used for foodstuffs for that reason and because yields have declined owing to insecurity, poor maintenance of the irrigation systems, and the damage done by parasites and erosion. The production per head of the population and that of maize, sweet potatoes, yams, soya, and groundnuts is still less than before the war. In 1956 an appeal had to be made to Italy and the United States for the supply of 3,700 tons of rice. Oil products (copra, palm oil, and palm kernels) are increasingly rendered down on the spot in a number of little factories for local consumption.

Fishing is far less productive than formerly through lack of nets, specialised boats, means of rapid transport, and packing-houses. Knowledge of fish migration is still rudimentary. Strenuous efforts have been made to increase the quantity of fish taken from inland waters, especially from streams and small lakes.

In 1954 the import figures in tons for Indonesia were more than double those in 1938. The import of foodstuffs reached its highest value in 1952, but was only a third of this high figure in 1955.

In Malaya the British have had a difficult struggle with bands of terrorists composed mainly of Chinese Communists who hide in the forests or, according to circumstances, change from the rôle of combatant to that of peaceful squatter. This is a war with weapons and has called for the use of as many as 300,000 men; but it is also a psychological struggle carried on with leaflets dropped from aircraft and by loudspeakers broadcasting appeals for surrender. In 1957 peace had not yet been secured, armoured cars patrolled the roads, and many of the plantations were still guarded by troops. Unrest had spread to the towns, especially Singapore, where the younger generation of the Chinese majority could not fail to be fascinated by the success of Communism in China. Strikes were frequent among office workers, dockers, and factory hands.

[1] Compare the following figures of tons exported:

	1938	1955
Tea	72,000	28,000
Copra	309,000	141,500
Palm oil	170,000	115,000
Tobacco	24,000	14,000 ⎱ Figures
Hard fibres (mainly sisal)	90,000	25,000 ⎰ for 1953

Nevertheless, the efforts and skill of the British, supported by Australia and New Zealand, achieved economic rehabilitation more rapidly than it was done in Indonesia. The plantations had once more been taken in hand by European experts, and the decrease in Indian labour had been compensated for by an influx of Chinese. The area under rubber cultivation is consequently greater than it was in 1937, largely owing to an increase in smallholdings. The acreage occupied by these is about one and three-quarter million and covers more than 60 per cent. of the total area of cultivation in the peninsula. Rubber production rose from 364,000 in 1938 to 709,000 tons in 1948, but fell to 649,000 tons in 1953. Since the proportion of hevea trees of more than twenty-five years of age had become too great, subsidies were granted for replanting both in the estates and small-holdings, whilst experiments aimed at overcoming the competition of synthetic rubber also received financial aid.

Vegetable oil production increased after 1948 from both coconut and oil palms. Great efforts have been made to diversify the crops for export and to develop the cultivation of cacao, tea, and pine-apples, which last had almost disappeared during the war.

Raw materials derived from agriculture contribute about two-thirds of the value of the exports from the Federation of Malaya and represent an important source of dollars. On the other hand, the production of foodstuffs is still inadequate to meet local demands, and 70 per cent. more rice had to be imported in 1955-6 than in 1954-5.

The Philippines have benefited to some extent from the fact that the great majority of their exports come, not from large under-takings, but from a host of Filipino smallholders for whom the problem of labour supply is of little importance. Risings, riots, and strikes have occurred in town and country, but there have been no general disturbances. The *hukbalahap*, who at one time spread terror up to the very outskirts of Manila, are now scarcely heard of. American aid has been of enormous assistance. But the revision of the Bell Trade Act in the middle of 1955 will have important con-sequences. Filipinos and Americans now have equal rights in both countries for every kind of economic activity; but free trade is to end, and import duties payable on Filipino goods entering the United States are to be gradually increased.

Now, the United States are by far the best customers of the Philip-pines, buying from them far more than any other country, as well as being the main source of their imports. In these islands, even more than in Malaya and Indonesia, most of the exports consist of agricultural produce. Of the major export crops copra has greatly exceeded pre-war production, the quantity rising from an average of

583,000 tons in the years 1925–39 to 942,000 tons in 1955, thus giving the Philippines a lead over all other countries as a source of this commodity. In addition to copra, 12,000 tons of coconut oil were exported in 1955. Cane sugar has now fallen to second place in the list of exports, but the quantity exported is increasing, and production which amounted to about a million tons in pre-war years rose to 1,250,000 tons in 1954–5. The restoration of the *abacá* plantations has been slower and has not yet been completed. The tonnage of fibre exported, which averaged 183,000 tons in 1935–9, had fallen to 87,000 tons in 1949–51 and by 1954–5 had not exceeded 110,000 tons. Tobacco production has also not reached its pre-war level.

In the Philippines, as in other parts of the Malay world, agriculture does not fully meet the demand for food in spite of the increase in the acreage under food crops, easy loans to cultivators, and the multiplication of minor drainage and irrigation schemes; and rice and various tinned foods have to be imported in greater quantities than before.

Mining, which was developed largely by foreign capital, occupies no mean place in the economy of the Malay lands. Reconstruction of mining plant has, however, proceeded very unequally from place to place. Many undertakings are now under more or less strict control by local government authorities or are subject to a mixed system of regulation which at times amounts to plain nationalisation. For example, most of the shares in the Dutch company which was formed in 1860 to work the tin deposits in the island of Belitong are now owned by the Indonesian Government. Besides the two State refineries in Belitong, the one in Banka, which was destroyed during the war, has been reconstructed. Tin mining in Indonesia was far more productive in 1956 than in 1935–9. Refining is not carried out wholly on the spot, a large proportion of the ore being taken to refineries established in Texas during the war by the Reconstruction Finance Corporation. In Malaya the recovery of the mines did not proceed very fast at first owing to a shortage of materials and coal and to the attacks of Chinese terrorists. But since 1951 the extraction of tin ore has exceeded the pre-war figure. In 1955, as in 1938, nearly twice as much ore was produced as in Indonesia, and almost all was exported in the form of metal, the refineries at Penang and Singapore having succeeded to a large extent in avoiding coming under American control.

The production of bauxite in Indonesia did not suffer too much from the war. The metal comes mainly from the Rhio, Bintan, and Kayan Islands, where it is extracted by a Dutch company. Its expansion is handicapped, however, by the scarcity of ships to carry the ore to market and by competition with Surinam, which is nearer the vast American market.

In 1954 ores and metals formed only 8·8 per cent. of the total value of exports from the Philippines, but their variety is greater than in either Malaya or Indonesia. The production of iron ore is increasing more regularly than in Malaya, though in the latter country great efforts are being made to develop this type of mining especially in the State of Trengganu, which lies in the northeast of the Federation. Both countries export their ore to Japan. On the other hand, in the Philippines the yield from gold mines tends to fall off in spite of Government subsidies. A similar falling off is noticeable in the deposits of chromium and manganese. Large quantities of copper ore seem to be available in the islands, and efforts are now being directed towards the extraction of this metal.

Situated between the enormous oilfields in the Middle East and the almost untouched potential fields in China, the Malay lands remain the chief source of petroleum for the Far East.[1] The big oil companies have quickly repaired the great damage suffered by their plant during the war, and since 1947 extraction has rapidly increased in the Palembang district and at Balik Papan. At the latter place the refinery has been reconstructed and modernised. Foreign companies have been able to keep for the purpose of restoring their productive capacity all the currency obtained from their export of oil. Production has therefore continued to increase and rose from 852,000 tons of crude oil in 1953 to 11,796,000 tons in 1955. Yet the future remains uncertain, for most of the fields being worked in Indonesia seem to have reached their peak of production, and several are even tending to fall off. It is doubtful whether the prospecting now being carried out, especially in Sumatra, the source of three-quarters of Indonesian petroleum, will discover fresh reserves. Refining capacity already exceeds production and cannot be fully used except by importing crude oil to Palembang from Brunei. Furthermore, Indonesian wells generally yield only a heavy oil which is difficult to refine, and aviation petrol has to be bought abroad.

It should be noted that in Indonesia eight oil companies have concessions running for seventy-five years. Since 1919 new concessions have been limited to forty years. Altogether, concessions for oil prospecting cover about one-twenty-fifth of the area of Indonesia.

The most striking fact of the oil industry during the past twenty years has been the rapid rise of Brunei, where crude oil production

[1] The Far East market, however, takes only 4 per cent. of world demand of this commodity.

M.I.B.P.—28

rose from 708,000 tons in 1938 to 5,630,000 tons in 1955. In this little country the oilfield employs about 5,000 labourers from the Asiatic mainland and in addition uses labour from villages in the interior. The rice needed to feed the numbers engaged in this work makes it necessary to import three-fifths of the quantity consumed in the territory. The crude oil is refined at Lutong in the neighbouring colony of Sarawak, whose oilfield at Miri is on the contrary declining, its output in 1955 having fallen to 60,000 tons.

On the whole, the volume of exports contributed to world trade by the Malay lands is still less than it was before the war. In recent years events have shown how greatly affected it is by fluctuations in world markets. Between 1945 and 1949 the fall in production as compared with pre-war years and the need to import both current consumption goods and the materials indispensable to the restoration of equipment damaged or destroyed by the war suffice to explain the deficit in the trade balance. The deficit, however, was largely covered by loans from the International Bank and by gifts and credits granted by the United States. In addition to all this there have been gifts of equipment from Australia, New Zealand, and the United Kingdom, together with 413 technologists and 1166 probationers from the last mentioned. The year 1950 and the beginning of 1951 formed a period of boom owing to the Korean war and the threat of its spreading to the rest of the world. The Great Powers began to build up their stocks of raw materials, and in consequence the price of rubber, tin, and other commodities soared up to the sky. About the middle of 1951 a reaction set in, and a slump followed. But whilst the bottom fell out of the raw materials market, the price of consumption goods, which had remained more or less steady in the boom, now began to rise, thus weakening still more the purchasing power of the already seriously undernourished masses and threatening the stability of the newly created States. In 1956 the price of foodstuffs and textiles at Jakarta rose by 50 per cent. in the course of a single week.

The situation may become particularly serious in Malaya and Indonesia because of the large number of smallholders, who are always especially hard hit by the great fluctuations which sometimes occur in the price of rubber. Of course, the Philippines have been relatively favoured, since they have been aided by the United States and because the fluctuations in the price of copra and sugar have not been so great as those in rubber and tin. But even when the balance of trade is favourable to the Malay countries, the balance of payments is not so, for money goes abroad to defray the cost of the services of ocean transport, banking, and insurance, to pay the dividends of foreign companies operating in the area, and to form the remittances sent home to China by Chinese through middlemen in Hongkong. The press in the Philippines often voices the national grievances due to the competition of Chinese shopkeepers, who almost completely monopolise the retail trade in Manila.

The deficit owing to these payments abroad leads to unbalanced national budgets 'and the depreciation of the currency. In 1950-1 Indonesia passed through a severe crisis, when bank notes were cut in two and their value, like that of all means of exchange, cut by a half. The adoption of a multiple system of exchange and the lack of foreign bills hinder economic progress by restricting imports.

The abolition of the Colonial status and the shock to the European economic system due to the war explain the progress made by the United States in the foreign trade of the Malay lands. But former ties are tending to be renewed. Of course, the United States still supplied 18·2 per cent. of the imports into Indonesia in 1953 and 14·6 per cent. in 1954; and they took 20·5 per cent. of the exports in 1953 and 16·8 per cent. in 1954. But trade is increasing with Western Europe, and especially with the United Kingdom and Federal Germany. Although the Netherlands lost heavily by the secession of Indonesia, they still maintain a considerable trade with the islands. Active dealings have sprung up between the Malay lands and other countries of the Far East, particularly Japan. This country, which supplied 15·1 per cent. of the imports into Indonesia in 1938, was the origin of 22·7 per cent. in 1954; and whilst in 1938 it took 3·3 per cent. of the exports of Indonesia and Hongkong, in 1954 it took 5·8 per cent.

Japan is an important purchaser of rubber in Indonesia. She buys mainly from smallholders, whilst the United States and Western Germany seem to prefer dealing with the large plantations. In 1956 the Government of Indonesia followed the lead of Malaya in deciding to export rubber to China and other Communist countries.

It is not surprising that a large part of the trade of Malaya should be carried on with the United Kingdom and the Asian countries of the Sterling Block, viz. Burma, Ceylon, Hongkong, India, Pakistan, and British Borneo. The total value of the trade of Malaya greatly exceeds that of Indonesia and the Philippines taken together. Singapore has resumed its profitable task of collecting and redistributing merchandise. Rubber, mainly from Sumatra and Borneo, remains the chief commodity in this transit business. In 1955 the high price of rubber changed the previously unfavourable balance of trade into a favourable one of 336 million Malayan dollars; but this fell far short of the boom due to the Korean war. It should be noted that Singapore's lead in exports is threatened by the existence of Port Swettenham, Penang, and other ports on the peninsula; by the direct shipment of oil in tankers from Palembang, Balik Papan, and Brunei; and by the loading of timber for Hongkong at the mouth of the River Rayang. But in imports Singapore reigns the unchallenged queen, the great shopwindow of Southeast Asia.

None of the former Protecting Powers seems to be more closely related commercially with their old dependencies than do the United States. This country has, however, been losing ground since 1948, when it still took 67 per cent. of the exports of the Philippines and supplied 82 per cent. of the imports; whereas in 1955 these figures had fallen respectively to 60·5 and 68 per cent.; and the fall will continue with the progressive reduction in the preferential tariffs agreed between the two countries until their total abolition in 1974. For this reason the Philippines are striving to find other markets. In 1954 the islands shipped 46 per cent. of their copra to Northwestern Europe, half being taken by the Netherlands. *Abacá* producers hope that the reconstruction of Japanese shipping will offer them a market. In recent years sugar production has coincided almost exactly with local demands and the quota allowed entry into the United States. In future it will be necessary to ensure the sale of large surpluses of the commodity by means of regional or international agreements.

British, American, and Western European ships carry most of the exports and imports of the Malay lands. Internal communications are regularly carried out by foreign shipping companies, among which are included some Chinese. In this connexion the famous Dutch K.P.M. still plays a very important part.

Air services have greatly increased. Local air lines have been, or soon will be, taken over by national organisations. They more or less compensate for the inadequacy in some districts of road and rail transport. In Indonesia the number of passenger-miles carried by air was more than doubled between 1948 and 1955.

The Economic Future. A glance at statistics seems to show that, though the Malay lands have not recovered their pre-war level of production, they have on the whole regained their position as great producers of raw materials; and considering the vast under-populated and underdeveloped areas included in their bounds, they still look forward to an enormous economic expansion.

But it is uncertain whether their basic products will be the same as before, for the fortunes of some of the commodities are by no means assured. Rubber has the most doubtful future of all. It heads the list of export values from the Malay world and used to be regarded by many people as the outstanding success in colonial exploitation. But the last war gave a great stimulus to its young synthetic rival when the United States were cut off from the chief rubber-growing regions. In 1956 the American synthetic rubber factories were denationalised and handed over to powerful firms (Firestone, Goodrich, Goodyear, du Pont, etc.) which manufacture chemicals and various articles made from petroleum and which have big interests in the production of synthetic rubber. In 1957 the 1,096,000 tons produced in 1955 will be increased to 1,510,000 tons. The competition of this dangerous rival is a principal factor in the fluctuations in the price of natural rubber which have occurred since 1955. Thus, from 25 pence per pound in March, 1955, prices rose to nearly 45 pence in August and September, but fell again to 29 pence in May, 1956, when synthetic rubber showed signs of being sold at 23 pence. Yet it is still doubtful whether the United States will in the near future give up the use of natural rubber. The two kinds of the commodity are said to be complementary, to have each its own uses, and frequently a compound of the two is actually to be preferred. It has been quietly suggested that in keeping their industrial plant going the United States merely want to make sure that they are not asked the high prices that they have had to pay in the past for natural rubber. It is said, too, that the States do not mean to tolerate another Stevenson Plan, but that they have an interest in maintaining the plantations in the Far East, since the rubber there produced lessens the large and dangerous credit balance they have in their trade with Western Europe. It is reckoned, too, that the uses of rubber may increase still further; for instance, for surfacing roads. The competition of synthetic rubber is, however, a serious threat to the natural article.

It is unlikely that Java will in the near future again become a large exporter of sugar. The areas on which sugar-cane was culti-vated alternately with rice are now being more and more devoted to food crops, since the island is so dangerously overpopulated. Sugar produced in the Philippines will soon come under an in-creasingly strict quota system in the United States, where it will be faced with the competition of sugar produced in the South, in the West Indies, and Hawaii. Besides, sugar-cane is being cultivated more and more in the Pacific Islands and around the Indian Ocean; for instance, in Fiji, India, Pakistan, and Madagascar.

Before 1941 the Philippines supplied 90 per cent. of world pro-duction of Manila hemp, most of it being grown on large estates. But during the war the *abacá* plantations were neglected, and as soon as the Japanese companies which worked them had closed down in 1945, the estates suffered from mishandling by the Filipino tenants; and now there is strong competition from Central America where during the war such large areas were put under the plant in the republics of Panama, Costa Rica, Guatemala, and Honduras that it seems possible that production in these countries will soon suffice to meet the needs of the United States in this commodity.

Since the discovery of synthetic febrifuges Java has lost the advantage of having a quasi-monopoly in the production of quinine. Kapok, whose chief producer is Indonesia, is now being very often replaced in its main uses (life-saving apparatus and stuffing for mattresses, pillows, and cushions) by sorbo rubber and plastic foam. The Malay world is still by far the leading producer of copra. In 1953 out of a global production of 2,760,000 tons the Malay world produced 1,763,000 tons. But both copra and palm oil are faced in the world market with an expanded production of palm oil in West and Equatorial Africa, as well as with the competition of butter in Western Europe, where butter is preferred to margarine; of animal fats in the United States and Australia; and throughout the globe of detergents made by petro-chemistry; all of which are deadly rivals of soap made from vegetable matter.

It should be added that the downfall of the colonial system has brought considerable changes in the methods of land use. The part played by large estates in producing raw materials has fallen off everywhere, though not always to the same extent. Many of the estates damaged during the Japanese occupation have not been rehabilitated owing to the anarchy which followed the war. Heavy welfare charges have been imposed on foreign firms. Besides, the cost of production has been increased, especially on coffee estates, by frequent pilfering and by the poor condition of the roads. Some of the large estates have been nationalised and have become 'people's plantations'. At the beginning of 1955 there were in Indonesia thirty-five State plantations covering a total of about 100,000 acres. This was distributed among the various crops as follows: 67,000 under rubber, 19,000 under oil palms, 9000 under tea, 2000 under gutta percha, and 1000 each under coconut trees, quinine, and coffee. These State plantations seem to be the main exporters today, except in rubber and coffee, and, as has been said above, the quantity of exports has greatly decreased. In comparison with pre-war conditions the proportion of smallholders producing rubber has increased owing to the suitability of the *ladang* system to a crop which contains an element of primitive gathering. This is noticeably so in the forest districts of Sumatra and Sarawak, where the smallholder can easily stop tapping his rubber trees and fall back on pepper, copra, sago, jelutong, and other crops. Then when there is a rise in the price of rubber in world markets, he resumes the tapping. In 1951 the quantity of rubber exported from Sarawak amounted to 43,000 tons, but in 1954 it was only 23,000 tons, the latter year being one in which the quantity of pepper exported was the highest on record.

The policy of the national governments is evidently to keep in the country most of the profits arising from the exports. They can hardly be blamed, but there is another side to the picture of spreading the wealth-bringing crops among the peasants and to that of the flexibility of the system of smallholding. In a host of little units it is difficult to modify the scientific methods of agriculture so as to enable the product to face the competition of the world market. A fairly long time will elapse before the native cultivators are co-operatively organised for protection and can take advantage of the results of research, the various technical improvements, and the flexible commercial organisation which will enable them to escape the toils of the middleman. It must also be remembered that European firms gave a livelihood in Java alone to about a million Indonesians before the war and that European firms supplied about three-fourths of the revenues of the Netherlands Indies.[1]

Thus, in 1954 Malaya and Indonesia together produced 52·5 per cent. of world production of tin. The future of this metal has become less assured through the invention of the electrolytic process of tin-plating, which reduces the quantity of metal used. The new process is favoured particularly by the United States, the world's largest consumers, who take about half the total world production, hold enormous stocks, and are thus able to regulate prices.

The Problem of Population. The Malay world is faced not merely with the problem of raising production to the pre-war figure. The rate of increase must be greater than that of the population. Though official statistics generally represent mere estimates, certain it is that the population continues to increase dangerously fast, as it does throughout Monsoon Asia and in most underdeveloped countries. According to the statistics published by the United Nations Organisation, Indonesia has a population of 82,500,000, Malaya one of 6,000,000 without counting the million and a quarter inhabitants of Singapore, British Borneo has 1,000,000, and the Philippines 21,000,000. Thus, the Malay world as we have defined it contains a total of 112,800,000 persons on an area of 820,866 square miles, which gives a mean density of 137 per square mile. This density exceeds 1030 in Java and Madura, but hardly reaches 13 per square mile in Borneo.

The mean demographic rate of increase seems to be between 1·5 and 2 per cent. per annum. As in so many underdeveloped countries in which the introduction of scientific technique has preceded psychological and social progress, the resulting decrease in the death-rate has not been compensated for by a fall in the birth-rate. Hence, the

[1] E. de Vries: *Problems of Agriculture in Indonesia*, in *Pacific Affairs*, June, 1949, pp. 130–2.

amount of food available per person is less both as regards the number of calories and, as occurs throughout the tropical world, through the insufficiency of animal protein. This leads to the need to import cereals, tinned milk, meat, fats, etc. Of course, it is possible to increase the area cultivated and the yield per acre by a far greater use of reserves of water and of hydraulic works. Dry farming, too, offers great potential returns so long as proper measures taken to avoid soil-erosion are strictly applied.[1] For instance, the results of an experiment carried out in 1953–4 in India on 390,000 acres showed that the introduction of a Japanese method of riziculture giving a high yield would afford some protection.[2]

But this demands detailed preparation, previous investigation, vigilant control, capital, skill, and time. Besides, there must be a transfer of population from overpopulated districts and a real internal colonisation of empty spaces. Experience has shown that spontaneous migration would not adequately achieve the desired transfer, even if this was limited to twenty or thirty thousand migrants a year instead of the 500,000 envisaged by the official Indonesian and Filipino plan of 1951. This reduced number is indeed but a small percentage of the rate of increase in the population of Java or Luzón and the Visayas. What is needed is official action and careful planning, not to mention the willingness to migrate that presupposes sufficient authority in the central government. A firm hand, generally accepted or submitted to, must replace the Dutch in directing movement towards still underdeveloped areas, such as exist in Sumatra, Borneo, and Celebes in Indonesia and in Mindanao in the Philippines, where the local rulers would try to regulate settlement in their own interests alone and in their own time. Western New Guinea, dubbed Irian by the Indonesian Government, seems to offer great possibilities not only because of

[1] Ormeling points out the continuous damage done by erosion in Timor. The Atonis, who have been driven into the mountains by the advance of the more efficient Belunese and Rotinese from the west, own large numbers of cattle which overgraze the natural pasture and thus cause the destruction of the soil and the low yield of the crops. Ormeling recommends their turning over to mixed farming, the cultivation of patches near the villages, an increase in minor irrigation systems, and official help to cottage industries. The damage done by shifting cultivation still continues in the mountain districts of the Philippines. (Spencer, pp. 50–6.)

[2] According to rough calculation, the area cultivated is but a small percentage of the total. In Indonesia it is about 7 per cent., in the Philippines 15 per cent., and in Malay 16 per cent. Irrigated soil forms only 3 per cent. of the total surface of the Malay world. The area is being increased in various ways. Thus, the Sungei Manik Irrigation Scheme has turned swamp forest in southern Perak into ricefields. But as a result the population of the district increased from 1500 in 1932 to 45,000 in 1953. Since 1918 agricultural productivity has increased in Malaya more than anywhere else in the Malay world.

its mineral wealth, especially in oil, but also because of its vast area of virgin land. But the special arrangement made for this bit of the Dutch East Indies seems to have been not only approved, but even demanded by the United States and Australia. The latter Power, which governs the eastern portion of New Guinea, sees in this large island not only agricultural and mining advantages, but also a rampart to protect her White Policy from the Yellow peoples. In this second view she is supported by New Zealand. It should be mentioned here that there is a plan to transfer to New Guinea any Eurasians in Indonesia who may desire it.[1]

Emigration would help to remedy unemployment, which is still considerable in the Malay world; but it would not suffice to absorb the surplus agricultural population. The proportion of the national revenue derived from agriculture relatively to the total national income is far less than the proportion of the agricultural population relatively to the total population. In other words, the density of population engaged in agriculture has increased without a corresponding increase in agricultural production. Overpopulation causes, as it often does in underdeveloped countries, a decrease in the yield per acre and per worker. Hence the need to import food in spite of the decrease in export crops. Technical improvements which would break this vicious circle and would destroy this socio-economic complex, seem difficult or even impossible, unless at the same time steps are taken to transfer part of the rural population to other types of work, especially industry.

As elsewhere in the world, there is no want of plans for fixing the stages and objectives of industrialisation, each plan being known by the name of some member of the Government. Praiseworthy attempts have been made to save and perfect the cottage industries, whose decline has been one of the factors of overpopulation, especially in Java. The plan is to associate craftsmen with a central institution which distributes raw materials, studies and gives information about better processes of manufacture, and helps to sell the finished articles. The State grants the initial capital and funds needed until the associated craftsmen forming a co-operative system have found their feet. Mechanisation is to be reduced to a minimum, since the chief aim is to avoid unemployment. By 1951 as many as fifty-two associations had been formed in Java, where there were twenty-one central institutions dealing with cottage industries in leather, wood, pottery, metal, textiles, parasols, and rubber. They controlled 4118 workshops and 44,650 craftsmen. But on the

[1] Controlled migration has moved from Java to Borneo and Sumatra a mere annual average of 26,000 persons. In addition, a few thousand peasants migrate spontaneously every year.

whole this plan does not seem to have had as much success as was hoped.

Industry is far from being able to absorb all the labour which troops in from rural districts, and unemployment is rife in the towns. In Indonesia Jakarta has a population of two million, Surabaya and Bandung each 800,000, Semarang 400,000, Bogor (Buitenzorg) 125,000, and these figures do not include the satellite towns. In Sumatra Medan has a population of more than 300,000, and Palembang nearly reaches that figure. Even in Borneo there are two towns of more than 100,000 inhabitants, viz. Banjermasin (175,000) and Pontianak (121,000). Macassar in Celebes has a population of 335,000.

Now, a state which aims at being modern cannot remain at the stage of cottage industry, a stage which is but a beginning and is to be quickly passed through. It is all a matter of prestige and a desire to reach Western levels as soon as possible. Industry on a grand scale seems indispensable to national independence. It is impossible to say how far this ambition will be realised, for industry has been on a very modest scale since the last war; and in spite of bold schemes, expansion has been slow and unmethodical. Besides, the cautious and laudatory character of official documents often makes it difficult to ascertain facts accurately. A cement factory which is being built at Gresik near Surabaya, with the help of American capital and technicians, is due to begin working in 1957 and to give an annual output of 200,000 tons. Seven rubber re-milling works with an annual output of 11,700 tons have been planned, but only two had been built at the beginning of 1955, one at Palembang and the other at Siak. At Chilachap in southern Java a cotton-mill has been built and fitted out with Japanese equipment. Filipino technicians have set up a desiccated coconut factory at Sukur in northern Celebes.

The average consumption of electric current in Indonesia was still only 10 kWh. a head in 1954. The production of coal—of a low calorific value—has fallen off in the nationalised pits. The petroleum raised is nearly all exported. Skilled workers and raw materials are even scarcer than power, especially in the textile industry. But in 1955 the value of the textiles imported into Indonesia was greater than that of any other article. Two great electric power plants have been envisaged by the Indonesian National Planning Board: one on the Asahan in northern Sumatra for aluminium works and timber mills; the other at Jatilahur in western Java for giving power to various industries and to serve the irrigation works covering 250,000 acres. It is hoped that the demand for electric power will be met by 1961. Indonesia is trying to hasten the training of technicians in the institutes at Bandung with the help of American and European teachers. The foreign private firms, especially the oil companies, have training schemes which will affect thousands of employees.

Owing to help from America, the index of industrial production is certainly a little higher in the Philippines, where 13 per cent. of the national revenue in 1954 was due to industry. The production of electric power increased about five times in Manila between 1938 and 1955, and the expansion continues. Most of the new industrial development has been concentrated around the capital, where it has the advantage of the presence of thousands of unemployed. Leather and rubber goods, cigarettes, electrical apparatus, and paper have increased in production. But the increasing manufacture of American cigarettes has proved disastrous to the local article; and as in Indonesia cotton goods find a difficulty in holding their own against imported textiles. Protection is sure to have an increasing finger in the industrial pie.

In the States of the Federation of Malaya, which are large producers of raw material, there is only cottage industry, apart from mining and the factories connected with the estates; but in Singapore many industrial undertakings of moderate size have grown up, including sawmills and factories for preparing and canning foodstuffs and for making rubber goods and electrical apparatus. But the frequent strikes in 1955 were a handicap. Power from electricity is produced in far greater quantity in Malaya and Singapore, taken together, than in either the Philippines or Indonesia; but on the peninsula only 204,000 tons of lignite were raised in 1955, whilst 480,000 tons were raised in 1938.

The new governments, whose ardent nationalist feelings should be understood, are aware of the need they have of foreign help, especially with capital and technicians of all sorts. In spite of the ruin of many of their businesses, the Dutch have not been altogether turned out of Indonesia. As was said above, they play a great part in shipping and commerce; they are still the most numerous of the Europeans in Jakarta. About two-thirds of the capital invested in Indonesia before the war was Dutch. A large proportion of this has now been returned to the Netherlands, and most of the British capital has been taken home. American dollars had been invested mainly in prospecting and raising mineral oil, but they are being used for other purposes now; for example, they are competing in rubber production with the British, Franco-Belgian, and Chinese. American firms have built motor construction works in Jakarta, and German and British companies have followed suit or are intending to do so. The great Dutch firm of Phillips, which makes electric

lamps and wireless sets, has an establishment in Surabaya.   Railway
requisites have been ordered from Krupps as well as from the Netherlands.   Since President Sukarno's visit to Bonn in 1955 negotiations
have been begun for the establishment of basic industries in Indonesia, including metallurgy, chemical products, textiles, bicycles, and
tyres.   Germany would also supply many kinds of medical requisites.   The eclecticism shown in placing orders in different countries
has the advantage not only of obtaining better terms, but also
of lessening the possibility of foreign economic domination.   Since
1950 negotiations have been going on with Sweden as well as with
Italy for the equipment of a cellulose factory for making paper.
The Indonesian Government has just given its consent to the formation of a Nippo-Indonesian bank, 49 per cent. of whose capital
would be supplied by Japan.   This bank is meant to assist industrial
development and to foster commerce between the two countries.

The need for foreign help is still very great.   In 1956 Indonesia
issued a cautious appeal to foreign capitalists, promising that
nationalisation would not take place for twenty years.   The length
of leases granted varies from ten to thirty and even forty years for
agricultural undertakings.   But foreign companies are required to
employ Indonesians in their businesses, to train Indonesian staffs,
and to re-invest a proportion of the profits in the concerns.

BIBLIOGRAPHY

I. GENERAL

1. J. O. M. Broek: *Diversity and Unity in Southeast Asia*, Geogr. Rev. 1944, pp. 175–95.
1a. K. Helbig: *Am Rande des Pazifik, Studien zur Landes- und Kulturkunde Südöstasiens*, Stuttgart, 1949.
2. J. Sion: *Asie des Moussons*, vol. 9, pt. 2, pp. 397–401 and 478–510, in the series *Géographie universelle*, edit. by P. Vidal de la Blache and L. Gallois and pub. in 1929.

II. DISCOVERY AND EARLY VOYAGES

3. W. Dampier: *A New Voyage round the World*, London, 1927.
4. Dobel: *Sept années en Chine*, Paris, 1838.
5. A. Guibon: *Sur les traces des Dieppois à Sumatra, 1529–34*, Dieppe, 1936.
6. W. Heyd: *Histoire de commerce du Levant au Moyen Age*, French edit., Leipzig, 1885, 2 vols.
7. A. Kammerer: *La Mer Rouge, l'Abyssinie et l'Arabie depuis l'antiquité*, pt. 2: *Les guerres du poivre*, in vol. 16 of the Memoirs of the Royal Egyptian Geographical Society, pub. in Cairo in 1935.
8. A. Kammerer: *Journal of the Embassy to China*, pub. in vol. 2 of J. Barrow's memoir of the embassy.
9. A. Olearius: *Voyages très curieux et très renommés faits en Moscovie, Tartarie et Perse*, Amsterdam, 1727, 2 vols.
10. Sonnerat: *Voyage aux Indes orientales et à la Chine*, Paris, 1806.
11. J. B. Tavernier: *Les six voyages de J. B. Tavernier en Turquie, en Perse, et aux Indes*, Paris, 1679–81, 3 vols.

III. GENERAL WORKS ON THE DUTCH EAST INDIES

12. G. Angoulvant: *Les Indes néerlandaises dans l'économie internationale*, Paris, 1926, 2 vols.
13. *Atlas van Tropisch Nederland*, pub. by the Roy. Nederlands Geog. Society in collaboration with the Survey Dept. of the Dutch East Indies; The Hague, 1938. (Reviewed by Ch. Robequain in Ann. Géogr. 1940, pp. 130–4.)
14. A. Cabaton: *Les Indes néerlandaises*, Paris, 1910.
15. J. S. Furnivall: *Netherlands India, a Study in Plural Economy*, Cambridge, 1944.
16. A. Hartmann: *Repertorium op de litteratuur betreffende de Nederlandsche Kolonien in Oost en West-Indië*, The Hague, 1895.
17. J. Nippgen: *Les Indes néerlandaises. Etude bibliographique*, Outre-Mer, Revue Générale de Colonisation, 1931, pp. 137–72. (This deals also with the Philippines and the British and Portuguese territories in the East Indies.)

18. J. Paulus, S. de Graff, and D. G. Stibbe: *Encyclopædie van Neder-landsch-Indië*, 2nd Edit., The Hague, 1917–35, 10 vols.
19. L. M. R. Rutten (editor): *Science in the Netherlands East Indies*, Roy. Acad. of Sciences, Amsterdam, 1930.
20. B. Schrieke (editor): *The Effect of Western Influence on Native Civilisations in the Malay Archipelago*, Batavia, 1929.
21. A. Vandenbosch; *The Dutch East Indies*, Berkeley, 1942.
22. B. H. M. Vlekke: *Nusantara, a History of the East Indian Archipelago*, Cambridge, 1944.

IV. GEOLOGICAL STRUCTURE AND RELIEF

23. F. Blondel: *Les connaissances géologiques en 1930 sur l'Extrême-Orient méridional*, in Bull. Soc. géol. Fr. 1930, pp. 323–432.
24. H. A. Brouwer: *The Geology of the Netherlands East Indies*, New York, 1925.
25. Transactions of the Int. Geogr. Congress at Amsterdam in 1938, vol. 2, sect. 2*b*: Oceanography: P. H. Kuenen: *Submarine Slopes of Volcanoes and Coral Reefs in the East Indian Archipelago*, pp. 93–98; J. H. F. Umbgrove: *On the Time of Origin of the Submarine Relief of the East Indies*, pp. 150–59; P. M. van Riel: *The Influence of the Bottom Configuration on the Properties of Sea Water in the Abyssal Layers*, pp. 18–26. Leiden, 1938.
26. W. M. Davis: *Fringing Reefs of the Philippine Islands*, in Proc. Nat. Acad. Sci. Wash., July, 1918, pp. 199–204.
27. J. Elbert: *Die Sunda Expedition des Vereins für Geographie und Statistik zur Frankfurt-am-Main*, 1911–12, 2 vols.
28. B. G. Escher: *Rapport sur les phénomènes volcanologiques de l'Archipel Indien* in Bull. volcan., Naples, 1937, pp. 127–78.
29. E. C. J. Mohr: *The Soils of Equatorial Regions with Special Reference to the Netherlands Indies*, New York, 1944. (Transl. from the Dutch by R. L. Pendleton.)
30. G. A. F. Molengraaff: *Modern Deep-Sea Research in the East Indian Archipelago* in Geogr. J. for Jan.–June, 1921, pp. 95–121.
31. P. M. van Riel (editor): *The Snellius Expedition in the Eastern Part of the Netherlands East Indies*, 1929–30, Utrecht, 1935–8. (Reviewed by G. Wüst in Z. Ges. Erdk., Berlin, 1936, pp. 347–58.)
32. L. M. R. Rutten: *Voordrachten over de geologie van Nederlandsch Oostindië*, Groningen, 1927.
33. L. M. R. Rutten: *De Geologie van Nederlandsch Indië*, The Hague, 1932.
34. G. Schott: *Geographie des Indischen und Stillen Ozeans*, Hamburg, 1935.
35. N. J. M. Taverne: *Vulkanologische Berichten*, Batavia, 1935.
36. N. J. M. Taverne: *Vulkanstudien op Java*, Batavia, 1926. (Summaries in English.)
36a. J. H. F. Umbgrove: *Structural History of the East Indies*, Cambridge, 1949.

V. CLIMATE

37. J. Boerema: *Rainfall Types in the Netherlands Indies*, Koninklijk Magnetisch en Meteorologisch Observatorium te Batavia, Verhandelingen, No. 18, 1926.
38. C. Braak: *Klimakunde von Hinterindien und Insulinde*, Manual of Climatology, vol. IV. Part R, Berlin, 1931.
39. C. E. Deppermann: *The Mean Transport of Air in the Indian and South Pacific Oceans*, Manila, 1935.
40. C. E. Deppermann: *Some Characteristics of Philippine Typhoons*, Weather Bureau, Manila Central Observatory, 1939.
41. E. H. G. Dobby: *Winds and Fronts over Southeast Asia*, in Geogr. Rev., April, 1945, pp. 204–18.
42. R. Eichelberger: *Regenverteilung, Pflanzendecke, und Kulturentwicklung in der östlichen Inselwelt* in Geogr. Z. 1924, pp. 103–16.

VI. VEGETATION

43. Allouard and Sallenave: *Les forêts de Malaisie et des Indes néerlandaises* in Bull. écon. Indochine, 1935, pp. 730–94.
44. H. Aymé-Martin: *Les forêts des Philippines* in Bull. Soc. Geogr. Comm. Paris, 1914, pp. 6–44.
45. C. A. Backer: *Plantes exotiques naturalisées dans Java* in Ann. Jard. bot. Buitenz., 1910, 3rd supplement, part 1, pp. 393–425.
46. E. Bordage: *Le repeuplement végétal et animal des îles Krakatoa* in Ann. Géogr. 1916, pp. 1–22.
47. W. H. Brown: *Vegetation of Philippine Mountains*, Manila, Bureau of Sci., publication No. 13, 1919. (A summary appears in No. 51 below.)
48. R. E. Dickerson: *Distribution of Life in the Philippines*, Manila, 1928.
49. F. W. Foxworthy: *Distribution and utilisation of the Mangrove Swamps of Malaya* in Ann. Jard. bot. Buitenz. 3rd. supplement, part 1, 1910, pp. 319–440.
50. H. Lehmann: *Der tropische Wald in Niederländisch-Indien* in Kol. Rdsch, 1934, pp. 204–227.
51. R. C. MacGregor: *Some features of the Philippines Ornis, with Notes on the Vegetation in relation to the Avifauna* in Philipp. J. Sci., 1920, pp. 361–437.
52. J. Massart: *Un botaniste en Malaisie* in Bull. Soc. Bot. Belg. 1895, pp. 151–341.
53. E. D. Merrill: *The Malayan, Australasian and Polynesian Elements in the Philippine Flora* in Ann. Jard. bot. Buitenz. 3rd. supplement, part 1, 1910, pp. 277–306.
54. R. Reinhard: *Die Tiekwälder und ihre Nutzung*, Wissenschaftliche Veröffentlichungen des deutschen Museums für Länderkunde, Leipzig, 1936, pp. 19–38.
55. A. F. W. Schimper: *Pflanzengeographie auf physiologischer Grundlage*, Jena, 1898.
56. G. G. J. van Steenis: *Maleische Vegetatieschetsen* in Tijdschr. ned. aardrijksk Genoot., 1935, pp. 25–67, 171–203, 363–98.

56a. G. G. J. van Steenis: *Hoofdlijnen van de Plantengeographie van de Indische Archipel op grond van de verspreiding der phanerogramengeschlachten* in Tijdschr. ned. aardrijksk Genoot., 1948, pp. 193–208.
57. W. N. Whitford: *The Forest of the Philippines,* Manila, 1911.
58. H. Zondervan: *Vegetationsbilder aus Äquatorial-Sumatra* in Geogr. Z. 1897, pp. 282–87.

VII. FAUNA

59. Th. Arldt: *Die Entwicklung des indoaustralischen Inselwelt* in Petermanns Mitt., 1917, pp. 341–48, 368–79.
60. J. Berlioz: *Notes ornithologiques au cours d'un deuxième voyage en Malaisie* in L'Oiseau et la Revue franc. d'Ornithologie, Nos. 3 and 4, 1936.
61. B. Rensch: *Die Geschichte des Sundabogens, Eine tiergeographische Untersuchung,* Berlin, 1936.
62. A. R. Wallace: *Island Life,* London, 1880.
63. A. R. Wallace: *The Malay Archipelago,* London, 1890.

VIII. PEOPLES AND CULTURE

64. M. Boule: *Le Sinanthrope* in Anthropologie, 1937, pp. 1–22.
65. G. H. Bousquet: *Introduction à l'étude de l'Islam indonésien* in Rev. étud. islamiques, 1938, vols. 2 and 3.
66. A. Cabaton: *Relations de l'Indochine avec les Indes néerlandaises* in Conférences à l'École Coloniale, Paris, 1911–12, pp. 57–69.
67. W. J. Cator: *The Economic Position of the Chinese in the Netherlands Indies,* Oxford, 1936.
67a. G. Coedès: *Le royaume de Crivijaya* in Bull. Ecol. Fran. d'Extrême-Orient, 1918, pp. 1–36.
67b. G. Coedès: *Les Etats hindouisés d'Indochine et d'Indonésie,* Paris, 1948.
68. O. C. Dahl: *Les convergences phonétiques entre le malgache et le maajan de Bornéo* in Bull. Acad. malgache, 1938, pp. 197–200.
69. G. Ferrand: *A propos d'une carte javanaise du 15e siècle* in J. asiat., 1918, pp. 158–69.
70. G. Ferrand: *L'empire sumatranais de Crivijaya* in J. asiat., 1922, pp. 1–105, 161–246.
71. L. Frobenius: *Die Kulturformen Ozeaniens* in Petermanns Mitt., 1900, pp. 204–15, 234–38, 262–71.
71a. D. C. E. Hall: *History of South-East Asia.*
72. J. P. Kleiweg de Zwaan: *De Rassen van den Indischen Archipel,* Amsterdam, 1925.
73. Th. Kluge: *Völker und Sprachen der Südsee* in Petermanns Mitt., 1942, pp. 369–71.
74. G. H. R. von Koenigswald: *Das Pleistocän Javas* in Quartär, Berlin, 1939, vol. 2, pp. 28–55.
75. A. Kramer: *Atlas der Völkerkunde, Westindonesien: Sumatra, Java, Borneo,* Stuttgart, 1927.
76. N. J. Krom: *Hindoe-Javaansche Geschiedenis,* The Hague, 1926.

77. B. Laufer: *The Relations of the Chinese to the Philippine Islands*, Smithsonian Misc. Collections, vol. 50, pt. 2, 1907, pp. 248–84.

77a. J. C. van Lewi: *Indonesian Trade and Society*, The Hague, 1955.

78. H. Marchal: *Rapport sur une mission archéologique à Java et à Bali* in Bull. Ecol. fran. d'Extrême-Orient, 1930, pp. 585-627.

79. N. Peri: *Essai sur les relations du Japon et de l'Indochine aux 16ᵉ et 17ᵉ siècles* in Bull. Ecol. fran. d'Extrême-Orient, 1923, pp. 1–136.

80. W. J. Perry: *The Megalithic Culture of Indonesia*, Manchester, 1918.

80a. V. Purcell, *The Chinese in Southeast Asia*, London, 1951.

81. P. Rivet: *Les Océaniens* in Præhistorica Asiæ Orientalis, Hanoi, 1932, pp. 35–46.

82. F. M. Schnitger: *Forgotten Kingdoms of Sumatra*, Leiden, 1939.

83. F. W. van Stapel: *Geschiedenis van Nederlandsch Indië*, Amsterdam. (In course of publication since 1938. Three vols. now out.)

84. W. F. Stutterheim: *Histoire des rapports entre l'Indochine et Java dans les temps anciens* in Extrême-Asie, an illustrated journal in Indo-China, June 1928, pp. 603–9.

85. W. F. Stutterheim: *Indian Influence in old Balinese Art*, London, India Society, 1935.

86. Ta Chen: *Emigrant Communities in South China*, New York, 1940.

87. P. Teilhard de Chardin: *Notes sur la Paléontologie humaine en Asie méridionale* in Anthropologie, 1937, pp. 23–33.

88. L. Unger: *The Chinese in Southeast Asia* in Geogr. Rev., 1944, pp. 196–217.

89. B. A. G. Vroklage: *Die sozialen Verhältnisse Indonesiens*, vol. 1: *Borneo, Celebes, and the Moluccas*, Münster in Westphalia, 1936. (Reviewed in Bull. Col. Inst. of Amsterdam, Nov. 1937, pp. 46–57, by J. C. Lamster.)

90. Vu van Quang: *Le problème des Eurasiens en Indochine*, Hanoi, 1939.

91. A. Werth: *Die alte (vorrussische) Nordgrenze des Ackerbaues in Asien* in Z. Ges. Erdk. Berl., 1941, pp. 379–87.

IX. MODES OF LIFE AND TYPES OF DWELLING

92. S. Bakker: *Cattle-breeding in the Netherlands Indies* in Bull. Col. Inst. of Amsterdam, 1940, pp. 111–30.

93. H. C. Delsman: *Fishing and Fish-culture in the Netherlands Indies* in Bull. Col. Inst. Amster., 1939, pp. 92–105.

94. A. W. Herre: *Philippine Fisheries* in Proc. 3rd. Pan-Pacif. Sci. Cong., Tokyo, 1928, vol. 2, pp. 2174–2203.

95. A. W. Herre: *The Sibutu Islands* in Proc. 3rd. Pan-Pacif. Sci. Cong. Tokyo, 1928, vol. 2, pp. 2357–2364.

96. H. Lehmann: *Das Antlitz der Stadt in Niederländisch Indien* in Festschrift Norbert Krebs, Stuttgart, 1938, pp. 109–139.

97. H. Lehmann: *Die Koloniale Oberschicht der Bevölkerung von Niederländisch Indien* in Kol. Rdsch., 1938, pp. 97–114.

98. E. C. J. Mohr: *The Relation between Soil and Population Density in the Netherlands East Indies* in Trans. Int. Geogr. Congr. at Amsterdam, 1938, vol. 2, sect. 3c, pp. 478–493.

99. Nguyen van Huyen: *Introduction à l'étude de l'habitation sur pilotis dans l'Asie du Sud-Est*, Paris, 1933.
100. E. de Vries and H. Cohen: *On Village Shopkeeping in Java and Madura* in Bull. Col. Inst. Amst., 1938, pp. 263–73.

X. MALAYA

101. T. A Buckley: *An Anecdotal History of Old Times in Singapore*, Singapore, 1902, 2 vols.
101a. H. P. Clodd: *Malaya's First British Pioneer: The Life of Francis Light*, London, 1948.
102. E. H. G. Dobby: *Singapore: Town and Country* in Geogr. Rev., 1940, pp. 84–109.
103. E. H. G. Dobby: *Settlement Patterns in Malaya* in Geogr. Rev., 1942, pp. 211–32.
104. R. Firth: *The Coastal People of Kelantan and Trengganu* in Geogr. J. for May, 1943, pp. 193–205.
105. D. H. Grist: *An Outline of Malayan Agriculture*, Kuala Lumpur, 1936.
106. A. W. King: *Plantation and Agriculture in Malaya* in Geogr. J., Feb. 1939, pp. 136–48.
107. S. W. Kirby: *Johore in 1926* in Geogr. J., March 1928, pp. 240–60.
107a. F. Léger: *Les influences occidentales dans la Révolution de l'Orient (Inde, Malaisie, China, 1850–90)*, Paris, 1955.
107b. Ooi Jin Bee: *Mining Landscapes in Kinta*, Malayan J. of Tropical Geogr., IV, January, 1955, 58 pp.
108. P. Schebesta: *Bei den Urwaldzwergen von Malaya*, Leipzig, 1927.
109. J. B. Scrivenor: *The Physical Geography of the Southern Part of the Malay Peninsula* in Geogr. Rev. 1921, pp. 351–71.
110. J. B. Scrivenor: *The Geology of Malaya*, London, 1931.
111. W. W. Skeat and C. O. Blagden: *Pagan Races of the Malay Peninsula*, London, 1906, 2 vols.
112. C. A. Vlieland: *The Population of the Malay Peninsula, a Study in Human Migration* in Geogr. Rev. 1934, pp. 61–78.
113. L. R. Wheeler: *The Modern Malay*, London, 1928.
114. R. O. Winstedt: *Malaya*, London, 1923.
114a. R. O. Winstedt: *Malaya and its History*, London, 1949.

XI. SUMATRA

115. R. W. van Bemmelen: *The Volcano-tectonic Origin of Lake Toba*, in De Ingenieur in Nederlandsch Indië, 1939, pp. 126–40.
116. O. A. Collet: *Terres et peuples de Sumatra*, Amsterdam, 1925.
117. F. J. J. Dootjes: *Deli, the Land of Agricultural Enterprise* in Bull. Col. Inst. Amster., Nov. 1938, pp. 45–56; Feb. 1939.
118. B. Hagen: *Die Orang Kubu auf Sumatra*, Frankfurt-am-Main, 1908.
119. K. Helbig: *Studien auf Sumatra und Nias* in Z. Ges. Erdk. Berl., 1934, pp. 103–23.
120. K. Helbig: *Der Insel Sumatra* in Geogr. Z., 1935, pp. 88–101.
122. K. Helbig: *Beiträge zur Landeskunde von Sumatra* in Wissenschaftliche Veröffentlichungen des deutschen Museums für Ländeskunde, Leipzig, 1940, pp. 133–238.

123. K. Helbig: *Die Insel Bangka* in Deuts. Geogr. Bl., 1940, pp. 133–210.
124. J. Jongejans: *Land en Volk van Atjeh, vroeger en nu*, Baarn Holland Drukkerij, 1939.
125. H. Lehmann: *Kulturgeographische Wandlungen in Südost Sumatra (Hinterland von Palembang)* in Z. Ges. Erdk. Berl. 1933, pp. 161–75.
126. H. Lehmann: *Die Bevölkerung der Insel Sumatra* in Petermanns Mitt. 1938, pp. 3–15.
126a. H. J. A. Promes: *De economische omwenteling in de Batak-Landen in de eerste helft van deze eeuw*, Tijd. voor Econ. en Soc. Geogr., 1955, pp. 159–65; 1956, p. 97–102, 126–34.
127. G. L. Tichelman: *Some Notes on the Central Batak Country* in Bull Col. Inst. Amsterd., June 1940.
128. J. Tideman: *Land en Volk van Bengkalis* in Tijdschr. ned. aardrijksk Genoot, 1935, pp. 788–816.
129. I. Tiemann: *Das Plantagengebiete der Östköste von Sumatra*, Leipzig, 1936.
130. W. Volz: *Nord Sumatra*: vol. 1: *Die Batakländer*, 1909; vol. 2: *Die Gajoländer*, 1912, Berlin. (Summarised in Ann. Géogr. 1914, pp. 367–70.)

XII. JAVA

131. R. W. van Bemmelen: *Korte Schets van de Geologie van Java* in De Bergcultures, 1937, pp. 1454–61.
132. R. W. van Bemmelen: *The Volcano-tectonic Structure of the Residency of Malang. (East Java)* in De Ingenieur in Nederlandsch Indië, Batavia, 1937, pp. 159–72.
133. J. Chailly-Bert: *Java et ses habitants*, Paris, 1901.
134. F. Junghuhn: *Java*, Leipzig, 1854, 3 vols.
135. G. Kuperus: *The Relation between Density of Population and Utilisation of Soil in Java*, Transact. Int. Geogr. Congr. Amsterd. 1938, pp. 465–77.
136. H. Lehmann: *Morphologische Studien auf Java*, Stuttgart, 1936.
137. C. Lekkerkerker: *Javas overbevolking* in Tijdschr. ned. aardrijksk. Genoot, 1937, pp. 866–86.
138. C. Lekkerkerker: *Land en volk van Java*, vol. 1, Groningen-Batavia, 1938.
139. E. Paravicini: *Die ländlichen Siedlungen Javas* in Geogr. Z. 1927, pp. 392–404, 451–66.
140. Wibo Peekema: *Colonisation of Javanese in the Outer Provinces of the Netherlands East Indies* in Geogr. J., April 1943, pp. 145–51.
141. S. van Valkenberg: *Java, the Economic Geography of a Tropical Island* in Geogr. Rev. 1925, pp. 563–83.
142. R. D. M. Verbeek and R. Fennema: *Description géologique de Java et Madura*, 1896, 2 vols. and maps.
143. P. J. Veth: *Java, geographisch, ethnographisch, historisch*, Haarlem, 1900–7, 4 vols.

XIII. BORNEO

144. C. M. Enríquez: *Kinabalu, the Haunted Mountain of Borneo*, London, 1927.
145. H. Fehn: *Die Insel Borneo*, Munchen, 1929.
146. T. H. Harrisson: *Borneo Jungle. The Story of the Oxford Expedition to Sarawak*, London, 1938.
146a. T. H. Harrisson: *Explorations in Central Borneo*, Geogr. J., Dec. 1949, pp. 129–50.
147. K. Helbig: *Bericht über eine Reise zu den Dayak* in Z. Ethn. 1939, pp. 389–414.
147a. K. Helbig: *Urwaldwildnis Borneo*, Brunswick, 1940.
147b. K. Helbig: *Die Insel Borneo in Forschung und Schriftum*, in Mitt. Geogr. Ges. Hamburg, bd 52, pp. 110–395 (Bibliography with 2410 entries; photographs).
148. C. Hose: *In the Heart of Borneo* in Geogr. J., July–Dec., 1900, pp. 39–62.
149. C. Hose and McW. Dougall: *The Pagan Tribes of Borneo*, London, 1912.
150. A. W. Nieuwenhuis: *Quer durch Borneo*, Leiden, 1904–7, 2 vols.
151. T. Posewitz: *Borneo*, Berlin, 1889.
152. O. Rutter: *British North Borneo*, London, 1922.
153. J. B. Scrivenor: *Notes on the Geology of Sarawak*, Malayan Branch R. Asiat. Soc., 1927, pp. 288–94.

XIV. CELEBES

154. E. C. Abendanon: *Expédition de la Célèbes centrale, 1909–10*, Leiden, 1916–18, 3 vols. and maps. (Reviewed by J. Sion in Ann. Géogr. 1923, pp. 179–83.)
155. N. Adriani: *Maatschappelijke, special economische Verandering der Bevolking van Midden-Celebes*, in Tijdschr. ned. aardrijksk Genoot., 1915, pp. 457–76.
156. M. Kornrumpf: *Mensch und Landschaft auf Celebes*, Breslau, 1935.
157. P. E. Sarasin: *Reisen in Celebes*, Wiesbaden, 1905, 2 vols. (Reviewed in Ann. Géogr. 1906, pp. 270–5).

XV. EASTERN INDONESIA

158. H. A. Brouwer: *Exploration in the Lesser Sunda Islands* in Geogr. J., July 1939, pp. 1–10.
159. J. W. Gregory: *The Banda Arc: its Structure and Geographical Relations* in Geogr. J., July 1923, pp. 20–32.
160. K. Helbig: *Eine tropische Insel landschaftlicher Gegensätze* in Z. für Erdkunde, Frankfurt-am-Main, 1939, pp. 357–79.
161. K. Helbig: *Nusa Penida, ein tropische Karstinsel* in Mitt. Geogr. Ges., Hamburg, 1941, pp. 391–409.
161a. F. J. Ormeling: *The Timor problem*.

162. G. Kuperus: *Het Culturlandschap van West Soembawa*, Groningen-Batavia, 1935. (Reviewed in Tijdschr. ned. aardrijksk Genoot., 1937, pp. 606-8, by C. Rhote.)

163. S. F. Wittouck: *Exploration of Portuguese Timor* in Geogr. J., Oct. 1938, pp. 343-50.

XVI. THE PHILIPPINES

164. W. H. Anderson: *The Philippine Problem*, New York, 1939.

165. R. F. Barton: *Ifugao Economics*, Berkeley, 1922.

165a. C. Benitez: *History of the Philippines*, Boston, 1940.

166. H. O. Beyer: *Population of the Philippine Islands in 1916*, Manila, 1917.

167. H. O. Beyer: *A Tabular History of the Philippine Population.—Table of Philippine Racial Ancestry* in Præhistorica Asiæ Orientalis, Hanoi, 1932, pp. 129-34.

168. E. H. Blair and J. A. Robertson: *The Philippine Islands*, 1493-1898, Cleveland, 55 vols., 1903-9.

169. F. Jagor: *Travels in the Philippines*, London, 1875.

170. F. M. Keesing and M. A. Keesing: *Taming Philippine Headhunters*, London, 1934.

171. F. M. Keesing: *Population and Land Utilisation among the Lepanto* in Trans. Int. Geogr. Congr. 1938, pp. 458-64.

172. A. Kolb: *Die japanisch Ackerbaukolonie in Davao* in Kol. Rdsch. 1938, pp. 209-18.

173. A. Kolb: *Die Industrialisierung der Philippinen* in Mitt. Geogr. Ges., Munchen, 1938, pp. 213-27.

174. A. Kolb: *Die Kulturschichtung auf den Philippinen* in Geogr. Z. 1942, pp. 1-20.

175. A. Kolb: *Die Philippinen*, Leipzig, 1942.

176. G. A. Malcolm: *The Commonwealth of the Philippines*, New York, 1936.

177. J. Mallat: *The Philippines*, Paris, 1846, 2 vols.

178. F. Maurette: *Les Philippines d'après le recensement de 1903*, Ann. Géogr. 1907, pp. 148-58, 254-64.

179. R. L. Pendleton: *Land Utilisation and Agriculture of Mindanao*, Geogr. Rev. 1942, pp. 180-210.

180. J. Ralston Hayden: *American Experience with Problems of Population in the Philippines and Puerto Rico*, Int. Studies Conference, 10th session, Paris, 1937.

181. M. Roosevelt: *The Philippines, a Treasure and a Problem*, New York, 1926.

182. Theodore Roosevelt: *Land Problems in Puerto Rico and the Philippine Islands* in Geogr. Rev. 1934, pp. 182-204.

183. W. D. Smith: *Geology and Mineral Resources of the Philippine Islands*, Manila, 1924.

183a. J. E. Spencer: *Land and People in the Philippines*, Berkeley and Los Angeles, 1954.

184. W. Tuckermann: *Die Philippinen*, Leipzig, 1926.
185. C. Worcester: *The Philippines Past and Present*, revised with additions by R. Hayden, New York, 1930.

XVII. ECONOMIC DEVELOPMENTS AND COLONIAL SYSTEMS

186. J. H. Boeke: *The Structure of the Netherlands Indian Economy*, Inst. of Pacific Relations, New York, 1942.
187. J. O. M. Broek: *The Economic Development of the Netherlands Indies*, Inst. of Pacific Relations, New York, 1942. See also Geogr. Rev. 1940, pp. 187–200.
188. W. J. M. Buch: *La Compagnie des Indes néerlandaises et l'Indochine* in Bull. Éc. Franc. d'Extrême-Orient, 1936—I, pp. 97–196; 1937—I, pp. 121–237.
189. H. Butler: *Labour Problems in the East*, I.L.O., Geneva, 1938.
190. H. G. Callis: *Foreign Capital in Southeast Asia*, Inst. of Pacific Relations, New York, 1942.
190a. E. Chassigneux: *Van den Bosch* in *Les techniciens de la colonisation*, Paris, 1946, pp. 278–96.
191. E. Dennery: *Foules d'Asie*, Paris, 1930.
192. P. Gonnaud: *La colonisation hollandaise à Java*, Paris, 1905.
193. J. F. F. Götz: *Railways in the Netherlands Indies, with special reference to the island of Java* in Bull. Col. Inst. Amsterd. 1939, pp. 267–90.
194. W. L. Holland (editor): *Commodity Control in the Pacific Area*, London, 1935. (See also the chapters by C. Rhote on the Netherlands Indies, No. 199 below.)
194a. O. T. Howe and F. C. Matthews: *American Clipper Ships*, Salem, 1927.
195. A. von Humboldt: *Essai politique sur le royaume de la Nouvelle Espagne*, 2nd Edit., Paris, 1825, 4 vols.
196. J. W. B. Money: *Java, or How to manage a Colony*, London, 1861, 2 vols.
197. J. Pelzer: *Die Arbeiterwanderungen in Südöstasien*, Hamburg, 1935.
197a. J. Pelzer: *Pioneer Settlement in the Asiatic Tropics*, Amer. Geogr. Soc., New York, 1945.
198. G. T. Raynal: *Histoire philosophique et politique des établissements et du commerce des Européens dans les deux Indes*, Geneva, 1781, 10 vols. and maps.
199. C. Rhote: *The Economic Situation of the Netherlands East Indies from 1928 to 1935* in Asiat. Rev. 1936, pp. 785–809; 1937, pp. 125–144.
200. Ch. Robequain: *Problèmes de colonisation dans les Indes néerlandaises* in Ann. Géogr. 1941, pp. 37–57; 114–36.
201. G. Schott: *Die Verkehrswege der transozeanischen Segelschiffahrt in der Gegenwart* in Z. Ges. Erdk. Berl. 1895, No. 3, pp. 235–300.
201a. W. L. Schurz: *The Manila Galleon*, New York, 1939.

XVIII. AGRICULTURE—NATIVE AND WESTERN TYPES

202. E. Andriny: *La production du caoutchouc indigène aux Indes néerlandaises* in Bull. Econ. Indochine, 1927, pp. 340–65.

203. W. Bally: *Quelques travaux récents sur l'économie des exploitations indigènes à Java*, Rev. Agric. Roma., 1932, E., pp. 91–106.

204. Ch. J. Bernard: *Le Jardin de Buitenzorg* in Bull. Soc. Bot., Genève. 1935-6, pp. 77–93.

205. F. Bernard: *Aménagement des eaux à Java: irrigation des rizières*, Paris, 1903.

206. V. Cayla: *L'esprit et la méthode dans les recherches agronomiques aux Indes néerlandaises* in Rev. Acad. Sci. Col., vol. 14, Paris, 1931.

207. V. Cayla: *Principaux enseignements à tirer de la production du sucre à Java*, Assoc. Colonies-Sciences, Paris, 1935.

208. V. Cayla: *Le perfectionnement de l'hévea brasiliensis*, Office Technique des Planteurs d'Indochine, Paris, 1937.

209. Seventh International Congress of Tropical and Subtropical Agriculture, Paris, 1937. (For the Dutch East Indies, see pp. 211–42.)

209a. P. J. S. Cramer: *La production du caoutchouc aux Indes néerlandaises* in Rev. Bot. appliquée et Agric. trop., 1941, pp. 157–206; 425–57.

210. K. W. Dammermann: *The Botaniçal Gardens at Buitenzorg as a Scientific Institution, its Past and Future* in Ann. Jard. bot. Buitenz., 1939, pp. 1–36.

211. G. Frontou: *La culture du quinquina dans l'Ouest de Java* in Bull. Econ. Indochine, 1927, pp. 545–86.

212. F. W. Fuchs: *Moderne Kolonisation in Niederländisch Indien* in Kol. Rdsch., 1938, pp. 316–42.

213. J. Goubeaux: *Le thé aux Indes néerlandaises* in Bull. Econ. Indochine, 1927, pp. 601–41.

214. J. Goubeaux: *Le tabac aux Indes néerlandaises* in Bull. Econ. Indochine, 1928, pp. 11–40.

215. C. J. J. van Hall: *An Outline of Agriculture in the Netherlands Indies*, Int. Studies Conference, Paris, 1937.

216. C. J. J. van Hall: *Le café aux Indes néerlandaises* in Bull. Econ. Inst. Amsterd., pp. 135–43.

217. Y. Henry: *Documents sur le palmier à huile à Sumatra* in Bull. Econ. Indochine, 1926, pp. 1–19.

218. Y. Henry: *Conditions techniques et financières de la production du sucre aux Philippines*, Hanoi, 1928.

219. *Institut de recherches pour les huiles de palme et les oléagineux: Semaine du palmier à huile et du cocotier*, Paris, 1943.

220. M. Kerbosch: *Some Notes on Cinchona Culture and the World Consumption of Quinine* in Bull. Econ. Inst. Amsterd., 1939, pp. 36–51.

221. G. H. van der Kolff: *The historical Development of the Labour Relationships in a remote Corner of Java as they apply to the Cultivation of Rice*, Int. Research Series of the Inst. of Pacific Relations, undated (1937).

221a. J. van der Linden: *Java Zucker* (*Geschichte, Pflanzungen, Fabrikat*), Aaran, 1946.

222. G. Le Fèvre: *L'épopée du caoutchouc*, Paris, 1927.

223. *Une plantation de canne à sucre à Java* in Bull. Econ. Indochine, 1930 B, pp. 709–19. Adaptation of an article by Moir in 'Facts about Sugar', No. 3, Jan. 1930.

224. G. Oudot: *Plantes à fibres* in Bull. Econ. Indochine, 1940, pp. 77–94.

225. R. Reinhard: *Künstliche Bewässerung in Java* in Geogr. Z. 1943, pp. 132–42.

226. M. Schoofs: *Stockage et transport de l'huile de palme*, Inst. de Recherches pour les huiles de palme et les oléagineux, Paris, 1944.

227. I. M. B. Smits: *Extension intensive et rationnelle des cultures indigènes*, Inst. Col. Int. de Bruxelles, session de Bruxelles, 1929, pp. 513–96.

228. I. M. B. Smits: *Population Density and Soil Utilisation in the Netherlands Indies* in Trans. Int. Geogr. Congr. at Amsterd. in 1938, pp. 500—506.

229. R. Soliva: *Vues économiques sur la production du caoutchouc*, Hanoi, 1931.

230. R. Soliva: *L'évolution de la culture du caoutchouc au cours des dix dernières années* in Rev. Bot. appliquée et Agric. trop., 1942, pp. 47–69.

230a. E. de Vries: *Problems of Agriculture in Indonesia* in Pacific Affairs, June 1949, pp. 130–43.

XIX. MINING AND INDUSTRY

231. J. van den Broek: *The Netherlands Indies as a Producer of Tin* in Trans. Int. Geogr. Congr. at Amsterdam in 1938, Dec. 1939, pp. 52–69.

232. Trans. Int. Geogr. Congr. at Amsterdam in 1938: vol. 2, sect. 3c, Colonial Geography: E. R. Hyde and F. Roman: *Industrialisation of the Philippines*, pp. 559–63; S. R. Mendinueto: *Industrial Philippines*, pp. 564–66; D. J. Hulshoff Pol: *The Desirability and Possibility of Industrialisation in the Netherlands Indies*, pp. 581–86; I. J. van der Waerden: *De Industrialisatie als noodzakelijke voorwaarde voor de handhaving van het welvaartspiel in dichtbevolkte tropische gebieden*, pp. 605–13.

233. J. S. Furnivall: *The Weaving and Batik Industries in Java* in Asiat. Rev., April 1936, pp. 365–76.

234. R. Reinhard: *Oel im Pazifik* in Geogr. Z. 1942, pp. 81–92.

235. C. Rhote: *Industrial Development and Home Consumption in the Netherlands East Indies* in Bull. Col. Inst. Amsterd. 1938, pp. 1–13. (See also Trans. Int. Geogr. Congr. at Amsterdam in 1938, pp. 594–600.)

236. P. H. W. Sitsen: *Industrial Development of the Netherlands Indies*, Inst. of Pacific Relations, 1942.

237. Alex. L. Ter Braake: *Mining in the Netherlands East Indies*, New York, 1944.

XX. MEDICAL ATTENTION AND HYGIENE

238. H. Home: *The Engineer and the Prevention of Malaria*, London, 1926.
239. Jansen: *Food in the Tropics* in Bull. Col. Inst. Amsterdam, 1938, pp. 56–62.
240. F. Kronecker: *Einiges über die Ursachen und die Verbreitung der Malaria auf der Insel Java* in Geogr. Z. 1897, pp. 79–88.
241. *Organisation d'un service de lutte antimalarienne sur les chantiers des travaux publics de l'Indochine*, Gouvernement Général de l'Indochine, 2e fascicule, Hanoi, 1930. (See Nos. 3, 4, 5, of the reports of the missions in Malaya of L. Lemai, Ch. Antonelli, and M. Dufeutrel.)
242. N. H. Swellengrebel and E. Rodenwaldt: *Die Anophelen von Niederländisch Östindien*, Jena, 1932.
243. N. H. Swellengrebel: *Malaria in the Netherlands Indies* in Bull. Col. Inst. Amsterd., Nov., 1937, pp. 37–45.

XXI. MISSIONARY WORK AND EDUCATION

244. H. H. Bartlett: *Vernacular literature in the Philippines* in Michigan Quarterly Rev., 1936, vol. 42, No. 23.
245. H. Bernard: *Les îles Philippines du grand archipel de la Chine: un essai de conquête spirituelle de l'Extrême-Orient*, 1571–1641, Tientsin, 1936.
246. Raden Lockman Djajadiningrat: *From Illiteracy to University*, Inst. of Pacific Relations, New York, 1942.
247. R. Ricard: *La conquête spirituelle du Mexique*, Paris, 1933.
248. H. A. Wyndham: *Native Education*, London and New York, 1933.

XXII. POLITICAL DEVELOPMENT

249. J. Th. P. Blumberger: *Le communisme aux Indes néerlandaises*, Paris, 1929.
250. G. H. Bousquet: *La politique musulmane et coloniale des Pays-Bas*, Paris, 1939.
251. R. Emerson: *Malaysia, a Study in Direct and Indirect Rule*, New York, 1937.
252. A. Labrouquère: *L'Indépendance des Philippines*, Paris, 1936.
253. A. A. Schiller: *Legal and Administrative Problems of the Netherlands Indies*, Inst. of Pacific Relations, New York, 1945.